CONTRIBUTORS

EDWARD B. ALLEN, M.D.
Senior Psychiatrist, New York Hospital–Westchester Division, White Plains, New York; Instructor in Psychiatry, Cornell University Medical College, New York, New York

KARL M. BOWMAN, M.D.
Professor of Psychiatry, University of California School of Medicine; Medical Superintendent, The Langley Porter Clinic, San Francisco, California

NORMAN CAMERON, M.D., Ph.D.
Yale University, New Haven, Connecticut

EUGENE DAVIDOFF, M.D.
Chief Psychiatrist, Ellis Hospital, Schenectady, New York; Associate Clinical Professor, Albany Medical College, Albany, New York

H. WARREN DUNHAM, Ph.D.
Professor of Sociology, Wayne University, Detroit, Michigan

DONALD M. HAMILTON, M.D.
Physician-in-Charge, Men's Service, New York Hospital–Westchester Division, White Plains, New York

EUGENIA HANFMANN, Ph.D.
Associate Professor of Psychology, Brandeis University, Waltham, Massachusetts

GEORGE A. JERVIS, M.D., Ph.D.
Director of Research, Letchworth Village, Thiells, New York

HAROLD E. JONES, Ph.D.
Professor of Psychology and Director, Institute of Child Welfare, University of California, Berkeley, California

FRANZ J. KALLMANN, M.D.
Professor of Psychiatry, College of Physicians and Surgeons, Columbia University; Principal Research Scientist (Medical Genetics), New York State Psychiatric Institute, New York, New York

OSCAR J. KAPLAN, Ph.D.
Professor of Psychology, San Diego State College, San Diego, California

NOLAN D. C. LEWIS, M.D.

Director of Research in Neurology and Psychiatry, New Jersey Department of Institutions and Agencies, Princeton, New Jersey

BENJAMIN MALZBERG, Ph.D.

Director, Bureau of Statistics, New York State Department of Mental Hygiene, Albany, New York

CLIVE M. McCAY, Ph.D.

Professor, School of Nutrition, Cornell University, Ithaca, New York

BELA MITTELMANN, M.D.

Associate Psychoanalyst, The Psychoanalytic Clinic for Training and Research, Columbia University, New York, New York

CURTIS T. PROUT, M.D.

Assistant Medical Director and Clinical Director, New York Hospital–Westchester Division, White Plains, New York; Consultant in Psychiatry, White Plains Hospital; Assistant Professor of Psychiatry, Cornell University Medical College, New York, New York

G. WILSE ROBINSON, JR., M.D.

The Robinson Clinic, Kansas City, Missouri

FRED V. ROCKWELL, M.D.

Chief Psychiatrist, Grasslands Hospital, Valhalla, New York; Associate Attending Psychiatrist, Payne Whitney Psychiatric Clinic, New York Hospital; Assistant Professor of Clinical Psychiatry, Cornell University Medical College, New York, New York

DAVID ROTHSCHILD, M.D.

Director of Clinical Psychiatry, Worcester State Hospital, Worcester, Massachusetts; Assistant Clinical Professor of Psychiatry, Tufts College Medical School, Boston, Massachusetts

NATHAN W. SHOCK, Ph.D., D.Sc. (Hon.)

Chief, Section on Gerontology, National Heart Institute, National Institutes of Health, Bethesda, Maryland, and the Baltimore City Hospitals, Baltimore, Maryland

EDWARD J. STIEGLITZ, M.D., F.A.C.P.

Consulting Internist, Suburban Hospital, Bethesda, Maryland; Consultant in Geriatrics, Veterans Administration; Lecturer on Industrial Medicine, Post-Graduate Medical School, New York University, New York, New York

PREFACE TO FIRST EDITION

MANY persons will be surprised to learn that there is already sufficient knowledge of the mental diseases of later life to fill a volume of more than four hundred pages. Although we are only at the threshold of our understanding of these puzzling conditions, we are moving from work that is primarily descriptive to inquiries concerned essentially with etiology. It is heartening to observe that the aura of inevitability is beginning to lift from these widespread maladies which have been viewed as hopeless in the past; certainly on the basis of existing data we are not entitled to resign ourselves to them.

This book is not and does not pretend to be an exhaustive treatment of the subject, nor does it represent itself as a full summary of the vast literature already available in this field. It is rather a collection of essays selected to indicate the level of present achievement in this area. I can hope for nothing better than that this volume will soon become obsolete and out of date; this seems destined to be its fate as the tempo of research with regard to the mental diseases of later maturity quickens.

Of the authors represented, Drs. Eugene Davidoff, George A. Jervis, G. Wilse Robinson, Jr., David Rothschild, and L. Erwin Wexberg were called into service before the completion of their manuscripts and had to work under very unfavorable conditions. The civilian authors were as busy as the men in service. The editor wishes to express his sincere thanks to all of the contributors; they completed a difficult job under war conditions.

I wish to take this opportunity to thank the following for the privilege of reproducing material originally published by them: C. V. Mosby Co., United States Public Health Service, E. P. Dutton & Co., The Century Co., Columbia University, Stanford University, The Family Welfare Association of America, and the American Psychological Association. Gratitude is also expressed to the publishers of the *Psychiatric Quarterly, Diseases of the Nervous System,* and the *American Journal of Psychiatry.* More complete acknowledgments are included in the text of the book.

Dr. Herbert S. Conrad made many valuable suggestions dealing with the organization and content of chapter iv. Mr. William Hawley Davis, editor of the Stanford University Press, has been patient and helpful, and his assistance is deeply appreciated; members of his staff also have contributed improvements.

In this book we see the pattern of future attack upon the mental diseases of later life, for only through the close collaboration of psychiatrists, statisticians, physiologists, sociologists, and psychologists can we obtain the fullest measure of triumph over these afflictions which today account for more than a fourth of all first admissions to American mental hospitals.

OSCAR J. KAPLAN

POCATELLO, IDAHO
April 17, 1945

PREFACE TO SECOND EDITION

A DECADE now has elapsed since the publication of the first edition of this book. The field of gerontology has experienced tremendous growth since 1945 and is certain to receive even more attention in the years ahead.

Activity and progress have not been uniform in the various areas represented in this book. Some chapters have required major revision; others are as up to date today as when they were written. The importance of heredity and the therapeutic usefulness of electric shock in geriatric psychiatry have been recognized by the addition of two new chapters.

Although the mental disorders of later life remain unconquered, they no longer are regarded as invincible. This book contains many research leads. It is issued as a challenge to resourceful and optimistic men.

OSCAR J. KAPLAN

SAN DIEGO, CALIFORNIA
December 15, 1955

TABLE OF CONTENTS

PAGE

Contributors v

CHAPTER

   I. *Introduction.* KARL M. BOWMAN 1

  II. *A Statistical Review of Mental Disorders in Later Life.*
      BENJAMIN MALZBERG 6

 III. *Genetic Aspects of Mental Disorders in Later Life.*
      FRANZ J. KALLMANN 26

 IV. *Physiological Aspects of Mental Disorders in Later Life.*
      NATHAN W. SHOCK 47

  V. *Psychological Aspects of Mental Disorders in Later Life.*
      HAROLD E. JONES AND OSCAR J. KAPLAN 98

 VI. *Sociological Aspects of Mental Disorders in Later Life.*
      H. WARREN DUNHAM 157

 VII. *Food for the Later Years.* CLIVE M. MCCAY 178

VIII. *Neuroses of Later Maturity.* NORMAN CAMERON 201

 IX. *The Involutional Psychoses.* EUGENE DAVIDOFF 244

  X. *The Presenile Dementias.* GEORGE A. JERVIS 262

 XI. *Senile Psychoses and Psychoses with Cerebral Arteriosclero-*
      sis. DAVID ROTHSCHILD 289

 XII. *The Toxic Delirious Reactions of Old Age.*
      G. WILSE ROBINSON, JR. 332

XIII. *Older Mental Patients After Long Hospitalization.*
      EUGENIA HANFMANN 352

XIV. *The Aged Subnormal.* OSCAR J. KAPLAN 383

 XV. *Psychosomatic Medicine and the Older Patient.*
      BELA MITTELMANN 398

XVI. *Psychotherapy in the Older Individual.* FRED V. ROCKWELL 423

XVII. *The Use of Electric Shock Therapy in Older Patients.*
      CURTIS T. PROUT, EDWARD B. ALLEN, AND DONALD M.
      HAMILTON 446

XVIII. *Mental Hygiene in Later Maturity.* NOLAN D. C. LEWIS . . 460

XIX. *Orientation of the Problems.* EDWARD J. STIEGLITZ . . . 476

Index 497

ix

Chapter I

INTRODUCTION

KARL M. BOWMAN

DURING recent years much work has been done on methods of preserving mental health and assuring normal mental development in children. Many studies have been made of both physical and mental growth and of development processes and the means of controlling them. Much of value has resulted from studies made of the role of the endocrines, diet, and prevention and treatment of the infectious diseases of childhood. The psychological development of the child has received attention as well, so that we now know at what age a child should be able to do certain types of intellectual and school work. We have also learned much about the emotional development of the child—such things as the importance and dangers of the child-parent relationship, sibling rivalry, and the need of security. From all this work with children the mortality rate from diseases of childhood has decreased; and we believe, although it cannot as yet be statistically proved, that mental health in childhood has improved.

Assuming this to be true, more children will grow up and live to a ripe old age and, accordingly, we are being faced more and more with the problems of physical and mental health of the aging person. In general, there has been less interest in the process of aging, as compared with the problem of childhood development. Comparatively little work has been done in studying this process and means of controlling it.

It is true, of course, that man has always been interested in the idea of rejuvenation. The theme runs through folklore and literature. Ponce de León searched for the fountain of youth in Florida. Faust undoubtedly represents the yearning of the aged for a return of the vigor and strength of youth. The search for the elixir of youth has gone on, but comparatively little scientific work has been done. Voronoff's announcement of rejuvenation by gland transplantation awakened a great deal of interest, but unfortunately other workers seem unable to confirm his optimistic findings. There have, however, been a few carefully controlled studies along physi-

1

ological and psychological lines. In the latter group, David Wechsler introduced the Wechsler-Bellevue Intelligence Test, standardized for varying ages in adults, and was the first to make some
allowances in an intelligence test for decline occurring in the later
decades.

It is often said that one is sure of only two things—death and
taxes. However, unless one dies early he is more and more likely
to live to be old. Will his later years of life be interesting and
productive, with preservation of physical and mental capacities,
or will deterioration set in to such a degree that he will only be a
burden to himself and to society, dragging out a miserable existence with death as a relief? While the span of life has been greatly
increased, it may be pointed out that merely to live on is not enough.
Most of us regret the preservation of life in spastic idiots and feel
that it would be a stroke of good fortune if something were to cut
short the lives of such individuals. Some even advocate euthanasia
for such conditions. Merely to keep the heart beating is of little
value. The important problem, therefore, is not to prolong the
years of life but to prolong the years of healthy living.

It is important to prevent, if possible, the periods during which
old persons linger on so mentally or physically deteriorated as to
be of no use to themselves or to society, a burden to their friends
and their families, often unhappy and protesting at this stage of
their existence or so deteriorated mentally as not to appreciate what
their condition is.

This whole problem is today more important because more persons now live to be old. The result is that there is a marked increase
of the types of mental disorders which occur among old persons,
particularly the arteriosclerotic and senile states. This is shown
by the statistics of state hospitals, and some superintendents have
even expressed the fear that the state hospital will become more
and more a home for the aged rather than an actual hospital for the
treatment of mental disorders.

Our problem is whether we can work out a mental hygiene program that will not only lower the incidence of mental disease among
old persons but will also give life an interest and meaning so that
they will not sit about just waiting to die. How can we utilize the
services of old persons so that they will not feel discarded and unwanted? Until the recent scarcity of labor due to war conditions,

industry would lay off men over 40. This has resulted in an attitude toward old age which has made it something to be feared and not desired. After the end of the war, shall we return to this idea in industry, or will public opinion, by forcing the use of crippled, blind, and handicapped veterans, develop new ways of utilizing all persons in industries and, from such techniques, work out a way by which older persons will find a worthwhile place in industry?

This volume concerns mental disease in later life. It points out some of the physical and psychological factors involved in aging, and discusses prevention and treatment. It also makes clear the wide gaps in our knowledge and the need for further research.

Life is not a fixed process from the cradle to the grave. The organism must make adjustments to its environment. Some of these are considered the processes of aging. To many the process of aging is something that begins around 40 or 50, when a person is said to be growing old. Actually the process of aging starts at birth, or rather from the moment of conception. The organism undergoes continual change, which finally results in deterioration and death.

Many diseases are concerned with age. Arteriosclerosis and cancer occur much more often after 40 or 50. Some diseases occur early in life, for example, the exanthemata. However, if one is not exposed to these diseases as a child and does not develop them then, he is likely to develop them later on, as is shown by the outbreaks of measles and such diseases in our Army camps. It has been said that we dig our graves with our teeth. Will the new science of nutrition aid us here? Will the newer knowledge of the use of vitamins, minerals, and proteins help in warding off some of the degenerative changes popularly attributed to old age? Will the use of endocrines also help?

Years before actual structural changes of degeneration appear, physiological changes occur which can perhaps be studied. The biochemical and physiological approach to the process of aging has, so far, received comparatively little attention. There is quite probably a basic difference between the young and the old cell. The ordinary processes of adjustment to life are an actual part of the aging process, and many of these are protective and adaptive on the part of the organism. Alteration in metabolic rate with increase of age is merely one of the many suggestive observations which need further and more intensive study. There is the question whether the mental disorders of old age are inherited. Does the development of cerebral arteriosclerosis arise primarily on the basis of a defect in the germ plasm? We know that arteriosclerosis does have some tendency to run in families. We know that certain racial groups seem to be rather free from the disorder, notably the Chinese. All this raises important questions of genetics, heredity, and eugenics.

We do discover remarkable cases of individuals living on in their eighties and nineties with excellent preservation of their mental faculties. Perhaps more intensive study of the person who survives in this fashion is indicated. We should not merely study why people break down but should devote more time to the positive side—why people remain strong and vigorous mentally and physically to a ripe old age. Careful study of such individuals may give us important data. We should further study the requirements of older persons in such matters as food, sleep, exercise, work, play, and mental activity. Does it vary greatly from person to person, or are there some general rules which can be laid down for all? Society is now arranging more and more for the retirement of persons as they grow old. Back of this is the laudable purpose of taking away the fear of old age as a period of dependency and want. We must, however, keep in mind that simply to drop out of all activities at sixty or seventy, or at whatever age may be elected for retirement, is not to insure a healthy old age. Retirement may have harmful effects on personality. It has been frequently noted that many active and capable persons go to pieces at once upon retirement. There is no point in stopping activity and then becoming depressed and just waiting to die. It is much better to die in harness. However, from all this it may be possible to work out some better plan, one which will avoid both extremes.

We should study the later changes in man as well as the developmental periods of childhood. One of the few worthwhile attempts of this sort has been the establishment of a Committee on the Biological Processes of Aging in the Division of Biology and Agriculture of the National Research Council. Continued interest and study along this line are indicated.

It is of interest that fewer old persons enter mental hospitals from rural life than from urban life. Does this mean that rural life is actually healthier, or does it mean that rural conditions are such that an old person can adapt to them and not require admission to a mental hospital? Admission to a mental hospital does not necessarily depend on the severity of the mental disease from which the individual is suffering. It may depend upon the environment in which he lives. The old person who becomes a little noisy at night will disturb others in a crowded apartment house in the city and cannot remain there; he may wander out in the street and get in front of an automobile. In the country it may be possible to care for him without these problems arising to such a degree as to necessitate transfer to a hospital.

The change in family attitude and in the public attitude toward old persons needs to be studied. If a culture considers old age undesirable and looks down on the old person, he feels unwanted and insecure. In most older cultures, age has carried prestige. It still does in some countries, as in France. When Pétain was put at the head of the French government and someone jokingly asked why an old man of eighty-one was placed in charge of the French government, the answer was that there was nobody ninety years old available!

Is it possible to work out some plan in our culture which will allow the older person to continue active with the feeling that he can still contribute to society, that he is important, and that he is wanted? These are very important points in the prevention of breakdowns in old age. Also, can we determine, from the study of such conditions as cerebral arteriosclerosis and senile atrophy, just what produces these changes, and can we work out methods of either treating or preventing them? These are but a few of the problems concerned with old age.

Chapter II

A STATISTICAL REVIEW OF MENTAL DISORDERS IN LATER LIFE

Benjamin Malzberg

It is a commonplace that the age structure of the general population has changed in an extraordinary manner. We may obtain a picture of these changes by considering the course of population in the United States since 1870, or shortly after the close of the Civil War. In that year the total population was 38,558,371. Those under 5 years of age included 5,514,000, or 14.3 per cent of the total. The school population, which may be considered to range from 5 to 19, included 13,641,490, or 35.5 per cent of the total. The adult part of the population may be divided into a younger group aged 20 to 44, and an older group aged 45 to 64. The former included 13,640,934, or 35.3 per cent. The latter totaled 4,602,424, or 11.9 per cent. The aged may be considered to embrace those aged 65 or over, and this group included 1,153,649, or 3.0 per cent.

How have these groups fared numerically since 1870? The child population increased decade by decade until 1920, when it totaled 11,573,230. From 1920 to 1930 it decreased by 128,840. During the next decade it decreased by 902,866. On a relative basis, this group decreased throughout the seventy years from 1870 to 1940. From 14.3 per cent of the total population in 1870 it decreased to 12.1 per cent in 1900, to 10.9 per cent in 1920, to 8.0 per cent in 1940, but increased to 10.7 per cent in 1950. The birth rate increased appreciably during the years following the war. Some demographers predicted that this would bring about a reversal in the downward trend of the child population. If earlier experience is repeated, however, this will probably prove to be a temporary phenomenon, and the population under 5 years of age may be expected to resume its long-term downward trend in numbers.

Those aged 5 to 19 totaled 13,641,490 in 1870. They increased during each succeeding decade, though at a decreasing rate, until they totaled 36,164,601 in 1930. Between 1930 and 1940 they

6

TABLE 1.—PERCENTAGE OF BROAD AGE GROUPS IN THE POPULATION
OF THE UNITED STATES, 1870 TO 1950*

Age Group (Years)	Per Cent								
	1870	1880	1890	1900	1910	1920	1930	1940	1950
Under 5	14.3	13.8	12.2	12.1	11.5	10.9	9.3	8.0	10.7
5–19	35.5	34.3	33.8	32.2	30.4	29.8	29.5	26.4	23.2
20–44	35.3	35.9	36.8	37.7	39.0	38.4	38.3	38.9	37.6
45–64	11.9	12.6	13.1	13.7	14.6	16.1	17.4	19.8	20.3
65 and over......	3.0	3.4	3.8	4.0	4.3	4.7	5.4	6.9	8.2
Unascertained ...	....	....	0.3	0.3	0.2	0.1	0.1	....	....
Total	100.0	100.0	100.0	100.0	100.0	100.0	100.0	100.0	100.0

* Abstracted from official censuses of the United States.

decreased, however, by 1,400,521, or 3.9 per cent. In 1870 this age group formed 35.5 per cent of the total population. On a relative basis, there has been a steady decline between 1870 and 1950. In the latter year those aged 5 to 19 included only 23.2 per cent of the total population.

Turning to the population aged 20 to 44, we find evidence of the continued industrial strength of the nation, in so far as this is measured by population alone. In 1870 this age group totaled 13,640,934. It increased during each decade since 1870, reaching a total of 56,691,454 in 1950. Though the rate of increase fell after 1910, owing largely to the outbreak of war in 1914, and to subsequent changes in the immigration laws, this age group remained almost constant in relation to the total population. In fact, from 1910 on, the group included from 38 to 39 per cent of the total population, as compared with 35.3 per cent in 1870, and 37.7 per cent in 1900.

The same trend was shown by the older working population, and in fact we begin, at this point, to observe the effects of greater longevity. Those aged 45 to 64 increased decade by decade from 4,602,424 in 1870 to 30,637,248 in 1950. The absolute, numerical increase was greater during each successive decade. In 1870 this age group represented 11.9 per cent of the total population. By 1950 this had increased to 20.3 per cent.

Finally, we may consider those aged 65 or over, or the old-age group, who numbered 1,153,649 in 1870, or 3.0 per cent of the total population. Decade by decade this age group has grown until it numbered 12,269,537 in 1950, or 8.2 per cent of the total.

Changes in the relative proportions of the several age groups have a direct relation to health. It is difficult to measure this in terms of disease, because such reporting, even with respect to reportable diseases, is far from adequate. Therefore recourse is almost always had to the consideration of death rates as a measure of health. Death rates are high in infancy, but drop to a minimum in childhood. The mortality curve rises thereafter to the end of the life span. It follows, therefore, that as the population grows older, there will be relatively fewer deaths at the younger ages and more at advanced ages. The total effect, however, has been a reduction in the general death rate, owing to remarkable progress in public health and the prevention of disease.

The death rate of the registration states of the United States was 14.7 per 1,000 population in 1910. Year by year the death rate has decreased, reaching a minimum of 9.9 in 1948. The death rate has decreased at all ages, though at varying rates. The greatest reductions occurred in infancy and childhood. In 1910 the infant death rate was 131.8 per 1,000, compared with 35.0 in 1948. The death rate at ages 1 to 4 fell from 14.0 to 1.6. At ages 5 to 14 the death rate fell from 2.9 to 0.7, and at ages 15 to 24 it fell from 4.5 to 1.4. The death rate also declined in the older age groups, but at an ever decreasing rate. At ages 45 to 54, for example, the death rate fell from 13.7 to 9.0, or by only 35 per cent. At ages 55 to 64, the death rate declined from 26.2 to 19.4, or by 26 per cent. Between 65 and 84, the death rates declined by about 20 per cent. Among those aged 85 or over, there is no evidence of a genuine decrease in the death rate.

The great decline in the death rate at the younger ages is the result of progress in medicine and in sanitation. For example, the death rate from typhoid and paratyphoid fever fell from 22.5 per 100,000 population in 1910 to 0.2 in 1948. The death rate from scarlet fever fell from 11.4 to 0.0 during the same interval. Deaths from whooping cough decreased from 11.6 per 100,000 to 0.8. The death rate from diphtheria fell from 21.1 to 0.4, and that from measles declined from 12.4 to 0.6. There has been a similar trend with respect to tuberculosis (all forms), the death rate from this cause falling from 153.8 per 100,000 population in 1910 to 30.0 in 1948. The death rate from pneumonia and influenza fell from 155.9 to 38.7. On the other hand, the death rate

TABLE 2.—DEATH RATES BY AGE, PER 1,000 ESTIMATED MIDYEAR POPULATION IN EACH AGE GROUP, IN THE REGISTRATION STATES OF THE UNITED STATES, 1910–48*

Year	All Ages	Under 1	1 to 4	5 to 14	15 to 24	25 to 34	35 to 44	45 to 54	55 to 64	65 to 74	75 to 84	85 and Over
						Death Rates by Age Group						
1910	14.7	131.8	14.0	2.9	4.5	6.5	9.0	13.7	26.2	55.6	122.2	250.3
1915	13.2	102.4	9.2	2.3	4.1	5.8	8.3	13.1	25.5	55.6	120.1	240.3
1920	13.0	92.3	9.9	2.6	4.9	6.8	8.1	12.2	23.6	52.5	118.9	248.3
1925	11.7	75.4	6.4	2.0	3.8	4.8	7.2	12.2	23.3	51.7	119.3	272.3
1930	11.3	69.0	5.6	1.7	3.3	4.7	6.8	12.2	24.0	51.4	112.7	228.0
1935	10.9	60.9	4.4	1.5	2.7	4.0	6.2	11.6	23.2	48.7	113.1	224.6
1940	10.7	54.8	2.9	1.0	2.0	3.1	5.2	10.6	22.0	48.2	110.9	230.1
1945	10.6	41.7	2.0	0.9	1.9	2.7	4.6	9.7	20.3	44.5	99.5	222.5
1948	9.9	35.0	1.6	0.7	1.4	2.0	4.0	9.0	19.4	44.0	96.3	247.1

* Abstracted from Table X, *Vital Statistics of the United States, 1948.* Part I, p. 19.

Benjamin Malzberg

TABLE 3.—CRUDE DEATH RATES FOR SELECTED CAUSES, PER 100,000 ESTIMATED MIDYEAR POPULATION, IN THE REGISTRATION STATES OF THE UNITED STATES, 1910–48*

Year	Typhoid and Paratyphoid Fever	Scarlet Fever	Whooping Cough	Diphtheria	Tuberculosis (All Forms)	Measles	Cancer and Other Malignant Tumors	Diabetes Mellitus	Intracranial Lesions of Vascular Origin	Diseases of the Heart	Pneumonia (All Forms) and Influenza	Nephritis
1910	22.5	11.4	11.6	21.1	153.8	12.4	76.2	15.3	95.8	158.9	155.9	94.8
1915	11.8	3.6	8.2	15.2	140.1	5.2	80.7	17.6	94.5	163.9	145.9	101.5
1920	7.6	4.6	12.5	15.3	113.1	8.8	83.4	16.1	93.0	159.6	207.3	88.8
1925	7.8	2.7	6.7	7.8	84.8	2.3	92.0	16.8	89.5	184.8	121.7	95.0
1930	4.8	1.9	4.8	4.9	71.1	3.2	97.4	19.1	89.0	214.2	102.5	91.0
1935	2.8	2.1	3.7	3.1	55.1	3.1	108.2	22.3	85.7	245.4	104.2	81.3
1940	1.1	0.5	2.2	1.1	45.8	0.5	120.0	26.5	90.8	291.9	70.1	81.4
1945	0.4	0.2	1.3	1.2	40.1	0.2	134.4	26.6	97.8	321.4	51.8	66.7
1948	0.2	0.0	0.8	0.4	30.0	0.6	134.9	26.4	89.7	322.7	38.7	53.0

* Abstracted from Table XI, *Vital Statistics of the United States, 1948.* Part I, pp. 20–21.

TABLE 4.—AGES OF FIRST ADMISSIONS TO ALL STATE AND LICENSED HOSPITALS
FOR MENTAL DISEASE IN NEW YORK STATE, FISCAL YEARS 1939–41,
AND AVERAGE ANNUAL RATES OF FIRST ADMISSIONS
PER 100,000 POPULATION

Age Group (Years)	Number			Per Cent			Average Annual Rate per 100,000 Population		
	Males	Females	Total	Males	Females	Total	Males	Females	Total
Under 5.....	7	5	12	...*	...*	...*	0.54	0.41	0.48
5–9	98	33	131	0.4	0.1	0.3	7.17	2.51	4.89
10–14	171	102	273	0.7	0.5	0.6	10.77	6.60	8.71
15–19	1,013	849	1,862	4.1	3.8	4.0	60.06	50.51	55.29
20–24	1,720	1,434	3,154	7.0	6.5	6.8	103.96	80.56	91.83
25–29	1,854	1,901	3,755	7.6	8.6	8.1	111.22	102.91	106.85
30–34	2,096	1,967	4,063	8.6	8.9	8.7	124.89	110.69	117.58
35–39	2,224	2,033	4,257	9.1	9.2	9.1	134.20	121.01	127.56
40–44	2,261	1,843	4,104	9.3	8.3	8.8	140.31	116.06	128.28
45–49	2,160	1,897	4,057	8.8	8.5	8.7	144.67	132.86	138.89
50–54	2,165	1,777	3,942	8.9	8.0	8.4	164.58	145.39	155.33
55–59	1,724	1,430	3,154	7.1	6.4	6.8	172.61	149.32	161.21
60–64	1,652	1,424	3,076	6.8	6.4	6.6	213.46	179.66	196.35
65–69	1,592	1,494	3,086	6.5	6.7	6.6	282.50	240.27	260.35
70–74	1,390	1,368	2,758	5.7	6.2	5.9	375.02	319.00	344.97
75 and over..	2,304	2,645	4,949	9.4	11.9	10.6	679.26	603.30	636.44
Total ...	24,431	22,202	46,633	100.0	100.0	100.0	121.90	109.22	115.51

* Less than 0.05.

TABLE 5.—FIRST ADMISSIONS TO THE NEW YORK STATE CIVIL HOSPITALS DURING
SELECTED FISCAL YEARS, CLASSIFIED ACCORDING TO AGE GROUPS

Age Group (Years)	Number				Per Cent			
	1920	1930	1940	1950	1920	1930	1940	1950
Under 15.......	21	57	133	247	0.3	0.6	1.0	1.5
15–19	309	413	561	634	4.7	4.6	4.3	4.0
20–24	583	735	844	1,119	8.9	8.1	6.5	7.0
25–29	775	835	1,031	1,236	11.8	9.2	7.9	7.7
30–34	745	866	1,074	1,103	11.3	9.6	8.3	6.9
35–39	756	1,008	1,119	1,172	11.5	11.2	8.6	7.3
40–44	628	894	1,022	1,071	9.6	9.9	7.9	6.7
45–49	570	809	1,061	993	8.7	8.9	8.2	6.2
50–54	495	706	1,096	1,043	7.5	7.8	8.4	6.5
55–59	393	568	860	1,012	6.0	6.3	6.6	6.3
60–64	368	506	914	1,078	5.6	5.6	7.0	6.7
65–69	309	482	910	1,161	4.7	5.3	7.0	7.3
70 and over.....	614	1,144	2,356	4,138	9.3	12.7	18.1	25.8
Unascertained ..	7	17	8	5	0.1	0.2	0.1	...*
Total	6,573	9,040	12,989	16,012	100.0	100.0	100.0	100.0

* Less than 0.05.

from cancer increased from 76.2 per 100,000 in 1910 to 134. in 1948. The death rate from diseases of the heart increased fro 158.9 to 322.7. It is possible that the entire increase in the diseases is not true statistically, in the sense that it results from greater weight exercised by the larger and older population no exposed to these diseases. When all possible corrections are mad however, with respect to age changes and to improvement in dia noses, there still remain increases in the death rates from degenei tive diseases, which must be accepted as evidence of the actu increase in the prevalence of these diseases.

Thus, progress in the control of disease has served to favor t young more than the old, and ever larger proportions of the poj lation are growing to the older ages at which degenerative disea still offer a challenge. The general result has been an increase the expectation of life, especially marked at birth and in the lov half of the life span. Among white males the expectation of l at birth increased from 50.2 years in 1909–11 to 66.5 years 1948. Among white females, the corresponding increase was fr 53.6 to 71.0. Similar increases, though on a smaller scale, curred through childhood into the years of full maturity (7).[1]

Changes in mortality have had a direct effect upon the pre lence of mental disease. Unlike the course of the death rate, rate of mental disease, as measured by first admissions to me hospitals, increases steadily from a minimum in childhood t maximum in old age. This is shown clearly in Table 4, which s marizes the distribution by age of first admissions to all me hospitals in New York State, during the three years ended June 1941.

At ages 5 to 9, there was an average annual rate of first ad sions of 4.89 per 100,000 population of corresponding age. rate increased rapidly to 106.85 at ages 25 to 29, increased slc but regularly to 196.35 at ages 60 to 64, and then grew rap to a maximum of 636.44 at 75 years or over. Males and fem showed similar trends, except for a drop among the latter at 40 to 44. In general, the male rates exceeded those of the fem

It is evident from this trend that, as the general popula changes its age proportions, there will be corresponding cha

---

[1] Figures in parentheses indicate the references to be found at the end of chapter.

TABLE 6.—FIRST ADMISSIONS TO THE NEW YORK STATE CIVIL HOSPITALS DURING
SELECTED FISCAL YEARS, CLASSIFIED ACCORDING TO PRINCIPAL GROUPS
OF MENTAL DISORDERS

Mental Disorders	Number				Per Cent			
	1920	1930	1940	1950	1920	1930	1940	1950
General paresis	820	932	844	420	12.5	10.3	6.5	2.6
Alcoholic	122	546	868	1,078	1.9	6.0	6.7	6.7
With cerebral arteriosclerosis	513	1,290	2,581	3,379	7.8	14.3	19.9	21.1
Senile	646	796	1,419	2,439	9.8	8.8	10.9	15.2
Involutional	243	235	838	1,093	3.7	2.6	6.4	6.8
Manic-depressive	882	1,160	794	373	13.4	12.8	6.1	2.3
Dementia praecox	1,926	2,369	3,373	4,658	29.3	26.2	26.0	29.1
With psychopathic personality	180	217	179	245	2.7	2.4	1.4	1.5
Psychoneuroses	128	161	437	603	1.9	1.8	3.4	3.8
Other	1,113	1,334	1,656	1,724	16.9	14.8	12.7	10.8
Total	6,573	9,040	12,989	16,012	100.0	100.0	100.0	100.0

in the age distribution of first admissions with mental disease.
Table 5 shows that the number of first admissions to the New York
State Civil hospitals increased from 6,573 during the fiscal year
ended June 30, 1920 to 16,012 during the year ended March 31,
1950. It shows that there were numerical increases at all ages during this period. But it also shows that the relative increases were
greatest beyond 55 years of age. In 1920, those under 55 years of
age included 74.3 per cent of the total; those over age 55 included
27.6 per cent. During each successive decade these proportions
changed, until in 1950 those under age 55 included only 53.8 per
cent of the total compared with 46.2 per cent aged 55 or over. Those
aged 60 or over included 19.6 per cent of the total first admissions
in 1920, 23.6 per cent in 1930, 32.1 per cent in 1940, and 39.8
per cent in 1950. The average age at first admission increased
from 42.7 years in 1920, to 44.9 in 1930, to 48.5 in 1940, to
51.9 in 1950.

The effect of the changes in the age distribution of the general
population, reflected in corresponding changes in the age distribution of first admissions with mental disease, is also shown in the
relative distribution of the major groups of mental diseases. In
1920 first admissions to the New York State Civil hospitals with
psychoses with cerebral arteriosclerosis included 7.8 per cent of

the total first admissions. By 1950 this had grown to 21.1 per cent. The senile psychoses included 15.2 per cent of the total first admissions in 1950, compared with 9.8 per cent in 1920. First admissions with involutional psychoses showed a relative increase of over 80 per cent. Thus, these three groups of psychotic disorders included 21.3 per cent of the total first admissions in 1920, but jumped to 43.1 per cent in 1950.

TABLE 7.—FIRST ADMISSIONS TO ALL STATE AND LICENSED HOSPITALS FOR MENTAL DISEASE IN NEW YORK STATE PER 100,000 GENERAL POPULATION, FISCAL YEARS 1919–21, 1929–31, AND 1939–41

Age Group (Years)	Males					Females				
	1919–21 (a)	1929–31 (b)	1939–41 (c)	b/a	c/b	1919–21 (a)	1929–31 (b)	1939–41 (c)	b/a	c/b
15–19	54.01	57.80	60.06	1.07	1.04	40.36	38.68	50.51	0.96	1.31
20–24	108.74	100.72	103.96	0.93	1.03	66.67	67.53	80.56	1.01	1.19
25–29	120.64	103.00	111.22	0.85	1.08	95.62	84.86	102.91	0.89	1.21
30–34	114.49	124.52	124.89	1.09	1.00	100.51	97.09	110.69	0.97	1.14
35–39	120.77	143.12	134.20	1.19	0.94	106.74	102.15	121.01	0.96	1.18
40–44	113.10	136.13	140.31	1.20	1.03	107.97	114.26	116.06	1.06	1.02
45–49	108.14	134.47	144.67	1.24	1.08	121.88	107.59	132.86	0.88	1.23
50–54	106.04	149.25	164.58	1.41	1.10	125.56	119.39	145.39	0.95	1.22
55–59	118.32	150.27	172.61	1.27	1.14	120.79	121.52	149.32	1.01	1.23
60–64	139.66	180.48	213.46	1.29	1.18	134.01	134.76	179.66	1.01	1.33
65–69	178.57	220.34	282.50	1.23	1.28	149.04	176.26	240.27	1.18	1.36
70–74	190.08	316.75	375.02	1.67	1.18	208.37	228.54	319.00	1.10	1.40
75 and over..	289.00	465.56	679.26	1.61	1.46	282.37	376.92	603.30	1.33	1.60

Table 7 shows the average annual rates of first admissions to all hospitals for mental disease in New York State in successive decades beginning with 1919–21. In general, the rates of first admissions increased among males in both decades, but the greatest rates of increase occurred at the advanced ages. Among females, there were no significant changes in the rates between 1919–21 and 1929–31 until old age, when the rates increased by from 10 to 33 per cent. The rates all increased sensibly between 1929–31 and 1939–41, but again the greatest rates of increase occurred at the advanced ages.

Thus, in addition to being highest in old age, rates of first admission have been increasing more rapidly at such ages than at any other period of life.

Rates of first admissions give the probability of a mental disease at a given age in a single year. A more significant measure, known as the expectation of mental disease, gives the probability at a given age of developing a mental disorder at any time after that age to the end of the life span. For example, the expectation of a mental disease at birth among males in New York State in 1920 was 48.2 per thousand. That is, 48.2 of every 1,000 males at birth would, according to the rates of first admissions and of general mortality in New York State in 1920, develop a mental disease before they died. In 1930, the corresponding expectation at birth was 63.9, an increase of 33 per cent. In 1940, the expectation had grown to 80.5, an increase during the decade of 26 per cent. Among females, the expectations of mental disease at birth in 1920, 1930, and 1940 were, respectively, 48.1, 55.8, and 82.0 per thousand. Between 1920 and 1930, the expectations at birth increased by 16 per cent. Between 1930 and 1940, it increased by 47 per cent. Between 1920 and 1940, there were increased expectations of mental disease at every age. But the rates of increase were all significantly greater at 60 years of age or over. These rates are summarized in Table 8.

TABLE 8.—EXPECTATION OF MENTAL DISEASE* IN NEW YORK STATE, 1920, 1930, AND 1940†

Exact Age (Years)	Males					Females				
	1920 (a)	1930 (b)	1940 (c)	b/a	c/b	1920 (a)	1930 (b)	1940 (c)	b/a	c/b
0.......	48.2	63.9	80.5	1.33	1.26	48.1	55.8	82.0	1.16	1.47
60.......	28.4	38.8	51.9	1.37	1.34	28.5	33.7	55.3	1.18	1.64
65.......	26.3	37.3	50.6	1.42	1.36	26.0	32.1	51.2	1.23	1.60
70.......	23.8	36.3	49.8	1.53	1.37	24.3	30.4	49.5	1.25	1.63
75.......	21.6	34.0	49.7	1.57	1.46	22.1	28.9	48.5	1.31	1.68
80.......	20.6	30.0	46.9	1.46	1.56	20.3	26.2	45.4	1.29	1.73
85.......	17.1	26.5	42.5	1.55	1.60	16.4	22.2	41.9	1.35	1.89
90.......	12.2	23.9	39.4	1.96	1.65	13.0	20.7	40.9	1.59	1.98
95.......	....	21.7	43.6	....	2.01	8.8	22.8	40.3	2.59	1.77
100.......	....	....	39.2	....	....	....	13.0	32.0	....	2.46

* Per 1,000 population at given age.
† Summarized from a chapter by Benjamin Malzberg in *Trends in Mental Disease* (New York: Kings Crown Press, 1945), p. 47.

Thus, among males the expectation of mental disease at birth increased by 33 per cent between 1920 and 1930. But between age 60 and age 90, the expectations increased during the interval by from 37 to 96 per cent. Between 1930 and 1940, the expectations increased among males by 34 per cent at age 60, and 101 per cent at age 95, compared with an increase of only 26 per cent at birth.

Among females there were similar increases at the advanced ages. Thus, between 1920 and 1930, the expectation of mental disease increased by 18 per cent at age 60, and 159 per cent at age 95, compared with 16 per cent at birth. Between 1930 and 1940, the expectation of mental disease increased by 64 per cent at age 60, and by 100 per cent or more toward the end of the life span, compared with an increase of only 47 per cent at birth.

The significance of the increase in mental disease at age 60 or over will be enhanced by a consideration of psychoses with cerebral arteriosclerosis, a disorder largely associated with advanced age. As shown in Table 9, in 1920 the expectation at birth among

TABLE 9.—EXPECTATION OF PSYCHOSES WITH CEREBRAL ARTERIOSCLEROSIS*
IN NEW YORK STATE, 1920, 1930, AND 1940†

Exact Age (Years)	Males					Females				
	1920 (a)	1930 (b)	1940 (c)	b/a	c/b	1920 (a)	1930 (b)	1940 (c)	b/a	c/b
0	51.2	113.9	191.6	2.22	1.68	37.4	95.4	186.3	2.55	1.95
60	83.2	172.6	262.9	2.07	1.52	49.7	119.8	226.1	2.41	1.89
65	75.3	168.6	256.6	2.24	1.52	41.6	111.5	210.5	2.68	1.89
70	56.3	157.3	234.3	2.79	1.49	34.8	97.0	184.7	2.79	1.90
75	44.9	135.2	206.0	3.01	1.52	28.6	82.6	154.2	2.89	1.87
80	33.9	103.5	160.5	3.05	1.55	18.0	59.9	105.6	3.33	1.76
85	26.7	68.8	129.7	2.58	1.89	13.7	37.9	77.8	2.77	2.05
90	28.6	40.1	125.0	1.40	3.12	12.6	21.7	50.1	1.72	2.31
95	....	....	129.3	....	....	....	....	28.4	....	....

* Per 10,000 population at given age.
† Summarized from a study by Benjamin Malzberg, *Psychiatric Quarterly*, 1943, 19: 130.

males of developing such a disease during a lifetime was 51.2 per 10,000. This grew to 113.9 in 1930, and to 191.6 in 1940. Between 1920 and 1930, the expectation at birth increased by 122 per cent. Between 1930 and 1940, it increased by 68 per cent. At ages 70 to 85, however, the expectation of such a psychosis increased by from 100 to 200 per cent between 1920 and 1930, and by from 50 to 90 per cent (and over) between 1930 and 1940.

Among females, the expectation of a psychosis with cerebral arteriosclerosis increased at birth by 155 per cent between 1920 and 1930, whereas it increased by amounts up to 233 per cent at the older ages. Among females, the expectation increased at all ages between 1930 and 1940, though the trend with age was not so marked as during the previous decade.

From these different lines of evidence we may draw the conclusion that mental disease is not only most frequent, relatively, among the aged, but that rates of mental disease have increased significantly among them since 1920. When it first became apparent that general rates of first admission were increasing, this was ascribed to the effect of the rise in the average age of the general population, and to increasing longevity. By making comparisons on the basis of a constant age distribution, however, it was shown that this is not a tenable explanation (1). The writer, therefore, suggested the following possible explanation of the rising trend of mental disease among the aged (1):

The upward trend in these disorders is probably associated with an increase in the degenerative diseases as a whole. The human organism must break down at some time. In younger persons, the organism is subject to one set of diseases, such as tuberculosis. The control of this disease in recent decades has extended the expectation of life, and consequently more people have reached that period of life at which circulatory and other degenerative diseases become manifest. A generation ago, those surviving to middle age probably constituted a better physical selection, on the whole, than those reaching the same age periods today. Consequently, in corresponding age periods, we now find greater morbidity and mortality from degenerative diseases. With these are associated the physical conditions that produce senility and cerebral arteriosclerosis. In brief, then, we find increasing rates of both senile and arteriosclerotic mental disorders, because the individuals constituting the susceptible age groups today are probably not selected as rigorously as were the corresponding age groups of an earlier generation.

SOME CHARACTERISTICS OF FIRST ADMISSIONS, AGED 60 YEARS OR OVER

During the fiscal year ended March 31, 1948, there were, as shown in Table 10, 6,249 first admissions to the state and licensed hospitals for mental disease, aged 60 years or over, of whom 2,926, or 46.8 per cent, were males, and 3,323, or 53.2 per cent, females. The sex difference is associated with the numerical excess of females in the general population at the older ages. Of the 6,249 first admissions, 5,697, or 91.2 per cent, were admitted to the civil state hospitals. Of the remainder, 513 were admitted to the private licensed hospitals. Ten were admitted to the two hospitals for the criminal insane in New York State, 23 to the two federal hospitals for mentally ill veterans, and 6 to the U.S. Marine Hospital. The

TABLE 10.—FIRST ADMISSIONS TO ALL STATE AND LICENSED HOSPITALS FOR MENTAL DISEASE IN NEW YORK STATE, AGED 60 YEARS OR OVER, YEAR ENDED MARCH 31, 1948

Mental Disorders	Total M.	Total F.	Total T.	60–64 M.	60–64 F.	65–69 M.	65–69 F.	70–74 M.	70–74 F.	75–79 M.	75–79 F.	80–84 M.	80–84 F.	85–89 M.	85–89 F.	90–94 M.	90–94 F.	95–99 M.	95–99 F.	100 or Over M.	100 or Over F.
General paresis	73	17	90	42	4	17	9	9	4	5	…	…	…	…	…	…	…	…	…	…	…
With other syphilis of central nervous system	6	1	7	3	1	1	…	2	…	…	…	…	…	…	…	…	…	…	…	…	…
With epidemic encephalitis	…	1	1	…	…	…	…	…	1	…	…	…	…	…	…	…	…	…	…	…	…
With other infectious diseases	3	2	5	1	1	…	…	2	1	…	…	…	…	…	…	…	…	…	…	…	…
Alcoholic	120	27	147	65	11	37	9	13	6	5	1	…	…	…	…	…	…	…	…	…	…
Due to drugs or other exogenous poisons	2	2	4	1	…	1	…	…	2	…	…	…	…	…	…	…	…	…	…	…	…
Traumatic	19	3	22	9	…	4	1	4	1	1	1	…	…	…	…	1	…	…	…	…	…
With cerebral arteriosclerosis	1,496	1,282	2,778	280	229	358	282	348	321	280	246	136	126	76	60	15	14	2	4	1	…
With other disturbances of circulation	21	14	35	9	7	5	3	3	4	2	…	2	…	…	…	…	…	…	…	…	…
With convulsive disorders	10	10	20	4	4	4	4	2	1	…	1	…	…	…	…	…	…	…	…	…	…
Senile	868	1,596	2,464	31	56	86	131	194	307	227	412	168	378	125	220	32	81	5	9	…	2
Involutional	101	135	236	69	95	26	27	5	10	…	3	…	…	…	…	1	…	…	…	…	…
Due to other metabolic, etc., diseases	8	6	14	4	2	2	…	2	3	…	1	…	…	…	…	…	…	…	…	…	…
Due to new growth	20	13	33	6	2	3	4	7	4	2	2	2	…	…	…	…	1	…	…	…	…
With organic changes of nervous system	14	13	27	4	2	6	6	3	5	…	…	1	…	…	…	…	…	…	…	…	…
Manic-depressive	42	58	100	22	8	13	27	6	12	1	9	…	1	…	1	…	…	…	…	…	…
Dementia praecox	36	59	95	18	34	14	14	4	10	…	1	…	…	…	…	…	…	…	…	…	…
Paranoia and paranoid conditions	11	16	27	5	7	5	3	1	4	…	2	…	…	…	…	…	…	…	…	…	…
With psychopathic personality	3	3	6	…	…	3	2	…	1	…	…	…	…	…	…	…	…	…	…	…	…
With mental deficiency	5	3	8	4	2	1	1	…	…	…	…	…	…	…	…	…	…	…	…	…	…
Psychoneuroses	27	44	71	17	21	5	14	5	6	…	2	…	1	…	…	…	…	…	…	…	…
Undiagnosed	9	4	13	5	3	2	…	…	…	1	…	1	1	…	…	…	…	…	…	…	…
Without psychosis	32	14	46	9	6	14	5	6	2	3	1	…	…	…	…	…	…	…	…	…	…
Total	2,926	3,323	6,249	608	519	607	529	613	698	531	678	309	507	201	281	49	96	7	13	1	2

fact that the vast majority are admitted to the civil state hospitals may be attributed, first, to the economic factor, and, second, to the fact that the private hospitals are not so likely to accept older and, presumably, chronic patients.

Of the 6,249 first admissions aged 60 years or over, 2,778, or 44.5 per cent, represented psychoses with cerebral arteriosclerosis, and 2,464, or 39.4 per cent, were senile psychoses. The involutional psychoses included 236, or 3.8 per cent. In contrast, the more significant of the remaining groups were as follows: general paresis, 90, or 1.4 per cent; alcoholic psychoses, 147, or 2.4 per cent; manic-depressive psychoses, 100, or 1.6 per cent; dementia praecox, 95, or 1.5 per cent. During the same years, there were 18,407 first admissions at all ages, of whom 5,052, or 27.4 per cent, were cases of dementia praecox. Psychoses with cerebral arteriosclerosis and senile psychoses represented only 17.3 and 13.4 per cent, respectively, of all first admissions, in contrast with 44.5 per cent and 39.4 per cent of the aged group.

ENVIRONMENT

Table 11 shows the environmental distribution of the 6,249 first admissions aged 60 or over. Following the definitions of the United States Bureau of the Census, those communities with a population of 2,500 or over are considered urban. The others are classed as rural. Upon this basis, 5,448, or 87.2 per cent, were from an urban environment, and 801, or 12.8 per cent, were from a rural environment. Of the latter, 649 were from the rural non-farm population, and only 152 from the farm population.

On April 1, 1940, the population of New York State aged 60 or over was divided into 77.8 per cent urban and 22.2 per cent rural

TABLE 11.—FIRST ADMISSIONS, AGED 60 YEARS OR OVER, TO ALL STATE AND LICENSED HOSPITALS FOR MENTAL DISEASE IN NEW YORK STATE, CLASSIFIED ACCORDING TO ENVIRONMENT, YEAR ENDED MARCH 31, 1948

Environment	Number			Per Cent		
	Males	Females	Total	Males	Females	Total
Urban	2,496	2,952	5,448	85.3	88.8	87.2
Rural	430	371	801	14.7	11.2	12.8
Farm	97	55	152	3.3	1.7	2.4
Non-farm	333	316	649	11.4	9.5	10.4
Total	2,926	3,323	6,249	100.0	100.0	100.0

(6). It is evident, therefore, that the urban population is overrepresented among the first admissions, while the rural population is underrepresented. This is especially true of the farm population, which represented 7.7 per cent of the total population aged 60 or over and only 2.4 per cent of the first admissions. First admissions from the rural non-farm population represented only 71.7 per cent of their quota.

MARITAL STATUS

As might be expected of a group of advanced age, the majority of such first admissions was either married or widowed. As shown in Table 12, the widowed included 2,998, or 48.0 per cent, of the total first admissions aged 60 years or over. There were some sex differences, the married representing 37.8 per cent of the male first admissions aged 60 or over, and 18.9 per cent of the females. On the other hand, the widowed included 34.4 per cent of the males but 59.9 per cent of the females. This is due to the fact that, because of their greater longevity, females outlive males. Though the numbers are small, it is also evident that males include larger percentages of first admissions who were separated or divorced from their spouses.

TABLE 12.—FIRST ADMISSIONS, AGED 60 YEARS OR OVER, TO ALL STATE AND LICENSED HOSPITALS FOR MENTAL DISEASE IN NEW YORK STATE, CLASSIFIED ACCORDING TO MARITAL STATUS, YEAR ENDED MARCH 31, 1948

Marital Status	Number			Per Cent		
	Males	Females	Total	Males	Females	Total
Single	548	561	1,109	18.7	16.9	17.7
Married	1,105	627	1,732	37.8	18.9	27.7
Widowed	1,008	1,990	2,998	34.4	59.9	48.0
Separated	165	75	240	5.6	2.3	3.8
Divorced	50	36	86	1.7	1.1	1.4
Unascertained	50	34	84	1.7	1.0	1.3
Total	2,926	3,323	6,249	100.0	100.0	100.0

According to the federal census of April 1, 1940, 12.0 per cent of the general population aged 60 or over were single; 48.3 per cent, married; 35.0 per cent, widowed; 4.2 per cent, separated; and 0.5 per cent, divorced (6). It is evident, therefore, that there are significant differences in the prevalence of mental disease among the aged in relation to marital status. The unmarried exceeded their quota by 47.5 per cent. The married, on the other hand, contributed only 57.3 per cent of their quota. The widowed differ significantly from the married, for they exceeded their quota by 37.1 per cent. This is significant in relation to sex, for the widowers exceeded their quota by 62.3 per cent, whereas the widows exceeded their quota by only 26.3 per cent. Those separated from their spouses reached only 90.5 per cent of their quota, but this was greatly in excess of the corresponding rate among the married. The divorced exceeded their quota by 180 per cent.

DEGREE OF EDUCATION

Of the 6,249 first admissions aged 60 or over, 4,972 were classified with respect to degree of education. These data are given in Table 13. Of the total classified, 2,945, or 59.2 per cent, had attended common (elementary) school. A fifth of the ascertained total had received no formal education, though 57 could read and 490 could read and write. Those who had received some degree of high-school education totaled 747, or 15.0 per cent. Those with some college education totaled 267, or 5.4 per cent.

Compared to all first admissions to the civil state hospitals, this shows a great excess of the illiterate and of those with an elementary education, but a marked deficiency of those with a high-school education. This may be attributed to the fact that the elderly patients belong to a generation that was not subject to the laws that require attendance at school up to a minimum age, which would have brought them to the high-school level.

TABLE 13. — FIRST ADMISSIONS, AGED 60 YEARS OR OVER, TO ALL STATE AND LICENSED HOSPITALS FOR MENTAL DISEASE IN NEW YORK STATE, CLASSIFIED ACCORDING TO DEGREE OF EDUCATION, YEAR ENDED MARCH 31, 1948

Degree of Education	Number			Per Cent of Ascertained Total		
	Males	Females	Total	Males	Females	Total
Illiterate	195	271	466	8.5	10.1	9.4
Reads only	24	33	57	1.1	1.2	1.1
Reads and writes............	236	254	490	10.3	9.4	9.9
Common school	1,389	1,556	2,945	60.7	58.0	59.2
High school	307	440	747	13.4	16.4	15.0
College	136	131	267	5.9	4.9	5.4
Unascertained	639	638	1,277	...	...	...
Total	2,926	3,323	6,249	100.0	100.0	100.0

A further comparison may be made with the general population. According to the federal census of April 1, 1940, 10.7 per cent of the population of New York State aged 60 or over had no education; 65.9 per cent had been to elementary school; 14.4 per cent had been to high school; and 5.3 per cent had been to college (6). If we consider the classifications "illiterate," "reads only," and "reads and writes" as equivalent to the census classification "no education," then the corresponding percentages among our first admissions were 20.4, 59.2, 15.0, and 5.4, respectively. This means that the group with no education exceeded its quota by 90.7 per cent. The group who had attended common school contributed only 89.8 per cent of its quota. Those with high-school or college education contributed almost their exact quotas. The outstanding fact is that the illiterate group exceeded by far its quota of first admissions.

ECONOMIC STATUS

Table 14 shows the economic status of the 6,249 first admissions aged 60 or over. Over 80 per cent were either in dependent or in marginal economic circumstances. Only 884, or 14.1 per cent, were found to be comfortable economically. Because of the absence of a comparable classification of the general population, it is impossible to compute rates of first admissions according to economic condition.

TABLE 14.—FIRST ADMISSIONS, AGED 60 YEARS OR OVER, ADMITTED TO ALL STATE AND LICENSED HOSPITALS FOR MENTAL DISEASE IN NEW YORK STATE, CLASSIFIED ACCORDING TO ECONOMIC STATUS, YEAR ENDED MARCH 31, 1948

Economic Status	Number			Per Cent		
	Males	Females	Total	Males	Females	Total
Dependent	1,059	1,355	2,414	36.2	40.8	38.6
Marginal	1,366	1,331	2,697	46.7	40.1	43.2
Comfortable	386	498	884	13.2	15.0	14.1
Unascertained	115	139	254	3.9	4.2	4.1
Total	2,926	3,323	6,249	100.0	100.0	100.0

The group does differ, however, from other groups of mental disorders. Thus, of 1,394 first admissions with involutional psychoses, 37.5 per cent were found to be in comfortable economic circumstances (4). It is also known that first admissions with manic-depressive psychoses tend to have a higher economic status than the average of all first admissions. On the other hand, first admissions with general paresis (2) and alcoholic psychoses (3) had low percentages of patients in affluent circumstances, and rank about the same as the group of aged first admissions. We may conclude, therefore, that the latter are probably drawn in disproportionate numbers from the poorer economic classes.

RACE AND NATIVITY

As shown in Table 15, of the 6,249 first admissions aged 60 years or over, 5,979, or 95.7 per cent, were white, and 262, or 4.2 per cent, were Negro. Eight belonged to other races, of whom 7 were Chinese.

TABLE 15.—FIRST ADMISSIONS, AGED 60 YEARS OR OVER, TO ALL STATE AND LICENSED HOSPITALS FOR MENTAL DISEASE IN NEW YORK STATE, CLASSIFIED ACCORDING TO RACE AND NATIVITY, YEAR ENDED MARCH 31, 1948

Race and Nativity	Number			Per Cent		
	Males	Females	Total	Males	Females	Total
White	2,801	3,178	5,979	95.7	95.6	95.7
Native	1,432	1,688	3,120	48.9	50.8	49.9
Foreign-born	1,352	1,475	2,827	46.2	44.4	45.2
Unascertained	17	15	32	0.6	0.4	0.5
Negro	117	145	262	4.0	4.4	4.2
Chinese	7	...	7	0.2	...	0.1
Other	1	...	1	...*	...	...*
Total	2,926	3,323	6,249	100.0	100.0	100.0

* Less than 0.05.

Of the general population of New York State aged 60 years or over on April 1, 1940, 97.9 per cent were white, and 2.0 per cent were Negro (5). Thus the white population in this age group contributed 97.8 per cent of its quota to the number of first admissions, whereas Negroes exceeded their quota by 110 per cent.

The white first admissions included 3,120 of native birth and 2,827 of foreign birth. These represented 52.2 and 47.3 per cent, respectively, of the total white first admissions aged 60 or over. In the general population of similar age, native and foreign whites constituted 56.8 and 43.2 per cent, respectively (5). Therefore, native whites contributed only 91.9 per cent of their quota, but foreign whites exceeded their quota by 9.5 per cent.

SUMMARY

1. For more than a half century the age structure of the population has been changing, the young showing a relative decrease, and the elderly a relative increase.

2. The decrease in death rates, primarily at younger ages, has acted so as to increase the expectation of life, and to enable a larger part of the population to reach advanced ages.

3. Mental disease varies directly with age. Because of the increase of the aged population, there has been a corresponding increase in the number of mentally ill.

4. Rates of first admission to hospitals for mental disease have increased more rapidly among the older elements of the general population than among the younger.

5. There has been a steady increase in the average age of first admissions to hospitals for mental disease, and in the relative rates of first admissions.

6. In association with the changing age distribution of patients with mental disease, there have been increases in the relative prevalence of psychoses with cerebral arteriosclerosis, senile psychoses, and involutional psychoses.

7. The expectation of mental disease increased at all ages between 1920 and 1940, but the rates of increase were greatest at the advanced ages.

8. Rates of first admission among those aged 60 or over are higher in urban than in rural areas. They are lowest in the farm population.

9. Of those aged 60 or over, rates of first admission were lowest among the married.

10. Of those aged 60 or over, that part without any formal education exceeded its quota by 90 per cent.

11. First admissions aged 60 or over appear to be drawn disproportionately from the less affluent classes.

12. Negroes have a higher rate of first admissions than whites of similar age.

13. Foreign whites aged 60 or over have higher rates of first admissions than native whites of similar age.

REFERENCES

1. Malzberg, B. "The Increase of Mental Disease," *Psychiatric Quart.*, 1943, 17: 488
2. ———. "A Study of First Admissions with General Paresis," *Psychiatric Quart.*, 1947, 21: 223
3. ———. "A Study of First Admissions with Alcoholic Psychoses," *Quart. Jour. of Studies of Alcohol*, 1947, 8: 288
4. ———. "A Statistical Study of First Admissions with Involutional Psychoses," *Psychiatric Quart. Suppl.*, 1948, Vol. 22, Part I, p. 149
5. United States Bureau of the Census. *Population. Second Series. Characteristics of the Population. New York.* Washington, D.C.: Government Printing Office, 1943
6. ———. *Sixteenth Census of the United States: 1940. Population.* Vol. 4, "Characteristics by Age. New York." Washington, D.C.: Government Printing Office, 1943
7. ———. *Vital Statistics of the United States, 1948. Part I.* Washington, D.C.: Government Printing Office, 1950
8. ———. *Seventeenth Census of the United States.* Vol. II, "Characteristics of the Population." Part I. "U.S. Summary." Washington, D.C.: Government Printing Office, 1953. Pp. 1–89

Chapter III

GENETIC ASPECTS OF MENTAL DISORDERS
IN LATER LIFE

Franz J. Kallmann

Professional interest in the potential significance of heredity as a determinant of variable adjustive capacities should not be perfunctory as to any part of the human life span, nor should it diminish toward the later stages of human life. Factual information about the genetic aspects of varying degrees of adjustment to senescence may still be incomplete, but the need of this information for an understanding of important geriatric problems is now largely unquestioned. On the whole, it has been realized that certain investigative imperfections, which may still be apparent in the available genetic data on senile disorders, are actually to be expected to be more or less proportional to current inadequacies in our knowledge of the general biological phenomena of aging and old age.

The sincerity of the assurance, that this statement is made without any recriminatory or apologetic reflections on behalf of the contemporary discipline of human genetics, is patent in view of the chronological (1951) and topographic (political) conditions under which it has been formulated. However, the reference may be helpful in recalling the prolonged uphill struggle, which was waged by the youngest branch of the biological sciences during the first half of the century in order to establish itself despite an utter lack of popular attractiveness. Obviously, the struggle was especially arduous in relation to the last sector of the human life cycle. From a clinical standpoint, this sector was likely to be the least rewarding, while methodologically it was certain to be among the most difficult subjects of genetic investigation. Apart from involving the longest possible period of observation and the extended maintenance of a durable and highly specialized research organization, genealogical studies of presenile and senile disturbances were apt to require complete, fully traceable, and adequately recorded life histories if they were to be useful for the scientific purposes of gerontological genetics.

Irrespective of the procedural difficulties inherent in the subject matter, it has become clear that the possible effect of genetically determined influences upon mental disorders in later life may express itself in three different ways:

1. Heredity may be largely responsible for the presenescent occurrence of disorders, physical or mental, which are likely to alter a person's adaptability to the vicissitudes of the senium. The range of disturbances in this category may extend from certain types of mental deficiency, epilepsy, and severe emotional instability (including schizoid personality traits and a tendency to compulsive drinking) to chronic pulmonary tuberculosis, cancer, or specific metabolic dysfunctions on the one hand and to schizophrenic or manic-depressive psychoses on the other.

2. Heredity may be a determining factor with respect to the normal average ability of man to survive till and through the period of old age. Evidently, a person must be sufficiently longevous to be capable of developing any kind of senile disorder. Besides, the tendency to break down with a typically senile psychosis presupposes the capacity for living through the earlier years of maturity without succumbing to another type of psychosis.

3. Heredity may play a decisive role in the etiology of mental disorders which are peculiar to the period of senescence. This group would include senile and presenile psychoses proper and possibly certain symptomatic types of psychosis associated with specific vascular or metabolic changes.

ADJUSTIVE VARIATIONS DURING THE SENIUM AS THE RESULT
OF THE PRESENESCENT OCCURRENCE OF GENETICALLY
DETERMINED DISORDERS

Especially limited is the volume of exact information about the mutual effects of aging and those chronic pathological conditions which fall into the first category described because they usually occur before the senile period. Relatively few longitudinal studies have been made on the manner in which prolonged physical or mental disorders tend to complicate, or are complicated by, the ordinary phenomena of old age, and most of these investigations have been in relation to chronological rather than biological age. However, since the interrelations between growth and decline are known to vary not only from one organic system to another within the same individual, but also from individual to individual, it is obvious that an appraisal of changes due to aging, if analyzed only in terms of chronological age, cannot be more than a gross approximation. Without this distinction it may often be difficult to determine, for instance, whether certain complications in the later stages of chronic conditions such as alcoholism or hypertensive disease fall into the period of senescence by coincidence or as the result of a causal constitutional relationship.

As a rule, the impact of the senium is assumed to intensify pre-existing maladjustment in that it is apt to lower a person's general resistance as well as the efficacy of specific protective defense mechanisms against progression of a chronic and not fully stabilized disease. Notable evidence of an increased tendency to mental deterioration in various types of mental deficiency is presented in Kaplan's section on the aged subnormal (chapter xiv), while extreme states of maladjustment in some old schizophrenics following prolonged hospitalization are described by Hanfmann in chapter xii. According to Gruhle (29), only minor changes attributable to the immediate effect of aging are observable in the clinical histories of chronic mental patients, except for those of alcoholics, who almost always show a marked decline in tolerance and general resistance. Some schizophrenics are said to become less autistic and socially more amenable with advancing age, and those few epileptics who reach the period of senescence despite an uncontrolled tendency to convulsions may perhaps be distinguished by a lessened degree of irritability.

Most of these observations do not seem to be compatible with the generalized emphasis placed by Riemer (59) upon the extended hospitalization of old schizophrenics "as a hedge against a senile psychosis." These patients are assumed by him to be spared the responsibility of coping with reality so that they will be relieved of consequent strains upon their systemic organization. Of course, the topic of this disagreement is entirely unrelated to the evidence in support of the theory that the potential vulnerabilities responsible for the generally presenescent occurrence of schizophrenic and manic-depressive psychoses are attributable to genetically specific, unexchangeable, and apparently single-factor types of inheritance (36).

The deleterious interrelationship between advancing biological age and declining constitutional resistance is least difficult to demonstrate in a chronic type of infectious disease such as tuberculosis, which shows genetically determined variations in relation to both deficient resistance to the infection itself and deficient resistance to the progression of the disease (37). Contrary to a rather widespread misconception, pulmonary tuberculosis cannot be classified as a disease which is likely to become more benign in later life. Instead, there are many indications that tuberculosis is aging as the population is aging (56), and that resistance to the disease is declining in proportion to whatever decline in general resistance is associated with ordinary changes of old age (10). Recent statistical data for the American population reveal that the majority of all deaths from tuberculosis occur after the age of 40 years. In fact, one out of six of these deaths is found in persons over 65 years of age. It is especially significant that many fatal cases observed in the older age groups appear to develop from lesions which become manifest only late in life (57, 58).

There is reason to believe, therefore, that the normal average capacity for adjustment to old age is adversely affected by chronic pathological conditions, which occur before senescence and either result from an interplay of specific genetic and environmental factors or tend to overstrain a person's general constitutional system of adaptive defense mechanisms.

HEREDITY IN RELATION TO ADJUSTMENT AND SURVIVAL IN THE PERIOD OF SENESCENCE

Much attention has been given to the procurement of data on variable biological survival values in old age, even if the implications of the central issue have not always been clearly understood. From a genetic standpoint, the basic problem is related to the question as to whether or not, in the absence of previous life-shortening adversity, man's ability to survive beyond the physiological age of creativeness and reproductivity without gross maladjustment shows a tendency to statistically significant variations. If affirmative evidence of variable survival values can be obtained, the primary basis of these vital differences may be traceable to genetically determined gradations in normal adaptational potentialities.

Earlier investigations of this problem, including those of Bell (7) and of Beeton and Pearson (6), were based on methods of vital statistics and were necessarily limited to the differential aspects of longevity. The most extensive statistical data on longevity were contributed by Nöllenburg (53), by Dublin and Lotka[1] (18), and especially by Pearl and his collaborators (54). All of these studies provided evidence of a positive correlation between the life spans of parents and their children, although there was some disagreement on the genetic interpretation of the observed relationship.

More recently, animal experiments and biochemical analyses such as those of Gorer (22) and Simms (66) and comparative twin studies have been used for the purpose of investigating the effect of genetic variations in relation to the total range of adaptation to aging and old age. Despite Grüneberg's skepticism (24), longitudinal twin studies have proved to be particularly useful, both genetically and psychiatrically, since they are directly applicable to human variations in adjustment during the period of senescence. In investigations of the interaction of genetic and environmental factors in the origin of human behavior disorders, one may generally expect to encounter more intricate problems of causality than is true in any other species.

It is rather fortunate, therefore, that the phenomenon of twinning supplies us with sets of genotypically identical persons, whose developmental and adjustive dissimilarities can be compared with those observed in the differential behavior patterns of ordinary siblings (35). Of course, such a comparison of intra-pair differences requires long-term observation and adequate sampling procedures, if the histories of the twin subjects used as index cases are supposed to be representative of the total population from which they have been drawn. As a rule, the sampling procedure applied may be expected to gain in effectiveness by being less arbitrary than, for instance, the one which was employed in the technically well-documented survey of Vogt and his collaborators (71). The results of this study have been interpreted in the sense of an inherited factor for senile conditions of the eye "hitherto regarded as due to wear and tear or to external influences."

In the comparative twin studies of senescence, conducted by the writer and his research staff (38, 39, 40, 41), a procedural refinement of the original twin-study method has been used, called the

---

[1] In the latest edition, in conjunction with Spiegelman.

twin-family method. By extending the number of genotypes available for comparison under similar conditions of culture and home milieu, this modified procedure combines the study of a random sample of both one-egg and two-egg twin pairs with a study of their full siblings, half-siblings, and step-siblings. In this manner, it has been possible to integrate controlled observations obtained with the twin-study method into a broad study of twin-family units, which are assembled by means of an approach combining the statistical requirements of Weinberg's sampling method as applied to the study of siblings (65) with the general principles of a procedure approximating a state-wide population census of twins in certain age brackets. The present number of index families, distinguished by an aged twin subject over age 60 and continuously observed within the area of New York State, has reached a total of 2,926 twin-index units.

It is indicated by an analysis of comparative twin data that differences in the intra-pair variance of general adaptational and adjustive potentialities, observed between one-egg and two-egg groups of twins tend to express themselves throughout life and are clearly correlated with the variable capacity for adjustment to aging and old age (38, 39, 40). As to physical signs of aging, a wide range of variability is the rule in two-egg pairs, even in those who always lived under comparable environmental conditions. Extreme dissimilarities, as displayed by the A. twins until age 65 (Fig. 1) or by the B. twins until age 83 (Fig. 2), are by no means an exception in genetically dissimilar pairs of two-egg twins.

By contrast, the general similarities between aging one-egg twins are apt to be much more pronounced and are frequently expressed against the potential effect of modifying influences arising from entirely different environments. These similarities extend to the degree of senile enfeeblement or its absence, to a decline in general adjustive plasticity, to measurable intellectual functions, and to the capacity for longevity. In many instances, including the pairs shown in Figures 3 to 5, one-egg twin partners continue to be as indistinguishable in various stages of senescence as they had been in childhood or in their earlier years of maturity, irrespective of striking differences in the social, economic, and other extrinsic aspects of their life histories.

The degree of dissimilar environmental circumstances in one-egg twins may be illustrated by the fact that one twin remained single while the other twin was married for many years, as has been true in both the C. twins (Fig. 3) and the D. twins (Fig. 4), or by prolonged separation with residence in different countries, which has been a distinguishing feature of the histories of the E. twins (Fig. 5). Permanent separation began at the age of 14 years in the C. twins, and at age 23 in the E. twins. In the latter pair, one twin was happily married to a prosperous jeweler for 45 years (16 children), while her twin sister was deserted by her husband, a shiftless gambler, after she had given birth to 15 children. The D. twins have been equally successful physicians and prominent citizens in different cities for more than four decades.

The most recent comparative data[2] on the life spans of senescent twin-index pairs, of whom both members died of natural causes after age 60, are summarized in Table 16. As to the total longevity score, the mean intra-pair difference in the length of life of one-egg twin pairs is approximately one-half that observed in two-egg pairs of the same sex. The total mean difference varies from 36.7 months in the one-egg group to 71.8 months in the same-sexed two-egg group, and to 126.6 months in two-egg pairs of opposite sex. The difference between the two same-sexed groups is statistically significant at the .02 level of confidence ($t = 2.48$; t_{02} with 66 degrees of freedom $= 2.33$), and it is particularly interesting that this total mean intra-pair difference shows no significant difference between the sexes.

Biologically it is to be expected, of course, that genetically determined differences in longevity between the two twin groups fall largely into the age group 60 to 74, and gradually disappear beyond age 75, revealing an important difference in favor of the female sex in view of a general sex difference in the average life span. In the age group 60 to 74, the difference in the mean length of life between the total twin groups of the same sex is significant at the .01 level ($t = 3.10$; t_{01} with 33 degrees of freedom $= 2.58$), but no significant difference in the mean intra-pair differences is observable any more in the age group 75 and over. In other words, if two-egg

[2] Miss Grenevere Freedman rendered valuable assistance in the statistical analysis of these data, which were treated in accordance with the method devised by Johnson and Neyman for "matched subgroups" (*Statistical Research Memoirs*, Vol. I, 1936), while Misses E. Bondy and C. Kimberg aided in recording the histories of these twin subjects.

TABLE 16.—MEAN INTRA-PAIR DIFFERENCES IN THE LIFE SPAN OF 69 DECEASED
TWIN-INDEX PAIRS OF THE SAME SEX*

Age Group Referring to First-deceased Twin Partner	Mean Intra-pair Differences in Longevity, Expressed in Months of Life					
	One-egg Pairs			Two-egg Pairs		
	Male	Female	Total	Male	Female	Total
60–74	47.1	24.8	39.7	97.9	106.9	101.1
Over 74	36.0	33.6	34.4	38.2	29.2	32.8
All pairs over 60.................	42.9	31.2	36.7	79.1	63.2	71.8

* Mean intra-pair difference for all opposite-sexed pairs over 60: 126.6 months.

twin partners are alike in the ability to survive until the eighth
decade of life, their variations in the remaining life expectancy will
be approximately the same as those of longevous one-egg pairs.

An equally revealing difference between one-egg and same-
sexed two-egg groups of twin partners distinguished by survival till
senescence has been observed in their psychometric test performances, although general similarities in the socioeconomic histories
of twin pairs available for testing in this age group have been found
to be of nearly the same order of magnitude for the two twin groups
(41). The mean intra-pair differences in the test scores of a random
sample of 240 senescent twin-index cases, which are compared in
Table 17, furnish interesting information about the potential effect

TABLE 17.—MEAN INTRA-PAIR DIFFERENCES IN THE TEST SCORES
OF SENESCENT TWIN PAIRS

Test	Male Pairs		Female Pairs	
	One-egg	Two-egg	One-egg	Two-egg
Vocabulary	2.47	3.89	2.22	4.77
Digits forward.....................	1.09	1.05	0.83	1.08
Digits backward....................	0.91	0.89	0.73	1.15
Digit symbol	5.34	6.92	4.42	9.25
Block designs	3.59	6.88	3.17	6.17
Similarities	2.69	2.95	2.45	4.17
Directions	4.64	6.43	4.92	4.62
Tapping	8.47	18.47	11.65	13.82
Reproduction of designs............	1.82	3.00	2.68	3.90

of genetic factors upon variable changes in intellectual abilities
during senescence. The basic trend in one-egg twins toward a similar
intellectual test performance in later life is demonstrable in all test
scores measuring abstract intellectual function. According to the

results of a detailed analysis presented recently by L. Feingold (20), the difference between the two twin groups is significant at the one-per-cent level of confidence for the Vocabulary, Digits Backward, Digit Symbol, Block Designs, and Similarities tests. Another interesting biological difference may be seen in the observation that some intellectual changes in senescent males seem to precede those displayed by aging females. This discrepancy apparently corresponds with specific sex differences in longevity and adjustive plasticity.

Notwithstanding various differences between the sexes, it is justified to conclude that the observed similarities in the intellectual performances, adaptive potentialities, and adjustive patterns of senescent one-egg twins generally exceed those seen in two-egg pairs. One may say, therefore, that the manner in which genetically determined variations in aging and longevity correspond with variations in intellectual and adaptational abilities provides conclusive evidence of the demonstrable extent to which genic elements influence a person's variable capacity for maintaining a state of physical and mental health throughout life.

HEREDITY IN RELATION TO SPECIFIC DISORDERS
OF THE SENIUM

Concerning the genetic aspects of distinctly pathological conditions peculiar to the period of senescence, it is safe to state that much of the existing uncertainty has been due to a frequent overlapping of clinical symptoms in a group of mental disorders, characterized by the complexities of a "polydimensional" structure (33). Additional reasons apparently include various inconsistencies in psychiatric terminology and diagnostic classification as well as a scarcity of clinical and genealogical data verified by histological and biochemical examinations.

It is in accordance with expectation, therefore, that some of the evidence relating to such specific disturbances as presenile brain atrophies, which are distinguished by prematurity, relative infrequency, and the circumscribed localization of gross pathological changes, tends to be clearer than is true for the data available in relation to the common forms of senile dementia. Provided that one is correct in ascribing certain pathological phenomena of senility to a progressive loss in the homeostatic capacities of the human organism (p. 49), it is evident that this loss will be most plainly discernible if it occurs dramatically, long before its time, and in a person who originally seemed to be endowed with a satisfactory capacity for health and longevity. Under conditions of this kind, one would not find it too difficult to think in terms of specific pathological dysfunctions produced by a particular mutant gene (single-factor type of inheritance).

Even in those three special types of presenile psychosis, however, which are described as Pick's, Alzheimer's, and Jakob-Creutzfeldt's diseases in another section (pp. 262–88), the observation of familial occurrence has been neither consistent nor entirely uniform. According to Newton (52), for instance, concurrence of apparently typical cases of Alzheimer's disease (2 siblings) and Pick's disease (father of the sibship) has been found in a family studied by James, while the simultaneous occurrence of Pick's disease and Huntington's chorea in one sibship has been reported by Korbsch (42). Other conditions, which have been observed among the blood relatives of patients affected by Pick's disease, comprise epilepsy and mental defect, including mongolism (9, 15), schizophrenia and various psychopathic personality traits (4), cerebellar ataxia and amyotrophic lateral sclerosis (15), and paralysis agitans (31). Analogously, presumably typical cases of senile dementia, involutional melancholia, epilepsy, and mental deficiency have been found associated with Alzheimer's disease in a few families (19, 45, 70). In fact, several investigators (52) favor the assumption of a close biological relationship between senile dementia and presenile brain atrophies, while in a report on verified cases of Alzheimer's disease in three siblings and their father, Grünthal and Wenger (27, 28) reject the theory that the various systematized forms of presenile cerebral atrophy are sufficiently explained by premature aging in different systems of the brain.

Additional instances of a familial tendency to Alzheimer's disease have been seen by Essen-Möller (19), Grosch (23), and Lüers (44) in one or two siblings and a parent; by McMenemey and his co-workers (45) in three siblings and a son of one of them; by Lowenberg and Waggoner (43) in four siblings and a father whose parents were first cousins; and by Van Bogaert, Maere, and Smedt (70) in four siblings as well as their mother and maternal grandmother in one family, and in three siblings, a son of one of these siblings, and a maternal aunt in another family. The operation of a single-factor type of inheritance seems to have been accepted by most of these investigators, but no further specifications of the probable mode of transmission have been worked out by them.

According to a recent comprehensive study of Sjögren and his collaborators (67), the hypothesis of a dominant gene influenced by other modifying genes is more plausible in Pick's disease than in Alzheimer's disease. In this study of 80 family units, the disease expectancy of parents and sibs appeared to be higher in the families of Pick's than of Alzheimer's cases (19 and 6.8 against 10 and 3.8 per cent, respectively). In spite of a preponderance of female patients, the theory of partial or complete sex-linkage was not substantiated.

As regards the etiology of Jakob-Creutzfeldt's disease, the present opinion appears to be in favor of the existence of both hereditary and nonhereditary forms. Familial incidence has been observed by Creutzfeldt (13) in two sisters, and by Meggendorfer (51) in a total of eight siblings. According to a recent report by Jacob, Pyrkosch, and Strube (34), the best-documented pedigree is that of the Backer family, in which histologically verified cases have occurred in three consecutive generations.

With respect to the type of inheritance which is assumed to prevail in Pick's disease, the opinions of Cruz (15), Becker (5), Bleuler (8), Curtius (14), and Sanders (60) are about equally divided between the simple forms of dominance and recessiveness. From the standpoint of familial accumulation, the most notable pedigrees recorded are those of Bebin and Parades (4), Braunmühl and Leonhard (9), Grünthal (26), Hǎskovec (31), and Schmitz and Meyer (62), who observed direct transmission in two, three, or four generations, as well as those of Cruz (four cases each in two consecutive sibships) and of Sanders, Schenk, and Van Veen (one family with seventeen cases). Discordant behavior toward the disease in a pair of one-egg twins has been observed by Becker (5) in a family, in which the twins' father, the paternal grandfather, and two siblings of the father had shown symptoms similar to those of the affected twin. By contrast, striking evidence of pronounced familial similarities has been placed on record by Mallison (47), Friedrich (21), Grünthal (25), and Malamud and Waggoner (46). The similarities

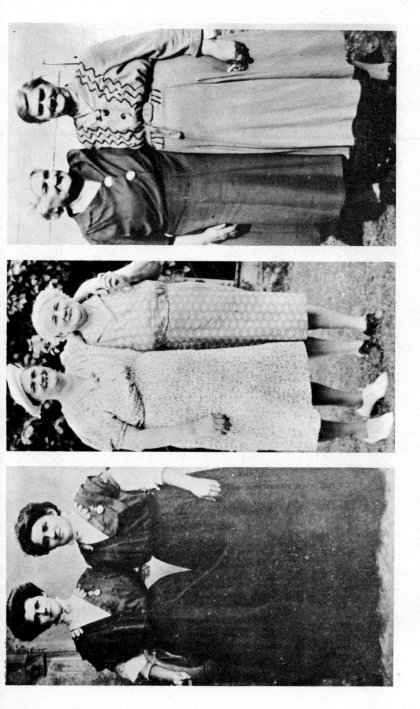

FIG. 1.—The A. twins at the ages of 21, 56, and 65 years.

Fig. 2.—The dizygotic B. twins at age 83.

FIG. 3.—The C. twins at the ages of 4, 16, 52, and 68 years.

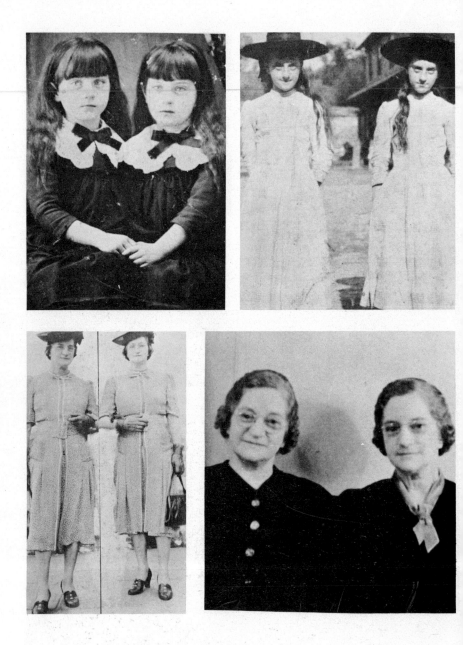

Fig. 4.—The D. twins at the ages of 6, 14, 60, and 68 years.

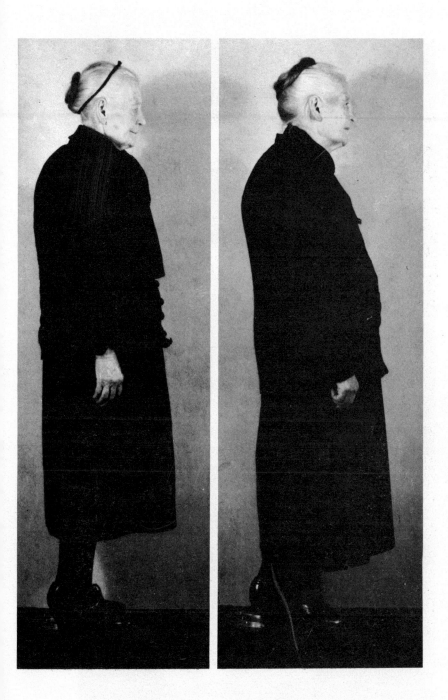

Fig. 5.—The E. twins at age 81.

Fig. 6.—The F. twins at the ages of 30 and 72 years.

FIG. 7.—The G. twins at age 80.

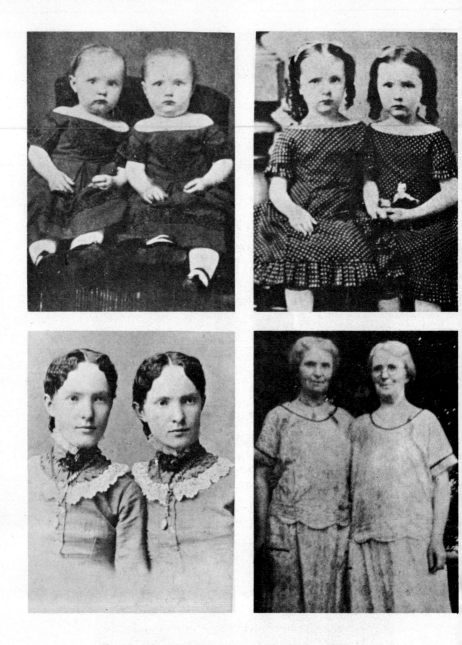

Fig. 8.—The H. twins at the ages of 1, 5, 25, and 70 years.

are said to extend to clinical symptomatology, localization of the process, histological findings, and age at onset of the disease.

The need of further genetic studies in statistically representative and clinically uniform samples of family units is even more apparent in relation to those psychoses in later life, in which cerebrovascular changes are the predominant feature. It is evident, of course, that arteriosclerotic symptoms are developed much earlier and more severely by some persons than by others, and that the ability to withstand cerebral damage is equally variable in man (3, 11, 55). In view of the investigations of Ayman (2), De Monchy (16), Donner (17), Gutmann (30), Schulz (63), and Weitz (73), it is also indicated that certain families show a specifically increased tendency to coronary artery disease, essential hypertension, or cerebral arteriosclerosis, especially in the presence of essential familial hypercholesterolemia which has been assumed by various investigators (1, 74, 75) to be produced by a dominantly transmitted biochemical dysfunction. In fact, a number of experts including Hines (32), Meggendorfer (51), and Stern (69) are inclined to believe that dominant genotypes are responsible for both a specific tendency to cerebral arteriosclerosis and its particular localization. On the whole, however, Rothschild seems justified in his conclusion that the etiology of arteriosclerosis is still "a much-disputed problem." Genetically it is entirely possible, for instance, that the hereditary aspects of arteriosclerosis (hypertensive disease) may be as complicated as are those of diabetes mellitus. In other words, the clinically observable syndrome of arteriosclerotic disturbances may be subdivided into a number of separate entities, for each of which a specific genetic mechanism may have to be considered.

General reservations of this kind appear especially warranted with respect to one of the most recent and certainly most impressive and extensive genealogical studies of essential hypertension, that of Søbye (68). In this survey, 94.6 per cent of the families of 186 index cases, distinguished by essential hypertension (elevated blood pressure without any known precipitating factor) and proteinuria in the absence of a history of renal disease, were found to include one or more additional cases of hypertensive disease, nephrosclerosis, isolated cardiac hypertrophy, or cerebrovascular accident. Søbye concluded, therefore, that the tendency to develop essential hypertension and nephrosclerosis appeared to depend on the effect of a dominant gene. However, an important presupposition of the given theory would be that the two conditions studied are a genetic entity, and this assumption does not seem as yet to be based on conclusive evidence.

It may be worth mentioning in this connection that the writer's sample of deceased senescent twin-index pairs, previously described in relation to longevity, includes three sets of one-egg twins who succumbed to cerebrovascular complications with an intra-pair difference in time of less than one month. Two pairs were five and twenty-five days apart when the twin partners died of cerebral hemorrhages at the ages of 85 and 69, respectively, and the members of the third pair died the same day of a similar cause at the age of 86, despite considerable differences in their life histories (39). In another one-egg pair with entirely dissimilar histories (Fig. 6), the twins developed equally severe symptoms of cerebral arteriosclerosis at practically the same time. However, there was a difference of almost two years in their ages of death at 83 and 85.

A similar degree of caution, as would still seem desirable regarding the assumption of a dominant unit factor for cerebral arteriosclerosis, is indicated with respect to the theory that the total group of disorders called senile dementia may be due to the effect of a dominant genotype of incomplete penetrance. The main supporters of this theory have been Cresseri (12), Meggendorfer (49), and Scheele (61). According to Meggendorfer, two dominant genes may be involved, one controlling longevity and one producing the psychopathological changes associated with senile dementia. The ensuant biological implications of this concept would not appear to be easier to reconcile with general genetic principles than is true for Weinberger's hypothesis (72), which is somewhat simplified and postulates only a specific genetic factor for the entity of senile dementia. Another point made by Weinberger was based on the fact that no evidence of a genetic relationship between senile dementia and schizophrenia was obtained. However, his sample of 51 senile patients, whose families yielded a total of 18 additional cases of senile dementia, did not include any senile psychoses with paranoid or depressive features.

In conformity with the diagnostic scheme adopted by Schulz (64) in his excellent study of the genetic aspects of senile psychoses distinguished by paranoid delusions, the occurrence of a paranoid-

depressive syndrome in the involutional and senile periods of life
has been given particular attention in the writer's analysis of psy-
chotic-twin-family data related to the senium (35). In fact, it is the
category of involutional psychoses (referring in this study to cases
in whom compulsive-delusional symptoms, nonperiodical forms of
depression, or agitated anxiety states are observed after age 50 and
before age 70), which was reported by Malzberg (48) to have shown
an especially alarming increase in first admissions to mental hospitals since 1930. According to Schulz, senile (involutional) psychoses with paranoid features occur in 1.7 per cent of the total
population over 70 years of age and in 0.47 per cent of all persons
over age 60.

That it is advisable—for biological and psychiatric reasons—to
separate the group of involutional psychoses from senile psychoses
on the one hand and from schizophrenic and manic-depressive psychoses on the other is clearly demonstrated by the comparative data
summarized in Table 18. In this analysis, collective and statisti-

TABLE 18.—DISTRIBUTION OF PSYCHOSES IN THE FAMILIES OF DIFFERENT
SAMPLES OF TWIN-INDEX CASES

Psychiatric Classification	Total Number	Schizophrenia*	Manic-depressive Psychosis*	Involutional and Senile Psychoses†
Senescence (without psychosis)	1,973	0.8	0.3	1.0
Involutional psychosis	96	4.3	0.8	10.0
Senile psychosis	108	2.0	...	5.8
Schizophrenia	953	9.7	0.1	6.6
Manic-depressive psychosis	76	...	21.2	1.8

* Related to all persons over age 14.
† Related to all persons over age 44.

cally not fully corrected psychosis rates for the parents and siblings
of a total of 3,205 twin-index cases, with and without psychotic
phenomena, are compared with respect to the distribution of the
various types of psychosis in the given groups of family units. It is
indicated by the differential rates that major psychoses tend to occur
more frequently among the blood relatives of psychotic index cases
than they do among those of senescent index cases without psychosis.
It is even more important that the general trend in the distribution
of the given psychotic entities is clearly in the direction of specific
genetic mechanisms for the different types of psychosis studied.

While the incidence of schizophrenia is increased especially in the siblings and parents of schizophrenic index cases, that of manic-depressive psychosis is excessive only in the consanguinity of manic-depressive index cases. Besides, there is a definite increase in involutional and senile psychoses, which is limited to the blood relatives of involutional, senile, and schizophrenic index cases. The observed increase in involutional psychoses is most pronounced in the siblings and parents of involutional cases, but is also considerable in the consanguinity of schizophrenic index cases. This excess of involutional psychoses in the families of schizophrenics corresponds with an increase in the incidence of schizophrenia among the blood relatives of involutional index cases. Although the latter increase is moderate, it is sufficient in magnitude to be compatible with the expectancy of schizophrenia among the siblings and parents of aged persons who are distinguished by schizoid personality traits and perhaps by a limited number of relatively mild and late-developing processes of schizophrenia precipitated only by the impact of the involutional period of life. By comparison, the increase in the incidence of schizophrenia in the blood relatives of senile index cases is rather insignificant.

Genetically, it is indicated by this part of the analysis that the principal causal relationship of that type of emotional instability which may lead to an involutional psychosis is to the group of schizoid personality traits and, therefore, indirectly to the entity of schizophrenia rather than to that of manic-depressive psychosis. Although it is probable that the clinical group of involutional psychoses does not fulfill the criteria of biological homogeneity, it is quite obvious that menopausal, presenile, and other types of involutional depression—in the absence of previous periodical mood swings—do not belong to the genetically distinct category of manic-depressive psychosis.

The hypothesis of a multifactorial etiology of involutional psychosis is strengthened by an analysis of age-specific expectancy rates related to the degree of consanguinity to an involutional twin-index case (Table 19). The given rates follow a sliding scale, which varies from an expectancy of 4.5 per cent for the half-siblings to 6.0 per cent for the siblings and two-egg co-twins, and to 60.9 per cent for the one-egg twin partners. It may be concluded from this finding that persons distinguished by a genotypically similar personality

TABLE 19.—EXPECTANCY OF INVOLUTIONAL AND SENILE PSYCHOSES
IN PSYCHOTIC TWIN-INDEX FAMILIES

Type of Psychosis in Original Index Case	Expectancy of the Respective Type of Psychosis According to the Degree of Consanguinity*				
	Parents	Half-siblings	Full Siblings	Dizygotic Co-twins	Monozygotic Co-twins
Involutional	6.4	4.5	6.0	6.0	60.9
Senile	3.4	...	6.5	8.0	42.8

* Related to all persons over age 44 with respect to involutional psychosis, and to all persons over age 59 with respect to senile psychosis.

structure (monozygotic twins) are more likely than dizygotic twins or ordinary siblings to be alike in those factors which favor the occurrence of a psychosis in the involutional period. Apparently, the development of such a psychosis requires not only the capacity for survival until the later years of maturity, but also certain combinations of etiologic components, which individually would not be sufficient to produce a psychotic reaction syndrome.

Psychiatrically it seems justified to assume that the scheme of interacting causative elements includes progressive impairment of general adaptability, cumulative emotional strain, and insecurity due to increasingly conspicuous signs of aging, and the coexistence of certain basic personality traits such as rigidity, compulsiveness, and oversensitivity, frequently associated with a schizoid personality structure or a mild schizophrenic defect. The long-range effect of these traits is toward a reduction of the adjustive plasticity of aging persons and, thereby, toward an impairment in their faculty of adaptation to involutional changes. Genetically, there is reason to believe that many of these emotionally unstable (schizoid) persons are heterozygous carriers of the recessive unit factor for schizophrenia, characterized by an inadequate state of constitutional resistance.

It is in accordance with expectation that the observed increase in the expectancy of a senile psychosis in the sibships of senile twin-index cases is also variable (Table 19). The increase parallels the marked variations in the expectancy of involutional psychosis in involutional family units, although it is more limited in scale. The given expectancy rates have a reduced frame of reference (persons over age 59) and vary only from 6.5 to 8.0 per cent for the siblings and dizygotic co-twins of senile twin-index cases to 42.8

per cent for the one-egg twin partners. Apparently, the interrelationship between a psychotic reaction syndrome in the senile period and the genetic entity of schizophrenia (schizoid personality traits) is much more diluted than is true with respect to involutional psychosis. In fact, that causal relationship seems largely replaced in the senile type of psychosis by an age-specific intensification of long-existing but minor deficiencies in general emotional adjustment. If this interpretation is correct, there would be no compelling reasons for the assumption of a specific, single-factor type of genetic mechanism as a basic determinant of a senile psychosis (senile dementia).

In any case, the observed difference between one-egg and two-egg groups of twins with regard to the expectancy of senile psychosis is statistically significant and indicative of the extent to which genetically similar personality types are more likely than ordinary siblings to be alike in those various factors interacting in the development of a senile psychosis. The essential part played by heredity in this intricate interplay may be seen in genetically determined variations in general personality structure and adjustive potentialities and in variable capacities for longevity and satisfactory adaptation to senescent decrepitudes. Since the capacity for aging and longevity is part of the normal equipment of man and is known to show many graded differences within the limits of normalcy, it seems reasonable to assume that the genetic phenomena responsible for variable deficiencies in adjustment to the senium follow the multifactor type of inheritance, which means that they are determined by the interaction of many genes.

The extent of possible adjustive variations in the senile period, observable in genetically dissimilar (two-egg) twin pairs despite very similar environmental and existential conditions, may be illustrated by the twin sisters shown in Figure 7. Throughout their lives, the G. twins had differed as much in their personalities and adjustive patterns as they did in their physical appearances and general signs of aging at age 80. The younger-looking twin, described as sociable, placid, and kind, remained active and well-adjusted until she died of a heart attack, a few months before her eighty-third birthday. Her taller and more intelligent twin sister, who had always been moody, ill-tempered, and vindictive, developed a depressive-paranoid psychosis around the age of 80. She died in a mental hospital three years later.

By contrast, the H. twins (Fig. 8) were monozygotic and displayed remarkable similarities in the type and symptomatology of a senile psychosis, in spite of marked differences in their life histories. They were 17 years old when they were separated through the marriage of one of them to a local grocer. The other twin remained single and supported herself as a factory worker and housekeeper until her retirement at age 67. Although they lived far away from each other and showed little interest in social activities because of an equally pronounced hearing defect, both were described as highly respected, kind, congenial, and well-adjusted. At the age of 73, however, the unmarried twin developed an acute anxiety state with mild confusion and agitation and with vague ideas of reference and persecution. She required admission to a mental hospital, where she died of cardiac decompensation within two years. A few months later, the survivor of the pair began to duplicate her twin's history in practically every respect.

It is demonstrated by observations of this kind that fully recorded twin data are helpful in investigating the challenging problems posed by severe maladjustment to aging and old age. Beyond question, further advancement in the understanding of involutional, arteriosclerotic, and senile psychoses will require the planning of more basic research in relation to the interplay of such complex determinative components as age-susceptible personality traits, reduced adaptive (homeostatic) plasticity, and those gene-specific biochemical phenomena controlling growth and decline. It seems rather certain, however, that adequate progress in the management of the clinical and psychological aspects of geriatrics will not be possible without a more thorough knowledge of the genetic background factors, which primarily determine man's variable capacities for maintaining a state of physical and mental health throughout life, including the senium.

REFERENCES

1. Adlersberg, D., Parets, A. D., and Boas, E. P. "Genetics of Atherosclerosis," *Jour. Amer. Med. Assoc.*, 1949, 141: 246
2. Ayman, D. "Heredity in Arterial (Essential) Hypertension," *Arch. Int. Med.*, 1934, 53: 792
3. Bauer, J. *Differential Diagnosis of Internal Diseases.* New York: Grune and Stratton, 1950
4. Bebin, J., and Parades, V. "Demencia presenil hereditaria por atrofia cortical," *Rev. Neuro-Psiquiatria*, 1947, 10: 177
5. Becker, P. E. "Genetische und klinische Fragen bei Pick'scher Krankheit," *Nervenarzt*, 1948, 19: 355
6. Beeton, M., and Pearson, K. "On the Inheritance of the Duration of Life,

and on the Intensity of Natural Selection in Man," *Biometrika*, 1901, 1: 50

7. Bell, A. G. *The Duration of Life and Conditions Associated with Longevity.* Washington, D.C.: Genealogical Record Office, 1918

8. Bleuler, M. "Die erbpathologische Forschungsrichtung in der Psychiatrie," *Schweiz. Arch. f. Neurol. Psychiatrie*, 1948, 62: 59

9. Braunmühl, A., and Leonhard, K. "Ueber ein Schwesternpaar mit Pick'-scher Krankheit," *Ztschr. f. ges. Neurol. Psychiatrie*, 1934, 150: 209

10. Chaves, A. D., and Leites, V. "Development of Pulmonary Tuberculosis in Persons Over Forty," *Geriatrics*, 1951, 6: 50

11. Cowdry, E. V. *Problems of Ageing.* Baltimore: Williams and Wilkins, 1942

12. Cresseri, A. "L'Ereditarietà della Demenza Senile," *Boll. Soc. Ital. Biol. Sperim.*, 1948, 24: 200

13. Creutzfeldt, H. G. "Ueber eine eigenartige herdförmige Erkrankung des Zentralnervensystems," *Nissl-Alzheimer Arb.*, *Ergänzungsband*, 1921, p. 1

14. Curtius, F. *Die organischen und funktionellen Erbkrankheiten des Nervensystems.* Stuttgart: F. Enke, 1935

15. De Gispert Cruz, J. "Síndrome demencial familiar presenil probable enfermedad de Pick," *Clínica y Labor.*, 1948, 46: 28

16. De Monchy, S. J. R. "Psychische stoornissen bij verkalking van de bloed vaten der hersenen," *Nederl. Tijdschr. v. Geneesk.*, 1923, 67: 726

17. Donner, S. E. "Arteriosklerose bei den Paralytikern und anderen Geisteskranken," *Ztschr. f. Konstitutl.*, 1926, 12: 564

18. Dublin, L. I., and Lotka, A. J. *Length of Life.* New York: Ronald Press, 1936

19. Essen-Möller, E. "A Family with Alzheimer's Disease," *Acta Psychiatr. Neurol.*, 1946, 21: 233

20. Feingold, L. "A Psychometric Study of Senescent Twins." Unpublished doctoral dissertation, Columbia University, 1950

21. Friedrich, G. "Pathologisch-anatomischer Nachweis des Vorkommens der Pick'schen Krankheit in zwei Generationen," *Ztschr. f. ges. Neurol. Psychiatrie*, 1940, 170: 311

22. Gorer, P. A. "Renal Lesions Found in Pure Lines of Mice," *Jour. Pathol. Bact.*, 1940, 50: 25

23. Grosch, H. "Alzheimer's Krankheit und prosektische Katatonie. Zur Auffassung vom Systemcharakter der Katatonie," *Psychiatrie, Neurol., Med. Psychol.*, 1949, 1: 302

24. Grüneberg, H. *Animal Genetics and Medicine.* New York: P. B. Hoeber, 1947

25. Grünthal, E. "Ueber ein Bruederpaar mit Pick'scher Krankheit," *Ztschr. f. ges. Neurol. Psychiatrie*, 1930, 129: 350

26. ———. "Klinisch-genealogischer Nachweis von Erblichkeit bei Pick'scher Krankheit," *ibid.*, 1931, 136: 464

27. Grünthal, E., and Wenger, O. "Nachweis von Erblichkeit bei der Alzheimer'-schen Krankheit nebst Bemerkungen über den Altersvorgang im Gehirn," *Monatsschr. f. Psychiatrie Neurol.*, 1939, 101: 8

28. ———. "Ergänzende Untersuchungen und Bemerkungen zu der Arbeit: Nachweis von Erblichkeit bei der Alzheimer'schen Krankheit nebst Bemerkungen über den Altersvorgang im Gehirn," *ibid.*, 1939, 102: 302

29. Gruhle, H. W. "Der Einfluss des Alters auf den Ablauf seelischer Störungen," *Ztschr. f. Altersforschung*, 1938, 1: 209

30. Gutmann, M. J. "Zum familiären Vorkommen des Schlaganfalls," *Arch. Rassen-Gesellschaftsbiol.*, 1927, 20: 70
31. Häskovec, V. "Pick'sche Krankheit," *Zentralbl. f. ges. Neurol. Psychiatrie*, 1934, 73: 345
32. Hines, E. A., Jr. "The Hereditary Factor in Essential Hypertension," *Ann. Int. Med.*, 1937, 11: 593
33. Hirschmann, J. "Ueber den mehrdimensionalen Aufbau der Alterspsychosen," *Arch. f. Psychiatrie Ztschr. Neurol.*, 1949, 181: 306
34. Jacob, H., Pyrkosch, W., and Strube, H. "Die erbliche Form der Creutzfeldt-Jakob'schen Krankheit (Familie Backer)," *Arch. f. Psychiatrie Nervenkr.*, 1950, 184: 653
35. Kallmann, F. J. "The Genetics of Psychoses—An Analysis of 1232 Index Families," *Congrès International de Psychiatrie, Vol. VI.* Paris: Hermann et Cie. 1950, 1
36. ———. "Twin Studies in Relation to Adjustive Problems in Man," *Transact. New York Acad. Sci.*, 1951, 13: 270
37. Kallmann, F. J., and Reisner, D. "Twin Studies on the Significance of Genetic Factors in Tuberculosis," *Amer. Rev. Tuberc.*, 1943, 47: 549
38. Kallmann, F. J., and Sander, G. "Twin Studies on Aging and Longevity," *Jour. Hered.*, 1948, 39: 349
39. ———. "Twin Studies on Senescence," *Amer. Jour. Psychiatry*, 1949, 106: 29
40. Kallmann, F. J., and Feingold, L. "Principles of Human Genetics in Relation to Insurance Medicine and Public Health," *Jour. Insur. Med.*, 1949, 4: 2
41. Kallmann, F. J., Feingold, L., and Bondy, E. "Comparative, Adaptational, Social, and Psychometric Data on the Life Histories of Senescent Twin Pairs," *Amer. Jour. Hum. Genet*, 1951, 3: 65
42. Korbsch, H. "Pick'sche und Huntington'sche Krankheit bei Geschwistern," *Arch. f. Psychiatrie*, 1933, 100: 326
43. Lowenberg, K., and Waggoner, R. W. "Familial Organic Psychosis (Alzheimer's Type)," *Arch. Neurol. Psychiatry*, 1934, 31: 737
44. Lüers, T. "Ueber die familiären, juvenilen Formen der Alzheimer'schen Krankheit mit neurologischen Herderscheinungen," *Arch. f. Psychiatr. Nervenkr.*, 1947, 179: 132
45. McMenemey, W. H., Worster-Drought, C., Flind, I., and Williams, H. C. "Familiar Presenile Dementia," *Jour. Neurol. Psychiatry*, 1939, 2: 293
46. Malamud, N., and Waggoner, R. W. "Genealogic and Clinicopathologic Study of Pick's Disease," *Arch. Neurol. Psychiatry*, 1943, 50: 288
47. Mallison, R. "Zur Klinik der Pick'schen Atrophie," *Nervenarzt*, 1947, 18: 247
48. Malzberg, B. "A Statistical Study of First Admissions with Involutional Psychoses to Hospitals for Mental Diseases in New York State," *Psychiatric Quart. Suppl.*, 1948, 22: 141
49. Meggendorfer, F. "Ueber die hereditäre Disposition zur Dementia senilis," *Ztschr. f. ges. Neurol. Psychiatrie*, 1926, 101: 387
50. ———. "Klinische und genealogische Beobachtungen bei einem Fall von spastischer Pseudosklerose Jakobs," *ibid.*, 1930, 128: 337
51. ———. "Alterspsychosen." In Just's *Handbuch der Erbbiologie des Menschen* (Berlin: J. Springer, 1939). Vol. V/2
52. Newton, R. D. "The Identity of Alzheimer's Disease and Senile Dementia and Their Relationship to Senility," *Jour. Ment. Sci.*, 1948, 94: 225

53. Nöllenburg, W. "Statistische Untersuchungen über die Erblichkeit der Lebenslänge," *Ztschr. f. Konstitutl.*, 1932, 16: 707
54. Pearl, R., and De Witt Pearl, R. *The Ancestry of the Long-Lived*. Baltimore: The Johns Hopkins Press, 1934
55. Platt, R. "Heredity in Hypertension," *Quart. Jour. Med.*, 1947, 16: 111
56. Pottenger, F. M. *Tuberculosis*. St. Louis: C. V. Mosby, 1948
57. Reisner, D. "Incipiency and Evolution of Pulmonary Tuberculosis," *Amer. Rev. Tuberc.*, 1948, 57: 207
58. Rich, A. R. *The Pathogenesis of Tuberculosis*. Springfield: Charles C. Thomas, 1944.
59. Riemer, M. D. "A Study of the Mental States of the Schizophrenics Hospitalized for over 25 Years into Their Senium," *Psychiatric Quart.*, 1950, 24: 309
60. Sanders, J., Schenk, V. W. D., and Van Veen, P. "A Family with Pick's Disease," *Verh. Kon. Nederl. Akad. Wetenschappen*, 1939, Sec. 2, 124
61. Scheele, H. "Ueber ein konkordantes zweieiiges Zwillingspaar mit seniler Demenz. Ein Beitrag zur Erbforschung bei der senilen Demenz," *Ztschr. f. ges. Neurol. Psychiatrie*, 1933, 144: 606
62. Schmitz, H. A., and Meyer, A. "Ueber die Pick'sche Krankheit mit besonderer Berücksichtigung der Erblichkeit," *Arch. f. Psychiatrie*, 1933, 99: 747
63. Schulz, B. "Ueber die hereditären Beziehungen der Hirnarteriosklerose," *Ztschr. f. ges. Neurol. Psychiatrie*, 1929, 120: 35
64. ———. "Ueber die hereditären Beziehungen paranoid-gefärbter Alterspsychosen," *ibid.*, 1930, 129: 147
65. ———. *Methodik der Medizinischen Erbforschung*. Leipzig: G. Thieme, 1936
66. Simms, H. S. "The Use of a Measurable Cause of Death (Hemorrhage) for the Evaluation of Aging," *Jour. Gen. Physiol.*, 1942, 26: 169
67. Sjögren, T., Sjögren, H., and Lindgren, A. G. H. *Morbus Alzheimer and Morbus Pick*. Copenhagen: E. Munksgaard, 1952
68. Søbye, P. *Heredity in Essential Hypertension and Nephrosclerosis*. Copenhagen: E. Munksgaard, 1948
69. Stern, F. "Arteriosklerotische Psychosen." In Bumke's *Handbuch der Geisteskrankheiten* (Berlin: J. Springer, 1930), Vol. VIII
70. Van Bogaert, L., Maere, M., and De Smedt, E. "Sur les formes familiales précoces de la maladie d'Alzheimer," *Monatsschr. f. Psychiatr. Neurol.*, 1940, 102: 240
71. Vogt, A., Wagner, H., Richner, H., and Meyer, G. "Das Senium bei eineiigen und zweieiigen Zwillingen: die Erbentstehung bisher exogen und durch Abnutzung erklärter Altersleiden," *Arch. J. Klaus Stiftg.*, 1939, 14: 475
72. Weinberger, H. L. "Ueber die hereditären Beziehungen der senilen Demenz," *Ztschr. f. ges. Neurol. Psychiatrie*, 1926, 106: 666
73. Weitz, W. "Zur Aetiologie der genuinen oder vasculären Hypertension," *Ztschr. f. klin. Med.*, 1923, 96: 151
74. Wilkinson, Ch. F. "Essential Familial Hypercholesterolemia: Cutaneous, Metabolic, and Hereditary Aspects," *Bull. New York Acad. Med.*, 1950, 26: 670
75. Wilkinson, Ch. F., Hand, E. A., and Fliegelman, T. "Essential Familial Hypercholesterolemia," *Ann. Int. Med.*, 1948, 29: 671

Chapter IV

PHYSIOLOGICAL ASPECTS OF MENTAL DISORDERS IN LATER LIFE

Nathan W. Shock

Although it would be presumptuous to assume, in the light of our present knowledge, that all mental diseases have identifiable physiological causes, many of the mental aberrations that are found in older people are accompanied by physiological changes. In order to assess the importance of physiological factors in mental diseases in later life, it is necessary to know something of the physiological nature of aging. Unfortunately we are still unable to give definitive answers about the basic physiological or biochemical causes of aging. We cannot decide whether aging is a normal physiological process inherent in all cells and tissues (37, 43, 64, 86, 177, 209, 216, 225, 250, 251, 326) or whether it results from successive and accumulated insults and injuries of living (207, 227, 315, 319). Truly, many of the histological characteristics of aged tissues, such as the presence of collagen, fibrin, etc. (3, 244, 245), may be reproduced in animals by many types of injury, ranging from toxic chemicals (205, 206, 207) through avitaminosis (338) to simple anoxia (317). On the other hand, the progressive loss of functional capacities with age in even healthy animals is offered as evidence of the nonpathological characteristics of aging. If acceptance of the normality and inevitability of aging leads to an attitude of scientific resignation—that therefore nothing can be done about the aging problem—then it would be better to reject this concept in favor of the one that aging is the end result of repeated injury and is essentially a pathological process. Even if false, the latter concept may serve the useful purpose of stimulating research and action to minimize physiological wear and tear throughout the life span.

Any fundamental description of the aging process must be based on the physiological processes of individual cells. What little we know of aging in individual cells indicates a wide range of longevity of different cells, even in the same animal. The length of life of individual cells, within the same organism, ranges from 3 or 4 days in individual neutrophiles to 60–70 years for individual

postmitotic nerve cells (73). Differences in longevity are undoubtedly related to differences in exposure of cells to oxygen, nutrient
media, or noxious influences. For instance, neural cells are well
buffered against sudden changes in their chemical environment and
are often protected from mechanical injuries by bony structures.
On the contrary, the neutrophiles are buffeted in the blood stream
and subjected to much greater stress, both mechanical and physiological, with consequently a much shorter life span.

By repeated transfer to fresh media, life may be maintained in
tissues cultures long beyond the life span of the body from which
the tissues originally came (73). Thus a certain degree of tissue
immortality may be conferred by maintaining optimal conditions
for nutrition and excretion (60, 61, 64, 250, 251). While this may
be true of tissues, or groups of cells, methods are not yet available
which make it possible to follow individual cells in such cultures,
let alone in their normal tissue environment. Nevertheless, we may
safely assume that the life of the individual cell is conditioned by
its ability to maintain its characteristic structural and functional
organization in the continual adaptation that it must make to changes
in its fluid environment. As cells grow older, their adaptability
probably decreases and they become more vulnerable to adverse
environmental conditions (73).

Although special histological techniques may permit the
identification of changes in cellular structure with increasing age,
such as the accumulation of so-called "wear and tear pigments" (3)
and alterations in the distribution of calcium in cells (175), the
chemical composition of individual cells is not a good index of their
age. On the contrary, aged tissues are readily distinguished from
young tissues by the presence of increased amounts of fibrin and
collagen deposits in the former (3, 40, 244). Such deposits are also
characteristic of even young tissues subjected to a wide variety of
injurious agents (205, 207, 317, 338). The increasing amounts
of inert material (including fat) may well interfere with the normal
exchange of metabolic products between cells and their environment, although direct evidence that such is the case is as yet lacking.[1] Since the maintenance of cellular organization is essential to

---

[1] Recent studies by Kirk and his co-workers, (162a, 182a) have indicated an increase
in permeability of the aorta with increasing age. No significant age changes in the permeability of the tentorium cerebelli in humans were found.

life, changes in permeability with aging probably occur as well; but here again direct evidence is lacking. Nevertheless, it seems probable that one of the chief characteristics of aging is a breakdown or interference with interrelationships between different cells of the body or between cells and their environment. This concept may be broadened to include the entire organism. The term "homeostasis," introduced into physiology by Cannon (54, 55, 56), to draw attention to the numerous mechanisms which function to maintain uniformity of the chemical environment of individual cells of the body (18), is particularly applicable to this concept of aging. The hypothesis that aging is characterized by a reduction in the homeostatic capacities of the organism is an attractive one under which much of our knowledge about aging may be organized (57, 291).

Whether this reduced homeostatic capacity is regarded as an expression of normal "wear and tear" of living or an expression of pathological processes seems immaterial at the moment. In either case, research may well be directed toward (a) a description of age changes in physiological capacities for homeostatic adjustment and (b) a search for the factors that influence or determine such capacities. The reduction in performance, ranging from diminished function of specific endocrine glands to slower performance in mental tests so often observed in aged individuals, may well be regarded as a reflection of reduced homeostatic capacity of the total organism. The performance of any task calls for readjustments within the cells of some organ system. If these cells are unable to execute the necessary function, or are slower in their reaction, the total performance or work output necessarily suffers.

The following sections will be directed toward (a) a review of the data available on changes in homeostatic capacities in humans with age, and (b) an attempt to evaluate the possible significance of such factors in the etiology of mental diseases in later maturity.

A. CHANGES IN HOMEOSTATIC CAPACITIES WITH AGE
I. REGULATION OF BLOOD AND TISSUE CHEMISTRY

Steady states of temperature, osmotic pressure, ionic concentration (H^+, Mg^{++}, Ca^{++}, Na^+, K^+, $BHCO_3^-$, Cl^-, PO_4^-, etc.), as well as uniform concentrations of other substances (glucose, proteins, lipids, cholesterol, urea, etc.), are necessary for the normal functioning of cells (18). This uniformity of the fluid environment must be maintained in spite of changes in the external environment and upheavals in the internal environment induced by activities of the cells themselves, as in physical exercise. The maintenance of such homeostatic balance is effected by numerous physiological processes involving different organ systems. The mechanisms by which homeostasis is maintained are much better known for certain chemical substances, such as sugar and acid-base equilibrium, than for others, such as protein or lipid concentrations. It should also be remembered that for many substances a number of mechanisms may be utilized for maintaining a proper homeostatic balance. Thus the body is often offered first, second, etc., "lines of defense" against extremes of variation in certain chemical or physical characteristics. It is essential to appraise the response of organisms and organ systems to physiological displacements if a true picture of their functional status is to be obtained. It is only when we know at what cost, or by what methods, the organism manages to maintain its uniform internal environment that we can adequately describe the physiological aspects of aging. It is also true that most organs or organ system possess great reserve capacities. For instance, 75 to 80 per cent of the kidney tissue must be destroyed in normal animals before clinical symptoms of kidney damage become observable (173, 203). Hence it is extremely important to obtain information about the physiological reserve capacities in older individuals. For such purposes, tests of reaction to physiological "stress" or "load" are necessary.

Physiological "load" or "stress" may be applied as a testing procedure in two ways. In the first type of test, attention is directed toward an appraisal of the reserve capacities of an organ system at the given time. For this purpose a physiological load must be selected which can be quantitatively evaluated and which will produce an immediate displacement in some physiological characteristic such as blood pressure, pulse rate, respiratory volume, or blood-sugar level, which can be reliably measured and for which the rate of displacement and recovery can be followed. As an example of such a test the administration of a single dose of glucose may be mentioned; the amount of glucose administered can be measured and the rate of rise and fall in blood-sugar levels can be accurately determined.

In the second type of test, attention is directed toward *changes* in physiological capacities which may result from repeated or continuous application of a physiological stress over extended periods of time. Although this type of experiment may yield important information about the aging process, few experimental applications of this method have yet been made. For instance, it has long been known that muscular hypertrophy and improved work output result from daily performance of nonexhausting exercise. It has also been shown that such hypertrophy does not follow if the daily exercise is continued to exhaustion (82, 276, 312). Thus the effects of continued stress are probably related to the extent to which reserve capacities are taxed (82).[2]

Similar relationships probably exist for other physiological stress situations for which data should certainly be collected. Such experimentation may provide data on which to base therapeutic recommendations to reduce disability in old age—a goal toward which the science of gerontology may well be oriented.

Regulation of blood sugar.—The successive "lines of defense" in maintaining physiological constancy of a blood constituent may perhaps be illustrated best for blood sugar. These processes will be considered in some detail for blood sugar, but limitations of space and inadequacy of physiological information will prevent a similar presentation for other blood constituents. Numerous studies have shown that the brain is particularly sensitive to deprivation of oxygen and glucose (137). While only one mechanism (the parasympathetic-insulin) acts to limit a rise in blood sugar, there are many mechanisms which operate to counteract a fall in blood sugar (the sympathetic-adrenalin system, the thyroid and posterior pituitary, as well as the anterior pituitary and adrenal cortex).

When blood sugar rises, from glucose either absorbed from the

---

[2] Repeated exposure to physiological stress may have cumulative effects not shown under conditions of continuous strain. For instance, animals continuously exposed to an altitude of 10,000 feet show an increase in their hemoglobin and red-cell count after a period of several days or weeks. On the contrary, rabbits taken to a similar altitude in an aeroplane for two- to three-hour periods each day failed to show this increase in red cells. In fact, a decrease in hemoglobin occurred, and after 30 days of repeated exposure most of the animals were definitely anemic and some actually died (9, 10).

Many clinicians believe that repeated exposure to disease throughout life plays an important part in the etiology of many of the chronic debilitative states encountered in old age (162), but experimental proof of this conception is still lacking. There is also some evidence that repeated severe stress may result in reduced efficiency of adaptive mechanisms (282, 339). Proctor, Dewan, and McNeel (259) have shown that, in schizophrenics, glucose tolerance may be diminished following insulin-shock therapy.

gut or released from the glycogen stores of the liver, insulin is secreted from the islet tissue of the pancreas through the direct stimulating effect of increased blood glucose on these tissues. Under normal circumstances there is an additional neural factor, since it has been shown that hyperglycemia serves as a stimulus to interacting parasympathetic nervous centers in the hypothalamus and the medulla oblongata (342). The islands of Langerhans of the pancreas receive branches from the vagus nerve along which these impulses are transmitted. Furthermore, when blood-sugar levels rise above 160 to 170 mg. per cc., excretion by way of the kidney occurs, thus affording the body additional protection against excessively high blood-sugar levels.

A diminution in blood-sugar levels represents a much greater physiological hazard than does a rise in blood sugar. This is because of the extreme sensitivity of the brain to deprivation of its chief source of energy. Function of the higher nervous centers becomes impaired when blood-sugar levels fall below 20 mg. per 100 cc. With lower blood-sugar levels the functional activities of the subcortical, mesencephalic, and even the diencephalic levels of the nervous system are progressively impaired (112, 334). The first line of defense against lowered blood-sugar levels is the sympathetic-adrenalin system (58). In response to diminished blood sugar, cerebral centers in the hypothalamus, pons, and medulla send impulses down the cord through the splanchnic nerves to stimulate the secretion of adrenalin by the adrenal medulla. This hormone mobilizes liver glycogen, which is released into the blood stream as glucose. In addition, augmented secretions of the thyroid (52) and the posterior pituitary gland accelerate the release of glucose from the liver into the blood stream. Secretions from the adrenal cortex (35, 146, 188, 196), as well as the anterior pituitary (273), may also aid in raising lowered blood-sugar levels by diminishing the rate of oxidation of glucose in the tissues. Another line of defense is found in the hormone from the adrenal cortex, which may also aid in raising blood-sugar levels by accelerating the transformation of protein to carbohydrates in the liver (306).

The effectiveness of the mechanisms involved in maintaining the blood sugar can be appraised by observing the speed with which the organism re-establishes normal levels following experimental displacements.[3] When glucose is given by mouth, the blood sugar temporarily rises sharply during the first half hour from levels of 80–100 mg. per 100 cc. to 130–150 mg. per 100 cc., and gradually returns to normal levels within 2 to 2½ hours. When such glucose-tolerance tests are made on older subjects, the maximum rise is greater, and return to normal level requires more than 3 hours (139, 140, 165, 210, 257, 268, 302). Figure 9 shows the glucose-tolerance curve for a 40-year-old normal male, and that obtained in an 83-year-old male (268). Marshal (210) found that 40 per cent of his normal subjects above the age of 65 showed curves similar to these, while less than 14 per cent showed normal curves. In another study of 12 subjects aged 60–67 (140), when the oral glucose-tolerance test was repeated on successive days in the same individual a notable lack of consistency in the curves was observed. Furthermore, interpretation of oral glucose-tolerance curves in terms of glucose metabolism is difficult (231) since the rate of absorption of the ingested sugar influences the shape of the blood-sugar response curve. By administering the sugar intravenously, the influence of absorption may be removed and much more uniform curves may be obtained (119, 322). Intravenous glucose-tolerance curves were determined in 68 males aged 20–89 years by Smith and Shock (304). There was a progressive drop in tolerance which became significant in the 70–79 and the 80–89 year groups when compared with the 20–29 year groups. Figure 9a illustrates the differences observed between the ages of 20 and 80 years. This diminution in glucose tolerance has been confirmed by Schneeberg and Finestone (279). Smith (303) has concluded that the reduced glucose tolerance in aged subjects cannot be attributed to a deficiency in insulin production, since the aged subjects showed a normal rise in blood pyruvate following glucose injection whereas the diabetes patients showed none. In short, there is no evidence that the diminished tolerance in the aged has the same basis as the pathological processes of diabetes. It should also be pointed out that

[3] In view of the numerous mechanisms by which blood-sugar levels may be maintained, it is not surprising to find that normal levels are ordinarily observed in older individuals under standard basal conditions. Different investigators have reported both high (148, 254, 257) and low (235) values for blood sugar in aged subjects under various conditions; but age changes in basal levels of blood sugar have usually been regarded as insignificant (43, 210, 238, 304). More recent studies, using analytical methods for determining true glucose, indicate a gradual rise in the glucose level of venous blood with increasing age (296b).

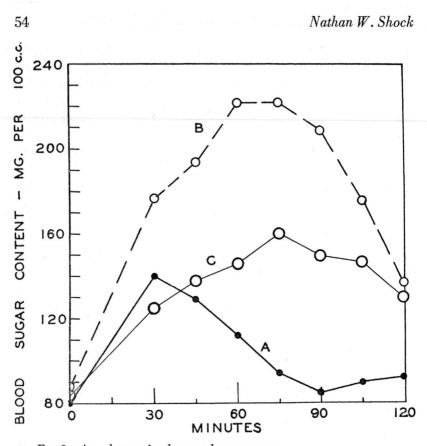

FIG. 9.—Age changes in glucose-tolerance curves.

●——●——● Blood-sugar levels after ingestion of 50 g. glucose by 40-year-old male.

—O— —O— —O— Blood-sugar levels after ingestion of 50 g. glucose by 83-year-old normal healthy male. Curve rises slowly to higher levels than in young adult, indicating impairment of removal or storage mechanism.

O——O——O Blood-sugar levels after ingestion of 50 g. glucose by 80-year-old normal healthy male. Curve shows slow rise and delayed fall. May be related to slow absorption of glucose as well as impaired storage mechanisms. Only about 10 per cent of aged subjects show curves like *A*; 60 to 70 per cent show curves like *B* or *C*. Data from Rømcke (268).

although the incidence of the beginning of diabetes increases with age, the peak incidence occurs at the ages 40–50 and that after the age of 70 the incidence diminishes (30, 91, 153, 232, 308).

The response to hypoglycemia has not been studied to any extent in normal older persons. In young adults, the injection of small amounts of insulin results in a rapid fall in blood sugar followed by recovery. Himsworth and Kerr (136) reported numerous subjects in the later years of life who failed to show this response to the injection of insulin. These authors attributed their results to an excessive secretion of the anterior pituitary gland, extracts of which can induce refractoriness to insulin in normal animals.

Regulation of acid-base balance of the blood.—The normal slightly alkaline reaction of the blood is maintained by a delicate balance between the excretion of volatile carbonic acid by the lungs and the excretion of nonvolatile acids by the kidneys. The acidity is determined by the ratio of bicarbonate to carbonic acid present in the blood, which is normally about 20:1. If the bicarbonate content is lowered by neutralization of excess nonvolatile acids, such as lactic, the carbon dioxide liberated is eliminated through the lungs. However, with the reduction in bicarbonate the alkalinity of the blood would decrease were it not for the fact that additional

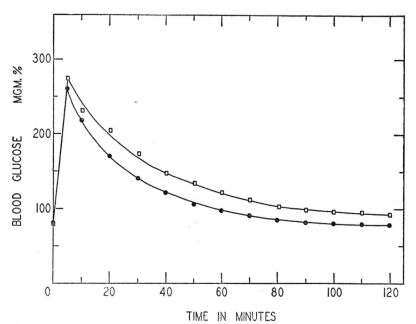

FIG. 9a.—Intravenous glucose-tolerance tests. Average curves ●——●——●, 20–29-year-old subjects; □——□——□ 80–89-year-old subjects. Note that the 80–89 year curve is above the young group throughout the test and has not returned to the fasting level at 120 minutes whereas the 20–29 year group has. Data from Smith and Shock (304).

carbon dioxide is eliminated by the increased respiration, so that the normal *ratio* of bicarbonate to carbonic acid is re-established, thus maintaining the normal alkalinity (pH) even though the total bicarbonate content of the blood has been diminished. Thus the pH is maintained at normal levels until the excess fixed acid (lactic) can be excreted by the kidney. Under circumstances of slight kidney damage it is possible for the lungs to maintain a normal blood pH through regulation of the respiration. Because of such interrelationships and a secondary "line of defense," normal levels for acid-base equilibrium are often found even when usual adjustive mechanisms have begun to fail.

It has been shown that total lung volume (333) and vital capacity diminish with age (124, 155, 187, 224, 234, 265) whereas the dead space increases (107). In addition there is a reduction in the maximum volume of air that can be voluntarily exhaled in a period of 15 seconds (123). It might be assumed that these respiratory changes might interfere with the elimination of carbon dioxide from the blood. However, such is not the case under resting conditions, since the carbon dioxide tension of arterial blood does not change with age (295).

Although there is a significant impairment in renal function with increasing age (78, 287, 292) there is only a slight increase in the acidity of the blood in aged subjects (295) under resting conditions. However, the application of an extra physiological load on the renal mechanisms brings to light certain limitations in the regulation of the acid-base equilibrium of the blood. The oral administration of acidifying or alkalinizing substances produces a temporary shift in the acid-base equilibrium of the blood. In young adults, recovery is effected within a period of 8–10 hours (293). On the contrary, when equivalent amounts of these substances are administered to older individuals, recovery is not completed for 24 to 72 hours (294). Figure 10 compares the rate of displacement and recovery of the acid-base equilibrium of the blood in a young and old subject following the administration of equivalent amounts of sodium bicarbonate. MacNider (208) has shown that young adult dogs recovered from the reduction in alkaline reserve of the blood, induced by administering morphine, more quickly than did old dogs.

Regulation of electrolytes and water.—The regulation of electrolyte and water balance of blood and tissues is a complex process

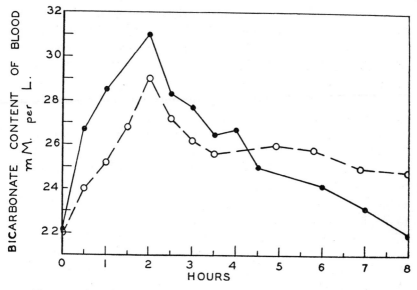

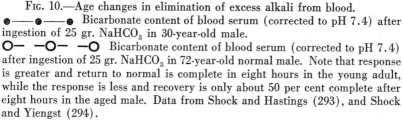

F<small>IG</small>. 10.—Age changes in elimination of excess alkali from blood.
●——●——● Bicarbonate content of blood serum (corrected to pH 7.4) after ingestion of 25 gr. NaHCO₃ in 30-year-old male.
O— —O— —O Bicarbonate content of blood serum (corrected to pH 7.4) after ingestion of 25 gr. NaHCO₃ in 72-year-old normal male. Note that response is greater and return to normal is complete in eight hours in the young adult, while the response is less and recovery is only about 50 per cent complete after eight hours in the aged male. Data from Shock and Hastings (293), and Shock and Yiengst (294).

involving the interplay of endocrine, circulatory, excretory, and even nervous mechanisms. It is beyond the scope of the present section to discuss in detail these mechanisms for individual electrolytes. Certain aspects of the problem have been selected for discussion to illustrate its complexity and the difficulties in interpreting data available which have a potential bearing on the aging process.

In considering age changes in water metabolism, it must be remembered that water loss takes place not only through the kidney but also through the lungs, the sweat glands, and the intestine (1). Water loss through any one of these channels may vary widely from time to time, and control of such loss is vested in a wide variety of physiological systems. For instance, water loss through the kidney is affected by alterations in blood pressure and blood flow through this organ. The endocrine secretions of the pituitary gland also have a controlling influence on the proportion of water that is resorbed in the kidney tubule and that which is excreted. Still another hormone, which is secreted by the adrenal cortex, influences the amount of water lost through the kidney by controlling the excretory level of sodium and potassium (114). Assessment of total water loss is complicated by the influence of respiratory rate and volume on the loss by vaporization in the lungs. Furthermore, the secretion of perspiration is influenced by nervous and circulatory factors associated with the control of body temperature. In the face of the many physiological systems involved in the control of water loss it is easy to see how difficult the interpretation of data based on urine volumes alone becomes. Even though quantitative data are difficult to obtain, or to evaluate, the clinical impression that the regulation of water balance is impaired in old age must be accepted. This impression is based on the relative ease with which edema may be produced in the aged, as well as on the rapid dehydration which is often observed in old patients.

It has long been assumed, on the basis of clinical examination and estimates of tissue water obtained by drying various tissues, that aging is accompanied by loss of water and dehydration of the tissues (89, 233). While this decrease in total water cannot be denied, it is true that the method of desiccation does not distinguish between intra- and extracellular fluid, a distinction which is of prime physiological importance (131, 253), since the degree of hydration of the active protoplasm is what really matters. The distinction between extra- and intracellular water and the degree of hydration of the metabolizing protoplasm can be made only by careful studies of electrolyte concentrations (Na^+, K^+, Cl^-, $BHCO_3^-$, etc.) of tissues and blood plasma. When such analyses were made on tissues of old and young rats, no differences in intracellular water were found, i.e., no evidence for dehydration in old tissues was observed (197).

Simms and Stolman (297) have compared the water and electrolyte composition of tissues obtained from 6 accident cases over 70 years of age with similar data from 40-year-old subjects. They found that the concentration of tissue water was 2 per cent higher in the 70-year-old cases than in the 40-year-olds. On a net-weight basis the concentration of sodium, calcium, and chlorine was greater (20 to 28 per cent) in old tissues than in young, while the concentration of potassium, magnesium, phosphorus, and nitrogen was from 7 to 12 per cent less in the old tissues.

Using chemical techniques, estimations of the total body water in intact animals can be made, provided the substance is excreted only slowly and is distributed equally in all the water of the body. Preliminary studies using antipyrine and heavy water have indicated only a slight reduction in total body water in aged humans (311). One possible interpretation of this apparent contradiction of earlier studies is that the increased amount of inert substances present in the old tissues simply takes up space, thus reducing the fluid space available. Apparently the cells which remain functional (i.e., consume oxygen) in old tissues have just as much water in them as young cells—but there are fewer cells present. More studies of this problem are needed before the question of tissue dehydration in aged cells can be finally decided.

The deposition of calcium in soft tissues, such as arteries, cartilage, etc., which is observed in many old persons, may be taken as evidence of failure of the regulation of calcium metabolism in old age. Regulation of calcium metabolism includes such diverse factors as functional activity of the parathyroid glands; dietary calcium, phosphate, and vitamin-D intake; degree of physical activity; acidity of intestinal contents; etc. Changes in calcium metabolism are characteristic of aging even in lower animals. Thus Lansing (175, 176, 178) has found that in rotifers, planaria, and toads calcium accumulates in the cell membranes of old organisms. Lansing and his co-workers (180, 181) have also shown that with increasing age calcium accumulates in the walls of blood vessels in mammals. The importance of local factors in the tissue is indicated by the fact that calcium deposition was much greater in the aorta than in the pulmonary artery. In mammals, the parathyroid hormone, together with vitamin D, is involved in the absorption and elimination as well as the deposition of tissue calcium (59). Reduced secretion of the parathyroids lowers the blood calcium and increases its excretion at the expense of calcium in the bones. Overactivity of the parathyroids increases blood calcium, also at the expense of the bones. The factors which control the abnormal deposition of calcium in soft tissues are essentially unknown. There are no clear indications either in the parathyroids or in the aging process itself that hypo- or hyperfunction of the parathyroids plays any significant part in the impairments of the aged. Blood calcium does not change systematically with age, according to studies by Kirk and his co-workers (163), although earlier studies (125, 264) had reported a decrease in serum calcium with age. The reputed decrease in the power of healing or repair of bones in old patients may be more closely related to circulatory impairments (arteriosclerosis or trauma at the time of injury) than to actual impairments of calcium metabolism or decreased activity of the parathyroid glands.

Regulation of protein and lipid metabolism.—The regulation of protein and lipid metabolism involves many interrelated physiological mechanisms which are still obscure. Kountz and his coworkers believe that elderly subjects require significantly higher protein intakes to maintain their body weight and efficiency than do young subjects (168). This finding implies some impairment in absorption or utilization of proteins in the aged. Carefully controlled metabolic balance studies indicate that older subjects are capable of absorbing protein from the diet and forming new tissue (27a, 27b). There is no evidence that the aged are any less efficient in this process than are the young. It is generally believed that the absorption of fats is impaired in aged subjects. Although no direct experimental evidence is available, it has been shown that the absorption of fat-soluble vitamin A is not appreciably altered in older subjects (341).

It has long been recognized that arteriosclerosis is related to fat metabolism (72, 184, 305, 337). Although no significant changes in blood fats (lipids) have been found (246, 247), there is a progressive rise in the cholesterol content of the blood up to the age of 60 years (118, 169, 260, 307), after which age there is a fall (159, 160). Further evidence of disturbed cholesterol metabolism is found in the increased deposition in arterial walls (184, 185, 244), the cornea of the eye, and other soft tissues (42, 44, 45, 46, 117).

Similar disturbances in lipid metabolism are observed in young individuals suffering from diabetes mellitus. Experimental studies on animals have led to the hypothesis that lipid metabolism is regulated in part of some endocrine secretion from the pancreas, other than insulin (90).

Recently, evidence has been presented to indicate that the combination of fats with proteins in the blood are more closely related to arteriosclerosis than are the fats (lipids) themselves. Thus Gofman and his co-workers (121) have separated a series of lipoproteins of varying molecular size from the blood by using high speed centrifugation in a medium of high specific gravity. According to these observations, the fractions of lower molecular weight, which increase with age, are of particular importance in the etiology of arteriosclerosis.

Imperfect as our knowledge of lipid and protein metabolism may be, it is not difficult to conceive that with increasing age certain co-ordinating influences which in youth prevent or minimize the accumulation of cholesterol in arterial walls operate less effectively (185).

II. REGULATION OF BODY TEMPERATURE

Uniformity of body temperature is maintained by a delicate balance between heat production and heat loss (93). Heat production depends on the oxidative processes that take place in the body. Underlying the basal rate of these oxidative processes is the continuous secretion of the thyroid gland; if that fails, heat production may be reduced as much as 40 per cent. Additional heat is produced whenever muscles or glands go into action.

Heat loss can occur through conduction, radiation, convection, and vaporization. The amount of heat lost through these four channels depends chiefly on the surface area of the body and the difference between its temperature and that of the surroundings. The temperature of the skin depends on the rate at which blood passes through the cutaneous vessels. Thus vasomotor changes in the skin capillaries are most effective in controlling heat loss by radiation and convection. Heat loss by vaporization of water occurs in the lungs and from the surface of the skin. Any increase in respiratory ventilation augments the heat loss by vaporization from the lungs, while nervous control of perspiration limits the heat loss by evaporation of water from the skin. Thus, the control of heat loss is effected by the interplay of a number of physiological processes—circulatory, respiratory, and nervous in character.

Studies on children have shown that the close co-ordination of these physiological processes is not present at birth but develops with the passage of time (15). In old age there is a progressive loss in the efficiency of co-ordination of these regulatory mechanisms. Although the internal temperature of elderly persons is maintained within the usual slight variation (43, 141, 211, 277), extremes of heat or cold in the environment produce greater variations in the

body temperature of old persons than of young adults (232). Krag
and Kountz (171, 172) have shown that aged subjects subjected to
both heat and cold show slower alterations in body temperature
than do young adults. Reduced basal heat production observed in
the elderly (288, 291, 296) may, in part, account for their greater
sensitiveness to cold. Inability to quickly dissipate excess heat at
high environmental temperatures is probably related to the sluggish
circulatory responses reported in the aged (49, 87, 156). In studies
on the maximal heat elimination from the hand, Pickering (255)
found that under standard conditions the output in calories per
minute per unit volume was about 33 per cent lower at age 70 than
at age 25. In senile subjects the rate of water loss from the surfaces
of the finger and toe tips was much less than in young subjects (50),
thus reducing the potential heat loss from evaporation.

The inability to dissipate heat is reflected in the increase in
mortality rate observed in institutions for the aged during periods
of prolonged high temperature (111). It has also been found that
the death rate from "heat stroke" rises sharply after age 60. In
Massachusetts, between 1900 and 1930, it increased from 8 per
100,000 for the ages 70 to 79, to 80 per 100,000 for ages 90 to 100
years (284).

Similarly, internal factors producing a rise in body temperature are less readily adjusted in older persons than in younger.
Temperature reactions to infections are often much more erratic in
old patients than in young (232).

III. REGULATION OF BASAL METABOLISM

The level of the basal metabolism (basal oxygen consumption
or basal heat production) is determined by the amount of thyroxine
produced by the thyroid gland. Numerous observations show that
the basal metabolism decreases in old persons (16, 21, 29, 169,
189, 265, 296). While the gross decrease cannot be denied, we
do not know whether the oxygen utilization of individual cells in
older organisms is changed or not.[4] This is because no method has

---

[4] A few studies have been made on the metabolic activity of individual tissues
which indicate a reduction in cellular metabolism with age. Lazovskaya (183) believes
that the decrease in oxygen uptake which he has observed in blood vessels of old rats
as compared with young ones is due to a fall in activity of specific enzyme systems.
There is also evidence for reduced activity of ester-hydrolyzing enzymes of the rat (241)

yet been found whereby the total amount of functioning protoplasm can be estimated for the intact human. Thus the reduction in total metabolism may be only a reflection of the accumulation of inert, nonmetabolizing material, such as collagen, fat, and fibrin, within the body of the aged. Since histological studies all indicate a reduction in the number of functional cells in old tissues of all kinds (3, 6, 113, 116, 229, 244, 267, 299, 319, 321), it is quite possible that this reduction in total metabolism is simply a reflection of the reduced number of metabolizing units (cells) present in the old organism. Additional weight is given to this interpretation of the fall in basal metabolism with age by observations reported by Shock, Yiengst, and Watkin (292a, 292b, 296a). In these studies, the basal oxygen consumption (BMR) was related to the total body water content of the subject, as determined by the antipyrine method. The results are illustrated in Figure 11. It may be seen that, although the basal oxygen consumption per unit of surface area diminishes with age, there is no change in oxygen uptake per liter of body water. If we accept total body water as an index of the amount of functioning protoplasm present, the fall in metabolism of the total animal can be accounted for on the basis of a progressive loss of cells with age. Decreased skeletal muscle efficiency, decreased muscle tone, and actual muscle atrophy do occur with advancing age (40), tending to reduce the amount of tissue present. Since the muscle mass contributes the major proportion of the total oxygen consumption, even slight reduction in the amount of this tissue would be reflected in a lower total oxygen consumption. It is possible that the cause of this degenerative process depends in part on the lower activity of the thyroid gland.

The concept of a general slowing up of the metabolic processes of individual cells with age gains some support from the evidence of partial involution of the thyroid gland (3, 69) reported in senes-

---

and rabbit (242). Rosenthal *et al.* (270, 271) have reported a decline in the respiratory power of aging articular cartilage which they attribute to a gradual failure of the oxygen-activating component of respiratory enzyme systems. Similar reduction in oxidation-reduction processes in muscle tissue of old animals has been reported (120). However, it is clear that not all tissues behave alike. For instance, Reiner (262) observed a marked decrease in oxygen uptake of brain-tissue homogenates prepared from aged rats, whereas no significant age changes were found in liver-tissue homogenates. The absence of age changes in oxygen uptake of liver tissue was confirmed by Rafsky *et al.* (261) but a significant diminution of metabolism of kidney tissue in old animals was reported.

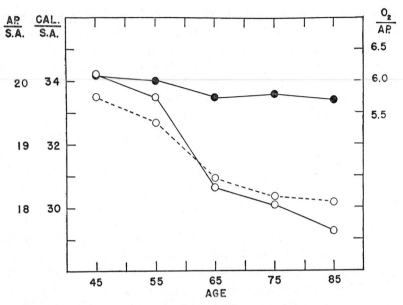

FIG. 11.—Age changes in basal metabolism. Mean curves o———o———o
Cal/sq. M/hr, o — — o — — o total body water (antipyrine space) liters/sq. M,
●———●———● basal oxygen uptake cc. O_2/liter body water. Data from Shock
(292*a*).

cent animals. According to Dogliotti and Nizzi Nutti (88), the number of follicles (which produce thyroxine) is reduced in the aged
thyroid gland, and in those follicles which remain the colloid may
be less and the epithelium hypertrophied. While of histological
interest, the interpretation of such observations in terms of physiological function is difficult, since the inference of functional activity from structural changes is fraught with dangers.

One may find other characteristics of the aged which look like
evidences of lowered thyroid function, such as dryness of the skin
and scalp, loss of hair, lowered resistance to infections—particularly those of the respiratory tract, weakness and atony of the skeletal muscles (106, 298), reduced speed of mental performance
(289), and slower reaction time (122, 221, 222, 223). However,
the similarity may be only superficial, and it is possible to relate
most of these symptoms to factors other than the thyroid. Furthermore, similar symptoms observed in cretins or myxedema respond

at least in part to administration of thyroid hormone. No striking results have been reported in these characteristics following administration of thyroid substance to aged persons or animals (166). Hence the attempt to attribute *all* age changes to a progressive hypothyroidism is unwarranted.

IV. PHYSIOLOGICAL ADJUSTMENTS TO EXERCISE

Whenever the body responds to stimuli, either external or internal, increased demand for oxygen results. This extra demand for oxygen may range from the tenfold increase often observed after exhausting muscular work (265, 285) to the almost undetectable increase in oxygen demand following activities of the higher nervous centers. Many interrelated physiological processes are directed toward delivering the extra oxygen needed by the functioning tissues. Vigorous exercise which results in lowered oxygen tension of the tissues and increased acid formation is accompanied by increase in heart rate, cardiac output, blood pressure, and circulation rate. More red corpuscles are forced from storage depots, such as the spleen, into the circulation to increase the oxygen- and carbon-dioxide-carrying capacity of the blood. Respiration increases in depth and rate, which increases the oxygen tension in the lungs and the rate of carbon dioxide elimination. The acid-base equilibrium of the blood is displaced toward the acid side. If the exercise is continued, the extra heat generated calls into play the mechanisms of temperature control, such as peripheral vasodilation and increased sweat secretion. The excess acid formed is eliminated through increased secretory activity of the kidney. Thus a wide range of physiological processes is called into play to maintain the homeostatic equilibrium in the face of the displacing stimulus of exercise.

In normal young adults these processes attain maximum effectiveness and co-ordination (285). With increasing age, various components of this system begin to show varying degrees of impairment (167, 298). For example, Robinson (265) found that pulse-rate increment after severe exercise was significantly less in older persons than in those of middle age (see Fig. 11*a*). On the other hand, a standard amount of light exercise produces a greater cardiovascular (238) and respiratory response in aged subjects than in

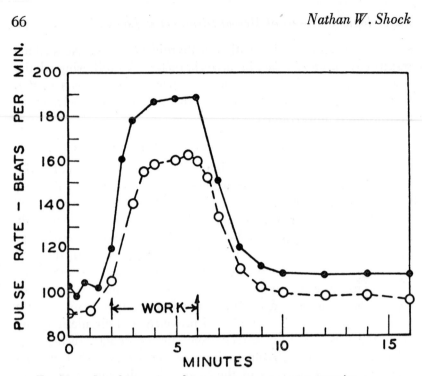

Fɪɢ. 11*a*.—Age changes in pulse rate response to severe exercise.

●——●——● Pulse rate response to exercise in young adult males (aged 20 to 29 years).

O— —O— —O Pulse rate response to exercise in aged males (aged 59 to 78 years). Note the more rapid rate of increase and decrease in pulse rate of young subjects than of old. Data from Robinson (265).

young adults (239). Observations on a single subject indicated a reduction of 50 per cent in work capacity between the ages of 41 and 71 years, although the mechanical efficiency remained about the same (83). Other studies on groups of subjects indicate a diminution in the mechanical efficiency of work in elderly subjects only at very low or high work rates (239). The elasticity of the arterial walls is diminished with age, as shown by direct measurements on excised strips of arteries (130, 170, 236, 274, 335), as well as by measurements of the pulse-wave velocity (33, 128, 138, 161, 248, 332). Even resting blood pressure tends to rise with advancing age (80, 135, 141, 191, 212, 272), although Robinson and Brucer (266), as well as Bruck (39), contend that the resting blood pressure does not change with age. This conclusion has been subjected to severe criticism on statistical and sampling grounds, and a gradual rise in average pressure seems established (212).

Many observations on old persons offer evidence of impaired functional capacity of the cardiovascular system. Irregularities of heart rate are often found even under resting conditions (27, 115, 141, 182). The electrocardiogram indicates no characteristic peculiarities to old age, although abnormal findings which are witness to pathological aberrations occur more frequently (81, 96, 108, 109, 182, 186, 195, 204, 215, 278, 310, 340). In such cases extrasystoles are common: evidence of left-heart hypertrophy predominates; the systolic phase is relatively lengthened, as is the P-R interval; and the duration of the QRS complex is more extended, while its form is often atypical. Although early studies were unable to demonstrate any significant reduction in resting cardiac output with age (190), the application of more precise methods has shown a significant reduction (33a, 70a). This reduction in cardiac output is associated with a slowing of the circulation as measured by the circulation time (132) and an increase in the total peripheral resistance (174a). The vasomotor responses are sluggish and less extensive in old persons (49, 87, 156, 237). Peripheral circulation is often deranged, resulting in lower skin temperature and local areas of cyanosis. The increased frequency of death from cardiovascular pathology in old persons offers mute evidence of the frequency of fatal breakdown in various components of this system (74, 91, 92, 179). It is not unreasonable to suppose that functional impairment has preceded the final pathological failure by a good number of years.

V. ALIMENTARY ABSORPTION AND DIGESTION

Few systematic studies of digestion and alimentary absorption in old age have been reported. Clinical observations show that normal digestion may be enjoyed by many aged persons (147). On the contrary, the incidence of dyspepsia and general gastric complaints increases with age. This is probably because of the ease with which the alimentary tract is reflexly influenced by mental states and by disease elsewhere in the body (327, 339). Thus there is no assurance that these complaints are related to age changes in the gastrointestinal tract itself.

With increasing age the volume of saliva as well as its enzymatic (ptyalin) activity diminishes (79, 217, 218). Thus less starch is digested in the mouth and stomach, but the pancreatic amylase is probably sufficient to provide for complete digestion of cooked starch. After the age of 40 the production of hydrochloric acid and pepsin by the stomach decreases (26, 79, 85, 220, 256, 324), and the incidence of achlorhydria markedly increases (26, 324). However, there is no evidence that such changes prevent adequate digestion. Gastric emptying time is no greater in old subjects than in young adults (323). The intestinal absorption of galactose is diminished in old age (219); but the absorption of vitamin A is practically unchanged (341).

VI. REGULATION OF EXCRETION

Anatomical studies have shown that the kidney undergoes structural changes with increasing age. These changes involve a progressive loss in the number of functional units in the kidney (6, 229, 244, 267) as well as a diminution in the number and form of vascular pathways (75, 292). Kidney tissue also loses its adaptability to demands upon its powers of structural and functional growth. McKay, McKay, and Addes (201, 202) observed that in old rats the compensatory renal hypertrophy following the surgical removal of one kidney was much less than in young rats. During the first month of life there was a 52 per cent increase in the weight of the remaining kidney, whereas at one year of age the hypertrophy amounted to only 32 per cent. Later studies have indicated that this difference is influenced in part by the protein intake in the diet (200).

Because of the great reserve capacity of the kidneys, routine clinical tests of renal function are unable to detect slight variations in excretory functions. Nevertheless Lewis and Alving (192) were able to demonstrate a gradual fall in urea clearance with increasing age. Using more sensitive tests which make it possible to distinguish between filtration and excretion in the kidney (301) it has been shown that with increasing age there is a linear decrease in the rate of glomerular filtration, rate of blood flow through the kidney, and the maximum rate of excretion and reabsorption in the renal tubule (78, 243, 287). Although the primary factor is vascular in nature, not all of the age changes can be attributed simply to a reduction in the number of vascular pathways and a structural narrowing of the blood vessels that remain (292).

VII. RESISTANCE TO INJURY AND DISEASE

Tissue growth and repair.—It is commonly believed that the healing and repair of tissues proceeds more slowly in old than in young subjects. Although early experiments on animals tended to confirm this belief (7, 94), more recent experiments in which infections could be eliminated by the use of antibiotics failed to show any deficiency in the rate of healing of skin and superficial wounds in older animals (31, 76). However, substances which inhibit the growth of cells in tissue cultures have been observed in the blood plasma (60) and the tissues (167) of old animals. The nature of the substance or the mechanism of its action has not been identified.

The reduced ability to form new tissue and the tendency to deposit collagen and fibrin in tissues may be regarded as part of the general picture of impaired homeostasis present in the older organism. For instance, the rate of regeneration of liver tissue is maximal in embryos and diminishes in old animals (11, 41, 240). Similarly, the rate of hypertrophy of the remaining kidney after unilateral nephrectomy is greater in young animals than in old (201, 202). This reduction of growth capacity with age is not a general characteristic of all cells, as is shown by the high incidence of benign hypertrophy of the prostate in old men (193, 230, 320) and the increased incidence of cancer in old age (20, 91, 232). In a total of 375 cases Moore (230) failed to observe hypertrophy of the prostate before the fifth decade. After this age, the incidence increased until at the ninth decade 75 per cent of prostates secured from consecutive routine autopsies were hypertrophied. This progression of incidence might permit the conclusion that benign prostatic hypertrophy is an inevitable consequence of altered homeostatic capacity in senility.

The increased incidence of cancer in advanced ages may also be taken as evidence of breakdown of regulatory mechanisms within the organism which normally control cellular growth. In certain instances there is evidence that some of the controlling influences are endocrine in character. For example, the recent studies of Kahle (154) and Huggins *et al.* (142, 143, 144) indicate that reducing the amount of male sex hormone by castration or even by endocrine neutralization through the administration of female sex hormones may retard the development of prostatic carcinoma and result in clinical improvement of the patient.

Susceptibility to drugs and toxic influences.—Clinicians have observed that aged patients are more sensitive to certain drugs, such as digitalis and strychnine, than are younger ones (38, 62, 84, 232). Systematic studies of this question, using animals, have shown that it is impossible to predict the influence of age on drug action. Some drugs, such as histamine dihydrochloride, sulfapyridine, "Seconal Sodium," or picrotoxin, are less toxic to young animals than to old ones, while other drugs, such as morphine or ephedrine hydrochloride, are more toxic to young animals (63). Dearing *et al.* (84) have shown that pathological changes in the heart are more easily produced by administration of digitalis in old animals than in young ones.

It has also been found that old animals are more susceptible to certain poisons than are young ones. For instance, MacNider (205) reported that small doses of chloroform or uranium produced much greater liver or kidney damage in the old than in the young animals. Young animals are much more resistant to the toxic influence of anoxia. Respiration and reflex activities continue at lower oxygen tensions, and resuscitation after severe anoxia is more successful in young than in old animals (100, 101, 133, 137, 281).

Immune reactions.—Experiments on animals have shown that the level of antibodies, agglutinins, and precipitins in the blood diminishes with age (13, 14, 134, 316). Kessler (157) found that old animals were much more susceptible to certain experimental infections than were young animals. It has also been observed that the rate of antibody formation is reduced in old animals (13, 14, 34, 164). Thus it is not surprising to find diminished resistance to certain infections in old persons (95, 275). All these findings are in accord with the concept of reduced homeostatic capacity in old age.

VIII. REGULATION OF REPRODUCTIVE FUNCTIONS

Menopause or climacteric.—Decreased function of the sex organs occurs with advancing age in both sexes. In women, the cessation of menstruation offers a clearly terminal milestone in their reproductive history, while in men the decreased function can only be inferred. Physiologically, the menopause may be interpreted as an inability of the ovary to maintain its endocrine secretory activity at a level capable of inducing the cyclic growth changes in the uterus, which are normally reflected in the menstrual process (2, 213). This physiological impairment of the sex glands with age has reverberations throughout the entire organism. For instance, hot flushes—vasomotor symptoms similar to blushing—are probably the most common symptoms reported by women during the climacteric. Many other symptoms, such as irritability, emotional instability, headaches, digestive disturbances, languor, and even depression of a frankly psychotic nature, are experienced. Many of these distressing symptoms have been reduced in patients by the therapeutic administration of female sex hormones (51, 53, 67, 77, 214, 328, 330).

Male climacteric.—Some clinicians have reported a similar "climacteric" in males, characterized by the vasomotor symptoms, impotence, lethargy, weakness, insomnia, etc., which responds to treatment with male sex hormones (198, 283, 329). However, the number of such patients seen, even in large clinics, is much less than the number of women complaining of similar symptoms. Furthermore, old men who show objective evidence of reduced sexual function, such as diminished excretion of male sex hormone in association with high excretion of gonadotrophic hormones, rarely report such symptoms (99). Consequently, the concept of the "male climacteric" is not generally accepted (12).

B. CHANGES IN SENSORIMOTOR CAPACITIES

In the preceding sections, emphasis has been placed on the loss of capacity of various physiological systems for maintaining homeostasis in aged persons. In the present section evidence of impaired functional capacity for sensorimotor performance will be presented. Such impairments in performance may eventually be traced back to a loss of homeostatic capacity—since any stimulus produces some physiological displacement in the organism. When readjustment is slow, as occurs with reduced homeostatic capacity, performance suffers.

I. VISION

With increasing age there is a reduction in visual acuity (23, 110, 194), the extent of the visual field diminishes (102, 289), the minimum threshold of light perception is raised (24, 103, 104, 263, 314), the ability to discriminate colors is diminished over the age of 60 (28, 300, 318), the critical flicker fusion frequency is reduced (289), and the incidence of lens opacities increases (105, 269). In interpreting the results of perceptual tests it is difficult to evaluate the role of structural changes in the eye itself. Thus Berens (17) believes that faulty circulation and degeneration resulting from vascular impairments are responsible for many of the visual disturbances of adults which are often attributed to age. Age changes in the lens begin at birth and proceed uniformly with increasing age, as shown by the progressive decrease in range of accommodation (110, 126). In fact, Bernstein (19) has obtained a reasonably close prediction of age at death from the knowledge of 4 or 5 serial refractions of the eye made between the ages of 40 and 50 years.

Visual perception span and speed gradually diminish after the age of 40. In a study by Price (258), letters, numbers, short sentences, colors, groups of lines, and common expressions faultily written made up the printed material, which was exposed to vision for a fixed time interval. The score consisted of the number of items seen and recorded correctly. The older subjects wore their glasses, and preliminary trials were given to assure optimal adjustment to test procedure. A residual age change in visual efficiency which was not overcome by corrective devices was observed.

The speed of visual perception is significantly reduced beyond the age of 30 years. Weston (331) compared the speed of identifying gaps in a series of Landolt rings in the same experienced observers after a 5-year interval. The subjects were aged 20–45 at the first testing. The decrement in performance shown by all subjects was greater in the 45-year-olds than in the 20-year-olds and was more apparent at lower levels of illumination. Other complex visual tasks, such as the perception of incomplete pictures, require more time in older subjects than in young adults (289). We may assume that the reduced efficiency in perception is more the result of changes in efficiency of central neural processes than changes in the physical characteristics of the eye.

II. HEARING

Impaired hearing for high-pitched sounds occurs so frequently in old people that it is regarded as a normal result of aging (47, 48, 66, 68, 71, 127, 226, 325). The decline in auditory acuity at low frequencies is less for men, while at the higher frequencies it is less for women (4, 5, 226). Although hearing loss for low tones is relatively slight by air conduction, marked impairment has been reported by bone conduction (66). In subjects with severe impairments of hearing for high tones, but with normal hearing for low tones, simple atrophy of the nerve or of the nerve end organ in the basal turn of the cochlea has been reported. The cause of the atrophy is not known (127). An analysis of the clinical histories of 3,732 males and 4,578 females indicated that the incidence of severely impaired hearing increases as an exponential function of age in years (4, 5).

The impairment in perception of higher tones observed in persons over 50 is of psychological significance since it is the higher frequencies which are important in understanding conversation in a social group (289).

III. OTHER SENSORY PERCEPTIONS

Although clinical observations indicate a reduction in sensitivity to pain in old age (232), quantitative data are very scanty. Chapman and Jones (61), using the Hardy-Wolff apparatus (129), have reported a decrease in sensitivity to pain in a small series of subjects. However, the wide range of individual differences and the extraneous factors that may influence pain-threshold determinations by this method (25, 129) render generalizations about pain thresholds based on a small number of subjects impossible. The progressive loss in vibratory sensitivity, which has been quantitatively demonstrated (252), may be related to changes in the posterior columns of the spinal cord. Corbin and Gardner (70) counted the number of myelinated fibers in the eighth and ninth thoracic dorsal and ventral nerve roots in 34 human cadavers ranging in age from 1 day to 89 years. The average curves, which show a decrease in the number of nerve fibers at the higher ages, are similar in form to the curve relating changes in vibratory sensitivity to age. While not conclusive, this suggests that the loss in vibratory sensitivity is associated with neural atrophy (22).

Anatomical observations of disappearance of perceptual end organs and neural pathways in old subjects may account for perceptual impairments. Arey *et al.* (8) examined the tongues of cadavers of different ages and found a reduction in the average number of taste buds from 208 in middle age to 88 at ages 74–85 years. Smith (299) has reported atrophy of the olfactory nerves in aged cadavers. No systematic studies of age changes in gustatory or olfactory perception have been made, although Laird and Breen (174) have reported a higher preference for tart pineapple juice in older subjects than in young.

IV. REACTION TIME

Systematic studies of reaction time, speed of muscular movement, and muscular co-ordination all show a gradual impairment of function with increasing age (36, 122, 222, 223, 298). This decline begins in the second or third decade of life and proceeds at a somewhat increasing rate to the end of life. Although the average curves show definite impairment in function, it is encouraging to note the great spread of individual differences in these measurements at any age level. Thus, about ⅓ of any given age group show performances equal to or better than the average age of the group 10 years younger. This wide range in individual differences among older subjects excludes the conclusion that the aged are *necessarily* slow in reaction.

C. POTENTIAL EFFECTS OF THESE CHANGES ON MENTAL LIFE

In previous sections, the clinical and experimental findings have been presented from which a general picture of reduced homeostatic capacities in old age emerges. It has been shown that because of the numerous "lines of defense" and different physiological mechanisms available, normal blood and tissue conditions at rest are usually maintained even in very old persons. However, the physiological cost of maintaining such conditions of equilibrium may become progressively greater, and more of the reserve mechanisms and capacities must be continuously activated and utilized to maintain this balance. Thus reserve capacities are chronically utilized so that extremes of physiological displacement are restored more slowly than in young animals. It is the purpose of the present section to examine the ways whereby this reduction in homeostatic capacities may influence mental life.[5] This discussion is admittedly speculative, since the physiological aspects of mental disease in general are little understood.

I. PHYSIOLOGICAL ASPECTS

Any hypothesis regarding the physiological basis of mental disease must assume an association between mental life and the metabolic activity and function of cellular elements of all tissues, but particularly those of the central nervous system. While such relationships have not yet been directly established in most mental diseases, we do know that interference with the normal oxygen or glucose supply to the brain results in impaired mental function. Studies of the mental effects of anoxia (or hypoglycemia) show a progressive impairment of mental function, beginning with a lack of critical judgment and ending with unconsciousness and death, as the oxygen supply to the brain is diminished (199). Furthermore, certain superficial resemblances between the mental symptoms of extreme senescence and acute anoxia may be traced—loss of memory for recent events, increased reaction time, loss of judgment, orientation, etc. Hence it is not unreasonable to suppose that mental deterioration and disease in old age are associated with impairment of physiological function within the individual cells of the aged organism. Since cells of the central nervous system are particularly sensitive to alterations in their environment, it is not difficult to see why impairment in homeostatic capacities may play an important role in the genesis of mental diseases.

Interference with normal cellular metabolism; impaired delivery of oxygen and nutrient materials.—Histological studies have demonstrated that in old tissues the amount of inert material, chiefly fibrin and collagen, is increased. Since even young cells respond to noxious and toxic substances by the formation of both fibrin and collagen, we cannot say whether the increased amount of these substances found in old tissues is the result of "normal" aging or the accumulation of a lifetime of physiological insults. However, the source of these materials is of little consequence to the argument. Their presence in increased amounts cannot be denied. Since these substances surround many cells, the normal diffusion of oxygen and foodstuffs to the metabolizing cells may be definitely impeded,

[5] See also Shock (286).

simply by mechanical means. Histochemical studies also show a diminution in the number of functioning cells in older tissues. Thus the distance over which substances must travel through intracellular space from capillaries to the metabolizing cells is increased. Coupled with this, the number of capillaries may be diminished, while the control of blood flow through the remaining capillaries is less adequate and periods of reduced flow may occur with greater frequency. As a result, areas of temporary anoxia may develop, setting in motion a vicious circle, since anoxic cells respond with the production of more fibrin, which in turn interferes further with the diffusion of oxygen even after the local blood flow is restored. Evidence for the cumulative destructive effect of repeated exposure to anoxia may be found in histological studies of the brain (317). The deleterious effects of anoxia may well extend to cells of the body other than those of the brain. The impairment of kidney function may be the result of repeated exposures to local anoxia. The deposition of calcium and cholesterol within the capillary walls (arteriosclerosis) may be a reflection of such impairment of cellular function. Changes in the semipermeability of cell membranes undoubtedly occur in old age, although precise studies of tissues in the intact animals are yet to be made.

Effects of inadequacies in enzyme systems; vitamins.—Recent studies of the important role of vitamins in the oxidation mechanisms of cells raise the interesting question of the possible vitamin requirements in old age. Since we know very little about the effect of age on the efficiency of absorption of substances from the gastro-intestinal tract, it is possible that even though the intake of such substances is maintained in older subjects, absorption becomes less adequate, so that the efficiency of cellular oxidation is reduced because of a lack of some of these essential components.

The brain is dependent for its normal functioning on a carbo-hydrate substrate (137), an adequate supply of oxygen (199), and various enzyme and coenzyme systems (98, 137, 150, 152). A disturbance in any of these constituents interferes with brain metabo-lism and therefore with brain function. At least three vitamins—thiamine, nicotinic acid, and riboflavin—are concerned with the proper metabolism of carbohydrate. Clinical syndromes involving mental symptoms which disappear with the administration of thia-mine or nicotinic acid have been described (32, 151, 152, 309). In view of the many other enzyme systems involved in brain metabolism, it is not improbable that additional vitamins are also important.

Thiamine-deficient diets are believed by some investigators to lead to easy fatigue, weakness, irritability, feelings of tenseness, quarrelsomeness, emotional instability, moodiness, subjectively poor memory, and difficulty of concentration (32, 149, 151, 336). These results could not be confirmed by Keys and his co-workers (158), so the precise conditions under which such results may be expected must still be defined.

Patients suffering from pellagra (due to a defficiency of nicotinic acid) often report nervousness, dizziness, headaches, and insomnia as early complaints. Varying degrees of mental depression with or without apprehension follow. In the more advanced stages, there is almost always a feeling of fear accompanied by hallucinations. Periods of mental haziness and disorientation develop which in some cases are followed by delirium (280). Memory loss, disorientation, and confusion are also reported (309). Clinical improvement in such patients quickly follows intravenous administration of large doses of nicotinic acid (280). Himwich (137) has reported a lower oxygen uptake of the brain tissue of pellagrins than in normal subjects, thus offering support to the theory that the mental changes are a result of impaired metabolic processes.

Since many of the mental symptoms encountered in the aged are similar to those described above, the effects of administering vitamins to aged subjects should certainly be studied. Stephenson, Penton, and Korenchevsky (313) have reported clinical improvement in senile subjects who were treated with large oral doses of vitamins of the B complex and vitamin C. Some improvement was noted in measurable qualities, such as co-ordination and muscle strength; but improvement in subjective symptoms such as delusions, nocturnal insomnia, day sleeping, and mental confusion was more striking. Some success in treatment of patients originally diagnosed as suffering from senile or arteriosclerotic psychoses has been reported by Palmer *et al.* (249), following dietary improvement and the administration of vitamins (A, B, C, and D). The therapeutic regime included: bed rest, followed by supervised exercise; occupational and physical therapy; high caloric and high vitamin diet; removal of sources of infection; correction of constipation;

and administration of abundant fluids. Reports of subjective improvement in aged subjects following the administration of nicotinic acid and thiamine have appeared (65, 228, 313), but more carefully controlled studies on much larger samples must be made before the effects of vitamins on senescence can be evaluated.

Summary.—According to the conception outlined above, the underlying basis of physiological changes in senescence is interference with the normal metabolic processes within individual cells. This interference operates through a reduced rate of transference of essential substances to the metabolizing cells, or through inadequacies of the enzyme systems required for normal metabolic processes within cells. Transference may be inadequate because of reduced supply, reduced circulatory delivery, or slower diffusion. The amount of essential substances which reach the metabolizing cells may be reduced because of greater distances over which diffusion must take place, reduced permeability, or the presence of inert substances through which nutrients diffuse with difficulty. The mechanism of impairment of mental functions is thus regarded as no different from that of the kidney, the gastro-intestinal tract, the liver, etc. It is simply the expression of effects in cellular metabolism of cells within the central nervous system, which we know are somewhat more susceptible to certain deleterious influences than are other cells of the body. While direct evidence for such a hypothesis is still lacking, it may form the basis for useful research.

II. PSYCHOLOGICAL ASPECTS OF PHYSIOLOGICAL INADEQUACIES

Although the hypothesis above may offer a cellular basis for aging, we are not yet in a position to relate complex human behavior to cellular activities. Until this is possible, it may be well to consider avenues whereby the gradual breakdown of homeostatic capacities outlined in the early sections of this chapter may influence behavior in the aged. Some of these influences may operate through the social environment as well as through the physiological environment (145, 286).

For instance, the sensory impairment of vision or hearing in older individuals may have important psychological reverberations. Paranoid characteristics often develop in persons with hearing defects. So also, the memory defects of old persons may lead to social rejection, with the development of undesirable behavior patterns. Thus the reaction of others toward the failings which become apparent in old age may be an important determinant of mental disease in later life. Many clinicians are well aware of the effects of acceptance or rejection of physical infirmity by the elderly patient on his potential recovery; but no controlled studies of this important variable have yet been made.

D. SUMMARY

The hypothesis is presented that most of the phenomena of aging can be attributed to a progressive loss in the homeostatic capacities of the organism. Biochemical and physiological evidence has been presented to indicate that with increasing age the body is less capable of maintaining the constancy of its internal environment. The degree of regulation of the internal environment which is attained in the aged requires the continued use of reserve capacities and mechanisms which are called into play only occasionally in younger individuals. The great reserve capacities and "secondary lines of defense" against physiological displacements inherent in the organism require the application of physiological stresses in order to assess early stages of physiological impairment. Thus the application, under standardized conditions, of a wide variety of "stress tests" to individuals of increasing age offers a fertile field of research in determining the changes in capacities for homeostatic adjustments. Such tests will give objective data on the changes in reserve capacities available to older individuals. Research should also be directed toward the long-term effects of repeated applications of physiological stress which occur as a result of infections and other disease processes. In such a research program, a study of the factors which influence or determine the physiological capacities for maintaining homeostasis will yield results which can be applied clinically to maintain levels of physical and mental performance in an aging population.

The mechanism of impairment of mental function in the aged is regarded as due to interference with the normal metabolic processes within individual cells and the breakdown of co-ordinating mechanisms between different groups of cells or organs. The physiological mechanisms of impairment of mental functions are thus regarded as basically the same as those involved in the impairment of kidney, gastric, or liver function in the aged individual.

While the physiological aspects of aging have been stressed in the present chapter, it is recognized that some of the effects of homeostatic breakdown may operate through the social as well as the physiological environment.

REFERENCES[6]

1. Adolph, E. F. "The Metabolism and Distribution of Water in Body and Tissues," *Physiol. Rev.*, 1933, 13: 336–70
2. Allen, E. "Female Reproductive System," Chapter 16 in E. V. Cowdry (ed.), *Problems of Ageing* (2d edition) (Baltimore: Williams & Wilkins, 1942), pp. 446–74
3. Andrew, W. *Cellular Changes with Age*. Springfield, Ill.: Charles C. Thomas, 1952. 74 pp.
4. Anon. *The National Health Survey: 1935–1936*. "Prevalence of Aural Pathology and Clinical History of Impaired Hearing Among Males and Females of Various Ages," *Pub. Health Rep., Hearing Study Ser.*, Washington, D.C., 1938, No. 3
5. Anon. *The National Health Survey: 1935–1936*. "Sex Differences and Age Variations in Hearing Loss in Relation to Stage of Deafness," *Pub. Health Rep., Hearing Study Ser.*, Washington, D.C., 1939, No. 6
6. Arataki, M. "On the Postnatal Growth of the Kidney, with Special Reference to the Number and Size of the Glomeruli (Albino Rat)," *Amer. J. Anat.*, 1926, 36: 399–436.
7. Arey, L. B. "Wound Healing," *Physiol. Rev.*, 1936, 16: 327–406
8. Arey, L. B., Tremaine, M. J., and Monzingo, F. L. "The Numerical and Topographical Relations of Taste Buds to Human Circumvallate Papillae Throughout the Life Span," *Anat. Rec.*, 1935, 64: 9–25
9. Armstrong, H. G., and Heim, J. W. "Factors Influencing Altitude Tolerance During Short Exposures to Decreased Barometric Pressures," *J. Aviat. Med.*, 1938, 9: 45–56
10. ———. "The Effect of Repeated Daily Exposures to Anoxemia," *ibid.*, 1938, 9: 92–96
11. Aub, J. C. "Regeneration of the Liver in Old Age," in N. W. Shock (ed.), *Conference on Problems of Aging*, 10th and 11th Conferences (New York: Josiah Macy, Jr. Foundation, 1950), pp. 17–18
12. Bauer, J. "The Male Climacteric; a Misnomer," *J. Amer. Med. Ass.*, 1944, 126: 914
13. Baumgartner, L. "Relationship of Age to Immunological Reactions," *Yale J. Biol. Med.*, 1933–34, 6: 403–34
14. ———. "Old Age and Antibody Production," *J. Immunol.*, 1934, 26: 407–29
15. Bayley, N., and Stolz, H. R. "Maturational Changes in Rectal Temperatures of 61 Infants from 1 to 36 Months," *Child Develop.*, 1937, 8: 195–206

[6] Although lengthy, the bibliography is not comprehensive. For additional references see Shock, N. W. *A Classified Bibliography of Gerontology and Geriatrics* (Stanford, Calif.: Stanford University Press, 1951) (290). For articles published after 1948 see the section, "Current List of Periodical Literature," published in the *Journal of Gerontology*, beginning April 1950.

16. Benedict, F. G., and Root, H. F. "The Potentialities of Extreme Old Age," *Proc. Nat. Acad. Sci.*, 1934, 20: 389–95

17. Berens, C. "Aging Process in Eye and Adnexa," *Arch. Ophthal., Chicago*, 1943, 29: 171–209

18. Bernard, C. *Leçons sur les propriétés physiologiques et les alterations pathologiques des liquides de l'organisme.* Paris: Baillière, 1859

19. Bernstein, F. "Law of Physiologic Aging as Derived from Long Range Data on Refractions of the Human Eye," *Arch. Ophthal., Chicago*, 1945, 34: 378–88

20. Bigelow, G. H., and Lombard, H. L. *Cancer and Other Chronic Diseases in Massachusetts.* Boston: Houghton Mifflin Co., 1933. 355 pp.

21. Binet, L., and Bourlière, F. "Nouveaux documents sur le metabolisme basal des vieillards," *Pr. méd.*, 1951, 59: 557

22. Birren, J. E. "Vibratory Sensitivity in the Aged," *J. Geront.*, 1947, 2: 267–68

23. Birren, J. E., and Bick, M. W. "Visual Acuity as a Function of Age and Retinal and Macular Degeneration," *ibid.*, 1948, 3 (Suppl. to No. 4): 9–10

24. Birren, J. E., Bick, M. W., and Fox, C. "Age Changes in the Light Threshold of the Dark Adapted Eye," *ibid.*, 1948, 3: 267–71

25. Birren, J. E., Casperson, R. C., and Botwinick, J. "Pain Measurement by the Radiant Heat Method; Individual Differences in Pain Sensitivity, the Effects of Skin Temperature and Stimulus Durations," *J. Exp. Psychol.*, 1951, 41: 419–24

26. Bloomfield, A. L. "Decrease of Gastric Secretion with Advancing Years," *J. Clin. Invest.*, 1940, 19: 61–65

27. Boas, E. P. "Aging of the Cardiovascular System," *Bull. N.Y. Acad. Med.*, 1940, 16: 607–17

27a. Bogdonoff, M. D., Shock, N. W., and Nichols, M. P. "Calcium, Phosphorus, Nitrogen, and Potassium Balance Studies in the Aged Male," *J. Geront.*, 1953, 8: 272–88

27b. Bogdonoff, M. D., Shock, N. W., and Parsons, J. "The Effects of Stilbestrol on the Retention of Nitrogen, Calcium, Phosphorus, and Potassium in Aged Males With and Without Osteoporosis," *J. Geront.*, 1954, 9: 262–75

28. Boice, M. L., Tinker, M. A., and Paterson, D. G. "Color Vision and Age," *Amer. J. Psychol.*, 1948, 61: 520–26

29. Boothby, W. M., Berkson, J., and Dunn, H. L. "Studies of the Energy of Metabolism of Normal Individuals. A Standard for Basal Metabolism with a Nomogram for Clinical Application," *Amer. J. Physiol.*, 1936, 116: 468–84

30. Bortz, E. L. "Diabetes Mellitus," Chapter 14 in E. J. Stieglitz (ed.), *Geriatric Medicine* (2d edition) (Baltimore: Williams & Wilkins, 1949), pp. 213–30

31. Bourlière, F., and Gourévitch, M. "Âge et vitesse de réparation des plaies expérimentales chez le rat," *C. R. Soc. Biol., Paris*, 1950, 144: 377–79

32. Bowman, K. M., and Wortis, H. "Psychiatric Syndromes Caused by Nutritional Deficiency," *Res. Pub. Ass. Nerv. Ment. Dis.*, 1943, 22: 168–89

33. Bramwell, J. C., Hill, A. V., and McSwiney, B. A. "The Velocity of the Pulse Wave in Man in Relation to Age," *Heart*, 1923, 10: 233–55

33a. Brandfonbrener, M., Landowne, M., and Shock, N. W. "Changes in Cardiac Output With Age" (Abstract), *Fed. Proc., Baltimore*, 1955, 14: (Pt. I): 16–17. *Circulation* (in press)

34. Brenner, L. O., Waife, S. O., and Wohl, M. G. "The Antibody Response in Old Age," *J. Geront.*, 1951, 6: 229–32

35. Britton, S. W. "Adrenal Insufficiency and Related Considerations," *Physiol. Rev.*, 1930, 10: 617–82

36. Brody, E. B. "Age and Weight Changes in Reaction Time of Dairy Cattle," *Growth*, 1942, 6: 179–84

37. Brody, S. *Bioenergetics and Growth; with Special Reference to the Efficiency Complex in Domestic Animals.* New York: Reinhold Publishing Co., 1945. xii + 1,023 pp.

38. Brown, C. F. G., and Dolkart, R. E. "General Remarks on the Care of the Aged," *Med. Clin. N. Amer.*, 1940, 24: 3–8

39. Bruck, M. "Gibt es eine physiologische Altershypertonie?" *Cardiologia*, 1940, 4: 165–203

40. Buccianti, L., and Luria, S. "Struttura dei muscoli voluntari dell' uomo nella senescenza," *Arch. ital. Anat. Embriol.*, 1934, 33: 110–87

41. Bucher, N. L. R., and Glinos, A. D. "The Effect of Age on Regeneration of Rat Liver," *Cancer Res.*, 1950, 10: 324–32

42. Bürger, M. "Die chemischen Altersveränderungen im Organismus und das Problem ihrer hormonalen Beeinflussbarkeit," *Verh. dtsch. Kongr. inn. Med.*, 1934, 46: 314–33

43. ——. *Altern und Krankheit.* Leipzig: G. Thieme, 1947. 413 pp.

44. Bürger, M., and Schlomka, G. "Untersuchungen am menschlichen Rippenknorpel," *Z. ges. exp. Med.*, 1927, 55: 287–302

45. ——. "Beiträge zur physiologischen Chemie des Älterns der Gewebe," *ibid.*, 1928, 63: 105–16

46. ——. "Ergebnisse und Bedeutung chemischer Gewebeuntersuchungen," *Klin. Wschr.*, 1928, 7: 1944–52

47. Bunch, C. C. "Further Observations on Age Variations in Auditory Acuity," *Arch. Otolaryng., Chicago*, 1931, 13: 170–80

48. Bunch, C. C., and Raiford, T. S. "Race and Sex Variations in Auditory Acuity," *ibid.*, 1931, 13: 423–34

49. Burch, G. E., Cohn, A. E., and Neumann, C. "Reactivity of Intact Blood Vessels of the Fingers and Toes to Sensory Stimuli in Normal Resting Adults, in Patients with Hypertension and in Senile Subjects," *J. Clin. Invest.*, 1942, 21: 655–64

50. ——. "A Study of the Rate of Water Loss from the Surfaces of the Finger Tips and Toe Tips of Normal and Senile Subjects and Patients with Arterial Hypertension," *Amer. Heart J.*, 1942, 23: 185–96

51. Burlingame, C. C., and Patterson, M. B. "Estrogen Therapy in the Psychoses," *J. Nerv. Ment. Dis.*, 1941, 94: 265–76

52. Burn, J. H., and Marks, H. P. "The Relation of the Thyroid Gland to the Action of Insulin," *J. Physiol.*, 1927, 82: 195–214

53. Caldwell, B. M., and Watson, R. I. "An Evaluation of Psychologic Effects of Sex Hormone Administration in Aged Women. I. Results of Therapy after Six Months," *J. Geront.*, 1952, 7: 225–41

54. Cannon, W. B. "Organization for Physiological Homeostasis," *Physiol. Rev.*, 1929, 9: 399–431

55. ———. The William Henry Welch Lectures. "I. Some New Aspects of Homeostasis," *J. Mt. Sinai Hosp., N.Y.*, 1939, 5: 587–97
56. ———. The William Henry Welch Lectures. "II. Homeostasis in Senescence," *ibid.*, 1939, 5: 598–606
57. ———. "Ageing of Homeostatic Mechanisms," Chapter 22 in E. V. Cowdry (ed.), *Problems of Ageing* (2d edition) (Baltimore: Williams & Wilkins, 1942), pp. 567–82
58. Cannon, W. B., McIver, M. A., and Bliss, S. W. "Studies on the Conditions of Activity in Endocrine Glands. XIII. A Sympathetic and Adrenal Mechanism for Mobilizing Sugar in Hypoglycemia," *Amer. J. Physiol.*, 1924, 69: 46–66
59. Carlson, A. J. "The Thyroid, Pancreatic Islets, Parathyroids, Adrenals, Thymus and Pituitary," Chapter 15 in E. V. Cowdry (ed.), *Problems of Ageing* (2d edition) (Baltimore: Williams & Wilkins, 1942), pp. 412–45. See also: Chapter 15 in A. I. Lansing (ed.), *Cowdry's Problems of Ageing* (3d edition) (Baltimore: Williams & Wilkins, 1952), pp. 347–80
60. Carrel, A., and Ebeling, A. H. "Age and Multiplication of Fibroblasts," *J. Exp. Med.*, 1921, 34: 599–613. "Antagonistic Growth Principles of Serum and Their Relation to Old Age," *ibid.*, 1921, 38: 419–25
61. Chapman, W. P., and Jones, C. M. "Variations in Cutaneous and Visceral Pain Sensitivity in Normal Subjects," *J. Clin. Invest.*, 1944, 23: 81–91
62. Chen, K. K. "Principles of Pharmacology as Applied to the Aged," Chapter 6 in E. J. Stieglitz (ed.), *Geriatric Medicine* (Philadelphia: W. B. Saunders, 1943), pp. 118–24
63. Chen, K. K., and Robbins, E. B. "Age of Animals and Drug Action," *J. Amer. Pharm. Ass.*, 1944, 33: 80–82
64. Child, C. M. "Senescence and Rejuvenescence from a Biological Standpoint," *Harvey Lect.*, 1930, 24: 25–44
65. Chittick, R. A., and Stotz, E. "Nicotinic Acid and Ascorbic Acid in Relation to the Care of the Aged," *Dis. Nerv. Syst.*, 1941, 2: 71–74
66. Ciocco, A. "Observations on Hearing of 1,980 Individuals; a Biometric Study," *Laryngoscope, St. Louis*, 1932, 42: 837–55
67. Cogswell, H. D., and Davis, S. C. "Post-traumatic Psychoses in the Aged; Treatment with Sex Hormones," *Amer. J. Surg.*, 1943, 62: 9–12
68. Colledge, L. "Hearing and Senile Deafness," *Practitioner*, 1943, 150: 335–40
69. Cooper, E. R. A. *The Histology of the More Important Human Endocrine Organs at Various Ages.* New York: Oxford University Press, 1925. xiv + 120 pp.
70. Corbin, K. B., and Gardner, E. D. "Decrease in Number of Myelinated Fibers in Human Spinal Roots with Age," *Anat. Rec.*, 1937, 68: 63–74
70a. Cournand, A., Riley, R. L., Breed, E. S., Baldwin, E. de F., and Richards, D. W. "Measurement of Cardiac Output in Man Using the Technique of Catheterization of the Right Auricle or Ventricle," *J. Clin. Invest.*, 1944, 24: 106–16
71. Covell, W. P. "The Ear," Chapter 10 in A. I. Lansing (ed.), *Cowdry's Problems of Ageing* (3d edition) (Baltimore: Williams & Wilkins, 1952), pp. 260–76
72. Cowdry, E. V. (ed.). *Arteriosclerosis: a Survey of the Problem.* New York: The Macmillan Co., 1933
73. ———. "Ageing of Individual Cells," Chapter 24 in E. V. Cowdry (ed.),

Problems of Ageing (2d edition) (Baltimore: Williams & Wilkins, 1942), pp. 626–63. See also: Chapter 3 in A. I. Lansing (ed.), *Cowdry's Problems of Ageing* (3d edition) (Baltimore: Williams & Wilkins, 1952), pp. 50–88

74. ———. *Problems of Ageing: Biological and Medical Aspects.* Baltimore: Williams & Wilkins, 1942 (2d edition). xxxvi + 936 pp.

75. Cox, A. J., Jr., and Dock, Wm. "The Capacity of the Renal Vascular Bed in Hypertension," *J. Exp. Med.*, 1941, 74: 165–75

76. Dalton, A. R., Lemmer, R., and Anschuetz, R. "Relation of Age to Wound Healing," *J. Geront.*, 1951, 6 (Suppl. to No. 3): 77

77. Danziger, L. "Estrogen Therapy of Agitated Depressions Associated with the Menopause," *Arch. Neurol. Psychiat., Chicago*, 1942, 47: 305–13

78. Davies, D. F., and Shock, N. W. "Age Changes in Glomerular Filtration Rate, Effective Renal Plasma Flow, and Tubular Excretory Capacity in Adult Males," *J. Clin. Invest.*, 1950, 29: 496–507

79. Davies, D. T., and James, T. G. I. "An Investigation into the Gastric Secretion of 100 Normal Persons Over the Age of Sixty," *Quart. J. Med.*, 1930–31, 23: 1–14

80. Davis, H. J. "Notes on Blood Pressure in Old Age," *Hum. Biol.*, 1930, 2: 264–76

81. Davis, J. O. "The Electrocardiographic Changes in the Aging Heart," *J. Geront.*, 1947, 2: 263–65

82. Dawson, P. M. *The Physiology of Physical Education.* Baltimore: Williams & Wilkins, 1938. xxxii + 938 pp.

83. Dawson, P. M., and Hellebrandt, F. A. "The Influence of Aging in Man upon His Capacity for Physical Work and upon His Cardio-vascular Response to Exercise," *Amer. J. Physiol.*, 1945, 143: 420–27

84. Dearing, W. H., Barnes, A. R., and Essex, H. E. "Experiments with Calculated Therapeutic and Toxic Doses of Digitalis; Effects on Myocardial Cellular Structure," *Amer. Heart J.*, 1943, 25: 648–64

85. Dedichen, L. "Anacidity in Old Persons," *Acta med. scand.*, 1924–25, 61: 345–50

86. Dhar, N. R. "Senescence, an Inherent Property of Animal Cells," *Quart. Rev. Biol.*, 1932, 7: 68–76

87. Di Palma, J. R., and Foster, F. I. "The Segmental and Aging Variations of Reactive Hyperemia in Human Skin," *Amer. Heart J.*, 24: 332–44

88. Dogliotti, G. C., and Nizzi Nutti, G. "Thyroid and Senescence," *Endocrinology*, 1935, 19: 289–92

89. Donaldson, H. H., and Hatai, S. "On the Weight of the Parts of the Brain and on the Percentage of Water in Them According to Brain Weight and to Age, in Albino and Wild Norway Rats," *J. Comp. Neurol.*, 1931, 53: 263–307

90. Dragstedt, L. R. "The Present Status of Lipocaic," *J. Amer. Med. Ass.*, 1940, 114: 29–30

91. Dublin, L. I., and Lotka, A. J. *Twenty-five Years of Health Progress.* New York: Metropolitan Life Insurance Co., 1937. 611 pp.

92. Dublin, L. I., Lotka, A. J., and Spiegelman, M. *Length of Life.* New York: Ronald Press, 1949. xxv + 379 pp.

93. Du Bois, E. F. *The Mechanism of Heat Loss and Temperature Regulation.*

Lane Medical Lectures. Stanford, Calif.: Stanford University Press, 1937

94. du Noüy, P. *Biological Time*. London: Methuen & Co., 1936. 180 pp.
95. Duran-Reynals, F. "Age and Infection; a Review," *J. Geront.*, 1946, 1: 358–73
96. Eliaser, M., and Kondo, B. O. "The Electrocardiogram in Later Life," *Arch. Int. Med.*, 1941, 67: 637–46
97. Ellis, R. S. "Norms for Some Structural Changes in the Human Cerebellum from Birth to Old Age," *J. Comp. Neurol.*, 1920, 32: 1–23
98. Elvehjem, C. A. "Relationship of Enzymes to Deficiency," *Res. Pub. Ass. Nerv. Ment. Dis.*, 1943, 22: 13–27
99. Engle, E. T. "The Testis and Hormones," Chapter 17 in E. V. Cowdry (ed.), *Problems of Ageing* (2d edition) (Baltimore: Williams & Wilkins, 1942), pp. 475–94. See also: Chapter 27 in A. I. Lansing (ed.), *Cowdry's Problems of Ageing* (3d edition) (Baltimore: Williams & Wilkins, 1952), pp. 708–29
100. Fazekas, J. F., Alexander, F. A. D., and Himwich, H. E. "Tolerance of the Newborn to Anoxia," *Amer. J. Physiol.*, 1941, 134: 281–87
101. Fazekas, J. F., and Himwich, H. E. "Anaerobic Survival of Adult Animals," *ibid.*, 1943, 139: 366–70
102. Ferree, C. E., and Rand, G. "Study of Factors Which Cause Individual Differences in Size of Form Field," *Amer. J. Psychol.*, 1930, 42: 63–71
103. Ferree, C. E., Rand, G., and Lewis, E. F. "Age as an Important Factor in the Amount of Light Needed by the Eye," *Arch. Ophthal.*, *Chicago*, 1935, 13: 212–26
104. Ferree, C. E., Rand, G., and Stoll, M. R. "Critical Values for the Light Minimum and for the Amount and Rapidity of Dark Adaptation," *Brit. J. Ophthal.*, 1934, 18: 673–87
105. Fisher, F. P. "Über Altersveränderungen des Auges," *Ophthalmologica*, 1941, 102: 226–32
106. Fisher, M. B., and Birren, J. E. "Age and Strength," *J. Appl. Psychol.*, 1947, 31: 490–97
107. Fowler, W. S. "Lung Function Studies. V. Respiratory Dead Space in Old Age and in Pulmonary Emphysema," *J. Clin. Invest.*, 1950, 29: 1439–44
108. Fox, T. T., Weaver, J. C., and Francis, R. L. "Further Studies on Electrocardiographic Changes in Old Age," *Geriatrics*, 1948, 3: 35–41
109. Freeman, Z. "The Electrocardiogram in Old Age," *Med. J. Aust.*, 1950, 1 (15): 499–503
110. Friedenwald, J. S. "The Eye," Chapter 20 in E. V. Cowdry (ed.), *Problems of Ageing* (2d edition) (Baltimore: Williams & Wilkins, 1942), pp. 535–55. See also: Chapter 9 in A. I. Lansing (ed.), *Cowdry's Problems of Ageing* (3d edition) (Baltimore: Williams & Wilkins, 1952), pp. 239–59
111. Friedfeld, L. "Heat Reaction States in the Aged," *Geriatrics*, 1949, 4: 211–16
112. Frostig, J. P. "Clinical Observations in the Insulin Treatment of Schizophrenia. I. Symptomatology and Therapeutic Factors of the Insulin Effect," *Amer. J. Psychiat.*, 1940, 96: 1167–90

113. Gardner, E. "Decrease in Human Neurones with Age," *Anat. Rec.*, 1940, 77: 529–36

114. Gaunt, R. "Adrenal Cortical Hormones and Related Hormones in Water Metabolism," in *Proceedings of the Second Conference on Renal Function*, Josiah Macy, Jr. Foundation, 1951, pp. 10–47

115. Geist, L. *Klinik der Greisenkrankheiten.* Erlangen: F. Enke, 1860. 650 pp.

116. Gellerstedt, N. "Zur Kenntnis der Hirnveränderungen bei der normalen Altersinvolution," Uppsala LäkFören. Förh., 1933, 38: 193–408

117. Gerritzen, P. "Beiträge zur physiologischen Chemie des Alterns der Gewebe," *Z. ges. exp. Med.*, 1932, 85: 700–11

118. Gertler, M. M., Garn, S. M., and Bland, E. F. "Age, Serum, Cholesterol and Coronary Artery Disease," *Circulation*, 1950, 2: 517–22

119. Gildea, E. F., McLean, V. L., and Man, E. B. "Oral and Intravenous Dextrose Tolerance Curves of Patients with Manic-Depressive Psychosis," *Arch. Neurol. Psychiat.*, Chicago, 1943, 49: 852–59

120. Glezina, O. M. "Old Age Changes of Oxidation-Reduction Processes in Muscle Tissue," *Biochem. J. USSR*, 1939, 13: 105–17

121. Gofman, J. W., Lindgren, F. T., Jones, H. B., Lyon, T. P., and Strisower, B. "Lipoproteins and Atherosclerosis," *J. Geront.*, 1951, 6: 105–19

122. Goldfarb, W. "An Investigation of Reaction Time in Older Adults, and Its Relationship to Certain Observed Mental Test Patterns," *Teachers College Contr. Educ.*, 1941, No. 831, viii + 76 pp.

123. Gray, J. S., Barnum, D. R., Matheson, H. W., and Spies, S. N. "Ventilatory Function Tests. I. Voluntary Ventilation Capacity," *J. Clin. Invest.*, 1950, 29: 677–81

124. Greifenstein, F. E., King, R. M., Latch, S. S., and Comroe, J. H., Jr. "Pulmonary Function Studies in Healthy Men and Women 50 Years and Older," *J. Appl. Physiol.*, 1952, 4: 641–48

125. Greisheimer, E. M., Johnson, O. H., and Ryan, M. "The Relationship Between Serum Calcium and Age," *Amer. J. Med. Sci.*, 1929, 177: 704–14

126. Gross, K. "Über Akkommodation im Alter," *Z. Sinnesphysiol.*, 1932, 62: 49–51

127. Guild, S. R. "The Ear," Chapter 21 in E. V. Cowdry (ed.), *Problems of Ageing* (2d edition) (Baltimore: Williams & Wilkins, 1942), pp. 556–66

128. Hallock, P. "Arterial Elasticity in Man in Relation to Age as Evaluated by the Pulse Wave Velocity Method," *Arch. Intern. Med.*, 1934, 54: 770–98

129. Hardy, J. D., Wolff, H. G., and Goodell, H. "Studies on Pain. A New Method for Measuring Pain Threshold: Observations on Spatial Summation of Pain," *J. Clin. Invest.*, 1940, 19: 649–57

130. Hass, G. M. "Elastic Tissue. III. Relation Between the Structure of the Aging Aorta and Properties of the Isolated Aortic Elastic Tissue," *Arch. Path.*, Chicago, 1943, 35: 29–45

131. Hastings, A. B. "The Electrolytes of Tissues and Body Fluids," *Harvey Lect.*, 1940–41, 36: 91–125

132. Heinrich, A. "Beiträge zur Physiologie des Alterns: lassen sich Anhaltspunkte dafür gewinnen, dass im Alter bei gesunden Menschen der Blutumlauf verlangsamt ist?" *Z. ges. exp. Med.*, 1935, 96: 722–28

133. Herrlich, H. C., Fazekas, J. F., and Himwich, H. E. "Survival of Infant

and Adult Rats at High Altitude," *Proc. Soc. Exp. Biol. N. Y.*, 1941, 48: 446–47

134. Hertel, H. "Das Verhalten der Präzipitation in den verschiedenen Altersstufen," *Z. Altersforsch.*, 1940, 2: 125–28

135. Hillman, C. C., Levy, R. L., Stroud, W. D., and White, P. D. "Studies of Blood Pressure in Army Officers; Observations Based on an Analysis of the Medical Records of 22,741 Officers of the United States Army," *J. Amer. Med. Ass.*, 1944, 125: 699–701

136. Himsworth, H. P., and Kerr, R. B. "Age and Insulin Sensitivity," *Clin. Sci.*, 1939, 4: 153–57

137. Himwich, H. E. *Brain Metabolism and Cerebral Disorders.* Baltimore: Williams & Wilkins, 1951. xi + 451 pp.

138. Hochrein, M. "Das Altern der menschlichen Aorta. I. Die Funktion der alternden Aorta," *Z. Kreislforsch.*, 1940, 32: 836–47

139. Hofstatter, L., Sonnenberg, A., and Kountz, W. B. "The Glucose Tolerance in Elderly Patients," *Biol. Sympos.*, 1945, 11: 87–95

140. Horvath, S. M., Wisotsky, R., and Corwin, W. "The Oral Glucose Tolerance Test in Old Men," *J. Geront.*, 1947, 2: 25–30

141. Howell, T. H. *Old Age* (2d edition). London: H. K. Lewis Co., 1950. 108 pp.

142. Huggins, C. "Endocrine Control of Prostatic Cancer," *Science*, 1943, 97: 541–44

143. Huggins, C., Scott, W. W., and Hodges, C. V. "Studies on Prostatic Cancer; Effects of Fever, of Desoxycorticosterone and Estrogen on Clinical Patients with Metastatic Carcinoma of the Prostate," *J. Urol.*, 1941, 46: 997–1006

144. Huggins, C., Stevens, R. E., and Hodges, C. V. "Studies on Prostatic Cancer; Effects of Castration on Advanced Carcinoma of the Prostate Gland," *Arch. Surg., Chicago*, 1941, 43: 209–23

145. Hunt, J. McV. (ed.). *Personality and the Behavior Disorders.* Vols. I and II. New York: Ronald Press, 1944. xii + 618 pp.

146. Ingle, D. J. "The Production of Glycosuria in the Normal Rat by Means of Stilbestrol," *Amer. J. Med. Sci.*, 1941, 201: 153–84

147. Ivy, A. C. "Digestive System," Chapter 10 in E. V. Cowdry (ed.), *Problems of Ageing* (2d edition) (Baltimore: Williams & Wilkins, 1942), pp. 254–301. See also: Chapter 20 in A. I. Lansing (ed.), *Cowdry's Problems of Ageing* (3d edition) (Baltimore: Williams & Wilkins, 1952), pp. 481–526

148. Johannessen, E. "Hyperglycemia Without Glycosuria in Older People," *Nord. Med., Stockholm*, 1940, 8: 2231–33

149. Johnson, R. E., Darling, R. C., Forbes, W. H., Brouha, L., Egaña, E., and Graybiel, A. "The Effects of a Diet Deficient in Part of the Vitamin B Complex upon Men Doing Manual Labor," *J. Nutrit.*, 1942, 24: 585–96

150. Jolliffe, N. "Effects of Vitamin Deficiency on Mental and Emotional Processes," *Res. Pub. Ass. Nerv. Ment. Dis.*, 1939, 19: 144–53

151. ———. "Treatment of Neuropsychiatric Disorders with Vitamins," *J. Amer. Med. Ass.*, 1941, 117: 1496–1500

152. ———. "The Neuropsychiatric Manifestations of Vitamin Deficiencies," *J. Mt. Sinai Hosp.*, 1942, 8: 658–67

153. Joslyn, E. P., and Dublin, D. I. "Studies in Diabetes Mellitus: Etiology," *Amer. J. Med. Sci.*, 1936, 191: 759–75

154. Kahle, P. J., Schenken, J. R., and Burns, E. L. "Clinical and Pathologic Effects of Diethylstilbestrol and Diethylstilbestrol Dipropionate on Carcinoma of the Prostate Gland. A Continuing Study," *J. Urol.*, 1943, 50: 711–32

155. Kaltreider, N. L., Fray, W. W., and Van Zile Hyde, H. "The Effect of Age on the Total Pulmonary Capacity and Its Subdivisions," *Amer. Rev. Tuberc.*, 1938, 37: 662–69

156. Kessler, M. "Über die Abhängigkeit der Kappillarfunktion vom Lebensalter," *Z. Kreislforsch.*, 1933, 25: 777–84

157. Kessler, W. R. "Age as a Factor in the Resistance of Splenectomized Rats to Infection with *Bartonella muris*," *J. Parasit.*, 1942, 28 (Suppl.): 26

158. Keys, A. "Physical Performance in Relation to Diet," *Fed. Proc.*, *Baltimore*, 1943, 2: 164–87

159. ———. "The Age Trend of Serum Concentrations of Cholesterol and of S_f 10–20 ("G") Substances in Adults," *J. Geront.*, 1952, 7: 201–6

160. Keys, A., Michelsen, O., Miller, E. v. O., Hayes, E. R., and Todd, R. L. "The Concentration of Cholesterol in the Blood Serum of Normal Man and Its Relation to Age," *J. Clint. Invest.*, 1950, 29: 1347–53

161. King, A. L. "Waves in Elastic Tubes; Velocity of the Pulse Wave in Large Arteries," *J. Appl. Physics*, 1947, 18: 595–600

162. King, J. T., Rizzoli, H. V., and Bell, J. P. "Chronic Valvular Disease," Chapter 26 in E. J. Stieglitz (ed.), *Geriatric Medicine* (Philadelphia: W. B. Saunders, 1943), pp. 405–15

162a. Kirk, J. E., and Laursen, T. J. S. "Diffusion Coefficients of Various Solutes for Human Aortic Tissue. With Special Reference to Variation in Tissue Permeability With Age," *J. Geront.*, 1955, 10: 288–302

163. Kirk, E., Lewis, W. H., Jr., and Thompson, W. R. "The Effect on the Plasma Calcium Content of Men," *J. Biol. Chem.*, 1935, 111: 641–42

164. Klondy, M. H. "The Influence of Age upon the Immunological Response of Rats to Infection with *Trypanosoma cruzi*," *Amer. J. Hyg.*, 1940, 31: 1–8

165. Kohl, H., and Dahmann, H. "Blutzuckerbelastungen in verschiedenen Lebensaltern," *Z. Altersforsch.*, 1940, 2: 310–17

166. Korenchevsky, V., Paris, S. K., and Benjamin, B. "Treatment of Senescence in Female Rats with Sex and Thyroid Hormones," *J. Geront.*, 1950, 5: 120–57

167. Kotsovsky, D. "Allgemeine vergleichende Biologie des Alters," *Ergebn. Physiol.*, 1931, 31: 132–64

168. Kountz, W. B., Hofstatter, L., and Ackermann, P. G. "Nitrogen Balance Studies in Four Elderly Men," *J. Geront.*, 1951, 6: 20–33

169. Kountz, W. B., Sonnenberg, A., Hofstatter, L., and Wolff, G. "Blood Cholesterol Levels in Elderly Patients. I. Relation of Age, Sex, Basal Metabolic Rate, Cardiac Decompensation, and Coronary and Peripheral Sclerosis to Blood Cholesterol Levels in the Aged," *Biol. Symp.*, 1945, 11: 79–86

170. Krafka, J., Jr. "Changes in the Elasticity of the Aorta with Age," *Arch. Path.*, *Chicago*, 1940, 29: 303–9

171. Krag, C. L., and Kountz, W. B. "Stability of Body Function in the Aged. I. Effect of Exposure of the Body to Cold," *J. Geront.*, 1950, 5: 227–235
172. ———. "Stability of Body Function in the Aged. II. Effect of Exposure of the Body to Heat," *ibid.*, 1952, 7: 61–70
173. Kretschmer, H. L. "Life After Nephrectomy," *J. Amer. Med. Ass.*, 1943, 121: 473–78
174. Laird, D. A., and Breen, W. J. "Sex and Age Alterations in Taste Preferences," *J. Amer. Diet. Ass.*, 1939, 15: 549–50
174a. Landowne, M., Brandfonbrener, M., and Shock, N. W.: "The Relation of Age to Certain Measures of the Performance of the Heart and the Circulation" (Abstract), *J. Clin. Invest.*, 1955, 34: 948. *Circulation* (in press)
175. Lansing, A. I. "Increase of Cortical Calcium with Age in the Cells of *Elodea canadensis*," *Biol. Bull. Wood's Hole*, 1942, 82: 385–91
176. ———. "Increase of Cortical Calcium with Age in the Cells of a Rotifer, *Euchlanis dilata*, a Planarian, *Phagocata sp.*, and a Toad, *Bufo fowleri*, As Shown by the Micro Incineration Technique," *ibid.*, 1942, 82: 392–409
177. ———. "Evidence for Aging as a Consequence of Growth Cessation," *Proc. Nat. Acad. Sci., Wash.*, 1948, 34: 304–10
178. ———. "Some Physiological Aspects of Ageing," *Physiol. Rev.*, 1951, 31: 274–84
179. ——— (ed.). *Cowdry's Problems of Ageing* (3d edition). Baltimore: Williams & Wilkins, 1952. xxiii + 1061 pp.
180. Lansing, A. I., Alex, M., and Rosenthal, T. B. "Calcium and Elastin in Human Arteriosclerosis," *J. Geront.*, 1950, 5: 112–19
181. Lansing, A. I., Rosenthal, T. B., and Alex, M. "Significance of Medical Age Changes in the Human Pulmonary Artery," *ibid.*, 1950, 5: 211–15
182. La Place, L. B. "Disturbances of Conduction and Rhythm," Chapter 25 in E. J. Stieglitz (ed.), *Geriatric Medicine* (Philadelphia: W. B. Saunders, 1943). See also: Chapter 25 in E. J. Stieglitz (ed.), *Geriatric Medicine* (2d edition) (Philadelphia: W. B. Saunders, 1949), pp. 371–84
182a. Laursen, T. J. S., and Kirk, J. E. "Diffusion Coefficients of Carbon Dioxide and Glucose for a Connective Tissue Membrane from Individuals of Various Ages," *J. Geront.*, 1955, 10: 303–5
183. Lazovskaya, L. N. ("The Change in Respiration of Blood Vessels with Age"), *Biokhimia*, 1943, 8: 171–76
184. Leary, T. "Genesis of Atherosclerosis," *Arch. Path.*, 1941, 32: 507–55
185. ———. "Cholesterol Lysis in Atheroma," *ibid.*, 1944, 37: 16–19
186. Levitt, G. "The Electrocardiogram in the Aged. A Study of 100 Men and Women Over the Age of 70 with Apparently Normal Hearts," *Amer. Heart J.*, 1939, 18: 692–96
187. Levy, B. "Die Vitalkapazität im höheren Lebensalter," *Zbl. inn. Med.*, 1933, 54: 417–20
188. Lewis, R. A., Kuhlman, D., Delbue, C., Koeuf, D. F., and Thorn, G. W. "The Effect of the Adrenal Cortex on Carbohydrate Metabolism," *Endocrinology*, 1940, 27: 971–82
189. Lewis, W. H., Jr. "Changes with Age in the Basal Metabolic Rate in Adult Men," *Amer. J. Physiol.*, 1938, 121: 502–16
190. ———. "Changes with Age in Cardiac Output in Adult Men," *ibid.*, 1938, 121: 517–27

191. ———. "Changes with Age in the Blood Pressures in Adult Men," *ibid.*, 1938, 122: 491–505

192. Lewis, W. H., Jr., and Alving, A. S. "Changes with Age in the Renal Function in Adult Men. I. Clearance of Urea. II. Amount of Urea Nitrogen in the Blood. III. Concentrating Ability of the Kidneys," *ibid.*, 1938, 123: 500–515

193. Life Extension Institute. "Incidence of Hemorrhoids and Prostatic Enlargement Among 15,700 Examinees by Age, Sex, and Weight Groups," *Proc. Life Ext. Examiners*, 1940, 2: 139–42

194. Lloyd, R. I. "Causes of Lowered Acuity in Senility," *Amer. J. Ophthal.*, 1944, 27: 232–43

195. Löhr, H., and Tillmanns, H. "Alterselectrocardiogram," *Z. klin. Med.*, 1939, 135: 453–56

196. Long, C. N. H., Katzin, B., and Fry, E. G. "The Adrenal Cortex and Carbohydrate Metabolism," *Endocrinology*, 1940, 26: 309–44

197. Lowry, O. H., and Hastings, A .B. "Histochemical Changes in Ageing," Chapter 27 in E. V. Cowdry (ed.), *Problems of Ageing* (2d edition) (Baltimore: Williams & Wilkins, 1942), pp. 728–55. See also: Chapter 5 in A. I. Lansing (ed.), *Cowdry's Problems of Ageing* (3d edition) (Baltimore: Williams & Wilkins, 1952), pp. 105–38

198. McCullagh, E. P. "Climacteric; Male and Female," *Cleveland Clin. Quart.*, 1946, 13: 166–76. Also in *Bull. Chicago Med. Soc.*, 1946, 49: 193–98

199. McFarland, R. A. "The Psycho-physiological Effects of Reduced Oxygen Pressure," *Res. Pub. Ass. Nerv. Ment. Dis.*, 1939, 19: 112–43

200. McKay, E. M., and McKay, L. L. "Age and the Effect of Unusual Diets," *J. Biol. Chem.*, 1930, 86: 765–71

201. McKay, L. L., McKay, E. M., and Addis, T. "The Effect of Various Factors on the Degree of Compensatory Hypertrophy of the Kidney After Unilateral Nephrectomy," *J. Clin. Invest.*, 1924, 1: 576–77

202. ———. "Influence of Age on the Relation of Renal Weight to the Protein Intake and the Degree of Renal Hypertrophy Produced by High Protein Diets," *Amer. J. Physiol.*, 1928, 86: 466–70

203. McKim, G. F., Smith, P. G., and Rush, T. W. "Twelve-Year Survival with One-Half of One Kidney," *J. Urol.*, 1943, 50: 769–74

204. McNamara, R. J. "A Study in the Electrocardiogram in Persons over 70," *Geriatrics*, 1949, 4: 150–60

205. MacNider, W. DeB. "A Consideration of the Relative Toxicity of Uranium Nitrate for Animals of Different Ages," *J. Exp. Med.*, 1917, 26: 1–17

206. ———. "The Aging Process and Tissue Resistance," *Sci. Mon., N.Y.*, 1942, 54: 149–84

207. ———. "Ageing Processes Considered in Relation to Tissue Susceptibility and Resistance," Chapter 25 in E. V. Cowdry (ed.), *Problems of Ageing* (2d edition) (Baltimore: Williams & Wilkins, 1942), pp. 664–79. See also: Chapter 4 in A. I. Lansing (ed.), *Cowdry's Problems of Ageing* (3d edition) (Baltimore: Williams & Wilkins, 1952), pp. 89–104

208. ———. "Stability of Acid-Base Equilibrium of Blood in Animals Falling in Different Age Periods," *Proc. Soc. Exp. Biol.*, 1943, 53: 1–8

209. Marinesco, G. "Études sur le mécanisme histobiochemique de la vieillesse et du 'rajeunissement,' " Berlin u. Köln: A. Marcus & E. Weber's Verlag. *Verh. Internat. Kongr. Sexualforschung*, 1927, 1: 117–77

210. Marshall, F. W. "Sugar Content of the Blood in Elderly People," *Quart. J. Med.*, 1931, 24: 257–84

211. Martsinkovski, B. I., and Zhorova, K. S. "The Question of Distribution and Regulation of Heat in Old Age," *Acta med. scand.*, 1936, 90: 582–92

212. Master, A. M., Dublin, L. I., and Marks, H. H. "The Normal Blood Pressure Range and Its Clinical Implications," *J. Amer. Med. Ass.*, 1950, 143: 1464–70

213. Masters, W. H., "The Female Reproductive System," Chapter 25 in A. I. Lansing (ed.), *Cowdry's Problems of Ageing* (3d edition) (Baltimore: Williams & Wilkins, 1952), pp. 651–85

214. Masters, W. H., and Allen, W. M. "Female Sex Hormone Replacement in the Aged Woman," *J. Geront.*, 1948, 3: 183–90

215. Mazer, M., and Reisinger, J. A. "An Electrocardiographic Study of Cardiac Aging Based on Records at Rest and After Exercise," *Ann. Intern. Med.*, 1944, 21: 645–52

216. Metchnikoff, E. *The Prolongation of Life.* New York: G. P. Putnam's Sons, 1908. xx + 343 pp.

217. Meyer, J., Golden, J. S., Steiner, N., and Necheles, H. "The Content of Human Saliva in Old Age," *Amer. J. Physiol.*, 1937, 119: 600–602

218. Meyer, J., and Necheles, H. "The Clinical Significance of Salivary, Gastric, and Pancreatic Secretion in the Aged," *J. Amer. Med. Ass.*, 1940, 115: 2050–53

219. Meyer, J., Sorter, H., Oliver, J., and Necheles, H. "Studies in Old Age. VII. Intestinal Absorption in Old Age," *Gastroenterology*, 1943, 1: 876–81

220. Meyer, J., Spier, E., and Neuwelt, F. "Basal Secretion of Digestive Enzymes in Old Age," *Arch. Intern. Med.*, 1940, 65: 171–77

221. Miles, W. R. "Age and Human Ability," *Psychol. Rev.*, 1933, 40: 99–123

222. ———. "Psychological Aspects of Ageing," Chapter 28 in E. V. Cowdry (ed.), *Problems of Ageing* (2d edition) (Baltimore: Williams & Wilkins, 1942), pp. 756–84

223. Miles, W. R., and Miles, C. C. "Principal Mental Changes with Normal Aging," Chapter 5 in E. J. Stieglitz (ed.), *Geriatric Medicine* (Philadelphia: W. B. Saunders, 1943), pp. 99–117. See also: Chapter 5 in E. J. Stieglitz (ed.), *Geriatric Medicine* (2d edition) (Philadelphia: W. B. Saunders, 1949), pp. 91–122

224. Miller, I. "Vital Capacity Studies in the Aged," *J. Lab. Clin. Med.*, 1941–42, 27: 737–40

225. Minot, C. S. *The Problem of Age, Growth, and Death.* New York: G. P. Putnam's Sons, 1908

226. Montgomery, H. C. "Analysis of World's Fairs' Hearing Tests," *Sci. Mon.*, N.Y., 1940, 50: 335–39

227. Moog, F. "The Biology of Old Age; Senescence and Death, Which to Man Seem Unavoidable, Are Not the Rule Among All Species of Living Things," *Sci. Amer.*, 1948, 178: 40–43

228. Moore, M. T., and Lichstein, J. "Effect of Nicotinic Acid and Thiamin Chloride on the Adverse Symptoms Encountered in Old Age," *Med. Rec.* N.Y., 1941, 154: 100–103

229. Moore, R. A. "The Total Number of Glomeruli in the Normal Human Kidney," *Anat. Rec.*, 1931, 48: 153–68

230. ———. "Male Secondary Sexual Organs," Chapter 18 in E. V. Cowdry (ed.), *Problems of Ageing* (2d edition) (Baltimore: Williams & Wilkins, 1942), pp. 495–517. See also: Chapter 26 in A. I. Lansing (ed.), *Cowdry's Problems of Ageing* (3d edition) (Baltimore: Williams & Wilkins, 1952), pp. 686–707

231. Mosenthal, H. O., and Barry, E. "Criteria for and Interpretation of Normal Glucose Tolerance Tests," *Ann. Intern. Med.*, 1950, 33: 1175–94

232. Mueller-Deham, A., and Rabson, S. M. *Internal Medicine in Old Age.* Baltimore: Williams & Wilkins, 1942. x + 396 pp.

233. Murray, J. A. "The Chemical Composition of Animal Bodies," *J. Agric. Sci.*, 1922, 12: 103–10

234. Myers, J. A., and Cady, L. H. "Studies on the Respiratory Organs in Health and Disease. XIII. The Effects of Senility on the Vital Capacity of the Lungs," *Amer. Rev. Tuberc.*, 1924, 9: 57–64

235. Nechaeva, P. V. ("Glycolytic Action of Blood in Subjects of Very Advanced Age"), *Trans. Conf. Senility, Kiev*, 1938, 345–46

236. Nelbach, J. H., and Herrington, L. P. "The Significance of the Tensility of the Aorta as an Index of the Aging Process in the Animal Body," *Amer. Heart J.*, 1941, 22: 661–82

237. Neumann, C., Cohn, A. E., and Burch, G. E. "A Study by Quantitative Methods of the Spontaneous Variations in Volume of the Tips of the Fingers and Toes and Postero-superior Portion of the Pinna of Hypertensive Patients and Senile Subjects," *Amer. J. Physiol.*, 1942, 136: 451–59

238. Norris, A. H., Shock, N. W., and Yiengst, M. J. "Age Changes in Heart Rate and Blood Pressure Responses to Tilting and Standardized Exercise," *Circulation*, 1953, 8: 521–26

239. ———. "Age Differences in Ventilatory and Gas Exchange Responses to Graded Exercise in Males," *J. Geront.*, 1955, 10: 145–55

240. Norris, J. L., Blanchard, J., and Povolny, C. "Regeneration of Rat Liver at Different Ages. Metabolism of Embryonic, Neonatal and Regenerating Rat Liver," *Arch. Path., Chicago*, 1942, 34: 208–17

241. Noyes, H. M., and Falk, K. G. "Studies on Enzyme Action. Time Changes in Ester-Hydrolyzing Actions of Extracts of Whole Rats of Different Ages," *J. Biol. Chem.*, 1927, 72: 449–65

242. Noyes, H. M., Falk, K. G., and Baumann, E. J. "Studies on Enzyme Action. Lipase Action of Extracts of Tissues of Rabbits at Different Ages," *J. Gen. Physiol.*, 1926, 9: 651–75

243. Olbrich, O., Ferguson, M. H., Robson, J. S., and Stewart, C. P. "Renal Function in Aged Subjects," *Edinb. Med. J.*, 1950, 57: 117

244. Oliver, J. "Principal Anatomic Changes with Normal Ageing," Chapter 4 in E. J. Stieglitz (ed.), *Geriatric Medicine* (Philadelphia: W. B. Saunders, 1943), pp. 72–98. See also: Chapter 4 in E. J. Stieglitz (ed.), *Geriatric Medicine* (2d edition) (Philadelphia: W. B. Saunders, 1949), pp. 67–90

245. ———. "Structural Aspects of the Process of Aging," in *The Social and Biological Challenge of Our Aging Population*" (New York: Columbia University Press), 1950, pp. 25–43

246. Page, I. H., Kirk, E., Lewis, W. H., Jr., Thompson, W. R., and Van Slyke,

D. D. "Plasma Lipids of Normal Men at Different Ages," *J. Biol. Chem.*, 1935, 111: 613–39

247. ———. "The Effect of Age on the Plasma Lipid Content of Man," *ibid.*, 1935, 111: 641–42

248. Paine, R. M. "Pulse-wave Velocity as an Index of Aging in the Cardiovascular System," *J. Geront.*, 1948, 3: 303–5

249. Palmer, H. D., Braceland, F. J., and Hastings, D. W. "Somato-psychic Disorders of Old Age," *Amer. J. Psychiat.*, 1943, 99: 856–63

250. Pearl, R. *The Biology of Death.* New York: J. B. Lippincott & Co., 1922. 275 pp.

251. ———. "Experiments on Longevity," *Quart. Rev. Biol.*, 1928, 3: 391–407

252. Pearson, G. H. J. "Effect of Age on Vibratory Sensibility," *Arch. Neurol. Psychiat.*, Chicago, 1928, 20: 482–96

253. Peters, J. P. *Body Water. The Exchange of Fluids in Man.* Springfield, Ill.: Charles C. Thomas, 1935. viii + 405 pp.

254. Picado, T. C. "Glucoregulación Sanguínea y edad. II," *Rev. méd.*, San José, 1940, 4: 327–28

255. Pickering, G. W. "The Peripheral Resistance in Persistent Hypertension," *Clin. Sci.*, 1936, 2: 209–35

256. Poeschel, R. "Magenfunktion bei alten Leuten," *Z. klin. Med.*, 1930, 113: 379–86

257. Porter, E., and Langley, G. J. "Studies in Blood Sugar," *Lancet*, 1926, 2: 947

258. Price, B. "A Perceptual Test for Comparing the Performance of Age Groups; Preliminary Report," *Psychol. Bull.*, 1931, 28: 584–85

259. Proctor, L. D., Dewan, J. G., and McNeel, B. "Variations in the Glucose Tolerance Observations in Schizophrenics Before and After Shock Treatment," *Amer. J. Psychiat.*, 1944, 100: 652–58

260. Rafsky, H. A., and Newman, B. "Cholesterol Studies in the Aged," *J. Lab. Clin. Med.*, 1942, 27: 1563–66

261. Rafsky, H. A., Newman, B., and Horonick, A. "Age Differences in Respiration of Guinea Pig Tissues," *J. Geront.*, 1952, 7: 38–40

262. Reiner, J. M. "The Effect of Age on the Carbohydrate Metabolism of Tissue Homogenates," *ibid.*, 1947, 2: 315–20

263. Robertson, G. W., and Yudkin, J. "Effect of Age on Dark Adaptation," *J. Physiol*, 1944, 103: 1–8

264. Robertson, J. D. "Calcium and Phosphorus Studies in Normal People Including Old Age," *Lancet*, 1941, 2: 97–100

265. Robinson, S. "Experimental Studies of Physical Fitness in Relation to Age," *Arbeitsphysiologie*, 1938, 10: 251–323

266. Robinson, S. C., and Brucer, M. "Range of Normal Blood Pressure. A Statistical and Clinical Study of 11,383 Persons," *Arch. Intern. Med.*, 1939, 64: 409–44

267. Roessle, R., and Roulet, F. *Mass und Zahl in der Pathologie.* Berlin: J. Springer, 1932. 144 pp.

268. Rømcke, O. "Der Blutzucker im älteren Alter, insbesondere bei hypertonischen Zuständen," *Acta med. scand.*, 1931, *Suppl. 39*, pp. 1–150

269. Rones, B. "Senile Changes and Degenerations of the Human Eye," *Arch. Ophthal.*, Chicago, 1938, 21: 239–55

270. Rosenthal, O., Bowie, M. A., and Wagoner, G. "Studies in the Metabolism

of Articular Cartilage. I. Respiration and Glucolysis of Cartilage in Relation to Its Age," *J. Cell. Comp. Physiol.*, 1941, 17: 221–33

271. ———. "The Dehydrogenatic Ability of Bovine Articular Cartilage in Relation to Its Age," *ibid.*, 1942, 19: 333–40

272. Russek, H. I., Rath, M. M., Miller, I., and Zohman, B. L. "The Influence of Age on Blood Pressure; a Study of 5,331 White Male Subjects," *Amer. Heart J.*, 1946, 32: 468–79

273. Russell, J. A. "The Relation of the Anterior Pituitary to Carbohydrate Metabolism," *Physiol. Rev.*, 1932, 18: 1–23

274. Saxton, J. A., Jr. "Elastic Properties on the Rabbit Aorta in Relation to Age," *Arch. Path.*, *Chicago*, 1942, 34: 262–74

275. Schäfer, W. "Lebensalter und Infektionsdisposition," *Z. Altersforsch.*, 1951, 5: 171–83

276. Schlesinger, E. "Körperform, Muskelkraft, und Turnleistung bei Kindern und Jugendlichen. III. Mitteilung über die Wirkung der Leibesübungen auf das Kind," *Arch. Kinderheilk.*, 1931, 92: 193–215

277. Schlesinger, H. *Die Krankheiten des höheren Lebensalters.* Vienna: A. Holder, 1914. Vol. I, 611 pp.; Vol. II, 541 pp.

278. Schlomka, G., and Kreuzmann, H. "Beiträge zur klinischen Elektrokardiographie Untersuchungen über den Einfluss des Lebensalters auf den Typ der Herzstromkurve des Gesunden," *Z. klin. Med.*, 1936, 129: 532–51

279. Schneeberg, N. G., and Finestone, I. "The Effect of Age on the Intravenous Glucose Tolerance Test," *J. Geront.*, 1952, 7: 54–60

280. Sebrell, W. H. "The Mental and Neurological Aspects of Vitamin B Complex Deficiency," *Res. Publ. Ass. Nerv. Ment. Dis.*, 1943, 22: 113–21

281. Selle, W. A. "Influence of Age on Survival of Respiration, Spinal Reflexes, Pupillary Responses and Heart Action," *Proc. Soc. Exp. Biol.*, *N.Y.*, 1941, 48: 417–19

282. Selye, H. *Stress.* Montreal: Acta Incorporated, 1950, 822 + 203 pp.

283. Sevringhaus, E. L. "The Male Climacteric," *Proc. Int. Assemb. Post-grad. Med. Ass. N. Amer.*, 1943 (1942), pp. 51–54

284. Shattuck, G. C., and Hilferty, M. M. "Sunstroke and Allied Conditions in the United States," *Amer. J. Trop. Med.*, 1932, 12: 223–45

285. Shock, N. W. "Physiological Changes in Adolescence," *Nat. Soc. for the Study of Educ.*, *43d Yrbk.*, *Part 1*, chapter iv, 1944, pp. 56–79

286. ———. "Physiological Factors in Behavior," Chapter 19 in J. McV. Hunt (ed.), *Personality and the Behavior Disorders* (Vol. 1) (New York: Ronald Press, 1944), pp. 582–618

287. ———. "Kidney Function Tests in Aged Males, *Geriatrics*, 1946, 1: 232–39

288. ———. "Metabolism in Old Age," *Bull. N.Y. Acad. Med.*, 1948, 24: 166–78

289. ———. "Gerontology (Later Maturity)," in C. P. Stone and D. W. Taylor (eds.), *Annual Review of Psychology* (Stanford, Calif.: Annual Reviews, Inc., 1951), Vol. 2, pp. 353–70

290. ———. *A Classified Bibliography of Gerontology and Geriatrics.* Stanford, Calif.: Stanford University Press, 1951. xxvii + 599 pp.

291. ———. "Ageing of Homeostatic Mechanisms," Chapter 18 in A. I. Lansing (ed.), *Cowdry's Problems of Ageing* (3d edition) (Baltimore: Williams & Wilkins, 1952), pp. 415–46

292. ———. "Age Changes in Renal Function," Chapter 23 in A. I. Lansing

(ed.), *Cowdry's Problems of Ageing* (3d edition) (Baltimore: Williams & Wilkins, 1952), pp. 614–30

292a. ———. "Some Physiological and Biochemical Aspects of Aging," in *Symposium on Problems of Gerontology.* The National Vitamin Foundation, Inc., New York, Nutrition Symposium Series No. 9, August 1954, pp. 1–23

292b. ———. "Metabolism and Age," *J. Chronic Dis.* (in press)

293. Shock, N. W., and Hastings, A. B. "Studies of the Acid-Base Balance of the Blood. IV. Characterization and Interpretation of Displacement of the Acid-Base Balance," *J. Biol. Chem.*, 1935, 112: 239–62

294. Shock, N. W., and Yiengst, M. J. "Experimental Displacements of the Acid-Base Equilibrium of the Blood in Aged Males," *Fed. Proc., Baltimore*, 1948, 7: 114–15

295. ———. "Age Changes in the Acid-Base Equilibrium of the Blood of Males," *J. Geront.*, 1950, 5: 1–4

296. ———. "Age Changes in Basal Respiratory Measurements and Metabolism in Males," *ibid.*, 1955, 10: 31–40

296a. Shock, N. W., Yiengst, M. J., and Watkin, D. M. "Age Changes in Body Water and Its Relationship to Basal Oxygen Consumption in Males" (Abstract), *ibid.*, 1953, 8: 388

296b. Silverstone, F. A., Brandfonbrener, M., Shock, N. W., and Yiengst, M. J. "Age Differences in the Intravenous Glucose Tolerance Tests and the Response to Insulin," *J. Geront.*, 1955, 10 (in press)

297. Simms, H. S., and Stolman, A. "Changes in Human Tissue Electrolytes in Senescence," *Science*, 1937, 86: 269–70

298. Simonson, E. "Physical Fitness and Work Capacity of Older Men," *Geriatrics*, 1947, 2: 110–19

299. Smith, C. G. "Age Incidence of Atrophy of Olfactory Nerves in Man," *J. Comp. Neurol.*, 1942, 77: 589–95

300. Smith, H. C. "Age Differences in Color Discrimination," *J. Gen. Psychol.*, 1943, 29: 191–226

301. Smith, H. W. *The Kidney.* (New York: Oxford University Press, 1951). xxii + 1049 pp.

302. Smith, L. E. "Glucose Tolerance in the Aged," *J. Geront.*, 1948, 3: 66–69

303. ———. "Blood Pyruvate Levels Following Intravenous Glucose Injections in Aged Males," *Amer. J. Med. Sci.*, 1950, 220: 78–83

304. Smith, L. E., and Shock, N. W. "Intravenous Glucose Tolerance Tests in Aged Males," *J. Geront.*, 1949, 4: 27–33

305. Solnzew, W. I. "Die Veränderungen des Fett-Lipoid-Stoffwechsels im Alter," *Z. Vitamin u. c Forsch., Wien*, 1951, 4: 94–107

306. Soskin, S., and Levine, R. *Carbohydrate Metabolism.* Chicago: University of Chicago Press, 1946. viii + 315 pp.

307. Sperry, W. M., and Webb, M. "The Effect of Increasing Age on Serum Cholesterol Concentration," *J. Biol. Chem.*, 1950, 187: 107–10

308. Spiegelman, M., and Marks, H. H. "Age and Sex Variations in the Prevalence and Onset of Diabetes Mellitus," *Amer. J. Pub. Hlth.*, 1946, 36: 26–33

309. Spies, T. D., Bradley, J., Rosenbaum, M., and Knott, J. R. "Emotional Disturbances in Persons with Pellagra, Beriberi, and Associated Deficiency States," *Res. Pub. Ass. Nerv. Ment. Dis.*, 1943, 22: 122–40

310. Sprague, H. B. "The Normal Senile Heart and Diagnostic Problems," Chapter 24 in E. J. Stieglitz (ed.), *Geriatric Medicine* (Philadelphia: W. B. Saunders, 1943), pp. 371–404. See also: Chapter 24 in E. J. Stieglitz (ed.), *Geriatric Medicine* (2d edition) (Philadelphia: W. B. Saunders, 1949), pp. 357–70

311. Steele, J. M. Berger, E. Y., Dunning, M. F., and Brodie, B. B. "Total Body Water in Man," *Amer. J. Physiol.*, 1950, 162: 313–17

312. Steinhaus, A. H. "Chronic Effects of Exercise," *Physiol. Rev.*, 1933, 13: 103–47

313. Stephenson, W., Penton, C., and Korenchevsky, V. "Some Effects of Vitamins B and C on Senile Patients," *Brit. Med. J.*, 1941, 2: 839–44

314. Steven, D. M. "Relation Between Dark Adaptation and Age," *Nature, London*, 1946, 157: 376

315. Stieglitz, E. J. *Geriatric Medicine.* Philadelphia: W. B. Saunders, 1943. xix + 887 pp. See also: 2d edition, 1949. xvii + 773 pp.

316. Thomsen, O., and Kettel, K. "Die Stärke der menschlichen Isoagglutinine und entsprechenden Blutkörperchenrezeptronen in verschiedenen Lebensaltern," *Z. Immunforsch.*, 1929, 63: 67–93

317. Thorner, M. W., and Lewy, F. H. "The Effects of Repeated Anoxia on the Brain. A Histopathologic Study," *J. Amer. Med. Ass.*, 1940, 115: 1595–1600

318. Tiffin, J. *Industrial Psychology.* (2d edition). New York: Prentice-Hall, 1947. 533 pp.

319. Tilney, F. "The Ageing of the Human Brain," *Bull. N.Y. Acad. Med.*, 1928, 4: 1125–43

320. Törnblom, N. "Contribution to the Discussion on the Etiology of Prostatic Hypertrophy in Man. I. The Weight of the Prostate and Seminal Vesicles in Men of Different Ages," *Acta med. scand.*, 1946, *Suppl. 170*, pp. 1–9

321. Truex, R. C., and Zwemer, R. L. "True Fatty Degeneration in Sensory Neurons of the Aged," *Arch. Neurol. Psychiat., Chicago*, 1942, 48: 988–95

322. Tunbridge, R. E., and Allibone, E. C. "The Intravenous Dextrose Tolerance Test," *Quart. J. Med.*, 1940, 9: 11–35

323. Van Liere, E. J., and Northrup, D. W. "The Emptying Time of the Stomach of Old People," *Amer. J. Physiol.*, 1941, 134: 719–22

324. Vanzant, F. R., Alvarez, W. C., Eusterman, G. B., Dunn, H. L., and Berkson, J. "The Normal Range of Gastric Acidity from Youth to Old Age," *Arch. Intern. Med.*, 1932, 49: 345–59

325. Voelker, C. H. "Tested Auditory Behavior Rather than Hearing; Acuity Is a Function of Age," *Amer. Ann. Deaf*, 1941, 86: 1–6

326. Warthin, A. S. *Old Age. The Major Involution.* New York: P. Hoeber, Inc., 1929. xvi + 199 pp.

327. Weiss, E., and English, O. S. *Psychosomatic Medicine.* Philadelphia: W. B. Saunders Co., 1943. 687 pp.

328. Werner, A. A. "Syndrome Accompanying Deficiency or Absence of the Ovarian Follicular Hormone," *Endocrinology*, 1935, 19: 695–700

329. ———. "The Male Climacteric; Report of Two Hundred and Seventy-three Cases," *J. Amer. Med. Ass.*, 1946, 132: 188–94

330. Werner, A. A., Kohler, L. H., Ault, C. C., and Hoctor, E. F. "Involutional Melancholia. Probable Etiology and Treatment," *Arch. Neurol. Psychiat., Chicago*, 1936, 35: 1076–80

331. Weston, H. C. "The Effect of Age and Illumination upon Visual Performance with Close Sights," *Brit. J. Ophth.*, 1948, 32: 645–53
332. Wezler, K., and Standi, R. "Die normalen Alterskurven der Pulswellengeschwindigkeit in elastischen und muskulären Arterien des Menschen," *Z. Biol.*, 1936, 97: 265–76
333. Whitfield, A. G. W., Waterhouse, J. A. H., and Arnott, W. M. "The Total Lung Volume and Its Subdivisions; A Study in Physiological Norms; Basic Data," *Brit. J. Soc. Med.*, 1950, 4: 1–25
334. Wilder, J. "Psychological Problems in Hypoglycemia," *Amer. J. Digest. Dis.*, 1943, 11: 428–35
335. Wilens, S. J. "The Postmortem Elasticity of the Adult Human Aorta. Its Relation to Age and to the Distribution of Internal Atheromas," *Amer. J. Path.*, 1937, 13: 811–34
336. Williams, R. D., Mason, H. L., Smith, B. F., and Wilder, R. M. "Induced Thiamine (Vitamine B_1) Deficiency and the Thiamine Requirement of Man," *Arch. Intern. Med.*, 1942, 69: 721–38
337. Winternitz, M. C., Thomas, R. M., and Le Compte, P. M. *The Biology of Arteriosclerosis.* Springfield, Ill.: Charles C Thomas, 1938. xxiii + 142 pp.
338. Wolbach, S. B. "Controlled Formation of Collagen and Reticulum. A Study of the Source of Intercellular Substance in Recovery from Experimental Scorbutus," *Amer. J. Path.*, 1933, 9 (Suppl.): 689–99
339. Wolff, H. G., Wolf, S. G., Jr., and Hare, C. C. (eds.). "Life Stress and Bodily Disease," *Res. Pub. Ass. Nerv. Ment. Dis.*, 1950, 29: 1–1135
340. Wosika, P. H., Feldman, E., Chesrow, E. J., and Myers, G. B. "Unipolar Precordial and Limb Lead Electrocardiograms in the Aged," *Geriatrics*, 1950, 5: 131–41
341. Yiengst, M. J., and Shock, N. W. "Effect of Oral Administration of Vitamin A on Plasma Levels of Vitamin A and Carotene in Aged Males," *J. Geront.*, 1949, 4: 205–11
342. Zunz, E., and La Barre, J. "Sur les causes de l'augmentation de la teneur en insuline du sang veineux pancréatique lors de l'hyperglycémie provoquée par injection de dextrose après l'hyperglycémie provoquée par injection de glucose," *C. R. Soc. Biol., Paris*, 1927, 96: 421–23

Chapter V

PSYCHOLOGICAL ASPECTS OF MENTAL DISORDERS IN LATER LIFE

HAROLD E. JONES AND OSCAR J. KAPLAN

PSYCHOLOGY has two major contributions to make to the understanding of mental disease in later life. It can contribute to the description of the behavior and capabilities of older psychotics, neurotics, aments, and psychopathic personalities, as seen against the background of normal age changes; even more important, it can provide us with new insights concerning process and origin, a task it shares with psychiatry, physiology, sociology, and other disciplines.

It is only recently that psychologists have shown serious concern regarding the course of mental change in senility, and interest in this field has not been commensurate with its importance. Carefully controlled investigations are almost totally absent in many phases of this vital subject, and it is hoped that this survey of the literature may call attention to existing gaps in our knowledge.

The presenile psychoses have been almost untouched by formal psychological inquiry, and involutional melancholia has not been extensively investigated by psychological methods. Therefore, this chapter will concern itself largely with the psychological consequences of so-called normal aging and with the status of mental functions in senile dements and in cerebral arteriosclerotics with psychosis; attention will be drawn to differences existing between normal and abnormal aged persons. Neurotic behavior in older individuals will be described by Cameron in chapter viii, and the psychological effects of age upon amentia will be covered by Kaplan in chapter xiv.

Measurement of psychological abilities in the normal aged is difficult enough; but the problems which arise in the study of those who are both senile and demented are even more difficult of solution. One of these problems involves differential diagnosis. As Rothschild points out (chapter xi), cerebral arteriosclerosis with psychosis cannot always be readily distinguished from senile dementia; in some institutions, limited in personnel, there is a tendency to place most older psychotics in the senile dementia category. Simon and Malamud (131) compared clinical diagnoses of senile psychoses with neuropathological findings obtained at autopsy. They found a high percentage of incorrect diagnoses. In particular, they found a tendency to classify senile dements as cerebral arteriosclerotics with psychosis.

Some of the confusion in the psychological description of the senile psychoses derives from this lack of discrimination in diagnostic procedures. Even where discrimination has been attempted, comparative study is sometimes handicapped by the fact that the individuals composing a group may be in different stages of the disease and may have entered upon the disease with markedly different backgrounds and endowments. In view of the variety of conditions that they present, great care must be exercised in offering generalizations appropriate to the diagnostic group as a whole. Moreover, we must bear in mind the fact that older patients in mental hospitals (the usual subjects for such inquiries) are not completely representative of noninstitutionalized psychotics.

In the view of the present writers the dividing line between normal aging and psychotic aging is statistical rather than abrupt. The study of normal aging will assist our understanding of the senile psychoses; and, since the latter may caricature the former, the study of mental disease in older persons will at the same time make more comprehensible the changes which take place in those who appear to be normal.

I. INTELLIGENCE

Memory, thinking, learning, imagination, judgment—these are facets of more general capacity. It has proved useful, for pedagogical reasons, to consider these functions as separate entities, though they are inextricably tied together. All intelligence tests have items based upon memory and learning. Imagination and thinking are also featured in such tests; these functions would be impossible in the absence of memory and would be seriously interfered with in cases of memory disturbance. It is therefore not surprising to find that profound memory loss in seniles is accompanied by alterations in thinking, imagination, learning, judgment, and general intelligence.

Old people decline with respect to the functions which intelligence tests measure. This cannot be denied. However, intelligence is a construct and one on which there is not universal agreement. Therefore in discussing the decline of intelligence in normal and psychotic seniles we must state our conclusions in terms of specific modes of inquiry. Some intelligence tests stress speed; others stress power. Some are heavily weighted with verbal items, such as vocabulary. Others assign emphasis to numerical abilities, spatial discrimination, etc. Since the components of "intelligence" may decline with age, or mental disease, at unequal rates, various results may be obtained, with different mental tests, according to their subtest structure.

Our intelligent tests have for the most part been standardized on young people and specifically designed for young people. Their use with older persons is open to the challenge that they are not wholly valid with such persons. In this connection it is important for us to remember the fundamental distinction between ability and capacity. We have no satisfactory way of measuring capacity directly; we can appraise capacity only indirectly by measuring the abilities manifested at a given time. All who have used intelligence tests know that there are many persons of normal or superior intelligence who lack the intellectual skills measured by some of our mental tests. Moreover, loss of ability does not always indicate loss of capacity. The college senior may have less ability in freshman subjects than the average freshman, but he may have equal or greater capacity. Old people often have well-practiced abilities not possessed by young people of the same or greater mental capacity.

II. METHODOLOGICAL PROBLEMS

The following discussion deals with some of the special problems that must be considered in interpreting the results from mental test studies of adults.

Motivation.—It has frequently been pointed out that with increasing age many individuals may have a reduced motivation in test performance. Tests are like school examinations; they involve incentives and habits of competitive effort which are now in the distant past and cannot easily be restored. Thus it may be argued that a poorer test performance on the part of older persons reflects a loss of interest in this kind of a task, rather than basically a loss of capacity.

We should consider at this point whether the argument refers merely to the test situation, or more broadly to intellectual activities. In the former case, the chief effect of a declining motivation is to make it hard to obtain subjects, and this sometimes results in average test scores which, due to a restricted sample of subjects, are spuriously high rather than spuriously low. Kay (73) has pointed out that although it may be more difficult to persuade older persons to enter an unfamiliar experimental situation, once they have agreed to participate they often show a strong competitive spirit, especially in relation to other age groups.

Where declining motivation applies to a person's mental life in a wider sense, we may not be justified in regarding this as a factor wholly separable from mental ability. Interest and functional activity play a role in developing and maintaining our abilities, and declining motivation may likewise play a role in the decline of abilities. If, as a result of this interaction, a person's mental test scores diminish, it may not be accurate to say that his abilities are still unchanged, if he were only willing to use them, or to assume that the apparent decline would be quickly reversible if the motivational pattern were altered.

Physical factors.—In the testing of older persons, care must be taken to distinguish between declining trends in mental abilities and in sensory or sensorimotor functions. Test performance may be impaired by failing to hear the instructions correctly, by a visual handicap, or by a difficulty in writing or in some other motor performance required by the test. Since tests are not usually devised with such problems in mind, they must be given special consideration in programs which extend beyond middle age.

Among younger persons, within a normal range physical factors and health bear only a small relationship to mental test abilities. Even this small relation is chiefly due to the influence of a common factor (social stratification) rather than to a physical-mental interaction. But it seems reasonable to suppose that, over a long term, diminishing health and vigor will exert both direct and indirect effects upon test performance: direct, through modifying habits of concentrated effort; and indirect, through changes in level of aspiration and in the maintenance of intellectual interests. To some extent this provides a basis for the declining motivation noted in the preceding section.

In a test of writing speed, Birren and Botwinick (12) reported that subjects in the sixties performed on the average only about half as well as subjects thirty years younger. When the test was extended to include free association (writing as many different words as possible, in two minutes) the loss was even more marked: 69 per cent as compared with 53 per cent. We may infer that older subjects are likely to be handicapped in any mental test in which writing speed limits the score, but where written materials convey mental processes the age decline involves more than merely sensorimotor retardation.

When physical deficiencies can be alleviated, the mental test trend may be changed, but this is easier to demonstrate in cases of definite pathology than within a normal sample. An aspect of this is illustrated in a study by Jetter *et al.* (63), who measured the intelligence of cerebral arteriosclerotics with psychosis before and after treatment with vitamins B and C. The improvement in IQ in a number of the cases led to the conclusion that this was related to an improvement in general health, as exemplified by the remission of clinical signs. Similarly, a positive effect of hormone therapy on some aspects of memory and learning has been demonstrated by Caldwell and Watson (21) in a carefully controlled experiment with elderly women. Mackay (92) has described the marked physical, emotional, and intellectual deterioration often manifested in the behavior of senile dements. Mental fatigability, poor concentration, and poor memory confront the examiner with special difficulties. In advanced cases, where disorientation exists, formal examinations are of course out of the question.

The factor of speed.—At some point in early maturity or beyond, the tempo of activity begins to slow down. This is shown in nearly all aspects of behavior. Since a mental test which places a premium on speed may handicap older subjects, it is necessary to consider whether an apparent decline in mental test performance is due to an actual change in intellectual level, to a change in the rate of mental work, or to some combination of the two.

We have sometimes assumed that there is no necessary relation between speed and efficiency, or that there may even be an inverse relation, as in some tests in which a slower rate is accompanied by greater accuracy. But it is also true that in many complex tasks the level of performance is affected if speed falls below a certain critical level. For example, in making comparative judgments about a series of events it is necessary to register impressions, to hold them, and to integrate them while the events are still in process. A person may fail in this task if his perceptions are too slow in emerging, or if mental integrations are too slow to keep up with a changing situation. This would be an instance in which levels of insight are directly related to speed. It is quite true that there are many life situations which do not require quick judgment. In such situations (not fully reflected in mental tests) the important factors may be experience, judicial attitude, emotional poise, and "sagacity," and in these characteristics it is younger rather than older persons who are often handicapped. But as Birren (9) points out, "under some very practical circumstances it appears that perceptions do not always flow through the consciousness of older persons quickly enough to permit effective behavior." This topic will be considered in greater detail in a later section.

Education.—The validity of intelligence tests, in individual or group comparisons, depends upon comparability of educational experience. Where a marked difference exists in education, low scores may reflect a deficiency in schooling rather than in ability. Since our educational practices and the average length of school attendance have changed greatly in recent decades, cross-sectional comparisons of younger and older persons must keep this factor in mind. In longitudinal studies, with repeated tests of the same individuals, we avoid this particular problem, although we may not avoid the effects of secular trends in communication and in the cultural content of daily life. To the extent that mental tests involve operations similar to those commonly practiced in school work, the older person may be handicapped merely because the task is more remote in his experience. There are several ways to control this factor: the use of practice tests; the use of repeated tests at short intervals, in which the criterion is rate of improvement; and the comparison of performance in tests which vary in their degree of relationship to school tasks.

III. MENTAL ABILITY STUDIES BASED ON NORMALS

The general form of the age curve.—We turn now to a survey of the principal studies which have presented mental test data for normal samples of adults. Three of the best-known investigations, which also include data for younger ages, are by Jones and Conrad (66), Miles and Miles (97), and Wechsler (148). Results for these three studies are given in Figure 12, in the form of smoothed age curves.[1]

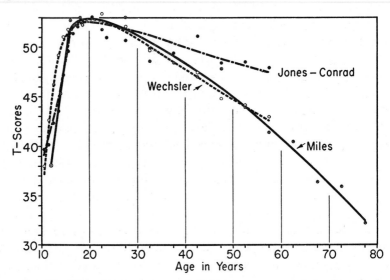

Fig. 12.—Mental test scores as related to age: a comparison of results from three investigations.

In view of the fact that three different tests were used in these studies, and with three very different samples, the similarity of results is quite striking. We should, however, inquire as to whether the various age groups, in each study, were genuinely comparable as to sampling. Jones and Conrad attempted to maintain a homogeneous group by systematically sampling entire villages and rural areas. They were able to show that errors in sampling tended to favor rather than to discriminate against older groups, for with increasing age the less competent individuals were more likely to

---

[1] In this chart the raw scores of each study have been transformed into comparable units by the T-score method. In each study the average of the three means for the age groups 25 to 40 has been given the arbitrary value of 50, and the average S.D. of these groups the value of 10. Average scores of other age groups are transformed into the same units. Thus, in the Jones-Conrad study the T-score of 40, obtained at age 11, signifies that the average at this age is 1 S.D. below the average for adults (age 25 to 40) in the same general population. At around the age of 20 the scores in each study rise about .2 to .3 S.D. above the average for middle maturity.

evade tests.[2] When special provisions were made to insure homogeneity, it was found that as the older groups became more strictly comparable with the younger (in terms of completeness of sample, or genetic homogeneity) the apparent rate of decline became greater. Miles and Miles sought a homogeneous sampling by testing the members of lodges and social groups in small California cities. Wechsler used an occupational stratification in a metropolitan area (New York), selecting a distribution which resembled, at each age, the occupational frequencies in United States census figures.[3]

Although the three studies show a general similarity, the question may be raised as to why the rate of decline is slower in the Jones-Conrad cases. The answer to this question serves to illustrate a common problem in mental measurement: the change with age in the meaning of a given test score. The Army Alpha (used by Jones and Conrad) gives a relatively heavy weight to two subtests involving vocabulary and information. Their proportional contribution increases with age, since these are functions which show little or no decline until after the age of 60. As a consequence, a given total score obtained by an older person includes a greater component of these functions than the same total score obtained by a younger person. And a test weighted with these functions (such as the Army Alpha) will show a relatively strong resistance to decline.

A number of studies have examined the relation between age and intellectual achievement, in terms of the peak of creative effort. This would be expected to fall considerably later than the peak for mental test scores, since achievement requires time, opportunity, and other factors which may be involved in the building of a career.

---

[2] The greater resistance of older persons to tests is illustrated in a study by Thorndike and Gallup (140), who incorporated a short, steeply graded vocabulary test in one of the weekly inquiries of the American Institute of Public Opinion. The percentage of persons refusing to co-operate increased from 1.5 per cent in the 20 to 30 age group, to 8.6 per cent in the age group 60 and over. Some of the technical problems in the intelligence testing of adults have been discussed by Conrad (33) and Conrad and Jones (34).

[3] Corsini and Fassett (36), using the Wechsler-Bellevue test with a prison population of ages 15 to 70, obtained somewhat different results on three of the verbal subtests. It is difficult to evaluate this study without additional information as to the comparability of their samples at different ages.

The age of peak performance might also be expected to vary in different fields.

Using published works as a measure of productivity, Dennis and Girden (38) compared successive age groups of psychologists and found the highest rate of publication in the age group 40 to 49, with a decline of about 50 per cent in the age group 60 to 69. This, of course, does not take direct account of the quality of production, but in a study of the records of over 4,000 scientists, Adams (2) found that on the average the age when they did their best work was in the early forties (ranging, in different fields, from age 37 in mathematics to 47 in anthropology).

In the most extensive series of studies as yet undertaken on this topic, Lehman (87) determined the age of highest creative activity in a large number of professional fields. Although variations were found in the peak of performance, the conclusion seems justified that the highest quality of work is usually accomplished before the age of 40. Political and social leadership involve maximum recognition at a much later age than is the case with scientific and artistic attainment.

Results in these areas are socially conditioned and will vary in different societies and in different periods of time. A great deal of attention is now being given to ways in which society can make the best use of abilities which are retained by older workers. This is an important social problem, but it may also be important for a society to learn how to use the highest levels of ability at the earliest possible age—rather than deferring opportunities for achievement through arbitrary systems of age grading or of seniority.

IV. STUDIES OF THE SPEED FACTOR

Examples of the speed handicap of older adults may be seen in tests of reaction time, swiftness of movement in simple or serial action, and speed of perception.[4] In some functions compensating factors may of course make up for this speed loss, at least to some degree. Solely by the criterion of motor and perceptual tests, individuals in the early twenties would be expected to be better automobile drivers than older persons. Nevertheless, they are greater insurance risks, and this is recognized in policy rates.

[4] Reviewed by Shock (129, 130).

In certain laboratory tests, Welford (151) has shown that older persons decline markedly in speed but tend to improve in accuracy. Whether this is a net advantage or a disadvantage obviously depends on the practical requirements of the task. Considerable weight, however, must be given to two studies (17, 31) of clerical workers and of semiskilled workers, in which it was found that the speed handicap is relatively small in simple tasks, but becomes marked in functions which involve complex processes or which emphasize precision. In one of the above studies, Brown and Ghiselli (17) showed that in simple arithmetic (addition, subtraction, multiplication) no losses occur up to age 50, but when the task involves "the integration of different aspects into a single numerical answer," time-limit tests show a peak performance before age 30 and a steady decline thereafter. Somewhat analogous results have been obtained in the study of seniles as compared with normal persons (10); in an addition test, seniles worked more slowly and less accurately when problem length was increased, indicating serious handicap in tasks requiring rapid integration of serial information.

A physiological basis for these changes in speed has been suggested by Welford (151) and by Birren (9), in terms of reduced sensory input. This may be partly due to sense organ impairment, thus lengthening the response time through reducing the maximum excitation that can be delivered to the nervous system. To a greater extent, however, it is probably dependent on central factors involved in the organization of perceptions. Birren points out that reduced sensory input affects unfamiliar tasks more than familiar ones, which operate on the basis of past experience more than on the receipt and integration of new data.

In the case of intelligence tests, Miles (101) has reported that the age decline obtained with the Otis test is reduced when the test is given without time limits. Similar results were obtained by Lorge (89), who administered a number of intelligence tests with time limits and the CAVD with unlimited time to 143 cases, ages 20 to over 70 years. The correlation with age was —.41 in the case of the Army Alpha, —.30 in the case of the CAVD. Although the difference between these coefficients is not large enough to be statistically significant, the consensus of evidence suggests that time limits tend to place older individuals at some slight disadvantage. We cannot be sure, however, that the removal of time limits actually improves the validity of a test for older individuals; if the motivation is adequate, a part of the effect may consist in placing a heavier weight on other factors, such as patience and persistence.

Lorge has investigated this matter further by selecting three groups of subjects (ages 20 to 25, 27.5 to 37.5, and over 40) matched in terms of CAVD scores; although equivalent in mental "power," the groups showed an age decline on such tests as the Otis and Army Alpha. Assuming that this decline was due entirely to a slower rate of performance in the older groups, Lorge developed a formula for modifying the Miles and Jones-Conrad curves for later maturity. The correction substitutes a level or slightly rising curve for the downward trends shown in Figure 12.

It is hardly justifiable, however, to attribute all of the age differences to a loss in speed. The speed factor can be analyzed more precisely if we consider age changes in items attempted, for different types of tests. This has been done by Jones (65) in a comparison of two Army Alpha subtests. Figure 13 presents curves for the number of items *attempted*, without reference to whether the answers were correct. The Information Test is one in which older persons do as well as younger persons, in terms of correct scores.

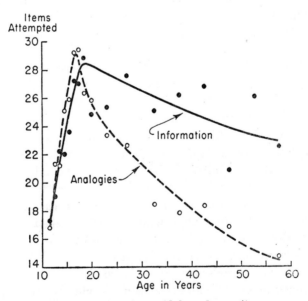

Fig. 13.—Age changes in two Army Alpha subtests (items attempted).

Hence we cannot say that the test becomes intrinsically more difficult with age. Nevertheless, the number of items which are attempted declines about 20 per cent from age 20 to age 55–59. It
is apparent that this represents a change in the speed of reading
and of the selective processes involved in choosing answers.

The Analogies Test is very similar to the Information Test in
superficial aspects. The reading difficulty is similar and there are
the same number of items—40 in each. The greater age change in
items attempted in this test (amounting to a loss of more than 50
per cent from the peak performance) must be due to some additional
factor or factors. The nature of these is suggested by Figure 14,

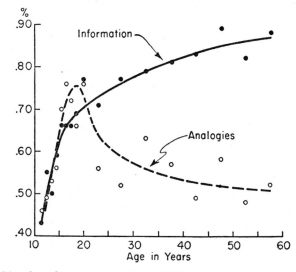

Fig. 14.—Age changes in two Army Alpha subtests (percentage of correct
answers of total answers attempted).

which eliminates speed by taking account only of the correct responses among those which an individual has time to attempt. The
contrasting slope of the curves indicates age gains in a test which
involves factual accumulation, but age loses in a test requiring
flexible adaptation to an intellectual task (analogical reasoning).

In a recent study based on a large sample of cases in Kansas
City, Wechsler (150) has investigated this problem by comparing
results from tests given with and without time limits. Since an age
decline was found under both conditions, it would appear that speed

is not the sole factor in handicapping older persons. A similar conclusion can be derived from a Belgian study (107) in which decline after the age of 25 was interpreted as due more to a capacity loss than to reduced speed.

When we concede that older individuals are slower, we admit a practical handicap in many everyday activities requiring mental work, as well as in formal tests involving speed of mental performance. But we have seen above that older individuals are (on the average) handicapped also in other ways more basic to mental capacity. The relationship of these cumulative handicaps to mental efficiency in later life depends of course upon the extent to which they are compensated by experience, stability, and improved work methods. Miles and Miles (97) have pointed out that a person of average intelligence may expect to fall to the 6 percentile by the age of 75 but that the person who starts in the highest 10 per cent will probably remain at or above the average of the population as a whole, even in the eighth decade. In terms of practical adjustments in everyday life, it may be easier to compensate a decline from the 90 to the 50 percentile than one from the 50 to the 10 percentile. This is, however, relative to many other factors, such as occupational demands and a person's own levels of aspiration. Camp (28) has expressed the view that the performance of older persons is often influenced by inferiority feelings which constitute an emotional handicap. Thus two individuals who have suffered the same actual decline may exhibit quite different levels of practical efficiency if they have made different adjustments to their change in ability.

V. AGE AND INDIVIDUAL DIFFERENCES

In group comparisons we frequently find that individual differences are much greater than group differences. In the Jones-Conrad study, the difference in means between age 20 and age 55 was approximately .5 S.D. But at each age the difference between the dullest and brightest was more than eight times this amount. This entails a considerable overlapping of the distributions, so that nearly one third of those aged 50 to 60 obtained scores above the average for age 20.

In studies of mental growth, it has been found that children differ not merely in scores at a given age but also in their rates of growth or growth patterns. It would be reasonable to look for differences also in rates of decline. These might be random in relation to earlier scores, or we might find a slower or a deferred decline among persons relatively high in the intelligence scale. It would be expected that losses in at least some mental abilities would be reduced in persons whose lives are rather largely organized around patterns of intellectual activity. If appropriate functioning serves to promote the growth of structure, we may also find that it postpones the atrophy of structure. Appropriate functioning also maintains mental resources and habits of work which may be important both in test performance and in life situations. Thus Sorenson (133, p. 738) has remarked, "Intellectual ability during adult years depends on native ability plus mental exercise, training, richness of intellectual stimuli. . . . Some adults will increase the currency in their intellectual banks, year by year; others will maintain a fairly constant mental level, while most adults through disuse allow their mental abilities to depreciate."

The studies represented in Figure 12 provide very little indication of a difference in rate of decline in relation to education or initial status. Miles and Miles, for example, found approximately parallel age curves for different educational classes. But different results are found when we deal with highly selected groups. Sorenson (133) reported that among teachers test scores in reading and vocabulary tend to increase slightly rather than to diminish from age 20 to 60. This may be attributed to the nature of the functions as well as to the sample studied. In a group of college professors age 60 to 80, as compared with a younger group (age 25 to 35), Sward (137) found that performance on a high-level mental test generally favored the younger men, except in the case of vocabulary. He believed that the two groups were comparable in initial ability, but that largely as a result of disuse of functions the older men had suffered some impairment in rate of performance, and "some real residual decline in general capability."

A more recent study, by Owens (109), has compared the performance on the Army Alpha at ages 19 and 50, for a group first tested as entering Freshmen at Iowa State College. This was not merely a college group but also a somewhat superior selection within the college group. Between the ages indicated Owens found a significant increase, of about .5 S.D., in the mean Army Alpha score. As could be expected, a large part of the gain in total score was due to the Information and Vocabulary tests in the Alpha. Since numerous studies have shown continued improvement in mental test scores of college students during the college years, it is possible that the small age changes reported by Owens between 19 and 50 were due chiefly to a gain in the early twenties; in some individuals this unmeasured gain may have masked an actual loss in the later decades. However, it is quite significant that in this selected group the scores on most subtests were, at age 50, no lower than the 19 year level, whereas in the more representative samples shown in Figure 12 they have declined to a point considerably below this level.

Additional evidence on age changes in the middle years of life (in a superior sample) may be found in a study by Bayley and Oden (6), based on a follow-up of the Terman group of gifted children.

A Synonym-Antonym test and an Analogies test were given to 768 members of this group at an average age of about 30 years, and repeated 12 years later. Gains occurred, averaging .56 S.D. in the Opposites test and .40 S.D. in Analogies. These gains are greater than would be predicted from the Owens study, but may reflect the more highly selected nature of this group. Gains, in a smaller degree, also occurred among the husbands and wives of the gifted.

The earlier results by Jones and Conrad, reporting an extremely marked age decline in an Analogies test, may differ from the results of Owens and especially of Bayley and Oden partly because of changes, with differing intelligence levels, in the nature of the function tested. In a general sampling, Analogies scores may be strongly influenced by individual differences in abstract reasoning ability. Among the highly intelligent, however, the margin of ability may be so great that test performance is not affected by differences in aptitude for the task, but only by knowledge of the words used. In such cases the test would become merely another vocabulary test, and the results would reflect the usual findings of a vocabulary improvement with age—especially marked among those with intellectual interests and habits.

It might be argued that the differential effects noted above are an artifact of the highly structured tasks in a mental test situation.

But somewhat similar differentials have been noted by Gurvitz (54) in relatively unstructured situations (Rorschach) applied over an age range.

V. DECLINE IN DIFFERENT FUNCTIONS

It has been indicated above that mental functions are quite unequal in their resistance to age. Tests especially difficult for older adults appear to be those which involve abstract reasoning or conceptualizing (41), the eduction of relations or correlates (8), and flexibility in thinking or in adaptation to new situations (55). Wechsler (149) has listed tests which "hold up with age" as including information, comprehension, object-assembly, and vocabulary. On the other hand, an especially conspicuous decline may be noted in such standard functions as digit-span, arithmetical reasoning, substitution, block-design, and similarities.

From data given by Jones and Conrad (66, pp. 251–52) the present writers have computed the differences between mean scores at 20.5 years and at 55 years, in terms of the S.D. at the earlier age. The results are shown in Table 20.

TABLE 20.—DECLINE IN SUBTESTS OF THE ARMY ALPHA

Subtest	Sigma Units	Subtest	Sigma Units
Analogies	—.80	Dissected sentences	—.36
Directions	—.54	Arithmetic	—.29
"Common-sense"	—.47	Opposites (Vocabulary)	—.19
Numerical completions	—.42	General information	+.02

Without reporting the numerical data, Willoughby (154) has presented age curves for a similar selection of subtests, derived from the Army Alpha, the Terman Group Test, and other sources; from inspection, it would appear that his results, based on an urban California sample, are substantially similar to those shown in Table 20.

A somewhat different approach to this problem can be made by analyzing the pattern of performance in adults and younger persons matched for mental age. This has been done by Jones (64) for a sample of mental defectives, with conclusions which provide an appropriate summary of the general findings in this field for normals as well as defectives: Adults tend to have an advantage in tasks in which they can draw upon their larger fund of experience; but they are relatively less efficient in tasks which demand ingenuity in adjusting to novel situations.

Little evidence is available concerning sex differences in age curves for mental scores. In general, the similarities are more striking than the differences. Conrad, Jones, and Hsaio (35) have compared mental growth and decline for 581 males and 607 females in the Army Alpha. A slight divergence of the curves occurred after the age of 40, the rate of decline being more rapid among males. This may have been due to sampling differences,[5] but it is worth noting that both Carter (29) and Price (114) have found larger negative correlations between age and test score in the case of men than in the case of women.

It is instructive to compare the age differences obtained for intellectual functions with those which have been noted in a variety of sensory, motor, and physiological characteristics. For a large sample of cases measured by Sir Francis Galton, Table 21 presents the difference between smoothed age means at ages 20.5 and 55.5, in terms of the S.D. at the earlier age:

TABLE 21.—DECLINE IN VARIOUS FUNCTIONS

	Sigma Units	
	Males*	Females†
Grip of stronger hand	− .49	− .68
Swiftness of blow	− .54	− .43
Vital capacity	− .74	− .93
Auditory pitch	−1.90	−1.94
Visual acuity	−1.89	−2.09

  * Ruger and Stoessiger (122).
  † Elderton, Moul, and Page (40).

As noted above, average scores which appear to show mental decline in later maturity must be evaluated with reference to many factors of sampling, test composition, and test procedure. In terms of the units employed, it is evident that from the 20's to the 50's the degree of decline in mental abilities is considerably less than in sensory functions such as visual acuity and auditory pitch. In

---

[5] It is conceivable that differences could arise from chance, from selective migration, or from differential mortality. A more probable factor is a slight superiority of women in verbal tests, and a tendency for verbal abilities to weigh more heavily in tests at later ages.

many mental functions, however, the decline is probably as great if not greater than that reported for vital capacity and for motor strength and speed, in terms of the unit employed in Table 21.

Studies based on psychotics.—Relatively little systematic work, with adequate samples, has been attempted on the intelligence-test performance of older psychotics. That the process of mental decline in different psychoses is marked by significant qualitative and quantitative differences is suggested by Rabin (115) and others, and is also apparent in the material to be discussed in subsequent sections on vocabulary, learning, etc.

Rabin (117) administered the Wechsler-Bellevue Scale to mental hospital patients aged 60–83, some of whom were psychotic. Total quantitative scores were lowest in those classified as senile dements. Differences in scores on the verbal and performance scales were largest in the senile dements, next largest in the arteriosclerotic psychotics, and least in the non-psychotics. In another study (116), he has reported that arithmetic and memory for digits are more impaired in arteriosclerotic psychosis than in other senile conditions but that there is a comparatively good preservation of the "abstract" (Goldstein) approach in the arteriosclerotics, as indicated by the results on the similarities and block-design tests. On the other hand, Pollack (111), using the Shipley-Hartford Retreat Scale, has found a marked deterioration in "abstract age" among arteriosclerotics. An explanation of inconsistencies sometimes reported has been suggested by Goldstein and Scheerer (53, p. 3) and also by Cleveland and Dysinger (32). The latter, in a small sample of senile patients, found a marked discrepancy between the ability to respond to *verbal* items on an apparently abstract basis and the ability to sort objects in terms of conceptual or abstract principles. The latter function, in common with other tests of the Wechsler-Bellevue Performance Scale, was very markedly deteriorated. Among schizophrenics less difference could be noted between the verbal and the performance items.

Attempts to describe the various psychoses of later life by psychometric procedures have been made by Roth and Hopkins (118), Fox and Birren (47), and Botwinick and Birren (14). There is hope that mental tests may differentiate affective and toxic psychoses from the so-called "organic" disorders.

The psychiatric literature is full of descriptive reports on the mental symptoms in the senile psychoses. Typical of these is one by Hirsch (59), who described the performance of deteriorated seniles. He found that they tend to perceive and define objects in utilitarian terms rather than in terms of composition and construction, that more attention is given to the parts of an object than to its total pattern, that color largely is ignored, and that inconsistencies and distortions tend to be ignored because of preconceptions.

Partly because of difficulties in obtaining co-operation, little is known concerning the mental-test performance of involutional melancholics. Since there are no demonstrable brain lesions, with adequate co-operation one would expect no important changes (as compared with normals) except the general slowing down of reactions, characteristic of this psychosis.

VI. VOCABULARY

Vocabulary long has been regarded as a useful component of a test of general intelligence. Among individuals of a given age and with similar educational opportunities, the acquisition of vocabulary is one of the more valid indices of mental ability. But if we use vocabulary tests to register age trends in ability, we should bear in mind that we are making comparisons between age groups which have had very unequal amounts of exposure to verbal learning.

An interesting use has been made of vocabulary scores in the Babcock Test of Mental Efficiency (5). The author of this test assumes that vocabulary survives without appreciable impairment until very late in life, and further assumes that recently acquired material is lost first and earliest acquired material is the last to disappear. Accepting the Terman vocabulary list as a valid measure of a person's intelligence at an earlier age (in early maturity), and using a series of speed and learning tests to measure present efficiency, Babcock has taken the difference between these two scores as an index of a person's mental deterioration. This procedure may give a useful rough estimate, but as will be noted later the assumption of constant vocabulary levels cannot be accepted without qualification.

Equating normals and abnormals in terms of the Binet vocabulary list, Feifel (44) found significant differences in the types of definitions given by members of the two groups. Yacorzynski (156) has pointed out that vocabulary scores may be maintained in later maturity chiefly because there are many different, acceptable ways of defining words. Deterioration may have eliminated some of the more difficult definitions or more elaborate contextual meanings, without disturbing the obtained scores. If attention were given to the process of defining words, rather than to end results, somewhat different inferences might be drawn; in this connection we may note Goldstein's finding that certain brain lesions which fail to destroy the ability to solve a problem may nevertheless profoundly influence the method by which the problem is approached.

Although vocabulary studies have had various outcomes, there seems to be general agreement that the ability to define words holds up fairly well with age in the absence of psychiatric disturbance. Fox (46) compared persons in their thirties with others in their seventies. Each group was representative of its age level in formal schooling and economic status. There were no significant differences in vocabulary size or in the quality of definitions. Brown (18), on the other hand, has reported evidence that even though the size of a working vocabulary may be fairly well maintained, the quality of definitions tends to decline.

Qualitative changes in vocabulary have also been demonstrated by Kaplan (70), in his longitudinal study of older morons. Although the general vocabulary level was usually maintained, changes occurred with regard to particular words. Some words which were passed on the first test were failed on the second and vice versa. Apparently this turnover has not previously been studied in either normals or psychotics. It casts further doubt upon the view that vocabulary remains fixed from early adulthood into the senile period.

Senile dements either experience more vocabulary loss than cerebral arteriosclerotics with psychosis, or else they have smaller vocabularies to begin with; at any rate, the senile dements, taken as a group, have fewer words at their command than the arteriosclerotics. This was the conclusion of Shakow *et al.* (127), who have also observed that the vocabulary performance of both groups is lowered below what would be expected on the basis of age alone; Brody (15) concurs in this conclusion. Ackelsberg (1), working with institutionalized senile dements, has demonstrated vocabulary loss commensurate with the general deterioration exhibited by the group.

In applying the Shipley-Hartford Retreat Scale to a small number of cerebral arteriosclerotics with psychosis, Pollack (111) found a marked difference in their vocabulary as compared with their ability in abstract reasoning. His subjects, with a median age of 69, had an average "abstract" age of 6.4 and an average vocabulary age of 12.9. Apparently, no studies of the vocabularies of involutional melancholia patients have been published, but one would expect little vocabulary change in such patients, since they are for the most part under sixty years of age.

In summary, it is generally agreed that vocabulary holds up better than most other intellectual abilities. Nevertheless, low vocabulary scores made by aged persons, either normal or demented, are not conclusive proof of inferior intelligence in earlier adult life. Much work remains to be done on the fate of vocabulary in the later years. However, it already is clear that wide individual differences exist. Differential decline is illustrated in a study by Foulds (45), who gave a vocabulary test to over 5,000 adults in various occupations. In the lowest quarter of the population a decline appeared after age 30, whereas in the top 5 per cent increases continued as late as age 55. In general agreement with this, Shakow and Goldman (126) have shown that persons of very high intelligence usually maintain high vocabulary scores until the eighth decade, while persons of only average intelligence often experience a drop several decades sooner. Occupation, hobbies, intellectual standards, physical health, and other factors presumably influence the course of change in a given individual.[6]

⅄ VII. LEARNING AND MEMORY[7]

Learning and memory are facets of a single process; the very existence of memory is dependent upon the prior occurrence of learning. However, the failure of memory is not conclusive proof

---

[6] Some of the conflicting results obtained in vocabulary studies derive from heterogeneity of samples and differences in methods. Shipley, for instance, uses a multiple-choice test of the written type, measuring recognition rather than recall. This is true also of the vocabulary elements in standard group tests. The Babcock Test is oral, employing the 1916 Terman vocabulary list.

[7] The earlier literature in this field has been ably summarized by Thorndike *et al.* (139) and by Ruch (120).

that the subject is now incapable of learning, nor does it offer conclusive proof as to the previous status of the individual. Memory failure—the inability to recall or recognize material known to have been in the possession of a patient—may be due to emotional blockage or repression, or may derive from organic changes in the nervous system.

A further point to bear in mind is that loss of *memories* is not always a trustworthy or certain indication of the status of the psychological function, *memory*. It is normal at any age to lose much even of that which we are anxious to retain. As persons grow older, the amount of material lost increases on an additive basis, quite apart from any increase in the rate of loss. Recency has a bearing upon retention; and whereas the period of childhood, for instance, may be close at hand to a 20-year-old, it is over half a century away to a 70-year-old.

Why then, it may be asked, is memory of past events more vivid than memory of recent events? One possible explanation lies in the nature of the remembered experiences, and in the frequency of review. The later years of life frequently are unpleasant, associated with loss and deprivation, characterized by a vegetative and uneventful existence. On the other hand, the years of early life are associated with struggle, with marriage, with new and exciting experiences. Emotional factors may have a bearing upon the material recalled, and may sometimes favor earlier as against later experiences. Experimental evidence on this point is to be found in the work of G. M. Gilbert (50), who reported that the "hedonistic tendency" in memory is more potent among 30- to 65-year-old adults than among children.

Studies based on normals.—It may be stated that there is a high correlation between the ability to acquire and the ability to retain that which has been acquired. We are therefore not surprised to find in seniles, both normal and demented, a marked impairment of both functions. A difference, however, must be recognized between rote memory and assimilation: a difference between material that can only be repeated and material that can be acted upon. This distinction should not be lost sight of in evaluating the memory function in seniles, both normal and abnormal. Kubo (78) studied rote memory of words in a group of 355 healthy men and women from 70 to 100 years of age. Rote memory did not show a sudden fall until the age of 82, after which a rapid decrease was noted. Notwithstanding the relatively late survival of rote memory in normal seniles, the integration of new memories with old memories and the exploitation of both in the solution of problems is unquestionably subject to difficulty in older persons. Memory for its own sake subserves no important purpose; it is only when memory becomes an instrument for the adjustment and survival of the organism that it possesses usefulness.

The study of learning ability at later ages is complicated by age changes in initial ability. In the most extensive series of experiments to date, by Thorndike and his associates (139), attempts have been made to control this factor, in some instances by partialing out initial ability, and in other instances by making age comparisons based on comparable segments of the learning curve. Using a large variety of experimental tasks, these authors came to the conclusion that learning ability is at a maximum at 20 to 24 years, with a gradual drop beyond 24. Older individuals were not as efficient in novel learning situations as were young people. In one experiment involving a comparison of individuals in the late 'teens with those in the late thirties (equated for intelligence and initial performance), the older group was found to improve only 64 per cent as much as the younger in a sensory-motor learning test involving what Thorndike termed "sheer modifiability."

In another sensory-motor test (mirror-drawing) Snoddy (132) has reported differences in learning curves related to the age of the learner. In the case of younger subjects curves could be analyzed into two phases, the first being termed "adaptation," characterized by rapid improvement, and the second being termed "facilitation." Older subjects showed learning curves consisting more largely of the second phase and marked by greater stability and slower gains.

Ruch (121) studied the differentiative effects of age on human learning in a population ranging in age up to 85. In one phase of the investigation subjects merely had to learn a new habit, either verbal or motor. In addition, they were required to learn a habit which was contradictory to a well-established habit or reaction pattern. Under the first condition, there was only a slight difference in the performance of the young and the middle-aged groups (12–17 and 34–59), while the older group (60–82) experienced only a 20 per cent loss. However, when old habits had to be broken down in favor of new ones, the oldest group suffered a 50 per cent loss of capacity. In another report Ruch (119) has presented further evidence indicating that the decline in learning ability with increasing age is not identical for all types of material, being at a maximum when there is interference or conflict between new and previously acquired material.

In evaluating the work of Ruch, it should be noted that the negative transfer effect of old habits in relation to new, contradictory ones is disadvantageous only when the new ways of behaving are superior. Much, perhaps most, nonlaboratory learning favors positive transfer. Kay (73) aptly has observed that "All adult learning involves transfer—an adult does not learn a new task *ab initio* so much as how it differs from an already acquired one." It would be informative to conduct more detailed studies of older persons in learning situations which permit them to exploit their past experience.

Jones and his associates (67) have studied the recall for the content of three motion pictures; 765 cases were tested, constituting a representative rural group from eight New England villages. The test blanks, containing completion and multiple-choice items specially printed in large type, were distributed immediately after each motion picture; for one picture a delayed recall was also obtained. Age curves, in terms of T-scores, were closely similar to the Miles age curve for intelligence (Fig. 12), rising to a peak shortly after the age of 20 and dropping to the 13-year level in the late fifties. Analysis of the data showed that the decline in the older ages was not due to a speed handicap in performing the tests, nor to special selection within the communities studied. It is interesting to note that within the ages studied the age decline was no greater in delayed recall than in immediate recall.

Differential changes in memory abilities have been noted by Gilbert (51), in line with those already found for intelligence. He matched 174 subjects aged 20 to 29 with the same number in the 60's, on the basis of vocabulary scores. The older subjects showed on the average a 60 per cent loss in a series of memory tests. Among the brightest 5 per cent, however, the loss was only about half as great.

Additional research is greatly needed on specific aspects of learning in later maturity. As Shock has pointed out (129, p. 361):

"In view of the social and economic importance of retraining programs for middle-aged and elderly people for their utilization in employment, it is surprising that there has been so little experimental work on defining the optimal conditions for learning in middle-aged and older people. With the current interest in learning theory, it would seem that age changes should be included as the independent variable on many of these studies."

Studies based on psychotics.—Although memory is conventionally spoken of in a restricted way, chiefly with regard to intellectual factors, its meaning can properly be extended to include the sum total of that which has been acquired and retained. Thus interpreted, complete memory loss would be tantamount to death. Even badly demented seniles often are able to dress themselves, to feed themselves, to walk, to talk, and to show the customary amenities. From the practical standpoint, these nonverbal retentions or "memories" represent functions which often are remarkably preserved.

Interesting, indeed, is the finding that those skills and acquisitions which are essential for social adjustment and which have been used repeatedly throughout life often are retained to the very end of life. Norman Cameron (27) has pointed out this remarkable preservation of the social amenities, even in senile cases of marked deterioration.

The difference between normal and pathological memory loss cannot be reduced to quantitative terms, for the discrepancy between the two is not always great, as Shakow *et al.* (127) have indicated. More important than the quantitative differences which exist between the memories of normal seniles and their psychotic peers are the differences in the integration of the survived material. However, generally speaking, the greater the amount of quantitative loss the more pronounced the disintegration of intellectual functioning.

That disturbances of memory and learning occur in senile dementia and in cerebral arteriosclerosis with psychosis is beyond dispute; the nature of the memory losses in these two psychoses is, however, not a matter of such universal agreement. Shakow *et al.* (127) have measured the memory function in senile dementia and cerebral arteriosclerosis with psychosis. The instrument used was an elaboration of the Wells Memory Test, consisting of old and new recall items. The new recall section included such items as repetition of figures forward and backward, sentence memory, and memory for ideas (a fifty-idea story). Among the old recall items were requests for personal information (e.g., where born, age, etc.), school information, and counting backward from 20 to 1.

The results of this investigation are represented in Figure 15. In comparing senile psychotics with a representative sample of

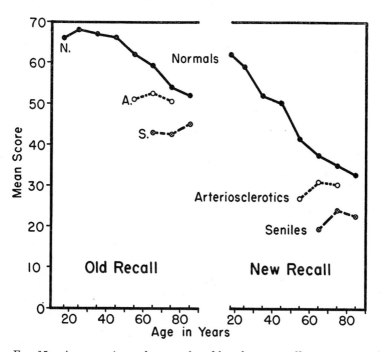

Fig. 15.—A comparison of scores for old and new recall among normals, arteriosclerotics, and seniles (127).

normal adults from the second through the ninth decades, consistently but not markedly poorer results were obtained with the psychotics; among the latter the senile dements were on the average poorer than the arteriosclerotics. Shakow and his associates (127) attribute their results mainly to the effects of age, pointing to the slight differences which exist between the normal and the psychotic groups. They admit, however, that their psychotic groups do not constitute fair cross sections of the pathological conditions under study, being rather a fair sample of the examinable and co-operative patients. The obtained differences between the normals and the psychotics may therefore be minimal rather than representative.

It is an interesting point that the senile dements had consistently higher coefficients in the interrelationships between new recall, old recall, and vocabulary, indicating a more generalized disturbance of memory in this group. The coefficients for the arteriosclerotics are the lowest, which is in agreement with the prevailing view that memory disturbance in this group is more sudden and selective. Shakow *et al.* (127, p. 47) raise the question: "Is the poorer performance in memory due to some generalized aphasic disturbance to be found in these patients, rather than to a difficulty in retention, and is this aphasic disturbance the fundamental basis for whatever memory difficulty we have found?" They leave their question unanswered, except to refer to their finding that memory for verbal material (sentences and ideas) is more severely affected than memory for digits.

The retention phase of remembering has been examined by D. E. Cameron (26), who compared 12 senile patients having a special retention defect with a control group of young people who had no retention disability. The test involved memorizing a series of three-digit numbers, with reproduction after varying periods of time. The periods between presentation and reproduction were divided into "unfilled" intervals and "filled" periods in which the subjects were required to spell a list of words. If no new activity was entered into, the seniles usually could retain the numbers for at least a few minutes. However, when the memorizing was followed by a period of other activity, recall of the digits became difficult or impossible. The normal controls showed no such disability.

Upon the basis of this evidence, Cameron suggests that "retention involves a process which permits of very fleeting maintenance of registration, and a second process of incorporation which is necessary for more extended retention. This latter process is apparently interfered with if some other activity is undertaken immediately after the individual has perceived the material." In other words, senile dements seem more subject to retroactive inhibition than are young adults.

When Cameron blindfolded patients suffering from retention

defects, he found that such patients suffered rapid distortions of their spatial images, forgetting the locations of certain objects in the room. Normal individuals are able to maintain spatial images of their surroundings for some time after they have been deprived of vision. Cameron also observed that where perseveration was marked in a senile patient, it might be impossible to register the second of a pair of objects presented in succession; hence there could be no remembering of this object.

Bearing in mind Cameron's findings, it is reasonable to suppose that the poorer memory of senile dements for present events is partly due to pathology of the impression process, and that senile dements are more lacking in learning ability than cerebral arteriosclerotics with psychosis. However, since senile dements also fare more poorly on tests involving past events it must be concluded that their poorer performance does not depend solely on defective registration.

N. Cameron (27), after a process of selection, found 22 seniles and 25 schizophrenics able and willing to co-operate with him in a study of thinking in senile deterioration and schizophrenic disorganization. Only 3 of the seniles could approximate their correct age, while the others made errors ranging from 5 to 50 years. Only 2 of the seniles could state accurately the length of their stay in the hospital, remember their marriage, or recall other intimate details of their past experience. Many of the senile patients gave nonsensical answers, such as stating that their children were older than themselves, that their children were born 3 years ago but are now 20 years of age, and that they are now only 40 but were married at 50. Immediate recall of spoken digits ranged from a maximum of 6 forward and 3 reversed to a minimum of 4 forward and none reversed. In almost all cases the ability to subtract serial sevens was impaired, only one person making even a fair showing. Most of the seniles could not name recent presidents of the United States.

In spite of serious memory defects and marked disorientation, the senile dements were superior in many ways to the schizophrenics who knew the year, the name of the experimenter, where they were, the season, and the date of their birth. Compared with the schizophrenics, the senile dements in many cases had far more insight into their condition; this was reflected in their dissatisfaction with

their efforts and in attempts to explain away their shortcomings.
The schizophrenics, in contrast, seemed well satisfied with jumbled
and incomplete answers. Jelgersma (62) also has noted the fact
that advanced senile dements may have insight into their loss of
memory.

Cameron continues with a comparison of the verbal productions and logical forms of senile dements and schizophrenics with
those of normal children and adults. It is interesting to note that
the language products of neither the seniles nor the schizophrenics
were similar to those of normal children. In view of qualitative
differences, it is obvious that the description of senility as "second
childhood" is unjustified. The senile dements rarely showed either
the loose-cluster form of organization (asyndesis) or the substitution of inexact approximations for definite terms and phrases usually found in schizophrenic material.

Many who have described the senile psychoses have accepted
uncritically Ribot's law of regression as applied to memory.
Briefly, this "law" holds that memory for recent events is poorer
than memory for events in the remote past. The role played by use
and repetition in the preservation of retained material is well
known to all students of psychology. It is reasonable to suppose
that material which has become strongly entrenched by use will be
more resistant to the aging process than material which has not
been equally favored. Though Ribot's formula for memory loss is
not without merit, it represents an oversimplification of the actual
course of memory loss.

The widespread impression that seniles have good memory for
past events is unfounded, and in older psychotics loss of memory is
by no means confined to present or recent events. When a woman
cannot remember the name of her husband, cannot state the number
of her children, and cannot remember her birth date, she assuredly
is not possessed of a good memory for past events. It is striking
that so many seniles cannot remember elementary facts which have
been the subject of so much emphasis and repetition all through
their lives.

The experimental studies of old versus new recall frequently
yield results which are dependent on the tests employed. Although
most published studies of old recall in senile psychotics are based
upon tests dealing with content believed to be of universal acqui-

sition (presidents, etc.), it is possible that this does not constitute a fair sample of material acquired in the distant past.

Löfving (88), in a recent study of the memory abilities of senile psychotics, found extensive memory loss for remote as well as recent events. When the statements of patients were carefully scrutinized, they frequently were found to be vague or inexact.

Ionasiu and Cupcea (61) have noted that memory for numbers fails before memory for images, and that memory for images is lost before memory for words is seriously interfered with. This is held to conform to Ribot's law of regression, since this finding is the inverse of that concerning acquisition—that which appears last disappears first, and conversely. Immediate memory was reported as lower for visual presentation than for auditory presentation.

Although a patient may recite many events of his past life, his reports are often untrustworthy. In advanced cases of the senile type there is much retrospective falsification and paramnesia. D. E. Cameron (23) has reported a greatly accelerated tendency toward secondary elaboration of memorized data in patients suffering from the psycho   .e senium. Minkowski (102) has pointed out the tendency   gross confabulation and false recognition, and the accentua   rientation in space and time in those afflicted with senile

                  .ich indicates that Ribot's law of regression must be
qu   .es in the form of a study by Trueblood (141), who
                 qualitative aspects of language change. The seniles were
                to name actual or pictured objects, were examined with
                .ion tests, and were asked for verbal interpretations of pic-
                . Trueblood concluded:

Senile language changes are found to be more and other than the "loss" of syntax or of parts of speech observed in aphasia. Moreover, they are not simply a reversal of language development in the individual. They should be considered as related to the frequency or intensity of the past occurrence of responses retained or lost, and not merely with the view that what is latest acquired is first lost.

Impartial redintegration of material is common in senile dements; here we have continuity without relevancy, association without logic. Memory disabilities indubitably figure in impartial redintegration at the senile level, for patients frequently forget the questions asked them before they bring their replies to a halt. One

point to be noted is that the loss of memories for past events sometimes has a benign effect upon the adjustment of the senescent individual, dulling the failures, bereavements, and disappointments of
earlier life periods.

A beginning has been made in the study of learning abilities in
old age, with experimental modification of some physiological factors. This opens a very large and important area, which as yet has
been hardly touched. Cameron (23) used oxygen inhalation and
vitamin therapy in an unsuccessful attempt to improve retention
among senile patients with retention defect. As already noted, more
positive results were obtained by Caldwell and Watson (21) in a
controlled experiment with female sex hormones.

In view of the difficulty of obtaining representative samples of
older persons for such studies, some investigators have favored the
use of lower animals for preliminary inquiries. Thus, Verzar-
McDougall (146) has demonstrated a great difference between
young and old rats in maze learning, under conditions involving
strong hunger motivation. At around 2 years of age, only 60 per
cent of the rats were able to learn at a rate within the normal range
for young rats. In retests after 5 to 9 months, young rats performed
efficiently on patterns previously learned, while older rats showed
a very marked memory loss. This demonstration of age changes,
comparable to those shown in human beings over a much longer
age span, suggests the possibility of numerous specific studies in
the animal laboratory of factors influencing behavioral aging.

In summary, it may be said that the loss of remembered material, for both normals and abnormals, depends upon factors other
than or in addition to earliness of impression. Among these
additional factors may be mentioned the degree to which the material has been utilized by the individual, the emotional connota-
tions of the material, and the intensity of the original experience.
At the risk of repetition, it should also be emphasized that simply
because two men are senile dements, or cerebral arteriosclerotics
with psychosis, it does not necessarily follow that they are in an
equal state of deterioration. Since memory defects are frequently
progressive, we are not justified in talking about senile memory as
a single condition. The fact remains that memory defects are, perhaps, the most salient psychological symptoms of aging, both normal and pathological.

VIII. EDUCATIONAL BACKGROUND OF OLDER PSYCHOTICS

Is education a protection against the psychoses of later maturity? This is a question which deserves more study than it has received; it cannot be answered unequivocally on the basis of the data to be presented.

Kaplan (69) studied the educational histories of senile dements, involutional melancholics, and cerebral arteriosclerotics with psychosis who were resident in the state hospitals of California and New York during the years 1935–39. The California data are shown in Table 22. Notwithstanding population and other differ-

TABLE 22.—EDUCATIONAL CLASSIFICATION (PERCENTAGES) OF THREE PSYCHOSES IN CALIFORNIA STATE HOSPITALS, 1935–39,* AND OF CALIFORNIA GENERAL POPULATION SIXTY AND OVER IN 1940†

Education	Involutional	Senile Dementia	Arteriosclerosis	General Population 60 and over
Total N	476	945	2,644	854,966
College	5.0	3.8	4.9	10.5
High school	18.5	9.6	10.3	24.6
Grade school	67.0	62.5	63.1	58.8
Reading and/or writing	6.7	12.5	11.0	....
Illiterate	1.9	6.3	6.5	4.5
Unknown	0.8	5.2	4.2	1.6

* Kaplan (69).
† U.S. Bureau of the Census (144).

ences between the two states, the results obtained are strikingly similar. In all three of the psychoses, and in both states, the majority of the cases had only grade-school education. There was, however, a higher percentage of persons with high-school or college education among the involutionals as compared with the senile dements and arteriosclerotics. Since the level of education in this country has been rising steadily, and since the involutionals, on the average, are younger than the other two groups, the involutional melancholia patients have been more favored by this trend than have the senile dements and the cerebral arteriosclerotics. Too much stress should not be placed upon the predominance of persons with grade-school education in all categories; it merely reflects the status of education in the United States four or five decades ago. This is borne out by the 1940 census of Californians aged sixty and over, most of whom were shown to have only grade-school education (Table 22). However, there were more than twice as many persons with college education among the general population of California aged sixty and over (on a percentage basis) as compared with senile dements, arteriosclerotics, and involutionals in the state mental hospitals.

Worthy of note is the fact that most of the hospital cases covered by the Kaplan study were marginal or dependent in economic status; the low percentage of institutional patients with college training or high-school attendance is, therefore, to be expected. Persons with a college background are more likely to be economically independent (and less likely to be institutionalized) than those who have had only a grade-school education or are wholly unlettered. This evidence, therefore, does not in general enable us to conclude that the psychoses of later life are less common among the better educated. The possibility remains, however, that in normal aging, without marked pathology, a high educational level and continued adult education may have some effect in postponing the decline of mental power.

Support for the view that education is favorable to the retention of mental ability in normals comes from the vocabulary study of Shakow and Goldman (126). These authors have reported that the drop in vocabulary which commonly occurs during the sixth decade was delayed until the eighth decade in subjects chosen from the highest educational groups. Many factors may be involved in this, including the factor of continued practice associated with cultural level and with intellectual interests. Moreover, in view of the relationship between educational status, economic status, and intelligence and physical health and constitution, it is quite possible that the slower decline in the educationally more privileged groups may reflect better physical conditions, better medical care, and a superior biological selection. It may also be explained on the basis of differences in native intelligence, since Lorge (91) has presented evidence that in homogeneous age groups there is a high correlation between intelligence and last school grade completed. Were it not for the fact that persons of the same or comparable intelligence do not always have equal opportunities for the acquisition of education, the correlation would be even higher. As mentioned, Gilbert (51) has gathered data which indicate that mental decline is slower in the more intelligent.

Although education tends to increase adaptability, and hence to prepare the individual for the psychological changes that accompany the aging process, it does not constitute a guaranty against psychotic symptoms attendant upon severe or extensive brain destruction; a college degree will not prevent paresis, arteriosclerotic changes, or other conditions essentially organic in character.

IX. PERSONALITY TRAITS

It is frequently emphasized that the pressures incidental to age do not fall r   ily upon all. Some enjoy physical health to the very end;   suffer varying degrees of physical handicap and discomfo   ie are financially secure, no matter how long they may liv   rs face the future with no certainty except that of privatic   me enjoy the declining years of life in the company of lov   es; others are doomed to years that become increasingly more friendless. Some are honored and favored; others are surrounded by a social atmosphere that might well be expected to nourish malignant attitudes.

The influence of these factors upon the individual depends, however, upon his own previous career and upon the personality traits that he has developed during his earlier life. Senile maladjustment may be thought of as a function of the ratio between what one used to have and what one has left. A college professor who drops to a mental age of ten may be far more maladjusted than a deteriorated laborer who never had a mental age much above ten. Sex maladjustment during the senile period is, at least partially, determined by the nature of the adjustment achieved during the preceding life period.[8]

Although it cannot be denied that there is a continuity in personality, and although earlier maladjustments may stand forth in sharp relief after the onset of a psychosis, it does not always follow that the earlier personality difficulties are completely responsible for the later behavior of the individual. The relationship between earlier and later personality is not necessarily primary, and, in

[8] Hamilton (56) has summarized some of the literature on sex adjustment in later life.

some cases, may even be fortuitous. It is, however, freely admitted that the problems attendant upon age may prove too much for a person with a long history of instability and that such problems may precipitate mental disease.

Lange (83) maintains that abnormal traits are the rule in the past histories of senile dements, especially those having delusions of persecution. Such persons often have been autistic, suspicious, quarrelsome, and loveless personalities, suggesting a relationship between senile dementia and schizophrenia. Apropos of this it may be mentioned that many persons do not become clinically diagnosable as schizophrenics until well into the senile period. Kaplan (69), using statistics provided by the New York Department of Mental Hygiene, tabulated data concerning the temperamental make-up of senile first admissions in New York state during the years 1935–39. Of a total of 4,998 cases, approximately one-half were declared to be "temperamentally normal," 941 were listed as irritable, 696 as seclusive, 548 as unstable, 418 as suspicious, 307 as depressive, 255 as overactive, 223 as egotistical, and only 4 as sexually abnormal and 4 as having criminal tendencies.

The personality traits of the involutional melancholic, in the prepsychotic stages, have been discussed from several points of view by Palmer (110), by Norbury (106), and by Davidoff in chapter ix of this volume. The earlier personality is of greater importance in involutional melancholia than in the senile psychoses, where disturbance is characteristically intellectual rather than affective. Malamud (93) points out that peculiarities of personality organization may involve susceptibility to mental disease, as a result either of physical disintegration or of increased social pressure.

It has been stated that the cause of many of the mental breakdowns in later life is to be found in the experiences of childhood and adolescence. It is commonly believed that early experiences play a prominent part in the etiology of schizophrenia and manic-depressive psychosis, and it is logical to suppose that the habits and attitudes which take root in childhood, and which are confirmed by repetition all through life, play a solid and recognizable part in the symptomology and etiology of such conditions as senile dementia and involutional melancholia. Unfortunately we have as yet little evidence of a longitudinal nature that can be effectively used in the study of these problems. Experience has proved that retrospective methods are not very trustworthy where the pre-psychotic personality is concerned, and the reports of relatives and friends often cannot be taken at their face value. Protocols gathered from secondary sources are often fragmentary and contradictory. The task still lies before us of following a sufficient number of individuals through life to give us objective knowledge of age trends in personality traits.

On a cross-sectional basis, C. C. Miles (96) has examined the relationship between age and several aspects of personality in adults. In a population of about 550 men and women of superior and average ability, she found that age was correlated positively with "persistence." No relation to age, however, was found for neurotic or introvert tendencies, self-sufficiency or dominance (as measured by the Bernreuter test). In analyzing the data from another personality questionnaire, Willoughby (155) found that women were significantly more emotional than men in the entire range from 20 to 70 years. The women exhibited an initial increase in emotionality until about 30 years, after which there was a drop until about 50, followed by a final rise. The men studied showed little or no change. It should be remembered that this also is a cross-sectional study and is not based on individual trends.

The restlessness and irritability of older psychotics may have their source in physical decline as well as in inability to cope with the environment. Apathy is often an outcome of the detachment of the individual from memories and events which have affective value. One of the effects of losing friends and relatives is to give the older person not only a feeling of being alone in the world but also a feeling that without social ties he is unprotected and insecure. An opposite factor is emphasized by Overholser (108), who suggests that in many cases we are overprotecting our old people, with resulting personality damage. The same errors of management which often retard the process by which a child matures into adult independence may at the other end of the age scale accelerate the entrance into a condition of dependent helplessness.

Related to this loss of independent activity is the experience associated with retiring from an occupation. Retirement often produces a psychological crisis, providing more opportunity for introspection, for self-evaluation, for the development of delusional ideas, and for regrets. Lawton (84) has pointed out that in this respect men are more likely to deviate from the norm than women. They live more strenuous, less protected lives than do women, and find it harder to accept frustration. (This is in agreement with suicide statistics.) The occupational transition is often more sudden for men than for women. On the other hand, many women are largely freed of their domestic responsibilities by the maturing and departure of their children, and have more time for morbid thoughts if their tendencies are in this direction. Men usually are occupationally active until forced into retirement, and their period of melancholic reflection is thereby in many cases deferred until later.

Older men are on the average more seclusive, more self-contained than are older women. Old-age-assistance statistics with regard to living arrangements for older men as compared with older women, as well as data gathered at the colony for older people at Millville, New Jersey, are cited in support of these views (84). In this connection it is interesting to observe that Landis and Farwell (81) have found that the median age at first admission is higher in senile dementia for females than for males (1.1 years) but is higher for males than for females in arteriosclerotic psychosis (1.0 years). It may be mentioned that males seem more susceptible to cerebral arteriosclerosis with psychosis and females succumb more frequently to senile dementia. Differences in habits of living have been held partially responsible for the sex differences referred to. Alcoholism, syphilis, and overindulgence are more common in men than women, and they are known to contribute to arteriosclerosis, at least in certain individuals.

Evidence on age changes in interests in normals has been supplied by Strong (135, chapter 13), who administered his *Vocational Interest Blank* to 2,340 men ranging in age from 20 to 59. They were recruited largely from those engaged in the professions. He found that differences between individuals are more easily accounted for in terms of occupation than in terms of age. Strenuous and dangerous activities, such as "walking along the edge of a precipice" or "being an aviator," were not as acceptable to the older as to the younger men. Interference with established activities is not enjoyed by older men, and their interests are less labile. Enjoyment of occupational activities drops with increasing age. Reading interests increase as persons grow older, and the older men prefer amusements that can be followed in isolation, whereas younger males enjoy social amusements. Little or no change in interests was found beyond age 55. We can do no more than conjecture the results that would be obtained with persons beyond the seventh decade. One would expect a generalized tendency toward constriction of interests and activities, with numerous exceptions in individual cases.

Recently Strong (136) has retested men who answered his *Vocational Interest Blank* 22 years previously. The subjects were young adults at the time of first examination. The median intercorrelation between scores was .75, indicating marked stability of interests during the middle maturity period.

Your Activities and Attitudes is currently the most widely used inventory for measuring the outlook and time-spending habits of older persons. Results obtained with the inventory have been summarized in a book by Cavan and her associates (30). The authors found increasing age correlated with decreased social participation, heightened religious activity, lowered feelings of happiness and personal worth, fewer close friends, and poorer health.

Bühler (19) made biographical studies of people of various ages and professions. Claiming a regular sequence in the events, experiences, and attainments of life, she maintains that the last part of life is a period of restriction, characterized by the relinquishing or loss of activities and position, by limitation of associations and income, and by fatigue. It is a period in which ambitions lessen and efforts decrease. Abilities and accomplishments also suffer a corresponding decrease. Psychological changes, however, are retarded in relation to biological changes, that is, increase is slower and culmination and decline are later than in the physical curve. Where biological factors such as beauty or strength are the crucial features in an individual life, there is greater similarity between the biological and the psychological curves. (Bühler considers parity between these two curves a matter of some significance.) The same holds for curves of attainment, those in the more intellectual pursuits being more favored than those engaged in manual occupations.

Prados and Fried (113), Dorken and Kral (39), Caldwell (20), Ames and her associates (3), and others have studied the

Rorschach protocols of aged subjects. Several of these investigators (3, 113), on the basis of Rorschach responses, conclude that senile psychotics are less subject to affective turmoil then aged normals. The most comprehensive publication on the use of this projective technique with older persons is the book published in 1954 by the Ames group. They report that the responses of the senile are stereotyped, restricted, and often similar from one subject to another. Anatomical or animal responses, or both, predominate.

For further references to the literature, the reader may consult the comprehensive review by Kuhlen (79). Research on the personality of the aged has been evaluated by Watson (147). He comments on the superficial nature of many of the published studies and calls for more systematic investigations. A more thorough understanding of the aging personality may lead to important advances in psychological theory.

X. AWARENESS OF AGING

The subjective awareness of aging has been studied by Giese (49) and L. W. Jones (68). Giese asked subjects how they noticed for the first time that they were growing old. Twice as many physical symptoms were mentioned as mental ones. He concluded that most people think of senescence in physical terms. Educated persons are more likely to mention mental symptoms. The principal physical symptoms of aging, in the order of the frequency with which they were cited, were: breakdown in the locomotor apparatus, nervous difficulties, sense-organ impairment, deterioration in the skin, hair, etc., increased tendency to fatigue, and greater need for sleep. According to Giese, most people suddenly realize that they are no longer young. Men frequently mention that they are less potent sexually.

L. W. Jones (68) ascertained that the average age of becoming subjectively old is 49 years, the range extending from 18 to 82. The physical symptoms reported showed a marked overlap with those mentioned by Giese. Bodily symptoms are mentioned twice as frequently as mental signs. Educated persons showed a higher percentage of mental symptoms. It may be repeated that Miles (101) has shown that functions which essentially depend upon physiological factors decline before those that are essentially mental.

The subjective appraisal of failing physiological and psychological functions is largely an individual matter and is relative to cultural pressures and level of aspiration. Malamud (94) points out that there is no one-to-one relationship between these different aspects of senile decline. Many of the psychological traits of the aged are due to the cumulative effects of experience, to frustrations and the awareness of limitations, rather than to any primary or essential consequences of physiological deficit.

XI. HAPPINESS

Since it is a good index of adjustment, happiness at various life periods is an item of psychological significance. Marcus (95) stresses the view that affective states may originate in experiences which occur during periods of transition; they may, however, persist only briefly, until equilibrium has been established. Since old age is a period associated with disintegration and loss, its characteristic feeling tone is likely to be one of unpleasantness as compared with earlier life periods.

By means of retrospective interviews, given to 450 individuals over 65, J. T. Landis (82) attempted to discover the period of life which they regarded as happiest. Of those interviewed, 7 per cent were unable to make a choice, 50 per cent named the period between 25 and 45 as happiest, 20 per cent chose the years between 15 and 25, 18 per cent declared childhood to contain their happiest moments, and only 5 per cent selected middle and old age. Marriage and family living appeared to be the chief reported source of happiness, although those who chose young adulthood as the happiest period were influenced by such factors as health and finances. Among those who selected the childhood period there were many who were still in the throes of an unhappy marriage. However, only one-third of the married people as against two-thirds of the single people were happiest in childhood. For those who marry, the reported happiest period is between 25 and 45.

In a similar study, Kuhlen (80) asked adults ranging in age from 20 to 80 to draw a line on a chart, indicating happiness levels at various life periods. Happiness ratings were highest in the first two adult decades, declining thereafter. The principal causes of unhappiness were listed as poor health, bereavement, and employment difficulties.

Factors influencing the happiness of persons over 60 in two Florida communities have been investigated by Lebo (86). Happiness was associated with good health, adequate income, and satisfactory interpersonal relationships.

Morgan (103) studied recipients of old-age allowances in New York State. Forty-nine per cent stated that the years from 25 to 45 were the happiest of their lives. Worries associated with financial insecurity are the greatest single source of worry, and the greatest reported sources of comfort were friends and family relationships. Eighty per cent of the upstate New York sample preferred to live alone rather than to take up residence with their children. This was less true of the urban group, which contained a high percentage of foreign-born individuals. As Dunham points out in a later chapter, cultural factors play a tremendous role in shaping the personalities of older persons and in delineating their privileges.

Lawton (84) has minimized the fear of death as a factor in the happiness of the aged, stating that most old persons are either oblivious to or unperturbed by the proximity of death. However, the increased interest in religion which is common in later life is no doubt partly due to an awareness of coming death.

XII. DELUSIONS

It is well known to those who have worked with delusional patients that the productions of such patients are understandable in terms of their past histories. The delusional productions of senile patients often caricature the basic worries of their normal peers. Fear of poisoning and bodily harm are very common among senile psychotics, particularly in those with a well-developed paranoid trend. Many senile dements and psychotics with arteriosclerosis are, however, quite free from delusions.

Old people often realize that they are not wanted, and this realization may become the source of delusional ideas. Klaesi (74), discussing the relationship between age and the forms which delusions assume, points out that older people are particularly subject to delusions of being robbed and being poverty-stricken. He contends that age expresses itself in differentiated dream symbolism. The delusion of being poisoned, for instance, may carry a different significance in later than in earlier ages. The character of senile delusions is also influenced by the serious intellectual deficiencies which usually accompany the delusions.

One aspect of imagination has been studied by Miles (98), through the use of the "kinephantom," which resembles an animated inkblot or Rorschach figure. This test revealed very little differentiation in relation to age.

XIII. SUICIDE

Although suicide is rare at all ages and among all races, its greater frequency among older whites as compared with younger ones is deserving of attention. As shown in Table 23, there is a steady increase in mortality due to self-destruction until the fifth or sixth decade is reached, after which the rate remains more or less constant. There have been no important changes in suicide rates among older persons of white race in the United States during the past fifty years. Fluctuations in the suicide rates of aged persons generally have been accompanied by fluctuations of similar direction within the younger age groups.

When the statistics are broken down on the basis of sex (Table 23), it is found that males of all races have higher suicide rates at all ages. Moreover, the gap between the sexes tends to widen with advancing chronological age, particularly among members of the Mongoloid and Caucasian races. For example, the suicide rate for 50- to 54-year-old whites is 37.8 in males and only 10.8 in females. At ages 75–79 the rate for males has jumped to 58.5, whereas for females in the same race and age group it has fallen to 8.4.

As shown in Table 23, non-whites of both sexes have lower suicide rates than whites at all ages. Rate differences are more pronounced in later life than in early adulthood. Significantly, Southern Negroes have lower suicide rates than Negroes residing in other sections of the United States. Inured to poverty and hardship, the Negro may find the economic and social disabilities attendant upon his age less weighty than does his white neighbor.

Economic and social conditions as well as other factors influence suicide rates. It is interesting to note that in 1930, a depression year, the rates were considerably higher than in 1940, and that in 1949 there were still further decreases in the rates of self-destruc-

TABLE 23.—Age-Specific Suicide Rates per 100,000 Estimated Population, 1949*

Population	All Years	20-24 Years	25-29 Years	30-34 Years	35-39 Years	40-44 Years	45-49 Years	50-54 Years	55-59 Years	60-64 Years	65-69 Years	70-74 Years	75-79 Years	80-84 Years	85 Years and Over
Total	11.4	6.4	7.8	10.0	13.8	17.2	18.7	22.8	25.9	28.6	31.5	28.7	30.0	31.7	39.0
White:															
Male	19.2	9.7	12.1	15.1	21.4	27.8	30.2	37.8	43.0	49.2	55.4	53.2	58.5	66.6	88.5
Female	5.5	3.7	4.2	6.0	7.8	9.0	9.8	10.8	11.7	10.7	11.7	9.1	8.4	6.4	10.1
Non-white:															
Male	7.0	6.4	9.8	10.1	13.0	11.6	12.8	12.2	14.4	20.6	17.5	17.3	15.4	14.3	12.5
Female	1.5	2.5	2.1	2.8	3.1	2.2	2.1	2.0	2.5	2.0	2.9	1.0	3.0	0.0	0.0

* Mortality summary for the United States; does not include armed forces overseas (104).

tion. Suicide rates for 1952 show decline in reference to 1949 (105). As might be expected, the greatest relative decrements occurred among white men in the older age brackets.

Not all suicides among older individuals can be attributed to poverty or impending poverty. The loss of a loved one often precipitates a suicidal attempt. Physical ailments of all kinds are more prevalent among older than among younger persons, and some of these conditions are of hopeless prognosis; many seek escape from these maladies by self-inflicted death. Another important cause of suicide in the later decades is mental disease; suicidal tendencies are particularly prominent in involutional psychosis. Suicidal attempts sometimes occur among senile dements and psychotics with arteriosclerosis, but they are not typical of persons in these categories.

XIV. CRIMINALITY

Even in the most crime-prone age groups of our population, the percentage of criminals is low; the rates become progressively lower beyond middle life. In 1940 only 171 persons aged 70 and over were sent to prisons or reformatories in the United States for felonious acts, and of these 169 were males (145). On the other hand, in the same year, 12,073 persons aged 21–24 were sent to institutions after being convicted of felonies, a figure more than seventy times that for the older age group mentioned above. There have been no appreciable changes in the relative crime rates of the various age groups since 1940 (43).

Further evidence to support the statement that crime rates for offenses of all kinds decrease after middle life is to be found in Table 24 (based on reference 43). This table shows the arrests made in the United States during 1952, with a breakdown by age and type of offense. The 1950 census indicates that the age group 40–49 contains over ten million fewer persons than the classification "50 and over"; yet in the younger group a larger number of arrests occur, not only for total offenses but for each separate offense listed.

One factor to be considered in this connection is the tendency of many judges and juries to regard old age as justifying lenience. Frequently sentences are suspended or the defendant is placed on parole; even where sentences are pronounced, they often are lighter

TABLE 24.—ARRESTS IN THE UNITED STATES BY AGE GROUPS, 1952*

Offense Charged	All Ages	Under 15	15–19	20–24	25–29	30–34	35–39	40–44	45–49	50 and Over	Not Known
Criminal homicide:											
Murder and nonnegligent manslaughter	1,288	12	99	204	246	199	160	137	82	146	3
Manslaughter by negligence	961	10	83	137	185	145	114	94	74	119	..
Robbery	6,554	370	1,744	1,751	1,210	666	379	238	100	96	..
Aggravated assault	11,882	189	972	1,981	2,261	1,910	1,580	1,163	696	1,130	..
Other assaults	45,539	350	3,077	7,382	9,398	8,158	6,095	4,443	2,829	3,785	22
Burglary—breaking or entering	22,744	5,577	7,524	3,747	2,386	1,402	843	549	328	382	6
Larceny—theft	39,871	7,975	9,721	5,207	4,477	3,357	2,623	2,159	1,576	2,772	4
Auto theft	11,996	1,592	6,183	1,873	1,039	607	324	172	81	125	..
Embezzlement and fraud	6,505	39	406	825	1,385	1,228	917	630	415	655	5
Stolen property; buying, receiving, etc.	1,767	155	305	279	216	245	189	143	113	122	..
Forgery and counterfeiting	3,969	42	454	815	843	655	451	281	203	223	2
Rape	2,051	41	556	522	327	219	156	93	52	85	..
Prostitution and commercialized vice	12,438	11	759	3,700	2,894	1,800	1,485	797	459	521	12
Other sex offenses	10,058	462	1,286	1,818	1,690	1,369	1,052	808	600	967	6
Narcotic drug laws	3,103	6	285	915	737	421	290	169	110	170	..
Weapons; carrying, possessing, etc.	8,039	190	1,120	1,439	1,526	1,206	871	634	415	633	5
Offenses against family and children	11,028	344	705	1,735	2,512	2,030	1,493	972	599	638	..
Liquor laws	16,217	62	2,157	1,854	2,169	2,161	2,111	1,870	1,402	2,423	8
Driving while intoxicated	41,259	16	933	4,597	7,080	6,968	6,503	5,491	4,072	5,590	9
Disorderly conduct	125,269	3,363	13,545	20,492	20,349	17,240	14,994	12,041	9,298	13,891	56
Drunkenness	506,023	129	8,380	34,306	51,423	62,058	72,574	75,174	69,645	131,715	619
Vagrancy	45,727	122	4,073	5,959	5,462	4,932	5,033	4,739	4,510	10,885	12
Gambling	26,738	39	674	2,252	4,085	4,460	3,955	3,552	2,775	4,911	35
Suspicion	44,350	1,143	9,277	9,013	6,975	5,047	3,978	2,978	2,090	3,427	422
All other offenses	105,299	11,373	20,341	16,038	13,389	11,065	9,361	7,537	5,759	10,118	318
Total	1,110,675	33,612	94,659	128,841	144,264	139,548	137,531	126,864	108,283	195,529	1,544

* Based on 232 cities over 25,000 in population (total population 23,334,305 in 1950 decennial census). See reference (43).

because of the age of the accused. Still another factor is the greater unwillingness of older persons to expose themselves to physical danger and the fact that they are physically less capable of undertaking successfully certain types of crime. Furthermore, many older persons have been imprisoned at some time during life, and by experience have learned that crime does not pay. Again, older persons, on the average, are better established (at least, until the onset of senility), and hence are less likely to undertake pecuniary crimes. These and other hypotheses have been offered in explanation of the known facts.

Although recognizing that the crime rate decreases with age, Dell'Amore (37) holds that dissociation in old age is responsible for the relative prevalence of calumny, sexual offenses, fraud, involuntary crimes, and similar offenses. The relative increase with age in these forms of delinquency can probably be attributed to senile personality changes. Pollack (112) points out that notwithstanding the general decline of the crime rate with advancing age, the percentage of first offenders among older criminals is high. He notes that older delinquents are particularly prone to commit certain sex crimes and embezzlement and to violate the narcotic laws.

Insight into the antisocial behavior of older persons is provided in the following statement by von Hentig (58):

The criminality of the older man resembles in many ways that of the woman. He is the instigator, or he commits crimes in which craftiness or the use of physical or chemical forces play a role. At the same time, feeling that the normal methods of defeating a competitor are not any longer at his disposal, the older man falls back on primitive means of violence. Even the weak can use force if he chooses a weaker object, a woman or a child, or if he turns to strength-saving devices, weapons, poison, and deceit. Arson is one of the crimes with a high old-age rate.

Government crime statistics do not differentiate between normal and psychotic aged. However, since the former are more numerous, more physically and mentally fit, and less frequently under supervision, it may safely be assumed that most senile crimes are committed by persons who are not psychotic. It can also be added that, although arrests include both normal and deranged, usually only those found to be normal are sent to prison.

Crime rates for the aged provide us with interesting suggestive material bearing upon the personality structure of seniles. They indicate, for one thing, that conformity to law increases as persons advance in age, being perhaps an outgrowth of their greater conservatism. They also show, in some measure, the cumulative effects of experience upon behavior. In some cases criminal acts represent pathological attempts to adjust to conditions influenced or imposed by age. Since the number of older persons is destined to increase, examination of current crime rates in the later decades provides us with clues to future over-all trends in this country.

XV. SEXUALITY

The recrudescence of sexuality in the aged has occasioned frequent comment in the literature. It is a phenomenon which is difficult to explain in purely physiological terms. One thing, however, is clear: it is not the same sort of sexuality that characterizes early adult life, being more largely of a compensatory nature. At least in part it may represent the individual's rebellion against the onset of old age, of which decreased sexual activity is a conventional symbol.

Assuming that feelings of impairment place emphasis upon sex, and that the waning of the libido causes depression and fear of death, Schilder (123) holds that this sexual inadequacy may lie at the root of many of the fantasies and projections so frequently seen in the aged psychotic, where a sex threat is experienced as coming from the outside. Schilder points to the frequency of senile delusional productions with regard to jealousy, rape, and marriage, the complaints about indecent suggestions and attacks, and the senile day-dreaming and fantasy about sex. He indicates that the apprehensions of the pre-senium and senium often disappear with further deterioration, a finding also observed in older schizophrenics. More than the schizophrenic, however, the senile dement remains to the end in a real rather than an imaginary world, though his understanding of that world may be limited appreciably.

The sexual frustrations so often observed in older persons have been related by Hamilton (56) to somatic and environmental handicaps carried over from early life. He observes that a common outcome is to throw older persons back upon the autoerotic and pregenital satisfactions of infancy, and reports an increase in masturbation in the seventh decade as compared with the fifth and sixth decades. Hamilton also stresses the incidence of anal eroticism, and suggests that it may be related to intestinal difficulties which are common at this stage. Attempting to explain the heightened sexuality of certain aged persons in Freudian terms, Hamilton believes that the ego becomes enfeebled with advancing age, making it more difficult to suppress the strivings of the id, and leading to accentuated guilt and anxiety feelings. He points out that there are definite and well-established social attitudes against sexual activity on the part of the aged, and that these attitudes are psychiatrically important. Physiological factors must also be considered in this connection. Thewlis (138) believes that excessive sex activity late in life is inimical to health, predisposing to cardiac and circulatory affections and hastening general mental decline.

Henninger (57) has offered a possible explanation for senile sexuality in terms of an increased libidinous drive, arising out of an unconscious desire to have offspring. He indicates that children are easy victims, and are susceptible to bribes. There is also the normal, natural affection of the aged for young children, which may be regarded either as a sublimation of the sexual drive or as part of an effort to regain their lost youth by identification. Homosexual acts with small boys are quite common, but there is an almost total absence of offenses against mature women. Most of the offenses are in the form of sex play, or genital manipulation, rather than attempts to secure the adult type of sex gratification.

There seems to be no correlation between the amount of mental deterioration and the probability that a senile male will commit a sex offense. This may be partially due to wide variations in family supervision of seniles. The more deteriorated seniles are less likely to commit serious sex crimes. In Stanford-Binet tests these senile offenders often show good insight and comprehension of relationships, but at the same time seem unable to manipulate and organize relationships toward a satisfactory solution of the problems presented. Not all of the older individuals who come to the attention of the courts for sex offenses are senile dements.

Examining senile sex offenders who were brought to trial in Allegheny County, Pennsylvania, Henninger (57) concludes that most senile sex offenders do not find their way to courts, largely because of the character of their offenses. He reports that senile men constituted 5 per cent of all male sex offenders exclusive of men charged with fornication and bastardy. When offenses against children were considered, older men constituted 12 per cent of those accused (and usually convicted) of sex crimes. There were all gradations of deterioration among these seniles, ranging from an almost imperceptible loss in mental alertness and slight recent memory failure to marked physical and mental decline. These individuals often had high standing in their communities. Some of the sex crimes which older men commit are attempted rape, indecent assaults, exhibitionism, and indecent conduct. Owing to the advanced ages of these persons, the disposition of their cases is a difficult matter.

Satyriasis mitis, according to Krafft-Ebing (77), often is seen in the early stages of senile dementia. Impotence and anaphrodisia, to which are added perverse fancies, conduce to perversities of the sexual act, and make these early senile dements particularly dangerous to young children.

Concurring in the opinion that increased sexual activity may be one of the first signs of senile dementia, Thewlis (138) adds that Bright's disease seems to increase sexual power in some older men. Thewlis describes the sexual drive of the aged as follows (p. 399):

It is in the paroxysmal form of recrudescence that an individual is driven by sexual fury, unrestrained by reason, to attempt rape, and a child being usually available the attempt is made upon the child. It is safe to say that most, if not every case of atrocious but unsuccessful attempt at rape upon a young girl by an old man occurs as a result of sexual recrudescence during the senile climacteric. When the recrudescence is prolonged, the sexual stress is apparently not so great and the individual is more likely to become infatuated with one woman, than to attempt indiscriminate or forcible intercourse.

XVI. CULTURE AND SENILE MENTAL DISEASE

Cultural factors have frequently been mentioned, in the present and earlier chapters, as important determinants in certain forms of senile mental disease. It is difficult to gauge the importance of these as compared with biological factors, for they vary with the individual and with the mental disease. They depend, too, upon the individual's evaluation of his problems, which may be influenced by his earlier status and aspirations, and by his community's attitude toward the aged. It would be presumptuous to elaborate upon the relationship between social environment and personality, so generally accepted is the existence of such a relationship, and so often examined in anthropological and psychological studies. Unfortunately, these studies have only rarely extended to older persons.

Attempting to weigh the relative significance of extrinsic and intrinsic factors in the development of senile and arteriosclerotic psychoses, Williams *et al.* (153) compared an equal number of patients suffering from these two psychoses. Seventy-seven per cent of the cerebral arteriosclerotics with psychosis were considered to have been "socially integrated." This was in sharp contrast to the senile dement group, only 15 per cent of whom were regarded as having good social integration. The writers concluded that "senile psychoses tend to arise in a characteristic setting. Social integration as well as financial independence have not been achieved or have been denied to the individual when most needed. In contrast, psychoses with cerebral arteriosclerosis tend to strike down the individual in a way similar to other disease processes. Personality and situational factors are relatively insignificant." Wexberg (152) concurs in this conclusion, stating that nonspecific exogenous (cultural and social) factors are important in senile dementia but that arteriosclerotic psychosis is "essentially a disease of the blood vessels."

Further support for this position comes from D. E. Cameron (25), who has found that a very considerable number of older persons who break down have suffered seriously from a lack of social integration, as exemplified by their marital and financial status. Rothschild, in a later chapter, deals more extensively with the problem of the relative importance of exogenous and endogenous factors in the etiology of the senile psychoses.

Klineberg (75) has described a study made by Jacobs among certain tribes of the northwest coast of British Columbia and Washington. In these tribes love affairs between younger men and considerably older women are of frequent occurrence. Jacobs has stated that many of the psychological problems which attend the aging process in women were eliminated under this cultural pattern.

Just as certain physical changes with age are beneficial to the individual (the gradual obliteration of the vermiform appendix), so certain changes in sociological status may promote mental

health. On the credit side of the ledger may be mentioned the respect shown the aged, even in our unmannered society. In China,
as Dunham will point out, older persons command even more respect. Our Bureau of the Census undoubtedly receives a somewhat
exaggerated report of the number of centenarians, partly for this
reason.

Race differences in susceptibility to the senile psychoses have
been attributed to cultural differences. Wexberg (152) points out
that Southern Negroes are more susceptible than whites to cerebral
arteriosclerosis with psychosis but less susceptible to senile dementia. He states: "It is not a question whether the Negro brain
is less susceptible to senile processes, but it is a question of how
the total personality of a particular social and cultural type stands
up under the wear and tear of civilization." In this connection it
may be recalled that Negroes have a suicide rate which declines
with age, in contrast to the trend in whites (Table 23). Senile
psychosis rates for Negroes are not uniform throughout the country.
Negro rates are much higher in New York State than in the South.
Commitment practices as well as differences in environmental stress
may be involved in these rate discrepancies.

The foreign-born, according to Landis and Farwell (81), are
contributing more than their share of mental hospital patients of
all ages but particularly in the ages beyond 60. This higher incidence of mental disease may be understood in terms of greater
difficulties in adjustment, difficulties accentuated by age. Economic
factors may be involved here, since the foreign-born are more commonly in the lower income groups.

Break-up of families, increasing social isolation, as well as unemployment and economic dependency, combine to form the socio-
psychological basis for mental disease in later life. However, the
relative importance of economic as against interpersonal factors
can be stated only in terms of individual cases; from the preventive
standpoint, attention must be directed to both. Mental hygiene,
public education, and better institutional facilities for the normal
aged may enable us to achieve better control of the interpersonal
factors. The economic causes of mental disease in senescence can
be dealt with in one of two ways: Either we must educate the masses
of our people to expect and to resign themselves to a much lowered
standard of living during the closing years of life, or we must

arrange in some way for the continuation of earlier standards even after retirement. Dunham, in the next chapter, presents additional data on the relationship between culture and mental disease in the aged.

XVII. LIMITATIONS OF PRESENT KNOWLEDGE

Exceptional care must be observed in drawing conclusions concerning the psychological changes which take place in old age. On some points, confirmatory follow-up studies are necessary, because of the unusual sampling hazards which characterize work in this field. On some points there is no information whatsoever, and sections of our knowledge are far from satisfying. Although it seems improbable that future research will greatly alter the symptomatic description of the senile psychoses, we are only at the beginning of our understanding of the dynamic psychological processes underlying the development of certain forms of mental illness in senescent persons.

Future research, it is hoped, will fill in many of the missing details in our knowledge, and aid in developing psychological techniques helpful in differential diagnosis. Very few studies of normals or dements have been carried beyond the age of 70, making hazardous the comparison of psychotics and nonpsychotics. Cross-sectional methods, being easier of application, have been the preferred methods in the study of the psychology of later life. Psychologists and psychiatrists know that case histories are no substitute for data carefully and scientifically collected on the same cases over a period of many years. If we were to follow a large group of middle-aged persons through the later years of life, we undoubtedly would find some who would yield to one or another of the senile psychoses. Such a study, taking into account medical as well as psychological records, might yield invaluable clues to the etiology of the later dementias.

The possibility must of course be considered that in the psychoses of advanced life the etiology may be multiple even for a given dementia, and even where cases conform to an established syndrome. Moreover, individual differences often overshadow generalizations based on statistical treatment of data. Although the description of certain "clinical entities" may be practically valuable, we must not lose sight of the fact that these stereotypes frequently do violence to the variety and complexity of actual behavior patterns.

REFERENCES

1. Ackelsberg, S. B. "Vocabulary and Mental Deterioration in Senile Dementia," *Jour. Abnorm. Soc. Psychol.*, 1944, 39: 393–406
2. Adams, C. W. "The Age at Which Scientists Do Their Best Work," *Isis*, 1945–46, 36: 166–169
3. Ames, L. B., Learned, J., Metraux, R. W., and Walker, R. N. *Rorschach Responses in Old Age.* New York: Hoeber-Harper, 1954
4. Anon. "Suicides Decline to New Low," *Statistical Bulletin*, Metropolitan Life Insurance Co., 1944, 25: 6–9
5. Babcock, H. "An Experiment in the Measurement of Mental Deterioration," *Arch. Psychol.*, New York, 1930, No. 117
6. Bayley, N., and Oden, M. H. "The Maintenance of Intellectual Ability in Gifted Adults," *Jour. Geront.* (*In press*)
7. Bellis, C. J. "Reaction-Time and Chronological Age," *Proc. Soc. Exper. Biol. Med.*, 1933, 30: 801–3
8. Berg, E. A. "A Simple Objective Technique for Measuring Flexibility in Thinking," *Jour. Gen. Psychol.*, 1948, 39: 15–22
9. Birren, J. E. "Age Changes in Speed of Simple Responses and Perception and Their Significance for Complex Behavior," in *Old Age in the Modern World* (London: E. and S. Livingstone, Ltd., 1955)
10. Birren, J. E., Allen, W. R., and Landau, H. G. "The Relation of Problem Length in Simple Addition to Time Required, Probability of Success, and Age," *Jour. Geront.*, 1954, 9: 150–61
11. Birren, J. E., and Botwinick, J. "Age Changes in Verbal Fluency," *Jour. Geront.*, 1951, 6: 62
12. ———. "The Relation of Writing Speed to Age and to the Senile Psychoses," *Jour. Consult. Psychol.*, 1951, 15: 243–49
13. ———. "Rate of Addition as a Function of Difficulty and Age," *Psychometrika*, 1951, 16: 219–32
14. Botwinick, J., and Birren, J. E. "The Measurement of Intellectual Decline in the Senile Psychoses," *Jour. Consult. Psychol.*, 1951, 15: 145–50
15. Brody, M. B. "A Psychometric Study of Dementia," *Jour. Mental Science*, 1942, 88: 512–33
16. ———. "A Survey of the Results of Intelligence Tests in Psychosis," *Brit. Jour. Med. Psychol.*, 1942, 19: 215–61
17. Brown, C. W., and Ghiselli, E. E. "Age of Semiskilled Workers in Relation to Abilities and Interests," *Personnel Psychol.*, 1949, 2: 497–511
18. Brown, M. M. "A Study of Performance on a Deterioration Test as Related to Quality of Vocabulary and Rigidity," *Amer. Psychol.*, 1948, 3: 372
19. Bühler, C. "The Curve of Life as Studied in Biographies," *Jour. Appl. Psychol.*, 1935, 19: 405–9
20. Caldwell, B. M. "The Use of the Rorschach in Personality Research with the Aged," *Jour. Geront.*, 1954, 9: 316–23
21. Caldwell, B. M., and Watson, R. I. "Evaluation of Psychologic Effects of Sex Hormone Administration in Aged Women," *Jour. Geront.*, 1952, 7: 228–44

22. California State Department of Mental Hygiene. *1952–54 Biennial Report*,—— Sacramento: State Printing Office, 1955

23. Cameron, D. E. "Certain Aspects of Defects of Recent Memory Occurring in Psychoses of the Senium," *Arch. Neurol. Psychiatry*, Chicago, 1940, 43: 987–92

24. ——. "Studies in Senile Nocturnal Delirium," *Psychiatric Quart.*, 1941,—— 15: 47–53

25. ——. "Present-Day Trends in Neuropsychiatric Research: A Round Table Discussion," *Amer. Jour. Psychiatry*, 1941, 97: 780

26. ——. "Impairment of the Retention Phase of Remembering," *Psychiatric Quart.*, 1943, 17: 395–404

27. Cameron, N. "A Study of Thinking in Senile Deterioration and Schizo—— phrenic Disorganization," *Amer. Jour. Psychol.*, 1938, 51: 650–64

28. Camp, C. D. "Discussion," *Mental Health in Later Maturity*, Suppl. No.—— 168, *U.S. Pub. Health Repts.*, 1942, pp. 17–19

29. Carter, H. D. "Family Resemblances in Verbal and Numerical Abilities," *Gen. Psychol. Monogr.*, 1932, 12: 1–104

30. Cavan, R. S., Burgess, E. W., Havighurst, R. J., and Goldhamer, H. *Personal Adjustment in Old Age*. Chicago: Science Research Associates, 1949

31. Chase, W. P., and Darley, J. G. "Age Changes and Occupational Test Scores Among Clerical Workers," in D. F. Patterson (ed.), *Research Studies in Individual Diagnosis*, Bulletin of the Employment Stabilization Research Institute (Minneapolis: University of Minnesota, 1934), Vol. 3, No. 4

32. Cleveland, S. E., and Dysinger, D. W. "Mental Deterioration in Senile Psychosis," *J. Abn. Soc. Psychol.*, 1944, 39: 368–72

33. Conrad, H. S. "The Measurement of Adult Intelligence and the Requisites for a General Intelligence Test," *Jour. Soc. Psychol.*, 1931, 2: 72–96

34. Conrad, H. S., and Jones, H. E. "Psychological Studies of Motion Pictures. IV. The Technique of Mental-Test Surveys among Adults," *Univ. Calif. Pub. Psychol.*, 1929, 3: 277–84

35. Conrad, H. S., Jones, H. E., and Hsiao, H. H. "Sex Differences in Mental Growth and Decline," *Jour. Educ. Psychol.*, 1933, 24: 161–69

36. Corsini, R. J., and Fassett, K. K. "Intelligence and Aging," *Jour. Genet. Psychol.*, 1953, 83: 249–64

37. Dell'Amore, D. "Della delinquenza senile," *Riv. sper. Franiat.*, 1937, —— 16: 137–76

38. Dennis, W., and Girden, E. "Current Scientific Activities of Psychologists as a Function of Age," *Jour. Geront.*, 1954, 9: 175–78

39. Dorken, H., and Kral, V. A. "Psychological Investigation of Senile Dementia," *Geriatrics*, 1951, 6: 151–63

40. Elderton, E. M., Moul, M., and Page, E. M. "On the Growth Curves of Certain Characters in Women and the Interrelationship of These Characters," *Annals of Eugenics*, 1928, 3: 277–335

41. Eysenck, M. D. "An Exploratory Study of Mental Organization in Senility," *Jour. Neurol., Neurosurg., & Psychiat.*, 1945, 8: 15–21

42. ——. "The Psychological Aspects of Ageing and Senility," *Jour. Ment. Sci.*, 1946, 92: 171–81

43. Federal Bureau of Investigation. *Uniform Crime Reports for the United*

States and Its Possessions, Vol. 23. Washington, D.C.: Government Printing Office, 1952

44. Feifel, H. "Qualitative Differences in the Vocabulary Responses of Normals and Abnormals," *Genet. Psychol. Monogr.*, 1949, 39: 151–206

45. Foulds, G. A. "Variations in the Intellectual Activities of Adults," *Amer. Jour. Psychol.*, 1949, 62: 238–46

46. Fox, C. "Vocabulary Ability in Later Maturity," *Jour. Educ. Psychol.*, 1947, 38: 482–92

47. Fox, C., and Birren, J. E. "Intellectual Deterioration in the Aged: Agreement Between the Wechsler-Bellevue and the Babcock-Levy," *Jour. Consult. Psychol.*, 1950, 14: 305–10

48. Garfield, S. L., and Blek, L. "Age, Vocabulary Level, and Mental Impairment," *Jour. Consult. Psychol.*, 1952, 16: 395–98

49. Giese, F. "Erlebnisformen des Alters. Umfrageergebnisse über Merkmale persönlichen Verfalls," *Deutsch. Psychol.*, Vol. 5, No. 2. Halle: Marhold, 1928

50. Gilbert, G. M. "The Age Difference in the Hedonistic Tendency in Memory," *Jour. Exp. Psychol.*, 1937, 21: 433–41

51. Gilbert, J. G. "Mental Efficiency in Senescence," *Arch. Psychol.*, New York, 1935, No. 188

52. ———. "Discussion," *Jour. Orthopsychiatry*, 1940, 10: 59–61

53. Goldstein, K., and Scheerer, M. "Abstract and Concrete Behavior: An Experimental Study with Special Tests," *Psychol. Monogr.*, 1941, 53: 1–151

54. Gurvitz, M. S. "Personality and Intellectual Correlates of the Aging Process as Measured by the Rorschach Technique" (abstract), *Amer. Psychologist*, 1953, 8: 360

55. Halstead, H. J. "A Psychometric Study of Senility," *Jour. Ment. Sci.*, 1943, 89: 363–73

56. Hamilton, G. V. "Changes in Personality and Psychosexual Phenomena," chapter 30 in E. V. Cowdry (ed.), *Problems of Ageing* (2d edition) (Baltimore: Williams & Wilkins, 1942), pp. 810–31

57. Henninger, J. M. "Senile Sex Offender," *Mental Hyg.*, New York, 1939, 23: 436–44

58. Hentig, H. V. *Crime: Causes and Conditions* (New York: McGraw-Hill Book Co., 1947), pp. 151–55

59. Hirsch, E. "Über senile Denk- und Sprachstörungen," *Psychol. Forsch.*, 1928, 10: 358–92

60. Hopkins, B., and Roth, M. "Psychological Test Performance in Patients Over Sixty. II. Paraphrenia, Arteriosclerotic Psychosis and Acute Confusion," *Jour. Ment. Sci.*, 1953, 99: 451–63

61. Ionasiu, L., and Cupcea, S. "Memoria in tulburarile mintale," *Rev. Psichol.*, 1938, 1: 195–98

62. Jelgersma, H. C., "Die Psychoanalyse der Dementia Senilis," *Ztschr. f. ges. Neurol. Psychiat.*, 1931, 135: 657–70

63. Jetter, W. W., Stiffle, A. M., Trowbridge, L., and Trowbridge, E. "Vitamin Studies in Cerebral Arteriosclerosis," *Dis. Nerv. System*, 1941, 2: 66–70

64. Jones, H. E. "The Pattern of Abilities Among Adult and Juvenile Defectives," *Univ. Calif. Publ. Psychol.*, 1931, 5: 47–61

65. ———. "Age Changes in Adult Mental Abilities," in *Old Age in the Modern World* (London: E. and S. Livingstone, Ltd., 1955)

66. Jones, H. E., and Conrad, H. S. "The Growth and Decline of Intelligence: A Study of a Homogeneous Group between the Ages of Ten and Sixty," *Genet. Psychol. Monogr.*, 1933, 13: 223–98
67. Jones, H. E., Conrad, H., and Horn, A. "Psychological Studies of Motion Pictures. II. Observation and Recall as a Function of Age," *Univ. Calif. Publ. Psychol.*, 1928, 3: 225–43
68. Jones, L. W. "Personality and Age," *Nature* (London), 1935, 136: 779–82
69. Kaplan, O. J. *Studies in the Psychopathology of Later Life.* Berkeley: University of California Library, 1940
70.———. "Mental Decline in Older Morons," *Amer. Jour. Mental Def.*, 1943, 47: 277–85
71. ———. "Psychological Aspects of Aging," *Annals Amer. Acad. Pol. Soc. Sci.*, 1952, 279: 32–42
72. ———. "Intellectual Changes of Normal Senescence," Chapter 5 in E. J. Stieglitz, *Geriatric Medicine* (3d edition) (Philadelphia: J. B. Lippincott, 1954), pp. 82–91
73. Kay, H. "Some Experiments on Adult Learning," in *Old Age in the Modern World* (London: E. and S. Livingstone, Ltd., 1955)
74. Klaesi, J. "Lebensalter und Wahnform," *Ztschr. ges. Neurol. Psychiat.*, 1938, 87: 265
75. Klineberg, O. "Discussion," *Mental Health in Later Maturity*, Suppl. No. 168, *U.S. Publ. Health Repts.*, 1942, pp. 85–87
76. Kolb, L. "The Psychiatric Significance of Aging as a Public Health Problem," *Mental Health in Later Maturity*, Suppl. No. 168, *U.S. Publ. Health Repts.*, 1942, pp. 6–17
77. Krafft-Ebing, R. V. *Psychopathia sexualis.* Brooklyn: Physicians & Surgeons Book Co., 1937
78. Kubo, Y. "Mental and Physical Changes in Old Age.," *Jour. Genet. Psychol.*, 1938, 53: 101–18
79. Kuhlen, R. G. "Age Differences in Personality During Adult Years," *Psychol Bull.*, 1945, 42: 333–58
80. ———. "Age Trends in Adjustment During the Adult Years as Reflected in Happiness Ratings," *Amer. Psychol.*, 1948, 3: 307
81. Landis, C., and Farwell, J. E. "A Trend Analysis of Age at First Admission, Age at Death, and Years of Residence for State Mental Hospitals, 1913–1941," *Jour. Abn. Soc. Psychol.*, 1944, 39: 3–23
82. Landis, J. T. "What Is the Happiest Period in Life? *Sch. & Soc.*, 1942, 55: 643–45
83. Lange, J. "Seelische Störungen im Greisenalter," *Münch. med. Wochschr.*, 1934, 81: 1959–64
84. Lawton, G. "Psychological Guidance for Older Persons," chapter 29 in E. V. Cowdry (ed.), *Problems of Ageing* (2d edition) (Baltimore: Williams & Wilkins, 1942), pp. 785–809
85. ———. "Happiness in Old Age," *Mental Hyg.*, New York, 1943, 27: 231–37
86. Lebo, D. "Some Factors Said to Make for Happiness in Old Age," *Jour. Clin. Psychol.*, 1953, 9: 385–87
87. Lehman, H. *Age and Achievement.* Princeton, N.J.: Princeton University Press, 1953
88. Löfving, B. "Diagnostic Value of Some Memory Tests with Selected Groups

of Senile Patients," in *Old Age in the Modern World* (London: E. and S. Livingstone, Ltd., 1954)

89. Lorge, I. "The Influence of the Test Upon the Nature of Mental Decline as a Function of Age," *Jour. Educ. Psychol.*, 1936, 27: 100–110

90. ———. "Psychometry: the Evaluation of Mental Status as a Function of the Mental Test," *Jour. Orthopsychiatry*, 1940, 10: 59–61

91. ———. "The 'Last School Grade Completed' as an Index of Intellectual Level," *Sch. & Soc.*, 1942, 56: 529

92. Mackay, J. "Symposium on Geriatrics," *Med. Clin. North America*, 1940, 24: 1–112

93. Malamud, W. "Current Trends and Needs in Research on Problems of the Aged," *Dis. Nerv. System*, 1941, 2: 37–45

94. ———. "Mental Disorders of the Aged: Arteriosclerotic and Senile Psychoses," *Mental Health in Later Maturity*, Suppl. No. 168, *U.S. Publ. Health Repts.*, 1942, pp. 104–11

95. Marcus, H. "Die Paradoxien des Gefühls," *Ztschr. f. angew. Psychol.*, 1927, 29: 197–228

96. Miles, C. C. "Age and Certain Personality Traits of Adults," *Psychol. Bull.*, 1933, 30: 570

97. Miles, C. C., and Miles, W. R. "The Correlation of Intelligence Scores and Chronological Age from Early to Late Maturity," *Amer. Jour. Psychol.*, 1932, 44: 44–79

98. Miles, W. R. "Movement Interpretations of the Silhouette of a Revolving Fan," *Amer. Jour. Psychol.*, 1931, 43: 392–405

99. ———. "Measures of Certain Abilities throughout the Life Span," *Proc. Nat. Acad. Sci.*, 1931, 17: 627–33

100. ———. "Age and Human Ability," *Psychol. Rev.*, 1933, 40: 99–123

101. ———. "Psychological Aspects of Ageing," chapter 28 in E. V. Cowdry (ed.), *Problems of Ageing* (2d edition) (Baltimore: Williams & Wilkins, 1942)

102. Minkowski, E. "Quelques remarques sur la psychopathologie de la démence sénile," *Jour. de Psychol.*, 1928, 25: 79–90

103. Morgan, M. "The Attitudes and Adjustments of Recipients of Old Age Assistance in Upstate and Metropolitan New York," *Arch. Psychol.* (New York, 1937), No. 214

104. National Office of Vital Statistics. "Deaths and Death Rates for 64 Selected Causes by Age, Race and Sex: United States, 1949," *Vital Statistics—Special Reports*, 1952, 36: 248, 262

105. ———. "Deaths and Death Rates for 64 Selected Causes, by Age, Race and Sex: United States, 1952," *Vital Statistics—Special Reports*, 1954, 40: 100–101

106. Norbury, F. P. "The Climacteric from the Viewpoint of Mental Disorders," *Med. Record*, 1934, 140: 605–9, 657–60

107. Nyssen, R., and Delys, L. "Contribution to the Study of the Problem of Intellectual Decline with Age," *Arch. Psychol.*, 1952, 33: 295–310

108. Overholser, W. "Orientation," *Mental Health in Later Maturity*, Suppl. No. 168, *U.S. Publ. Health Repts.*, 1942, pp. 3–5

109. Owens, W. A., Jr. "Age and Mental Abilities: a Longitudinal Study," *Genet. Psychol. Monogr.*, 1953, 48: 3–54

110. Palmer, H. D. "Involutional Psychoses: Melancholia," *Mental Health in*

Later Maturity, Suppl. No. 168, *U.S. Publ. Health Repts.*, 1942, pp. 118–24

111. Pollack, B. "The Validity of the Shipley-Hartford Retreat Test for 'Deterioration'," *Psychiatric Quart.*, 1942, 16: 119–31

112. Pollack, O. "The Criminality of Old Age," *Jour. Crim. Psychopath.*, 1941, 3: 213–35

113. Prados, M., and Fried, E. G. *"Personality Structure in the Older Age Groups,"* *Jour. Clin. Psychol.*, 1947, 3: 113–20

114. Price, B. "The Perceptual Ability of Persons over Fifty Years of Age," Master's Thesis, Stanford University, 1931

115. Rabin, A. I. "Test-Score Patterns in Schizophrenia and Nonpsychotic States," *Jour. Psychol.*, 1941, 12: 91–100

116. ———. "Wechsler-Bellevue Test Results in Senile and Arteriosclerotic Patients," *Psychol. Bull.*, 1942, 39: 510

117. ———. "Psychometric Trends in Senility and Psychoses of the Senium," *Jour. Gen. Psychol.*, 1945, 32: 149–62

118. Roth, M., and Hopkins, B. "Psychological Test Performance in Patients Over Sixty. I. Senile Psychosis and the Affective Disorders of Old Age," *Jour. Ment. Sci.*, 1953, 99: 439–50

119. Ruch, F. L. "The Differential Decline of Learning Ability in the Aged as a Possible Explanation of Their Conservatism," *Jour. Soc. Psychol.*, 1934, 5: 329–37

120. ———. "Adult Learning," *Psychol. Bull.*, 1933, 30: 387–414

121. ———. "The Differentiative Effects of Age upon Human Learning," *Jour. Gen. Psychol.*, 1934, 11: 261–86

122. Ruger, H. A., and Stoessiger, B. "On the Growth Curves of Certain Characters in Man (Males)," *Annals of Eugenics*, 1927, 2: 76–110

123. Schilder, P. "Psychiatric Aspects of Old Age and Ageing," *Amer. Jour. Orthopsychiatry*, 1940, 10: 62–72

124. Schroeder, P. L. "Criminal Behavior in the Later Period of Life," *Amer. Jour. Psychiatry*, 1936, 92: 915–24

125. Semrad, E. V., and McKeon, C. C. "Social Factors in Old Age Psychosis," *Dis. Nerv. System*, 1941, 2: 58–62

126. Shakow, D., and Goldman, R. "The Effect of Age on the Stanford-Binet Vocabulary Score of Adults," *Jour. Educ. Psychol.*, 1938, 29: 241–356

127. Shakow, D., Dolkart, M. B., and Goldman, R. "The Memory Function in Psychoses of the Aged," *Dis. Nerv. System*, 1941, 2: 43–48

128. ———. "Discussion," *Mental Health in Later Maturity*, Suppl. No. 168, *U.S. Publ. Health Repts.*, 1942, pp. 49–52

129. Shock, N. W. "Gerontology (Later Maturity)," *Annual Review Psychol.*, 1951, 2: 353–66

130. ———. "Aging and Psychological Adjustment," *Rev. Educ. Research*, 1952, 22: 439–58

131. Simon, A., and Malamud, N. "The Inadequacy of Clinical Diagnosis in Geriatric Psychoses." *To be published*

132. Snoddy, G. S. "Learning and Stability," *Jour. Appl. Psychol.*, 1926, 10: 1–36

133. Sorenson, H. "Mental Ability over a Wide Range of Adult Ages," *Jour. Appl. Psychol.*, 1933, 17: 729–41

134. ———. "Differential Effect of Age and Experience on Mental Abilities," *Psychol. Bull.*, 1936, 33: 805–6

135. Strong, E. K., Jr. *Vocational Interests of Men and Women.* Stanford, Calif.: Stanford University Press, 1943

136. ———. "Permanence of Interest Scores over 22 Years," *Jour. Appl. Psychol.*, 1951, 35: 89–91

137. Sward, K. "Age and Mental Ability in Superior Men," *Amer. Jour. Psychol.*, 1945, 58: 443–79

138. Thewlis, M. W. *Geriatrics* (2d edition). St. Louis: C. V. Mosby, 1924

139. Thorndike, E. L., Bregman, E. O., Tilton, J., and Woodyard, E. *Adult Learning.* New York: The Macmillan Co., 1928

140. Thorndike, R. L., and Gallup, G. H. "Verbal Intelligence of the American Adult," *Jour. Gen. Psychol.*, 1944, 30: 75–85

141. Trueblood, C. K. "The Deterioration of Language in Senility," *Psychol. Bull.*, 1935, 32: 735

142. United States Bureau of the Census. "Mortality Summary for U.S. Registration States: Suicide," *Vital Statistics—Special Reports*, 1942, 16: 157–60

143. ———. *Sixteenth Census of the United States: 1940. Population: Special Report on Institutional Population Fourteen Years Old and Over.* Washington, D.C.: Government Printing Office, 1943

144. ———. *Sixteenth Census of the United States: 1940. Population.* Vol. 4, "Characteristics by Age." Part 2, "Reports by States," Table 19, p. 236, Washington, D.C.: Government Printing Office, 1943

145. ———. *Prisoners in State and Federal Prisons and Reformatories: 1940.* Washington, D.C.: Government Printing Office, 1943

146. Verzar-McDougall, E. J. "Learning and Memory Tests in Young and Old Rats," in *Old Age in the Modern World* (London: E. and S. Livingstone, Ltd., 1955)

147. Watson, R. I. "The Personality of the Aged. A Review," *Jour. Geront.*, 1954, 9: 309–15

148. Wechsler, D. *The Measurement of Adult Intelligence.* Baltimore: Williams & Wilkins Co., 1939

149. ———. "Intellectual Changes with Age," *Mental Health in Later Maturity*, Suppl. No. 168, *U.S. Pub. Health Repts.*, 1942, pp. 43–49

150. ———. "The Measurement and Evaluation of Intelligence of Older Persons," in *Old Age in the Modern World* (London: E. and S. Livingstone, Ltd., 1955)

151. Welford, A. T. *Skill and Age: An Experimental Approach* (London: Oxford University Press, 1950), p. 161

152. Wexberg, L. E. "Discussion," *Mental Health in Later Maturity*, Suppl. No. 168, *U.S. Pub. Health Repts.*, 1942, pp. 19–20

153. Williams, H. W., Quesnel, E., Fish, V. W., and Goodman, L. "Studies in Senile and Arteriosclerotic Psychoses. I. Relative Significance of Extrinsic Factors in Their Development," *Amer. Jour. Psychiatry*, 1942, 98: 712–15

154. Willoughby, R. R. "Family Similarities in Mental-Test Abilities," *Genet. Psychol. Monogr.*, 1927, 2: 235–77

155. ———. "The Relationship to Emotionality of Age, Sex, and Conjugal Condition," *Amer. Jour. Sociol.*, 1938, 6: 920–31

156. Yacorzynski, G. K. "An Evaluation of the Postulates Underlying the Babcock Deterioration Test," *Psychol. Rev.*, 1941, 48: 261–67

Chapter VI

SOCIOLOGICAL ASPECTS OF MENTAL DISORDERS IN LATER LIFE

H. Warren Dunham

Sociological study of the several abnormal psychological conditions in later life implies an attempt to isolate relevant social factors which make for distortions in the conduct, feeling, and thinking of the aged members of any society. More specifically, of course, the immediate concern is with the attempt to locate such factors in our own society, with the confidence that such an analysis may provide insight on the mental breakdowns of persons in other societies. In fact, the position and role of the aged vary in different societies, and this might prove to be crucial in accounting for variations in the rate of breakdown in different societies. Even so, Western culture, which is largely Euro-American and which might be described as urban, industrial, technological, competitive, and individualistic, does have an old-age problem of some magnitude. Part of this problem is reflected in the increase of the mental disease rate as age advances (5), and it is this aspect of the problem which we wish to consider.

Here, it seems feasible to make clear certain limitations of a sociological analysis. On the sociological level it seems that we can proceed in a broad, general fashion to clarify some of the social factors which make for an inadequate psychological adjustment of our aged members. In other words, one facet of inquiry is to isolate those factors which will act adversely upon the existing psychological organizations of the aged persons in our society. Another facet for sociological investigation is to show the manner in which abnormal conduct and thought processes of the aged are reflected in the relationship between personality structures and given social situations. We use the generalized concept of adjustmen here because we think that sociological analysis can reveal only the particular conditions of the situation of the aged where certain persons will experience a mental breakdown, and cannot predict which persons will become mental cases. Social factors will act upon persons with a differentiating effect because of variations in constitutional make-up, content of emotional life, diversity of reactions to the totality of life experience, and character of the self conceptions.

Thus our major concern in this paper will be directed toward an analysis of those relevant social factors in our culture which appear to play some crucial role in the development of psychopathological conditions in later life. To do this, we intend to examine the following: (*a*) Certain statistical and ecological data concerning the prevalence of psychotic conditions among older people will be presented. (*b*) The current role of our familial and economic institutions in making for social and psychic maladjustments of the aged will be analyzed. (*c*) Certain materials will be presented bearing on a comparison of Chinese and American cultures with respect to the role and adjustment of elderly persons. Study and analysis of these materials should be instrumental in revealing the nature of some social factors which are significant in making for certain psychotic conditions experienced by aged persons in our society.

I. ECOLOGY OF AGED PSYCHOTICS

The presentation of statistical and ecological data is not made with a view to giving any detailed quantitative analysis but rather for the purposes of (*a*) obtaining an over-all view of the mental breakdowns of older persons in the United States and (*b*) utilizing these data to point toward some of the cultural factors which make for some of the adjustment problems of the aged.

A statistical analysis of the mental disease rates for persons 45 years of age and over in the United States for 1940 is shown in Table 25. Here, one notes that the mental disease rates in the two decades between the ages 45 and 64 are the highest in the categories labeled "other functional" and "other organic," while in this age period the "senile psychoses" category has the lowest rate. In addition, the male rate is higher in the "other organic" category, while the female rate is the highest in the group labeled "other functional" psychoses—a reflection, perhaps, of the stress of the menopause. Approximately the same size rates in this period are shown for the two major functional disorders, dementia praecox and manic-depressive psychoses. Among older persons above the age of 65

TABLE 25.—RATES FOR MENTAL DISEASE IN THE UNITED STATES BY SEX AND BY MAJOR DIAGNOSTIC CATEGORIES IN POPULATION ABOVE 45 YEARS OF AGE*

Psychoses	Age 45–64						Age 65 and Over					
	Male		Female		Total		Male		Female		Total	
	No.	Rate	No.	Rate	No.	Rate	No.	Rate	No.	Rate	No.	Rate
Dementia praecox	1,330	9.9	1,477	11.6	2,807	10.8	76	1.7	105	2.3	181	2.0
Manic-depressive	1,550	11.6	1,831	14.4	3,381	13.0	164	3.7	174	3.8	338	3.7
Senile psychosis	403	3.0	473	3.7	876	3.4	3,928	89.1	3,899	84.5	7,827	86.8
Cerebral arteriosclerosis	2,748	20.6	1,960	15.4	4,708	18.0	4,444	100.9	3,090	67.0	7,534	83.5
Other functional	3,251	24.3	4,624	36.4	7,875	30.2	500	11.3	459	10.0	959	10.6
Other organic	6,116	45.7	2,115	16.6	8,231	31.6	959	21.8	396	8.6	1,355	15.0
Other functional without psychosis	1,092	8.2	346	2.7	1,438	5.5	292	6.6	153	3.3	445	4.9
Other organic without psychosis	2,749	20.6	490	3.9	3,239	12.4	199	4.5	39	0.8	238	2.6
Total	19,239	14.4	13,316	10.5	32,555	12.5	10,562	24.0	8,315	18.0	18,877	20.9

*Data in all tables, except Table 26, compiled from *Patients in Mental Institutions, 1940*, U.S. Bureau of the Census, includes all first admissions to veterans', state, county, and private hospitals.

TABLE 26.—RATES FOR MENTAL DISEASE IN THE UNITED STATES BY SEX AND BY MAJOR DIAGNOSTIC CATEGORIES IN POPULATION ABOVE 45 YEARS OF AGE*

Psychoses	Age 45-64						Age 65 and Over					
	Male		Female		Total		Male		Female		Total	
	No.	Rate	No.	Rate	No.	Rate	No.	Rate	No.	Rate	No.	Rate
Dementia praecox	1,552	10.2	2,336	15.3	3,888	12.7	107	1.8	152	2.3	259	2.1
Manic-depressive	1,364	8.9	2,050	13.4	3,414	11.2	221	3.8	324	4.9	545	4.4
Senile psychosis	408	2.7	536	3.5	944	3.1	5,601	98.0	6,689	101.1	12,290	99.7
Cerebral arteriosclerosis	2,182	14.3	1,859	12.1	4,041	13.2	6,381	111.7	5,187	78.4	11,568	93.8
Other functional	1,323	8.7	1,247	8.1	2,570	8.4	394	6.8	282	4.2	676	5.4
Other organic	6,840	45.0	6,504	42.6	13,344	43.8	1,269	22.2	813	12.3	2,082	16.8
Other functional without psychosis	5,839	38.3	2,647	17.3	8,486	27.8	955	16.7	637	9.6	1,592	12.9
Other organic without psychosis	3,734	24.6	766	5.0	4,500	14.7	315	5.5	70	1.0	385	3.1
Total	23,242	15.3	17,945	11.8	41,187	13.5	15,243	26.6	14,154	21.4	29,397	23.9

* Data compiled from *Patients in Mental Institutions, 1948*, National Institute of Mental Health, all first admissions to state and private hospitals. Rates based on population census, 1950.

the categories having the highest rates are the "senile" and "arterio-sclerotic." The other categories have extremely low rates in comparison.

A rough comparison of changes which have taken place during the decade is seen on the examination of similar data for 1948 in Table 26. The coverage is not quite comparable to 1940, as the 1948 census did not include veterans' or county hospitals. While the over-all sizes of the total rates are smaller in each age and sex category this is probably a reflection of the difference in coverage. However, during the decade the rates for both old-age psychoses show a definite increase above 65 years, although there is slight decrease in the rates for these disorders in the 45–64 age group. In addition, a marked shift is also noted in the rates for the "other functional" and "other organic" groups. While in 1940 these rates were approximately equal in the 45–64 age group, in 1948 the "other organic" rate has increased by twelve units and the "other functional" shows a decrease of twenty-two units. This holds constant for each sex. It possibly reflects an improvement in psychiatric diagnostic skill in making the differential diagnosis. The same pattern is also noted for these categories in the older age groups but here the increase in rates is not so marked.

The 1940 data can be seen in terms of their distribution in the various sections of the United States in Table 27. In this table we note that the highest rates in both age categories are to be found in the Middle Atlantic, the New England, and the Pacific sections. This finding points to the fact that in the older and more urbanized

TABLE 27.—NUMBER OF ADMISSIONS AND RATES TO HOSPITALS FOR MENTAL DISEASE IN THE UNITED STATES BY AGE AND BY DIVISIONS—1940

Division	Age 45–64		Age 65 and Over	
	No.	Rate	No.	Rate
New England	2,203	119.0	1,905	266.3
Middle Atlantic	7,269	122.5	5,473	291.3
East North Central	6,159	108.5	3,691	187.5
West North Central	2,513	89.0	1,879	168.9
South Atlantic	2,876	99.5	1,477	152.4
East South Central	1,283	74.9	842	137.4
West South Central	1,725	79.3	864	120.2
Mountain	351	45.7	345	137.4
Pacific	2,572	114.1	1,699	214.4
Total	26,951	103.3	18,175	201.5

sections of the country, where the institution of the family has developed its greatest strains and tensions, are to be found the largest numbers of older people suffering from mental disorders. The high rate in the Pacific area is, no doubt, a partial reflection of the number of older people who have migrated to this section from the Middle Western states. Conversely, the low rates in those divisions most rural in character possibly reflect the traditional tendency of an agricultural people to care for its aged. Exactly the same picture is revealed in Table 28, where the old-age psychoses are considered separately.

TABLE 28.—NUMBER OF ADMISSIONS AND RATES OF PSYCHOSIS WITH ARTERIO-
SCLEROSIS AND SENILE PSYCHOSIS TO HOSPITALS FOR MENTAL DISEASE
IN THE UNITED STATES BY DIVISIONS—1940

Division	No.	Rate
New England	2,010	78.3
Middle Atlantic	6,362	81.5
East North Central	4,188	54.8
West North Central	1,965	49.9
South Atlantic	1,790	46.4
East South Central	825	35.5
West South Central	1,175	40.6
Mountain	371	36.4
Pacific	2,054	67.4
Total	20,740	59.1

These statistical data gain some additional significance when compared with the ecological distribution of the senile psychoses and psychoses with arteriosclerosis in Chicago (6). In this study it was found that the highest rates for both of these psychoses occurred in the rooming-house and Negro communities within the city. Both of these areas are characterized by low economic conditions, a loose and disorganized family life, and a high mobility rate of the population. Certain correlations which were computed attest the character of the concentration of these two old-age psychoses. The senile psychosis rates correlated with the percentage of home ownership—.75±.05; while the combined rates for both senile psychosis and psychosis with cerebral arteriosclerosis correlated with the percentage of population on relief .82±.03, and with the percentage of the population of native white of native parentage—.87±.03. This ecological study points to the fact that older people in a poverty situation and in communities of disorganized family life are more likely to be identified as psychotic cases than those older persons who live in more acceptable economic surroundings and still enjoy a fair degree of familial support.

These statistical and ecological data provide clues for appraising and evaluating the type of social factors and their role in the development of the psychopathology of the aged. Specifically, they point to the necessity for considering the character of the familial institution in our society and the nature of its recent changes. In addition to changes in the familial institution there have also been changes in our economic institutions which have abetted the development of our old-age problem. Since these changes in two of our major social institutions are intimately associated, we shall consider them together.

II. INSTITUTIONAL CHANGES

Sociologists for over three decades have been pointing to changes in the family, which also have produced certain problems for the aged. The large family unit consisting of grandparents, parents, and children, and perhaps even a stray bachelor or widowed uncle or aunt, is now a thing of the past. This reduction in the size of the family is a concomitant of the economic changes which have taken place throughout our entire society and also of the development of large cities and swift means of transportation which have led to increased mobility on the part of our people. During the past decade, war and its aftermath have also contributed to affect the stability of the family. In addition to these factors, our economic organization has tended, at least partially, to stress the desirability of the employment of younger people.[1] Consequently, many older persons in the population, especially in the white-collar group, have found themselves displaced by ambitious and aggressive younger persons.[2] Here, it is relevant to note that in this new and complex

[1] There are indications that this trend may be reversed somewhat as we become more fully aware of the loss to the community and the effects on the older persons of depriving them of their economic functions.

[2] This is a phase of our old-age problem which needs a thorough and careful investigation. While an agricultural economy always provided economic functions for older persons, a machine industrial economy seems likely to provide fewer jobs. As the machine economy moves to some ideal state of perfection, one might expect that economic functions for oldsters would steadily decline. On the other hand, advances in

urban society many states have had to pass laws compelling children to support their aged parents, a type of requirement which would have had no significance or meaning in an older agrarian society in which mutual duties and obligations are rigidly defined by the mores. Thus, these older people who are parents and who have supported themselves in previous years find many of their habitual props—their children, their homes, their possessions, their friends, and their club memberships—suddenly taken from them and a new situation created in which their psychic and emotional insecurity becomes magnified. The insecurities and frustrations of childhood and early adolescence become duplicated in the insecurities and frustrations of old age. Thus, in our culture a cycle has been completed: from childhood insecurity to old-age insecurity. But there is this difference: in the insecurity of childhood there is a future; in the insecurity of old age there is nothing but a past, and it is this past which the oldsters must call upon to make an uncertain present livable. But making it livable is difficult without the customary and habitual supports.[3]

It is, of course, recognized that the beginning of old-age insecurity varies considerably with the person, depending upon such factors as state of physical health, constitutional energy, and personality organization. When the final glimmer of hope has departed, the oldster begins to resurrect his past glories. It is then that the emotional insecurities, stereotyped attitudes, fixed habits, and unsatisfied libidinal strivings tend to find expression in exaggerated and unacceptable forms.

Previously we have shown the manner in which our new urban social organization has modified the traditional family structure. In addition to this, however, there is the role which is played by actual family disintegration as reflected in the rising divorce rate.

medical knowledge have been steadily increasing the average age of life. Thus is created a situation where on the one hand the number of oldsters in the population is increasing, and on the other hand the number of jobs in which older people can still find satisfaction in being useful is steadily decreasing. For a further discussion of the significance of an aging population, see Nathan Israeli, "Psychiatric Aspects of a Declining Population," *Jour. Soc. Psychol.*, 1942, 15: 341–5.

[3] For an important and relevant discussion of the time factor in the aging process, see A. L. Vischer, "Psychology of the Aged," *Jour. Amer. Med. Assoc.*, 1942, 118: 661. In this article Dr. Vischer calls attention to the fact that when the consciousness of the future disappears, the general framework of the life of the person may be said to break down. Thus, the time of the older person is seen only in terms of the daily present and his animal functions.

While it is established that approximately fifty per cent of divorced people eventually remarry, one may ask what becomes of the other fifty per cent? Certainly many of them will be destined to an insecure, lonely old age. It is of some significance to note in this respect that divorced persons in contrast to the other marital-status groups have the highest rate for mental disease, and the evidence shows that this rate increases as age advances. In such a manner this trend follows the general insanity rate.[4]

The changes which the family has been experiencing are buttressed by new social attitudes and practices which are emerging in connection with family life. A new psychology of child training has taken away from old persons many of the pleasures which they once had in guiding their grandchildren. Any suggestions which oldsters may offer with respect to child training are generally regarded as old-fashioned in the light of current practices. Then too, as Folsom points out, a new cultural attitude has arisen which emphasizes that it is undesirable for the young person at marriage to make his home with the parents (8). In addition, the older custom which required children before marriage to turn over all their earnings to the parents has practically disappeared. The modern young person, if working and living at home, is more likely to pay board and room or keep all that he makes.

These changes which our familial and economic institutions have undergone have created an abnormal social situation in which the oldsters have found many of their customary and habitual cultural supports removed. The numerous organizations of older people (which appeared during the '30's) with a political program demonstrated that canny politicians can make capital out of the disappearance of these essential supports. These supports, libidinal and economic, are as essential for oldsters as they are for the other age groups in the society. For the aged to continue to live effective and useful lives these traditional supports must be returned to them, even though in some new form.

III. CHINESE AND AMERICAN FAMILIAL STRUCTURES

An examination of a society where the cultural situation is markedly different from our own may enable us better to isolate

---

[4] For example, see B. Malzberg, *Social and Biological Aspects of Mental Disease* (Utica, N.Y.: State Hospital Press, 1940), pp. 116–30.

some of the factors which are significant with relation to the development of psychopathological conditions in our aged. For example, take China, which for the most part has preserved its traditional orientation toward life and stands in sharp opposition to the utilitarian, individualistic, personality-expressing type of life found in Western society. Its culture has been closed, until recently, to the influences of Western technology; and, while today such influences are felt, China still maintains—especially in the great sections of its interior—many of the cultural and institutional forms which were found also in ancient China. This is particularly true of the institution of the family. With respect to family life there are two factors in Chinese culture which have tended to keep the traditional structure relatively well preserved. Here, we are referring to their religious system of ancestor worship and the traditional ideology emphasized in the early writings of Confucius and other Chinese sages which places immense value upon the ties binding children to their parents and the obligations of children toward their parents. In addition, the family throughout China has been institutional and patriarchial in character, composed not only of father, mother, and children, but also frequently of the older paternal grandparents and, in some instances, other adult members of the father's family. The Chinese family, unlike the family in the United States, has not experienced much change with respect to its institutional character. Even as late as 1939, Hsiao-Tung Fei, writing of the peasant life in the Chinese section (7), points out that *chia*, which stands for the enlarged family group, still emphasizes the interdependence of parents and children and that this traditional structure tends to insure lasting co-operation among its members.

This type of family, where the existing practice is for the sons to bring their wives to the parental roof, provides a security for the older parents which our present type of social organization has denied them. On this point, Hsiao-Tung Fei writes (pp. 74–75):

If the parents have in their old age still a share of the land and are not able to work it themselves, the son will cultivate it for them. Another form common when one of the parents is dead, is that the remaining one will reincorporate into the son's *chia* and live there. If there are two sons, they support their parents alternately.

Older people in China are definitely assured of security. In fact, it has been pointed out by some writers on China that the possession of a son is the same as an old-age pension for the parents. This same observation is made (13) by Ross[5] on his trip to China about 1910:

Nothing is more creditable to the domestic organization of the Chinese than the attractive old people it produces. The old women, it is true, are not so frequently a success as are the old men, the years of pain from their bound feet and the crosses they have had to bear as women, often sour the temper, and kindly faced grannies seem by no means so common as with us. . . . . On the other hand, I think I have never seen old faces more dignified, serene and benevolent as I have met with among elderly Chinese farmers. . . . . The rights of the parents are such that every man with grandsons is practically endowed with an old-age pension; hence you notice more serene brows, calm eyes and carefree faces among Chinese farmers than among old American farmers.

These observations of Hsiao-Tung Fei and Ross relating to the institutional life of the Chinese family are emphasized also by Professor Sing Ging Su (16):

Aged parents and relations are zealously taken care of: they are never allowed to suffer want and always have first consideration in any matter of physical comfort. The benevolent communism of the Chinese family makes unnecessary institutions of public charity.

This writer also points out that as long as either parent is living the family remains intact, and that the family system, being both patrilineal and patrilocal, can be regarded as the chief socializing agency for the child.

These observations concerning the character of the Chinese family reveal a sharp contrast to the present family structure in the United States. The inference from these observations is clear, namely, that the family structure which remains relatively intact for succeeding generations serves as an insurance for all its members in their advanced ages and thus provides for them a psychological as well as a physical security. We were unable to secure data which might serve to determine definitely the role of the institutional family as a protective influence against the development of mental illness for its aged members, and thus we can only state

[5] No doubt, this older work by a first-generation American sociologist would appear somewhat ethnocentric today when viewed from the standpoint of current anthropological methodology. However, it can be said in its behalf that Ross was a good observer and had some shrewd insights with respect to people and social conditions. It is these insights we have attempted to make use of in comparing the position of the aged in Chinese culture with their position in American culture.

this inference as a hypothesis. To establish this hypothesis it would be necessary to contrast the rates for mental disease in the later life of the Chinese with comparable rates for the United States; and, more to the point, it would be necessary to break down the former rates according to size of family — for example, "no family," "small family," and "large family." While it can be shown that the larger institutional family of China, in contrast to our small, democratically organized family, serves to bring a continuity to the individual lives of its members and thus assure a person of an easy, secure transition from the middle years to the later years of life, nevertheless it does not follow that a reconstruction of the institutional family would be a desirable solution for us. Rather does it point to the fact of a "cultural lag" in our society. While, on the one hand, we have been busy in effecting a reorganization of our family life and buttressing it with new cultural supports, we have not, on the other hand, very satisfactorily provided for one of the consequences of this change, namely, the necessity of constructing a new cultural device which may enable our aged family members to live out their lives with a continuing security. What we have done is to provide only legal makeshifts.

Thus, while the institutional family may serve as such a protection to all its members, its resurrection is not necessarily indicated as suggested by Professor Sorokin (15). Rather, it seems that the trend which the family is taking in this country is toward a development of the more democratic companionship type of family (16). In fact, until the transition period is completed and the companionship type of family perfects itself, one may assert that many of the psychological difficulties which older people develop is the price we have to pay for the new family organization—unless it is possible now to develop new social instruments which will facilitate the adjustment of the older people and give them the type of security which was provided at one time by the institutional family. Whether we can accomplish this now depends partially upon our ability to evaluate correctly the needs of older people and particularly their own conception of their needs.

IV. ATTITUDE OF SOCIETY TOWARD THE AGED

A complete picture of the situation of the aged in our society is not obtained unless the current attitude toward the aged is exam-

ined. This attitude, which is best described as "urban," is gradually permeating the entire society. It is, of course, a city product
and arises in the industrial society where advancing age brings
lowered productive capacity, decreasing income, contraction of
talents and abilities, and increased reliance upon one's children.
This secular attitude is divorced sharply from the attitude of deference to the aged which is found in the older agricultural societies,
in China and in certain American Indian groups. In such societies
the aged are regarded as repositories of ancient wisdom and knowledge which are useful in directing the youth and guiding the society. In these societies the older people still have a role to play in
the productive life, and thus their status is assured.

This developing secular attitude which more or less sharply
relegates the older persons to the position of "has-beens" is of significance when juxtaposed with the cultural factors which, as we
have seen, are slowly but surely adding to the mental tensions and
insecurities of the aged. Both the attitude toward the aged and
these cultural factors are products of the same social forces; and
they tend to enmesh, thus making for a complete insecurity for
many of our aged.

Up to this point we have examined the conditions making for
psychic abnormalities of the aged primarily in terms of cultural
change. We have attempted to locate certain relative cultural factors operating in our society which make for increasing anxiety
and insecurity among its old-age members. We have pointed to the
following factors: the breakdown and passage of the institutional
family in our society, the development of new attitudes connected
with family life, the change from a sacred to a secular attitude
toward the aged, and the fact that our economic institutions tend
to function by providing a decreasing number of jobs where older
people might fit. These factors have two implications which are
crucial with reference to the development of psychological difficulties in later life. First we would point to the fact that the new
companionship form of family and the new attitudes and practices
which have been developed by the younger persons of our society
make for an increasing social isolation of our older persons. They
are often treated courteously and, if they have status in the community, with respect, by younger people; but because of the current
changes in our culture and the development of new ways to accom-

plish older ends they are often excluded from participation in many phases of our common social life. They still need love, affection, and the feeling of being useful and wanted as always; but the functioning of the cultural forces has merely set them apart, separating them from their own families where normally these needs would be met. Their habitual channels of communication and social intercourse tend gradually to be eliminated.

The second implication of the functioning of these factors is that more and more old people in our society are being forced to make rearrangements in living conditions at the very period when they most need a placid and routinized existence. Economic difficulties make it impossible, in many instances, to continue living on the same level as in the past. Thus, in their later years, many old persons face the matter of readjustment. Old habits which have been built up in the course of the years are broken off suddenly. If they are forced to live with their children, they find themselves in a situation where they are not wanted—their suggestions are criticized, their old habits of life are unable to function.[6]

V. INTERRELATION OF PERSONALITY AND SOCIAL FACTORS

The prevailing notion that every person would become a mental case if he lived long enough indicates that cultural factors operate with a differentiating influence upon different persons. So far in this analysis we have pointed to the increasing social isolation and the disruption of the living conditions in an older person's life which make, in turn, for increasing emotional instability, anxiety, and psychic tensions. However, the functioning of these factors for one older person will not be productive of an equal quantity and quality of emotional instability for another older person. Thus, one has to take into consideration the degree of integration and the type of personality structure which has developed in the course of life. A well-integrated personality combined with a satisfactory adjustment in past adult life should be able to cope with an abrupt change better than a personality which has not achieved integration and previous adjustment. A workable life philosophy, as a phase of this integration, should be of definite value.

---

[6] For an interesting fictional account of the social situation which we have described, see Josephine Lawrence, *Years Are So Long* (Frederick A. Stokes, 1934).

The aging process in every person is indicated by certain grad- ual changes in behavior, attitude, and personality structure even though these changes will not occur in each person at the same age. In behavior it is observed that the gait of the older person is less certain, his motor movements begin to show a lack of co-ordination, and his hands show a development of more tremors. In attitude the older person shows a marked tendency toward stereotypes and fixed viewpoints, a narrowing of interest, and an exaggeration of fears. The older self looks back on the self which previously ex- isted and constructs a self-picture which is often at a marked vari- ance with the past reality situation. This is a partial result of the general impairment of intellect, judgment, and memory which comes with old age and partially the result of the human tendency to see the past as one wishes it rather than as it was. These changes which we have described, and which do occur with the aging proc- ess, are, of course, within limits, normal but are often identified with simple senile deterioration. Our contention in this analysis is that these oncoming behavioristic and psychic changes are often accelerated in our society by our rapidly changing familial and economic institutions. Kardiner (10) states our needs in this re- spect.

For an ideal society we would demand for the aged that their activities should never be abruptly stopped, but changed in accordance with their altered capacities; for, as long as the individual is alive, in addition to food and love he needs the opportunity to be both functioning and effective.

What happens, however, is in marked opposition to Kardiner's ideal society. Our cultural changes swiftly develop a new family structure which makes no allowances for the resulting impacts upon the older persons in our society. Our therapy in the form of old- age assistance, old-age pensions, and hospitalization follows in the wake of these impacts and often provides no more than insufficient patches on a society crumbling at the apex of its age pyramid. Semrad and McKeon (14) point to the fact that most old patients have a history of long-standing personality and financial difficul- ties. They make the point that disruption of the original home is an important precipitating factor. In their reflections upon this problem these authors certainly glimpse the role of the social fac- tors which we have attempted to describe. This is reflected in their final question: Are the mental aberrations of the aged purely a result of the functioning of the economic organization?

We have attempted here to carry our analysis a step farther by showing that cultural factors must operate with a differentiating effect on persons because of the degree of variation in the integration of their respective personalities. Specifically, with respect to the development of mental disease in later life, we contend that our analysis is more likely to apply only to the senile psychoses and the schizophrenic reactions appearing in later life. Numerous recent studies in the literature would appear to support this contention. Williams (17) in a comparative study of forty-seven cases of senile psychosis and psychosis with arteriosclerosis reports that the former arises in a situation where family solidarity and financial independence have not been achieved or have been denied the person, while the latter psychosis acts in a fashion similar to other disease processes. He regards personality and situational factors as relatively unimportant with respect to psychosis with arteriosclerosis. Without attempting to contrast the two mental diseases, Diethelm and Rockwell (4) make the same point with reference to the senile psychoses—they attempt to show the interrelationship of the social factor and the personality of the individual.

VI. SOME PROPOSALS FOR SOCIOLOGICAL RESEARCH
IN THIS AREA

The preceding analysis has proved to be somewhat predictive of the direction which some sociological research has taken during the past decade. To be sure, the tempo of research and research planning has gone forward on many fronts—biological, physiological, psychological, and sociological—but our concern here is to record some of the developing sociological perspectives in this area. Here, it is difficult to separate out that sociological research which bears directly on the problem of the production of mental disorders in later life from that research which relates to the area of aging in general. This is so because some of the latter research, especially that bearing on adjustment problems of the aged and needed essential services for the aged, may eventually prove to have a preventive role with respect to some of the mental breakdowns of the aged.

Pollak's research planning report of 1948 (12) centered the

sociological research interest in geriatrics squarely on the special problems of adjustment faced by aged persons. The attitude is marked, in the recent literature on this aspect, that the accumulation of more specialized knowledge in this area should be helpful in alleviating some of the mounting tensions among the aged and hence prevent some of the mental breakdowns which otherwise might be inevitable. Consequently, some attempt has been made to secure measures of adjustment of older people. One of the most systematic efforts to construct an instrument to measure personal adjustment of older people was made by E. W. Burgess, R. S. Cavan, and R. J. Havighurst (15). Actually, two instruments were constructed, one a device for measuring social participation, and the other a device for measuring personal adjustment. The first is concerned with getting at the degree of participation in activities and the second is directed toward objectifying the attitudes toward these activities. The correlation between them proved to be $.78 \pm 10$, which indicated that at least 60 per cent of one variable was accounted for by the other.

Some recent research has attempted to get at the self-conceptions of oldsters or to what age group they tended to think of themselves as belonging. Lawrence K. Frank pointed up this problem in the opening article of the new journal (9) devoted to gerontology when he inferentially suggested that a given chronological age has a different conception for different persons. These suggested lines of inquiry all point to the attempt to secure some more positive knowledge about the situation of the aged in order to develop services which may be helpful to them in making adjustments in later life.

More specifically, in New York State the Mental Health Commission under the Department of Mental Hygiene has started a large epidemiological study of the aged psychotic in order to determine where a preventive program in the community might be most effectively introduced. They then propose to set up a research design to measure the effectiveness of any such program of services for the aged which is developed. Through such efforts they hope to secure some knowledge about how most effectively we can reduce the incidence of our older psychotics as well as the type of program which might best achieve this end.

Ivan Belknap and H. J. Friedsam (1) recently have outlined a research proposal to isolate, at least by inference, the social factors which might play a role in the production of the mental disorders of later life. They point out, as I have done, that some of the empirical work in this area gives strong support to hypotheses involving social factors as affecting the incidence of mental disorders of later life. They propose that age and sex statuses be regarded as sociological variables with which the incidence of these mental disorders could be correlated. As our previous analysis has indicated, they correctly see that abrupt interruptions in the habitual functions of the person is likely to lead to a poor adjustment. Belknap suggests two hypotheses:

For males:

When family intergenerational continuity is maintained and when spatial and social mobility are at a minimum, and when the status of orientation (the key status of a given culturally determined life cycle) is of maximum length and does not begin or terminate abruptly, the mental disorders of later maturity, organic and functional, should be at a minimum.

For females:

If family intergenerational continuity is maintained, and if the attrition of the feminine status of orientation is accompanied by new sanctioned statuses, the mental disorders of later maturity, organic and functional, should be at a minimum.

These hypotheses could probably be subjected to appropriate tests by the examination of contrasting situations. They portray the position which results from our own above analysis, namely, that the abrupt changes introduced into the lives of many older persons by changes in familial and other social institutions have been responsible for the increased incidence of mental disorders in later life. The task which we face—and some current research is marking it off—is to perfect some social inventions which will make easier the necessary adjustments for older people which our rapid social changes have required them to make.

VII. CONCLUSIONS AND IMPLICATIONS

The implications of our analysis to this point are that the psychic disturbances of the aged which are labeled as senile psychosis and late schizophrenia are (*a*) brought to light by the operation of cultural factors and (*b*) precipitated by the breakdown of the customary channels of communication and the interruption of the routinized ways of living. Thus the detection and identification of

some of the psychic abnormalities of later life are closely inter-
woven with the changing character of our familial and economic
institutions, the new attitudes regulating family life, and the evolving secular attitude of society toward its older members, and these
have proven to be exactly some of the areas which current research
will attempt to investigate.

When we examine this picture from the reverse side, namely,
from the standpoint of personality integration, we are forced to
recognize that our society, in general, has tended to form personalities in many aged persons which find it difficult and well-nigh
impossible to cope with a world of change. By this we mean that
many personalities among the aged were formed by institutional
structures in which stability was the order of the day and the possibility of radical changes in human affairs was, for the most part,
ignored. This view is reflected in the unsophisticated statements
of numerous oldsters who claim that the world is still the same old
world but the people in it have changed—supposedly for the worse.
One sees it also in the nostalgic longing for a return to "the good
old days" and, in the political and economic spheres, in the "back
to normalcy" movement.

The research studies in this area, however, appear to support
the contention that those persons who are selected as senile psychotics in our society have generally displayed previous personality upsets and derive from social and economic surroundings
lacking in stability. This latter factor is a reflection of the economic
insecurity which a large number of people experience.

Throughout our discussion the assumption has been implicit
that there is a constitutional factor which may be highly variable
among individuals. The character of this factor is, for the most
part, unknown and undetermined. We have implicitly recognized
it by pointing out that the age of the psychic breaking point varies
for different persons. This breaking point, while variable, is not
only a result of constitutional differences which are unknown but
also is related to the quality of emotional life, the character of the
personality organization, and to the disruptions in the cultural
order. What we have just said implies the necessity of making some
careful clinical studies of senile patients, taking note of age at breakdown and correlating it with observable constitutional differences
and also with the general life conditions of the patient.

The attempt to cope with these mental disorders of later life on the preventive level suggests two prerequisites. First, there is a need for a cultural reorganization of our familial and economic institutions which will provide not only the appropriate physical security for the old-age period as well as other life periods but also the assurance of continued emotional satisfactions and libidinal ties during the later years of life. Secondly, there is the need for our educational process to mold personalities who will find it easy to adjust to a world that may never again know the stability of past epochs. A new cultural organization requires a new personality structure. This requirement is being met by investigations into the perception and learning capacities of older persons and also by certain educational institutions which are encouraging oldsters to take up their education again.

Current devices for aiding the aged with their problems in our society are, for the most part, preoccupied with the problem of physical security and hence reflect the mechanical, impersonal, formalized, legalistic, rationalized, and secular characteristics of our contemporary culture. These devices perforce cannot be used to deal with the breaking of emotional and libidinal ties of the aged. But this area of life is also of great importance, especially to the old whose future gradually fades to nothing. This position could be supported by the daily observations of those social workers engaged in the task of administering benefits to the aged through our Federal Social Security program.

The continuing shifts in the age structure of the population in the United States may serve to create conditions in which our society will have to deal with the psychological abnormalities of old age sooner than some might expect. The prediction by certain population experts (11), that by 1960 the population above the age of 65 may be 10 or 12 per cent of the total, should furnish a notion of the extent of our future problem. If current trends continue, the financial burden in old-age pensions alone may prove to be somewhat staggering. Before that consummation is reached we should attempt to devise supports for existing institutions, economic and familial, calculated to absorb this possible future social strain. If we succeed, we shall not only make a contribution to the later years of life and thus alleviate many of the current psychic difficulties but we shall also assure a continuance of the strength of the nation by releasing the energies of persons who are still in their productive years. If these factors, as described, have some influence in the development of certain mental troubles of later life—and we think that they do—the best means of prevention will be directed toward the development of a new cultural situation in which these factors will diminish in their effectiveness. Our investigations thus point to the need for the development of new social inventions designed to insure the physical and mental welfare of aged persons in our society.

REFERENCES

1. Belknap, I., and Friedsam, H. J. "Age and Sex Categories as Sociological Variables in the Mental Disorders of Later Maturity," *Amer. Sociol. Rev.,* 1949, 14: 367–76
2. Burgess, E. W. "Effect of War on the American Family," *Amer. Jour. Sociol.,* 1942, 48: 343–52
3. Cavan, R. S., Burgess, E. W., Havighurst, R. J., and Goldhamer, H. *Personal Adjustment in Old Age* (Chicago: Science Research Associates, 1949), pp. 102–48
4. Diethelm, O., and Rockwell, F. V. "Psychopathology of Aging," *Amer. Jour. Psychiatry,* 1943, 99: 553–56
5. Dorn, H. F. "The Incidence and Future Expectancy of Mental Disease," *U.S. Pub. Health Repts.,* 1938, 53: 1991–2004
6. Faris, R. E. L., and Dunham, H. W. *Mental Disorders in Urban Areas* (Chicago: University of Chicago Press, 1939), pp. 134–42
7. Fei, H-T. *Peasant Life in China* (New York: E. P. Dutton & Co., 1939), pp. 28, 74–75
8. Folsom, J. K. *The Family in Democratic Society* (New York: John Wiley and Sons, Inc., 1943), p. 186
9. Frank, L. K. "Gerontology," *Jour. Gerontology,* 1946, 1: 3–16
10. Kardiner, A. "Psychological Factors in Old Age," *Family Welfare Association of America,* 1937, pp. 14–26
11. Overholser, W. "The Problem of Mental Disease in an Aging Population," *National Conference of Social Work,* 1941, p. 459
12. Pollak, O. *Social Adjustment in Old Age: A Research Planning Report.* New York: Social Science Research Council, 1948
13. Ross, E. A. *The Changing Chinese* (New York: Century Co., 1911), p. 198
14. Semrad, E. V., and McKeon, C. C., "Social Factors in Old Age Psychosis," *Dis. Nerv. System,* 1941, 2: 58–62
15. Sorokin, P. A. *The Crisis of Our Age* (New York: E. P. Dutton & Co., 1941), p. 203
16. Su, S. G. *The Chinese Family System* (New York: Columbia University, 1922, Doctoral dissertation), p. 95
17. Williams, H. W., *et al.* "Studies in Senile and Arteriosclerotic Psychoses: Relative Significance of Extrinsic Factors in Their Development," *Amer. Jour. Psychiatry,* 1942, 98: 712–15

Chapter VII

FOOD FOR THE LATER YEARS

Clive M. McCay

In the field of nutrition there is a vast reservoir of human knowledge extending over many centuries. In spite of substantial progress in creating a science of nutrition during the past century, much human guidance can still rest upon experience by many generations of men. Knowledge is useful in application without regard to whether it was acquired last year in a study of older women in Michigan (13) or whether it originated in the experiments of Louis Cornaro (1464–1566) in Italy (4). Men often follow avidly the latest teachings or discoveries and neglect past knowledge which may have far more importance in guiding them toward healthier living.

In a series of scholarly articles, Zeman (23) has indicated that much of our current philosophy in regard to age was well understood many centuries ago. Likewise, much of our modern knowledge in regard to the best use of foods was known by a small group of our forefathers.

Cornaro taught the virtues of moderation in the amount of food eaten, four centuries ago. His teachings are equally important today for all those who tend to eat and become fat. This lesson is especially vital for older people with good appetites. In the later years, pleasures are fewer and many live from one meal to the next. Exercise is less and basal metabolism decreases. Hence, one can become fat upon less food.

One of the most useful of the older works dealing with human nutrition in relation to old age is that of John Sinclair (18) (1754–1831). More than a century ago, Sinclair set himself the enormous task of putting useful knowledge into "codes." He compared his services to the refining of gold, useless in a ton of crude ore, but capable of being carried by a child after refinement. Even today, his books can serve as useful guides in many fields of applied nutrition.

In Sinclair's "Rules for the Preservation of Life," he stated:

1. Breathe pure air. 2. Use a moderate proportion of liquid food. 3. Consume no more solid food than the stomach can easily subdue. 4. Preserve the organs of digestion in good order. 5. Take regular exercise without over fatigue. 6. Sleep as many hours as may be necessary to restore the strength of body and mind. 7. Control the passions and bear with fortitude the disappointments of life.

Some of Sinclair's simple statements about nutrition, which need to be learned by many, are:

Physicians have therefore almost universally preferred simplicity of diet, as satiety is sooner produced by one, than by many substances.

He (Bacon) admits that to be lean with a settled temper denotes long life; but then he contends that persons who are inclined to corpulency cannot expect long life, unless it is joined to choler, and a stirring and peremptory disposition.

Health is the reward of temperance rather than the effect of constitution.

Everyone ought to lay it down as a general rule never to disappoint nature in regard to discharge from the bowels. The inclination if not yielded to goes off.

A costive habit may be removed by certain articles of diet such as roasted or boiled apples, pears, stewed prunes, raisins etc. Broths with spinage, leeks and other pot herbs, also beet root and turnips; bread made of fine flour ought to be avoided; rye bread or a mixture of wheat and rye is laxative as also is barley meal porridge.

London bread has a great tendency to promote costiveness. It is commonly watered with a solution of alum, to render it light and to give it whiteness.

Destroying the enamel of teeth, which there is reason to believe, is the only substance in the body, that is not constantly renewed so that when once lost, it is never regained.

Much more could be quoted from Sinclair that might prove more useful than modern statements. Thus, in a recent discussion of constipation in the aged, consideration was given only to two drugs, namely, "Urecholine" and cascara, while the article opened with the statement, "constipation has been one of the most frequent complaints in people above 60 and one of the most vexing problems, therapeutically" (19). In applied nutrition, today, advantage must be taken of the rich backlog of knowledge provided by past centuries and the wealth of experimental facts that has developed during the past fifty years.

I. NUTRITION, MENTAL DISEASE, MALNUTRITION

Most people render lip service to better foods in the interests of better health but it is doubtful if a substantial fraction of our population are really convinced that nutrition is related to well-being. The reason for this is that nutritional deficiencies in man, especially when diets are marginal, take months or years to develop. Furthermore, it is very difficult to relate cause and effect of symptoms. Finally, the results of dietary improvements are often equally slow and difficult to measure in short periods of time.

As to the part that nutrition plays in the health of animals, the segment of the American population that has no doubt about it is the farmer. Animals respond quickly to their diets and the results spell profit or loss. For this reason most of the nutritional research throughout the world is found in agricultural colleges and most of the discoveries are made there. Both the teaching and research programs in the science of nutrition are very modest in medical schools.

Finally, due to the development of vitamins, sulfa drugs, atomic bombs, cortisone, and antibiotics, the public has come to expect miracles from the biochemist. The future would seem to hold fewer such single specific compounds of use in nutrition but would seem to offer vast opportunities for the over-all improvement of the many marginal substances in human diets.

The past is soon forgotten in relating nutrition to mental diseases and the slow rate of acquiring effective knowledge for application. More than two centuries were required to correct the diets that produced pellagra and its associated insanity. Pellagra was described clearly in 1730. In 1914 Beall (2) stated, "nervous phenomena occur in all cases of pellagra, and in 5 or 10 per cent of cases there is insanity." He could also state, "the diet should be full and nutritious and contain considerable quantities of animal protein." Much later it was found that pellagra-producing diets lacked tryptophane, nicotinic acid, and possibly some of the factors related to vitamin B_{12}. More than two centuries were needed to make these discoveries, and the end is not in sight.

Many early students of pellagra were struck by the fact that pellagrins became prematurely senile (7). Some early workers ascribed the cause of both pellagra and senility to autointoxication. Although poisoning from products created by bacteria is given modest attention today, the field of nutrition is giving much consideration to the creative activities of the intestinal flora. Less attention is paid to the possibility of injurious products and more to potential failures of intestinal bacteria in providing such essentials as vitamin K.

Many believe that malnutrition is impossible in a large nation with a high living standard because purchasing power is large and the food surplus is huge. But in the United States most of the millions of older people have little income. In central New York in 1951 the food allowance for old patients living alone on relief was $26.50 per month. At rates then current this represented twenty-six hours or less of common labor. This food allowance in the hands of an educated and intelligent person is more than enough to provide an adequate diet, but few relief clients have sufficient knowledge for such wise expenditure.

In a nation with large surpluses even of secondary foods such as meat, milk, and eggs, it is necessary that large numbers live upon primary foods such as cereals and plant products because these are much cheaper. Furthermore, in a free economy there is constant and tremendous pressure to divert the purchasing power away from wholesome foods—and even away from all food—toward attractive gadgets such as television sets.

Greater dangers beset the aged because such factors as poor dentures accentuate otherwise unfavorable influences. Meats, salads, and vegetables are often abandoned or overcooked to produce tenderness. Overcooking may destroy vitamins and leach out minerals.

Probably the greatest food factors leading people toward malnutrition in later life are the trends during the past century toward increased consumption of sugar and alcohol. The annual per capita consumption of sugar today is nearly a hundred pounds. Such an extensive use of a food that provides nothing but calories pushes out of the average American diet about 500 pounds of wholesome foods such as milk, fruit, and potatoes. Furthermore, the extensive use of hard liquors displaces other valuable foods. Alcoholic beverages account for 4 per cent of the calories consumed by Americans. However, all of these beverages cannot be considered antagonistic toward sound nutrition since malt beverages carry a substantial amount of water-soluble vitamins and wholesome ingredients.

Excessive use of white fats and white flour also tends to promote faulty nutrition, although the fats of butter, eggs, and liver are important because they provide liberal allowances of certain vitamins.

Among the greatest foes of sound nutrition are hard liquors and soft drinks, commonly called "pop" or more specific names such as cola beverages. It is estimated that the American public now spends more than three quarters of a billion dollars each year for soft drinks alone. No one can estimate the improvement in public health that might result if the same sum were invested in milk.

II. NUTRITIONAL NEEDS OF OLDER PEOPLE

As age creeps forward, the need for energy in food declines because of less physical exertion and lowered basal metabolism. Unfortunately the requirement for protein, vitamins, and minerals does not decrease, and may even increase.

The older person who continues his lusty appetite and grows fat speeds his end; the one who has been reducing her diet to "foodless" white crackers, tea, and sugar is also insuring a lingering death following years of ill health. A marginal diet in middle age may prove to be a deficient one in later years when the amount of food consumed is reduced to about half that eaten during middle life.

Calories and protein.—The mean basal metabolism for a group of 15 older women was found to be 1,367 calories per 24 hours, with a range of 1,130 to 1,735 (1). Most of these women were moderately active and ate enough food to provide 1,500 calories per day. These data accord with various earlier studies made during the past century (5).

Older men have a comparable value of 1,400 calories for basal metabolism and need 2,200 to 2,300 calories for moderate activity (15). Older women seem to need about 55 grams of protein daily and older men about 65. Some seem able to live upon less and to remain in nitrogen balance (13, 15). Some older patients seem to need much more (9).

In the case of low-energy diets it is very difficult for a person to eat enough protein. The problem becomes especially acute in the case of many bedridden patients that consume only enough food to provide a thousand calories or less (22).

Vitamins and minerals.—Only a modest amount of information is available from either human experience or animal experiments in regard to the levels of vitamins and minerals needed in later life. The limitations of both types of information need be recognized. Studies upon older people are few in number, usually limited to few subjects, and always have been conducted for brief time periods. Needed greatly are long-time studies upon patients in mental hospitals, those in homes for the aged, and life-term prisoners. All these studies are possible and would usually be welcomed because of the personal attention given the patient and because of the partial escape from boredom, provided by participation in research.

A few long-time studies upon animal species—white rats, hamsters, and dogs—have increased basic information and provided useful guides for human nutrition. Fortunately, rodents such as the rat and hamster pass from birth to death in extreme old age during a period of a thousand days. During this period many of the phenomena of age, e.g., deterioration of the bones and skin, can be observed. While rodents have many of the chronic afflictions of man such as cancer and degenerative changes in the kidneys, they also suffer in later life from a high incidence of bronchiectasis which may modify nutritional requirements.

All evidence thus far indicates that older people need the same amounts of vitamins as younger ones. The problem is to insure this vitamin intake by adequate consumption of foods that are rich in essentials. Many older people who have existed upon poor diets, profit by enrichment of their diets with natural, vitamin-rich foods such as yeast, eggs, wheat germ, and liver. Occasionally single pure vitamins have proved very useful, as described in cases suffering from painful leg muscles (3).

Only a few inorganic substances are liable to be lacking in the diets of older people. These are iron, iodine, and calcium. The iron intake is likely to be low if meat and eggs are little used in the diet. However, even a vegetarian diet provides adequate iron if it contains liberal amounts of vegetables, whole-wheat bread, and dark molasses. Whole-wheat bread contains the wheat germ, which is a remarkable storehouse for many inorganic essentials such as iron and manganese. Organ meats—liver and kidneys or chicken giblets—are rich in iron.

Iodine is not a problem since most people can afford iodized salt. Many institutions, however, even in iodine-deficient areas such as inland New York, do not use iodized salt.

Calcium is a major problem for man and animals during the later third of life, as well as during the first third, when the bones and teeth are being formed. When men and animals pass into the last third of life several factors tend to accelerate the loss of calcium from the bones. This is especially evident in the case of women entering the postmenopausal period (1). Little is known about men of comparable age.

Experimental animals such as old dogs and rats undergo the same type of loss of calcium from the bones as they enter the last third of life.

Several factors combine during the later period of life to throw the body into negative calcium balance. There seems to be an endocrine effect, probably related to the parathyroids and the thyroid, that increases the rate of release or decreases the rate of deposition of bone calcium. In studies with dogs, using radioactive calcium, it has been found that calcium (taken into the stomach as the lactate) appears in the blood in substantial amounts within an hour and reaches a peak level in about four hours. In the case of young dogs this calcium leaves the blood in the course of 24 hours, but in old animals measurable amounts are found at the end of 6 days. This indicates that the major problem is the movement of calcium from the blood into the bones or out through such channels as bile, saliva, and the kidneys in the case of old animals.

Limited evidence also indicates that exercise tends to improve calcium storage while lethargy puts the body into negative balance. No one has determined if patients confined to bed for long periods can ultimately adjust, so that the balance is maintained upon modest intake allowances.

The decrease in gastric acidity in the case of older people may cause a failure in conversion of insoluble calcium into assimilable forms but the literature contains no evidence concerning this.

In older animals and man, the utilization of fats declines and the additional free fatty acids in the feces tend to bind and dissipate calcium. Hard fats waste more calcium than soft ones in the case of old animals.

At all times in life human diets tend to be low in calcium. The

human need has been set at a level of a gram per day for about
half a century. This comprises about 0.2 per cent of the diet on a
dry basis. Animal nutritionists always advocate much higher levels.
Thus, most dog feeds contain at least 0.5 per cent of calcium and
many contain several times this amount. This subject of calcium
need has been reviewed more extensively elsewhere (12).

Even when the diet is providing only 1,500 calories daily it was
found possible, in the case of three out of four women over 70, to
maintain the calcium equilibrium by the use of 1½ cups of milk
daily (13).

In a study of food eaten by 100 older women, Ohlson (13) computed the essentials ingested (Table 29). For purposes of com-

TABLE 29.—CALORIES INGESTED AND INTAKES OF SPECIAL NUTRIENTS

Calories	Protein (gm.)	Calcium (gm.)	Thiamin (mg.)	Riboflavin (mg.)	Vitamin A (I.U.)	Vitamin C (mg.)
2,400 to 3,500	65	0.63	1.31	1.54	4,222	53
2,000 to 2,399	75	0.56	1.29	1.50	4,286	63
1,500 to 1,999	55	0.44	0.91	1.13	4,766	53
1,000 to 1,499	42	0.36	0.70	0.87	3,225	53
Less than 1,000	33	0.21	0.61	0.57	1,931	29
1,037 (Danish study)	37	0.34	0.47	0.67	1,395	28

parison, data from a Danish study (22) on debilitated patients have
been included. These latter probably reflect the use of more soured
skim milks, since the calcium and riboflavin are higher while the
thiamin and vitamin A are lower.

III. ACHIEVING ADEQUATE DIETS IN MENTAL HOSPITALS

Some of the major factors that have led to substantial improvement in the entire nutritional program in the twenty-seven mental
hospitals of New York State during the postwar period can be listed,
without attempting to place them in order of relative importance.

1. A commissioner of mental hygiene who was a physician and
an internist but especially interested in food. This commissioner
was willing to back his food managers and dietitians in developing
a better program.

2. The establishment of an excellent training school, for up-
grading cooks and bakers as well as introducing new equipment and
recipes.

3. The employment of a mature, experienced dietitian who understood institutional feeding, had original ideas, understood economics, co-operated with food managers, consulted with research laboratories, and was not afraid of a state bureaucracy.

4. The standardization of recipes after extensive testing in several hospitals.

5. The creation and putting into use of bread formulas of the highest nutritive value.

6. The constant study of equipment and sanitation by a highly experienced, former naval officer.

7. The improvement of menus and the attempt to integrate these with farm production.

8. The improvement of farm production.

9. Interesting administrative officers as well as those working with foods in the production of better products from the point of view of taste and nutritive value.

10. Development of a system of cost accounting that did not permit patients to have a poorer diet so that caretakers could have better meals.

11. The introduction of special inexpensive foods of high nutritive value, such as soy flour and dry skim milk, into the dietary. In the course of two years the use of dry skim milk and soy flour were each increased by more than a million pounds annually.

12. The development of a dry mixture, constituting a complete diet, for mixing with hot water and feeding to patients such as the spastic feebleminded.

13. Operating a fat-salvage program so that all trimmings including beef and mutton were rendered and used as fat in baking. Previously much of this fat was removed from food channels because it was processed into soap, of so low a grade that it injured the bed linen in the laundry.

A few of these subjects deserve brief but special discussion.

The importance of making genuine use of well-trained and well-paid dietitians in improving the food service for both patients and employees is often not appreciated. Too often the dietitian is put off in a corner weighing up special diets for a few diabetic patients; too often the food program is left almost entirely in the hands of some accountant who has no knowledge of nutrition and no training in dietetics.

Many bread formulas have been tested from the point of view of taste and high nutritive value. In the course of years the best formula evolved, for white bread, contains, for each 100 pounds of unbleached, high-protein white flour, the following: wheat germ, 2 pounds; high-fat soy flour, 6 pounds; and nonfat dry milk solids, 8 pounds. The best whole-wheat bread formula can use the same supplements but substitutes for the white flour a mixture of white flour (40 pounds) and whole-wheat flour (60 pounds) (11). Such breads spread with butter or fortified margarine are nearly complete foods and are far superior to ordinary breads. They can be made very well by any experienced baker.

Some institutions prefer to make their own whole-wheat flour and small mills from the Lee Nutritional Foundation of Milwaukee are now available for this purpose at a cost of about four hundred dollars. These have a capacity of more than a pound per minute and produce either a very fine or coarse flour. The author has tested one of these and knows that it works.

Other baked goods for mental hospitals, like doughnuts, cookies, and cakes, can be made with substantial amounts of dry skim milk, dry yeast, and soy flour. These afford inexpensive methods of introducing adequate protein and vitamins as well as calcium into low calorie diets. The cook book by Davis (6) has many recipes for using these special products. Cornell University in Ithaca has also issued special recipes for the use of yeast and soy products.

The problem of interesting medical and food officers as well as cooks and bakers in the improvement of the nutritive value of food may often seem insolvable but two examples indicate this is not so.

One large mental hospital had the reputation of being against all change in the improvement of food. When an improved bread formula was put into production they were asked to provide the bread for biological testing in a university nutrition laboratory. Some months later the food manager and his baker visited the rat laboratory and saw the excellent condition of animals reared upon their bread and the poor, undersized rats reared upon ordinary bread. A few months later they came to visit again. This time they brought the hospital superintendent, who was a former pathologist, turned psychiatrist. All were fascinated by the difference shown in the animals fed superior or ordinary bread. This hospital became one of the most enthusiastic supporters of the head dietitian and the improvement of basic foods.

A second example of creating co-operative enthusiasm within institutions is shown by an annual exhibit at a state fair. In spite of substantial opposition from second-line administrative officers, but with support from the top, the head dietitian decided to set up an exhibit showing the baking of better bread. She was allowed almost no funds—because the mental hygiene department had invested a number of thousands of dollars in illuminated "funny pictures." However, through co-operation of makers of equipment, suppliers of bread ingredients, and the services of two of the best bakers from outstanding mental hospitals, the exhibit was created.

The exhibit ran for ten days, with fresh bread being baked all day long. In the course of this period a quarter of a million people stood in line at various times to get samples of bread and butter. This exhibit created pride among the hospitals in their progress; it made relatives realize that genuine attention was being devoted to providing good food for patients; and it stimulated a number of local bakers to initiate production of better bread in their communities.

Both examples illustrate the importance of employing dietitians with initiative and the value of support from top administrators so that underlings cannot block progress.

The development of a dry mixture, for patients such as spastics that are difficult to feed, was considered worth while. Such a mixture was made as a complete diet that was already cooked and only needed to be mixed with hot water. Such a mixture provides a more adequate diet than many patients are liable to get, because they often reject the more valuable foods such as meat and vegetables. Hence they are liable to get very deficient diets from such menu items as macaroni or potatoes without supplements.

The dry mixture used consisted of dry yeast, 3 pounds; wheat germ, 3; powdered skim milk, 6; full-fat, heat-treated soy flour, 10; potato flour from cooked potatoes, 41; cooked breakfast cereal (corn flakes, shredded wheat, or puffed rice), 10; powdered eggs, 10.5; sugar, 12; salt, 2.5; alfalfa-leaf meal, 0.5; human-grade, low-F bone meal, 1.5; irradiated yeast, 1/2,000 of weight of the dry mixture. From time to time some ground meat and fat were cooked and added to this mixture, which is low in fat. In addition, the children were given some fresh milk to drink and vitamin supplements to provide vitamin A and ascorbic acid.

A year of use has proved that this mixture is very satisfactory. The inclusion of the potato flour makes the mixture inexpensive and gives it a sticky consistency that improves the mechanics of feeding. Such mixtures can be improved greatly but this one forms an excellent starting point.

The fat-salvage program in mental hospitals developed from experiences of the Army and Navy during the last war. They found they could save substantial sums of money by rendering fat in their steam-jacketed kettles and then using this fat for frying or baking. Even tallows work very well as shortening in bread. Strongly flavored fats, such as those from ham, can be washed readily in the kettle with water while the fats are in the melted state.

Fat salvage pays substantial dividends in money and better nutrition, since the amount saved allows each person the equivalent of a third to a half ounce of fat per day. If the diet is low in fat, this raises the level; if it is adequate, funds are released for the purchase of other special foods such as low-fat, dry, ice-cream mixes.

These few instances demonstrate that every institution feeding the aged can improve its program regularly if it takes advantage and makes use of advances in knowledge of food technology and nutrition.

The diet consumed by the average old person in a special hospital established for older people is indicated in the data of Rackow shown in Table 30 (16); for comparison are included some of the data gathered by Pyke in the almshouses of England (15). Unfortunately, this special hospital established for undisturbed senile patients had to be turned back to the Armed Services at the beginning of 1951. This study of segregation and improvement of the nutrition of the older patient had to be abandoned by New York State.

Improvements cannot be the same throughout the nation because budgets differ and even available food supplies are not identical. Thus some states are obliged to use locally grown soft wheats in their bread. Such states cannot use the same bread formulas as states that employ hard wheat flours because the low-protein, soft

TABLE 30.—ESTIMATES OF NUTRIENTS CONSUMED BY OLDER PEOPLE

	Rackow		Pyke		
Nutrients	Men	Women	Women	Men	Women
Calories	2,653.00	2,103.00	1,434.0	2,160.0	1,316.0
Protein (g.m.)	90.00	68.00	68.0	107.0	75.0
Fat (g.m.)	93.00	76.00	24.0	69.0	91.0
Carbohydrates (g.m.)* ...	364.00	287.00	...	...	...
Calcium (g.m.)	1.07	0.87	0.5	0.8	0.6
Phosphorus (g.m.)*	1.60	1.22	...	...	...
Iron (m.g.)	18.00	13.00	8.0	15.0	7.0
Vitamin A (I.U.)	8,932.00	5,143.00	2,500.0	3,600.0	1,450.0
Vitamin B$_1$ (m.g.)	1.90	1.20	0.7	1.4	0.8
Riboflavin (m.g.)	2.50	1.80	0.8	1.3	0.9
Niacin (m.g.)	17.40	12.70	7.0	16.0	7.0
Vitamin C (m.g.)	76.00	65.00	12.0	33.0	16.0
Vitamin D (I.U.)	....	....	74.0	90.0	101.0

* Not given in Pyke's data.

wheat products cannot be combined with the same level of nonglutinous supplements such as soy flour or dry milk.

IV. BETTER NUTRITION THROUGH COMMUNITY ACTION

The improvement of the nutrition of older people in communities of a half million or less has proved feasible. No one has demonstrated that this is possible in the largest cities. In all communities, the older folks are cared for either in private homes or in institutions such as nursing homes or county farms. Part of these people are public charges, part have independent means, and part are supported by families.

Progressive community action in providing better nutrition for older people divides itself into three areas.

Leadership by nutritionists.—In the first place, the nutrition specialists of the region must provide determined, practical, imaginative, courageous, and continuous leadership over long periods of time. The nutrition specialist who sits in his ivory tower, refuses to contaminate his daily life with practical matters, but offers pearls of wisdom mixed with contempt to his fellow men, creates little respect for his specialty. Furthermore, active leadership forces the nutritionists to take definite stands which are often contrary to special interests that back given food products because of financial profit, without regard to the effect of these products upon the health of the people.

Food marketing.—The second important factor in providing better foods involves assistance from those who operate groceries, food markets, bakeries, and meat shops. These people need education and assistance in marketing products of special merit that are not backed by national advertising. Often the poorer the nutritive value of a product, such as hard liquor or soft drinks, the greater the margin of profit that can be invested in national advertising.

In contrast to a century ago, few foodstuffs are manufactured today in the area in which they are eaten. Bread and baked goods afford an exception and these products play a special role in the nutrition of older people, as indicated previously. Every community can improve its bread and baked goods by concerted action on the part of the housewives. In some areas the smaller bakers assume the leadership in this field. In one small city the baker not only bakes the best products he can, but he also grinds his own whole-wheat flour and sells bread ingredients to housewives who desire to do home baking.

One of the greatest advances toward better baked goods has started in some cities. Bakers are being encouraged and in some cases obliged by housewives to state the amounts of ingredients on the wrappers. This has long been done in various parts of the nation in the case of feeds for livestock. Someone has remarked that this is one reason the farmer does a better job of feeding his stock than he does in providing for his children. He knows what he feeds his pig if he reads the label but he cannot tell what his bread contains unless his wife bakes it.

Open-formula bread and foods make it possible for the housewife to judge relative merits of products. A bread containing two or three per cent of milk or even none may taste nearly as good as a bread containing wheat germ, soy flour, and milk, but it has much less value. Open-formula labels on products such as bread guarantee the nutritive value of foods eaten by the aged. Competition under a condition of open-formula labeling forces improvement because the intelligent housewife will select a high-milk bread in preference to a low one if she knows what she is buying. Secret formulas encourage low-grade ingredients because the cheapest possible substances are employed in the interests of competitive advantage.

To get high-quality special foods offered for sale, housewives must arrange with one or more stores and then trade at those places. If storekeepers are left stranded with special products on their shelves such as dry skim milk they lose money and soon fail to co-operate with local enthusiasts for better foods.

In some cities that have active co-operative stores, as in New Haven, Connecticut, many special products are sold—dark molasses and sugar, whole-wheat and unbleached white flour, dry yeast, wheat germ, and other products such as dry skim milk. Such stores render service to the whole community and especially to the older people who must have high quality in their low-calorie diets.

Marketing is very important in providing better foods in communities. Thus, in areas in which milk is sold from dispensing machines, it has been found that the sale of soft drinks from a neighboring machine is reduced to one-third its volume, especially if the community has had an active educational campaign of teaching the relative merits of soft drinks and milk.

Community education and nutrition of the older people.—A continuous education program within communities probably affects the children and the intelligent older people more than any other groups. Many older people have become aware that the years of life are limited. They desire health. Therefore, they are seeking to learn all they can about better foods. By way of contrast there is also a difficult segment of the older population, represented by the grouchy old man who insisted that he have extra sugar from the relief worker during the rationing period of the war. Such people represent the least informed and the most difficult of the older group. They are often the most costly to the community, since they tend to find themselves partial invalids in nursing homes living at public expense.

Several organizations contribute very effectively to nutrition education in the communities of New York State, where the writer has had a quarter of a century of experience, though knowing little about nutrition education in other states.

Half of the population, or about seven million people living in the metropolitan area of New York City, are almost untouched by knowledge of modern nutrition except for that gained by reading in current magazines. The usual agencies that influence the rest of the state's population have little influence in this large urban area and are not considered in this discussion.

The housewives of most counties are the best informed of any group in nutrition knowledge, due largely to the long continued activities of the home bureaus. The leaders of the home bureaus are brought to the university regularly in order that they may keep up to date in their knowledge of foods and nutrition. The typical home-bureau agent is probably equal or ahead of the usual home-economics teacher in her knowledge of nutrition because of this regular training program. In New York State the women members of the home bureaus exceed a hundred thousand and these are usually the most intelligent citizens. They are widely dispersed and hence represent sources, throughout the entire state, of knowledge about better foods for older people.

In many smaller communities the local teachers of home economics are the most effective agents in teaching better nutrition in their communities. Part of this knowledge passes through the children to the older people and part is extended through outside activities of the teacher. A substantial fraction of knowledge in regard to foods also originates in the activities of 4-H clubs with specialized leaders in the field of foods.

In some areas the dentists play an important role in teaching better nutrition to both old and young. The dentist has an unusual opportunity since he comes in contact with all age groups.

Relief workers are in contact with a substantial group of older people but they seldom have specialized training in nutrition.

In some areas, as around Ithaca, the health agencies play a consistent role in spreading information about better nutrition. Thus the county health unit has a nutritionist who trains nurses and sets up nutrition exhibits in such places as the local co-operative grocery. Likewise, the Tuberculosis and Health Association, which is an old but active private agency supported by the sale of Christmas seals, carries on a modest but continuous nutrition program by providing a trained worker for the normal schools of the state and by local activities such as exhibits and special teachers in the country schools.

Many special food-producing agencies also promote special programs stressing their products but teaching the best in modern nutrition. Thus the dairy industry employs a group of well-trained nutritionists for such a purpose. Likewise, the co-operative grocery stores usually conduct continuous educational programs teaching the public how to select and buy to best advantage from the point of view of nutrition.

During wartime, state and county nutrition committees play an active role; but after the war, when rationing is past, they tend to disappear or enter semihibernation.

These agencies that participate in nutrition education are little recognized but play important roles in helping the older people select and obtain better foods.

V. SPECIAL FOODS FOR OLDER PEOPLE

Milk is probably the most important food for older people. Fortunately, in this nation some form of milk is available that fits most tastes and all purses. Whole milk is nearly a complete food. When pasteurized it is low in vitamin C. It lacks four trace elements, namely, iron, copper, manganese, and iodine. Enough of these are readily obtained in most other natural foods such as whole-wheat flour, liver, or eggs. If whole milk is considered too expensive when fresh, it can usually be bought cheaper as evaporated milk or as a powder.

Hundreds of combinations of whole milk are possible. Many are unique. One writer of well-known books, in her years past 70, lived mostly upon whole milk soured by the addition of the juice of two lemons to each quart. For those who prefer soured milks this mixture is pleasing. Likewise, tomato juice and milk blend well.

Since the days of Metchnikoff and his work on the prolongation of life, issued forty years ago, the popular enthusiasm for soured milks has waxed and waned. Soured milks afford valuable foods for older people since they are often made from dry skim milk and hence are low in calories but rich in calcium, lactose, and protein. These milks are much used in the Scandinavian countries.

The problems of senility and the use of these soured milks have been discussed by Danish workers (14) who are familiar with the problems. They conclude that such products as yogurt alone cannot transform the microorganisms of the intestinal tract because the bacteria present in such soured milks are destroyed by the acid of the gastric juice. However, they believe that soured milks are very worth while for older people. They advise the use for breakfast of both soured milks and whole milk or some product rich in lactose, in order to replace the putrefactive organisms of the large intestine. These Danish workers believe the decline in the acidity of the gastric juice of many older people permits the passage of proteins into the intestine without the customary digestion in the stomach. Furthermore, they believe milk is especially wholesome for older people because the proteins of milk do not putrefy as easily as those of products such as meat and fish.

Soured milks can be prepared in every home without difficulty. The cheapest are made from dry skim milk suspended in water. Cultures for making such soured milks are sold by many companies. Furthermore, a product such as yogurt can be purchased and used for making more of the product, thus serving to provide the culture of bacteria. Some families carry no milk with them when they go to their summer homes in out-of-the-way areas. They take a liberal supply of dry skim milk and some culture. From this they make their own "buttermilk," and do not have to labor with home pasteurization of questionable milk.

Dry skim milk is one of the bargain foods in America. It has about twice the protein value of meat as well as liberal amounts of minerals and vitamins. Older people who cannot afford whole milk, eggs, and meat can buy this form of milk. It can be used in baked goods and in many mixtures such as hot chocolate. The U.S. Department of Agriculture issues a bulletin on the use of dry milks (21).

The mental hospitals of New York State use more than a million pounds of dry skim milk per year in bread and other recipes. Skim milk is one of the most useful products for older people. However, large amounts of it are still wasted even in the United States. In some areas such as New Zealand it is estimated that enough milk is thrown away each year to manufacture several hundred millions of pounds of dry skim milk. This represents an unfortunate wastage against the interests of the old and young in many lands.

The question is often raised concerning the relative food value of milk and other human foods. Many tables are available showing such values. One of the least expensive can be purchased from the Superintendent of Documents, Washington, D.C. for ten cents (20).

A few older people cannot tolerate milk because of allergy, and must seek supplements of calcium, protein, and vitamins elsewhere. In many nations the bones of fish provide useful minerals. The heads of large fish are cooked until soft so the bones can be eaten.

Minnows are dried and eaten whole, as sardines are in some areas such as the Philippines. Salmon bones are usually eaten in this country.

Special bone meals are prepared and available in powder form by drying the bones of calves, which are low in fluorine. This bone meal can be kept on the table in salt shakers or sugar bowls. A half teaspoon per day affords a liberal supplement of calcium as well as phosphorus and some protein. Newer developments are in progress in the crushing of whole fresh bones which may soon make them very useful in soup. Some of the calcium of bone goes into solution in such foods as pickled pigs' feet. In some parts of the world the shells of eggs are dissolved in vinegar and thus consumed.

Some plant foods such as sesame contain substantial amounts of calcium. Sesame seeds are staple articles of diet in many areas. Such seeds should be eaten without removal of the husks because these contain the calcium. Sesame is a cheap food in America and can be used in many baked products such as cookies and doughnuts.

Many plant products—soybean flour, almonds, dandelions, and other foodstuffs—provide substantial amounts of calcium. Other rich products can be discovered by the use of the common tables.

Many excellent proteins can also be obtained from plant sources such as soy flour, wheat germ, corn germ, rice cereals, potatoes, and dry yeast (10). Centuries of human experience have demonstrated the value of the proteins in these products. Numerous studies with rats and other species have confirmed this experience and have formed a rational background in formulating combinations of these proteins.

Soy flour is outstanding in value and especially useful in supplementing wheat protein. Hence it is very useful in all types of bread. The optimum level is about six per cent in baked goods such as bread, cookies, and doughnuts. Many people have learned to use whole, sprouted soy beans in such dishes as chop suey. In the course of sprouting, the soy bean undergoes changes that make it require very little cooking. In some parts of the world such as Java, the changes are effected by the use of molds acting for a day or two. Products similar to cheese and easily assimilated by man are thus produced.

The germs of grains, like wheat and corn, can be eaten as breakfast cereal or combined in baked goods. These germ products are inexpensive but rich in vitamins, minerals, and protein. Some excellent white flours are left unbleached and have the wheat germ ground back into them as part of the milling process.

The protein level of both rice and potatoes is relatively low but masses of people subsist upon these products with little other food. For three centuries the peoples of Ireland, Poland, Wales, and many other parts of the world have derived both energy and protein from the potato. In most cases the supplemental foods have consisted of buttermilk with a little fish and meat. The long history of the use of the white potato attests to its value (17). Human experience as well as a substantial amount of animal testing have indicated the high value of the protein of rice.

Cereal proteins such as those from wheat and rye are cheap but need to be supplemented with soy, milk, yeast, or germ proteins.

Dry yeast is a unique food that is coming into modern use. In olden times men drank yeast suspended in beer and the bakery was often located near the brewery since the former drew its supply of live yeast from the latter. In modern times much yeast is dried after it is removed from making beer. A pound of dry yeast is produced from every hundred gallons of beer. Yeast is very rich in all water-soluble vitamins except B_{12}. It contains about twice as much protein as meat and this protein is a very good supplement for wheat proteins. Thus bread containing six per cent has high protein value.

Dry yeast is an inexpensive food as it leaves the producer, at a price of about thirty cents per pound. When sold in pound units by grocers it is retailed at about twice this price, or substantially less than meat.

Yeast is commonly eaten on pancakes or waffles when combined with syrup. Some is eaten on ice cream since it has a nutty flavor. Many people cook it with meat-flavored dishes, or bake it into cookies and bread. Some people keep yeast in the powdered form on their tables in a sugar bowl, and use it as their tastes demand.

Some yeast is eaten by older diabetics in order to diminish their use of insulin. Others drink a spoon of yeast suspended in water a half hour before meals in order to reduce their appetite and avoid obesity. Many find the use of one or two teaspoons of yeast daily helps avoid constipation. A few older people cannot consume dry yeast because they are subject to gout and believe the purines of yeast are injurious.

Some claims have been made that the yeast nucleoproteins have special merit for individuals who cannot synthesize them readily. These claims are not adequately founded, however.

The problem of adequate bulk in the diet and the prevention of constipation is very important for older people. Some cannot tolerate the fiber in dark breads such as those made from rye or whole wheat; others thrive upon whole cereal products. Individuals must make their own decisions.

Potato skins, apple peelings, and fruits such as prunes, raisins, dates, and figs, have long been useful in maintaining the functioning of the intestines. Many fruits—apples, for example—are also valuable because they contain pectin. Some other products promise to come into wider future use. The rinds of citrus like orange and grapefruit deserve more extensive trials since they contain pectin as well as vitamin C.

Marmalades retaining this vitamin can be made, although most commercial products destroy it by cooking. Likewise, the tomato pulp which remains when the juice is expressed is a very useful product in maintenance of functioning of the intestines. This so-called "tomato pomace" is widely used for this purpose in commercial dog feeds but not in human diets. An increased consumption of raw canned tomatoes would prove worthwhile for many who tend to overcook canned tomatoes before they are eaten.

Older people need to reduce their consumption of sugar but when they use sweetening they will find brown sugar and dark molasses to contain some essentials such as iron.

In modern times much discussion has been devoted to the reduction in the use of vitamin-rich foods such as liver, eggs, butter, and cream by older people. These have been deleted from many dietaries because thes foods contain substantial amounts of cholesterol. The human body can make cholesterol. Fats, even those of vegetable origin that contain no cholesterol, cause the blood to increase in fatty fractions such as true fats, phospholipids, and sterols. The evidence is too imperfect to justify cessation in the use of such valuable foods as those that contain cholesterol on the grounds that they may help older individuals avoid arteriosclerosis (8).

Some milks are now being prepared by removing the butter fat and substituting a vegetable fat for it. Such products are more economical than whole milk becaues vegetable fats are cheaper than cream, but they cannot be justified, on the basis of existing evidence, to keep the blood cholesterol at a low level. All evidence points in the opposite direction.

In summarizing briefly the nutritional needs for older people, one can subscribe to many of the older rules, like the need for drinking adequate water and the prevention of constipation. As a general rule, the use of sugar, soft drinks, hard liquors, refined flour, and white fats should be severely restricted. Liberal use of milk products and many special natural foods will insure an adequate amount of protein and minerals as well as vitamins. There is no sound evidence that the average person should not make moderate use of coffee, tea, beer, and other common beverages. Individuals may always differ from the average, however. Many special products such as dried milks, wheat germ, dry yeast, and dark molasses may fit the needs of various people. The evidence against foods rich in cholesterol is not adequate today to justify restriction in the use of eggs, liver, and cream in the diet of older people. Moderation in food consumption and the avoidance of obesity are twin essentials; and moderate exercise usually stimulates better nutrition.

REFERENCES

1. Albright, F., and Reifenstein, E. C. *Parathyroid Glands and Metabolic Bone Diseases*. Baltimore: Williams & Wilkins Co., 1948
2. Beall, K. H. "Pellagra," in Osler and McCrae, *Modern Medicine*, Vol. 2, p. 472
3. Chieffi, M., and Kirk, J. E. "Vitamin Studies in Middle Aged and Old Individuals," *J. Gerontol.*, 1950, 5: 326
4. Cornaro, L. *The Art of Living Long*. Milwaukee: Wm. F. Butler, 1903
5. Cowdry, E. V. *Problems of Ageing* (2d edition). Baltimore: Williams & Wilkins Co., 1942
6. Davis, Adele. *Let's Cook It Right*. New York: Harcourt, Brace and Co., 1947
7. Harris, H. F. *Pellagra* (New York: The MacMillan Co., 1911), p. 177
8. Keys, Ancel. "The Relation in Man Between Cholesterol Levels in the Diet and in the Blood," *Science*, 1950, 112: 79
9. Kountz, W. B., Hofstatter, L., and Ackermann, P. "Nitrogen Balance Studies in Elderly People," *Geriatrics*, 1947, 2: 173
10. McCay, C. M. "Increasing the Use of Plant Proteins," *Federation Proceedings*, 1944, 3: 129

11. ———. "What the Consumer Should Know About Bread." *J. Home Ec.*, 1949, 41: 179

12. ———. "Diet and Aging," *Vitamins and Hormones*, 1949, 7: 147

13. Ohlson, M. A., Jackson, L., Boek, J., Cederquist, D. C., Brewer, W. D., and Brown, E. C. "Nutrition and Dietary Habits of Aging Women," *Am. J. Pub. Health*, 1950, 40: 1101

14. Orla-Jensen, S., Olsen, E., and Geill, G. "Senility and Intestinal Flora," *J. Gerontol.*, 1949, 4: 5

15. Pyke, M., Harrison, R., Holmes, S., and Chamberlain, K. "Nutritional Value of Diets Eaten by Older People in London," *Lancet*, 1947, p. 461

16. Rackow, J. R. "A Dietary Study of Four Hundred Elderly Patients in a New York State Mental Hospital." Unpublished Master's thesis, Cornell University, 1950

17. Salaman, R. N. *History and Social Influence of the Potato.* Cambridge: Cambridge Press, 1948

18. Sinclair, J. *The Code of Health and Longevity* (6th edition). London, 1844

19. Sorter, H., Berg, M., and Mecheles, H. "Constipation in the Aged. Attempts at Therapy," *J. Gerontology*, 1949, 4: 121

20. Swickard, M. T. *Tables of Food Composition*, U.S. Department of Agriculture, Misc. Publication No. 572, Washington, D.C., 1949

21. ———. *How to Use Whole and Nonfat Dry Milk*, U.S. Department of Agriculture Bulletin AIS-86, Washington, D.C., 1950

22. Vinther-Paulsen, N. "Investigation of the Actual Food Intake of Elderly Chronically Hospitalized Patients," *J. Gerontol.*, 1950, 5: 331

23. Zeman, F. D. "Life's Later Years. Studies in the Medical History of Old Age, Roman Attitudes and Opinions," *J. Mt. Sinai Hosp.*, 1945, 11: 300

Chapter VIII

NEUROSES OF LATER MATURITY

Norman Cameron

Among the clinical disorders of later life the neuroses occupy a conspicuous place. This fact is hardly surprising when one considers what fundamentally important problems are raised for the aging person by his biological involution and the frustrations with which our culture burdens him. What is really surprising is that the subject is virtually ignored by contemporary psychopathology and psychiatry. For although the incidence of neurotic reactions in later maturity is high in comparison with deteriorative psychoses of the presenium and senium, the latter are given a relatively huge proportion of attention in current psychiatric journals, monographs, textbooks, and lecture courses. One important result of this is that the average graduating physician, nurse, or social worker almost invariably looks upon neurotic manifestations appearing in late senescence at once as signs of inevitable decay, about which no more can be done for the patient than to render him quiet and reasonably comfortable.

This attitude of therapeutic nihilism is of course based upon ignorance. There is actually no more justification for dismissing neurotic reactions in aging persons as simply the beginnings of brain decay than there is for regarding gastric dysfunction, without further study, as early carcinoma. In neither instance can anyone afford to overlook such a possibility; but in the very great majority of cases neither suspicion is confirmed. There is nothing radically different about the neurotic patterns one finds in later maturity. What modifications they do show can be attributed to the characteristics of biological aging and to the peculiar status given to the senescent and normal senile by our society. The same general mechanisms are present that operate in the neuroses of early maturity. They respond to the same general therapeutic procedures; and there is good reason to believe that by appropriate preventive measures their severity, their duration, and even their incidence may be materially reduced.

201

A. THE DYNAMICS OF NEUROSES IN LATER MATURITY

The neuroses of senescence and senility represent patterns of inadequate and unsuccessful attempts at adaptation to personal difficulties, just as do the neuroses appearing in earlier periods of life. Although we have insufficient data upon which to base a final statement, it is probable that most aging persons who develop neurotic reactions have shown similar maladaptations under stress when younger. Certainly for many of them, as their histories show, the neurosis is only a continuation of earlier inadequate behavior with some increase in severity and with modifications in the pattern that grow out of changes in their total situation. In some persons, particularly in those who have tasted lifelong success in dominating others or in being more or less the center of attention, the neurosis comes as a reaction of disappointment and frustration over their altered circumstances and as something quite new in their life. But, regardless whether or not there is a background of periodic or of continuous maladaptation, the presence of disturbing neurotic behavior in the aging calls for a study of all the antecedent and existing factors that may be responsible, whether these be in the person's biological status, in his changed environmental relationships, or in his personal reactions to the role of the oldster which he is called upon to play. As a rule it will be found that each of these ingredients enters into the formula for producing neurotic maladjustment in later life.

I. BIOLOGICAL FACTORS

The human machine normally begins to slow down long before it shows signs of wearing out. Miles (32) has summarized psychological research in this field, establishing beyond a doubt the fact that, as the average person moves into and beyond the forties and fifties he undergoes a gradually accelerating decline in the speed and precision of motor performance, of perception, and of learning and immediate recall. Sensory acuity eventually suffers in all spheres. Neural and humoral co-ordinations, muscular and secretory responses are apt to show some decrement in efficiency. The somatic musculature begins to fatigue more easily and to recover more slowly after exertion. Tonic and phasic action becomes less steady and less well co-ordinated. Ultimately there is increasingly obvious atrophy of muscle and bone which, together with the gradual reduction in subcutaneous and retrobulbar fat, results in the characteristic form, posture, and facies of the aging and the aged. The skin also undergoes progressive change, becoming less elastic, more creased and folded, drier, discolored, and usually marked with pigment deposits, keratoses, or xanthomata. The hair loses its pigmentation and grows sparse or disappears from the head. Changes in the viscera, with increasing age, are much less visible than skeletal and surface changes; but they are certainly no less important in reducing the general competence of the organism. Visceral musculature tends normally to grow less active, to atrophy, and, particularly in the blood vessels, to lay down calcium deposits which make it less and less responsive to the demands of sudden or prolonged increases in organic activity. The glands undergo involutionary atrophies and troublesome compensatory hypertrophies. To all these changes must be added the major and minor pathological changes which everyone picks up through accidents, disease, and repair processes as he runs his age course.

It is a mistake to belittle the significance to the aging person of these inescapable signs of decline and to overemphasize the fact that they can be and frequently are compensated for through other abilities and through deliberate shifts into other channels of gratification. It is doubtful whether any normal man or woman welcomes them; and for most individuals they necessitate fundamental and often very difficult re-orientations which are not carried through equally well by all. In this chapter we are primarily concerned, not with the happy and successful, but with that not inconsiderable minority of persons who fail to meet effectively the unwelcome challenge of biological waning and who, in the course of trying to work out their solutions, fall back upon or develop anew some pattern of maladaptation. These maladaptive reactions we call neuroses.

In senescence and senility the biological factors that seem to cause most difficulty in adaptation are: in men, the general decrease in strength, skill, and endurance, and the waning of sexual prowess; in women, the progressive loss of attractiveness, which may itself lead to a pessimistic neglect of personal appearance (Barker, 3), and the onset of infertility. Of cardinal importance in both men and women are also their reactions to any reduction in drives and gratifications, common visceral dysfunctions that may be harm-

less in themselves but suggest to the person a threat of illness, invalidism, and death, suspicions of neoplasms, deforming and disabling changes, and any serious impairment of hearing or vision
that tends progressively to exclude them from active participation
in the affairs of others and increases their painful sense of isolation. Our information concerning the relative importance of these
dynamic factors in later life neuroses is still too meager and im-
pressionistic to warrant our setting up a finalistic formulation. In
general, for a given individual the importance of one or another
biological impairment, or of his anticipation of it, will be in part
determined by the relative significance it possessed in his earlier
life and by the degree to which his personal status, security, and
gratifications have been tied up with it.

Strength and endurance.—Although the reduction in strength
and endurance in senescence is usually very gradual, one's realization of it may come quite abruptly as the result of illness, injury,
cumulative fatigue, or some unexpected failure in competition with
younger persons. Not infrequently an individual's recognition that
he is not what he used to be follows some bit of friendly caution
or ridicule, or results from an unexpected show of special consideration by the young. It may arise out of a casual conversation on
the subject, followed afterward by some rumination, or from reading and listening to ghoulish patent-medicine advertising. Maladaptations to decreasing vigor and endurance usually take one of
two opposite directions. The aging person may give up too easily
and too completely, perhaps justifying this course by complaints
of fatigability, weakness, nervousness, incapacity, and visceral disorder. On the other hand, he may refuse to accept his actually
changing biological status and attempt to demonstrate to others and
himself that he is just as good as ever, which of course he is not.
Most commonly this protest takes the form of mere rationalization
with tiresome insistence upon his competence, often tinged with
resentment toward the younger generation.

A more aggressive rejection of biological aging leads to generally increased effort and to energetic overcompensatory activities
that tend in time to wear the person down and eventually compel
him to give up, instead of merely slowing up (36). During the
overcompensatory energetic phase there often develops a state of
tense anxiety in which the striving individual grows restless, sleep-

less, and irritable, and may resort to alcohol for both support and relaxation. When these protesting persons finally give up the struggle, they too are apt to fall back upon hypochondriacal complaints, utilizing their quite genuine fatigue or some physiological component of their tension state, such as a minor visceral disorder, headache, or inappetence. A patient of the writer's, referred from neurosurgery after ventriculography, whose chief presenting symptoms had been headache, diplopia, and disturbed sleep, complained repeatedly of "getting old," of being unable to "take the punishment any more," and of having many "physical ailments," although actually he was but 44 years of age, in good general health, and only moderately presbyopic. On the neurosurgical service he had expressed genuine disappointment and disbelief when told that he was not to have a brain operation; he had previously accepted a tentative diagnosis of brain tumor as the satisfactory explanation for his inability to keep up his earlier pace. He was a civil servant who had for several years been striving without success to advance himself rapidly and had recently succumbed to the fatiguing struggle. Unaware of the possibilities presented by a brain tumor, he had felt relieved by the diagnosis and quite hopeful that an operation would restore his vigor.

Some middle-aged enthusiasts whose bodily vigor has always been their pride adopt rigorous physical-culture routines when it begins to diminish. What then appears to be only a strong interest in health may turn out actually to have its roots in an anxious attempt to deny to themselves their inescapable decline in physique, or at least to delay its progress.

Attractiveness.—In women especially the principal emphasis is apt to be less upon strength and endurance and more upon the retention of youthful appearance and liveliness. For upon the preservation of these assets may to some extent depend their success in holding the affection and respect of their immediate relatives and friends. Youth, comeliness, and fertility are among a woman's strongest means of gaining and holding a privileged and secure status. Hence their fading may be reacted to by her, not without justification, as a serious personal threat. When a woman's direct attempts to cover up the signs of aging by cosmetic and other devices fail, she may slip into complaints of fatigue, malaise, and disorders of the reproductive, gastrointestinal, and cardiovascular systems. This she can do even more easily than the male because of the greater familiarity she has gained with visceral discomfort and indisposition through the menses, pregnancy, and child-bearing, and because of the generally indulgent attitude that prevails in our culture toward sickness and weakness in the female. If these complaints succeed in bringing back some of the attention and consideration which the woman had formerly earned through her attractiveness and charm, they are likely to become unintentionally organized into fixed neurotic patterns. Even when they fail in this respect, they may persist because they provide her with a focus for self-interest and a plausible explanation to others and herself of her loss in affection and prestige. To some men, also, the loss of a youthful appearance, particularly through baldness and obesity, raises problems touching upon their prestige, economic security, and sources of gratification to which some react with body over-concern or neurotic depression.

Sex life.—A great and unnecessary hardship has been visited upon many elderly men and women by the traditional demand that all human beings, as they grow old, shall also grow asexual. Miles (32) believes that, in general, society has built up a "convention of expectation" with respect to drive and capacity in later maturity on the basis of the normal individual's balance between them. This may be true of other drives; but in the sexual field it seems also to be derived from one ancient prejudice identifying sex with sin and another denying the right of sinning to elderly men and women. These prejudices do not square with the well-known fact that some persons suffer little reduction in sexual ability up to an advanced age, and with at least the casual evidence at hand to indicate that most persons retain some personal sex interest almost to the end of their lives. The social stereotype of the sexless normal senile has its counterpart in the stereotype of the sexless normal child which Freud and his disciples have done so much to dethrone.

Although decline of the sex life may refuse to follow the curve of conventional expectation, it does undergo a progressive reduction during senescence. Hamilton (17) found "usually a marked reduction in potency" among his clinical patients during their fifth and sixth decades. There is, however, greater variability reported for sex activity throughout maturity than in many other functions

(Pearl, 34). Reactions to a declining sex life are most varied. A common aggressive attempt at compensation is that of stepping up the level of sexual behavior and indulging in sex adventures, the goal of which is to gain reassurance as to one's general sexual competence. Revenge against what are felt to be critical and belittling attitudes on the part of spouse or children frequently enters into the motivation; and failing social compensations and rewards in other spheres of activity may also be involved. More than one senescent person has been launched upon an ill-advised adventure by a sudden feeling that life is slipping away. This motive seems to be commoner among women than among men. Such active protests in middle and later life often lay one open to further hazards. If, as is very likely to be the case, the aggressor fails to live up to the expectations of his respondent, or fails to derive the return he had anticipated, he is sure to suffer an intensification of his sense of inadequacy and to invite serious retaliations. Family opinion and public opinion are very sure of what one has a right to demand of older people and very severe when these demands are flouted. When in these circumstances a sexual misadventure befalls the elderly person, the threat he anticipates of failure, ostracism, or social retaliation is likely to light up in him the fear, guilt, anxiety, and remorse to which he has long been conditioned; and these in turn may lead to neurotic patterns of anxiety, hypochondria, compulsion, or depression.

Another aggressive reaction to the biological and social restrictions laid upon sexual behavior in later life takes the form of active resentment toward its manifestations in others. The maladjusted senescent may then join the ranks of the morally indignant in crusades against or gossip about the depravity of modern times. This solution can solve the personal problem by providing constant preoccupation with sex without arousing guilt. But it is very hard on the community, and sometimes leads to needless distortions of its social life. Other substitute avenues of more personal domination and attention-getting are followed by many. These range all the way from compensatory aggression in business and professional life to the more disguised aggressions of hypochondriacal complaints of illness and demands upon one's spouse and offspring for care and attention, which, if successful, hold them under neurotic domination.

Equally important in the dynamics of later life neuroses are
the more passive reactions to sexual decline; and among these none
is more prevalent than fantasy. When they are visited by sex pri-
vation and frustration which they are unable to overcome, the aging
and aged resort to sexual fantasies for their gratification just as
they once did in childhood and adolescence and as normal mature
persons usually do during enforced deprivation. The tensions thus
built up they also may relieve through autoerotic and pregenital
measures (Hamilton, 17). If this sequence comforts the lonely,
unhappy, misunderstood oldster, as it comforted him earlier in his
life course, it is likely to persist as a solution. Unfortunately, even
without the help of others, he is likely also to be revisited by the
conflicts formerly attached to such behavior. Each indulgence in
forbidden fantasies, with or without recourse to autoerotism, may
be followed by increased anxiety and a deepened sense of unworthiness and inadequacy. Such a cycle favors the development of
anxiety states, reactive depressions, and, secondarily, compulsions
and chronic complaints of fatigue. Autoerotism also leads in some
persons to hypochondriacal concern, especially over the reproductive organs, but over other systems as well.

Vision and hearing.—The fading of vision or hearing not only
robs a person of a large share of pleasure and diversion but also
tends to isolate him from participation in the activities of his social
group. Such *social disarticulation* (9, 10) may seriously reduce
the effectiveness of an individual's personality organization at any
age. One's opinions and attitudes remain appropriate to those of
the real community only if sufficient interchange is kept up through
effective communication with one's social environment. Partial
isolation, particularly when it eliminates the daily conversation of
others, encourages misunderstandings and misinterpretations on
both sides which usually require a great deal of patience and for-
bearance to correct. The half-deaf and half-blind are notoriously
given to suspicion; and suspicion makes few friends when one is
old, fretful, and unhappy. If suspicions go uncorrected, they tend
to build upon themselves. The real motives of the real community
become distorted into the imagined motives of a hostile or indifferent pseudo-community (Cameron, 11). The loss of emotional support which such social disarticulation entails leaves the isolated
elderly person with increased anxieties, fear, and discouragement.

Occasionally sensory impairment actually reduces the severity of old neurotic reactions, and particularly in persons chronically oversensitive to noise and light.

To a somewhat lesser degree the partial isolation imposed upon aging or aged persons by deformities and disfigurement tends to arouse neurotic conflicts. These accidents diminish their opportunities for active participation in the activities of their family group and community, increase their sense of loneliness and uselessness, and make them more than ever dependent upon the good will of others. Normal communication with others is not, however, as seriously disturbed as with partial deafness or blindness.

Visceral dysfunction.—Body overconcern does not arise in senescence and senility merely because a person is idle, disaffected, or lonesome. Normal old organs are seldom as efficient as they were in their prime, and this in itself may indirectly increase one's sense of insecurity. For when older viscera are subjected to prolonged or sudden strain they do not meet the emergency as well as they once did, and they take longer to recover equilibrium. The little and usually unimportant dysfunctions that appear are experienced by the patient as changes which call attention to themselves. It is then not difficult for an already anxious, discontented, or inactive person to build up secondarily the habit of watching and complaining about them. Anxiety, insecurity, and discontent with life become anxiety, worry, and dissatisfaction over visceral performance. These reactions themselves in turn add their own contributions to the visceral disturbance and the stage is set for hypochondria. If such a pattern has been built up earlier in life, in response to disappointment and apprehension, it is so much the more likely to reappear in later life. On some such basis may also develop the hypochondriacal but not irrational fear of neoplasms with their threat of suffering and invalidism.

The brain.—Wide differences of opinion are current regarding the role of the brain in the behavior disorders of later life. Kahn (19) regards the onset of cerebral impairment in old age as crucial, in that it breaks the previous continuity of the personality and brings bewilderment, despair, loneliness, and isolation to the aging person. Rothschild (39), working on senile dementia, has been unable to find any exact correlation between the intensity of clinical symptoms and the severity of post-mortem findings. He attributes this lack of correspondence to differences in the capacity of different individuals to compensate for their cerebral damage.

The question of cerebral impairment has an important, though indirect, bearing upon the neuroses of later life. Considered as a co-ordinative organ, the brain plays an indispensable role in our complex behavior. Impairment of its efficiency by any means is known to reduce the general competence of the human organism in its social environment. In late senescence and senility the modern human being is called upon to meet environmental situations that would tax the adaptability of even young adults—social restrictions, reductions in security, and declining usefulness, significance, and regard. When cerebral impairment develops to the point where, for example, new learning and immediate recall are noticeably difficult, the aging person, unless his surroundings are unusually kind and helpful, is likely to develop reactions of inadequacy, insecurity, and dejection, attitudes which favor the appearance or reappearance of neurotic manifestations. Compensatory mechanisms that have successfully held earlier neurotic trends in check are then no longer able to operate with the necessary effectiveness.

It is well known that neuroses appear or reappear in senescence and senility without any signs of impairment in cerebral function, and clear up again or greatly improve under appropriate therapy. The important question, therefore, is not whether the neuroses of later life are or are not dependent upon brain damage, but rather to what extent cerebral impairment may reduce the general competence of a person and so make him no longer able to handle his difficult environment or his own unresolved conflicts. Of course, if cerebrovascular disease produces focal neurological signs that discommode or worry the patient, these can operate in the same way that signs of trouble in any other important organ may, provoking anxiety, hypochondriacal fears, and depressive reactions.

Emotion.—What has been said concerning general cerebral functioning applies equally well to the signs of emotionality. It is as easy to minimize unduly the possibility of a histopathological component in the emotional reactions of later maturity as it is to exaggerate it. There is abundant clinical evidence that at any age, from childhood on, the after-effects of brain damage following head trauma or disease can adversely influence the mechanisms of emotional adaptation. The result is sometimes a permanently unstable emotional equilibrium, somewhat modifiable with training, but not entirely curable. The increased emotional lability of the otherwise normal senile seems also to be associated with central-nervous-system pathology, as well as with vascular and other visceral changes that render emotional equilibrium less steady and that delay a return to the midpoint once that equilibrium has been disturbed. There are wide individual variations within a given age group in this as in other biological changes.

Although it must be recognized that emotionality is more likely to suffer distortion in late senescence and senility than earlier in life, one must guard very carefully against the too common error of assuming at once that any emotional disturbance during this period is just a sign of parenchymatous degeneration or cerebro-vascular disease. Even though some emotional reactions in late maturity may be exaggerated, there is always some reason for their occurring at all. The lot of many elderly persons seems very hard to them—lonely, tired, loveless, and without hope. To those who have always depended heavily upon affection and a privileged status for their security and happiness, there is every reason to develop patterns of grief, anxiety, anger, resentment, and even mild panic when these melt away and an individual is for the first time in decades left out in the cold. A younger person with a completely normal brain, raised to expect a similar privileged position and emotional support, would show very similar responses if his preferred status were denied him. In either case the general reaction is of course to be considered not as normal but as neurotic. In the elderly person it is still neurotic and still potentially treatable, whether or not decline in the biological mechanisms allows the expressive responses to be exaggerated and prolonged.

General capacities.—In addition to the rather specific functions of the organism already discussed, its more general abilities, i.e., its more general interrelationships with the human environment, also appear to suffer impairment in most aging persons. With respect to later life neuroses two main questions present themselves here: (*a*) Are these reductions in general abilities themselves irreversible and irremediable? And, if they are, to what degree can they be compensated for in the over-all picture by other activities, attitudes, and sources of gratification? (*b*) To what extent should actual impairment of complex interpersonal functions be taken into account in recognizing, interpreting, and treating the neurotic and prepsychotic manifestations of later life, and ultimately in predicting and forestalling them? We are quite sure that certain complex abilities, e.g., new verbal and perceptual learning and immediate recall, become inferior in most aging persons. But, because of the intricate intertwining of restrictions on a biological basis with those imposed by social traditions and expectations, a great deal more careful observation and experiment will be necessary before clear distinctions can be made between the effects of one and the effects of the other.

In late life a person's ability to carry out even his usual work and other familiar activities is nearly always reduced (Allen, 1). On the basis of psychometric studies, Lorge (30) reported finding no gradual decline with age provided the data be corrected statistically for "the penalty of age," i.e., slowness, remoteness in time from schooling, disutility of some functions, etc. Although such corrected data have their usefulness, we cannot, in considering maladaptive developments, dismiss the influence of decline by thus analyzing it into its components and discounting these, unless they in turn are reversible and can somehow be eliminated from the patient's reactions. What counts in the genesis of neurotic symptoms is just this growing incapacity to cope with life situations because of the slowing down of the aging organism, its remoteness from early training, its lowered general adaptability, disuse and disinterest, the changes in sense organs, muscles, and glands, etc. Miles maintains that psychological factors in aging always depend to some degree upon physiological regression. The degree of psychological impairment depends in part upon the extent to which it involves perceptual speed and precision, muscular strength, swiftness, and the exactitude of gross movement. It is therefore least noticeable in interpretation and imagination. Wide individual differences are found within any group of functions in a given age group; and this is attributable to biological differences, variations in individual familiarity with and skill in certain activities, and the degree to which unimpaired functions are employed to compensate for impaired ones (32). Robbins advises that we regard senility as a normal physiological entity and not simply as pathological maturity (37). The implication of this attitude for the

neuroses is very fundamental. It means that neurotic manifestations appearing or increasing during senescence or senility must
be looked upon, at least in part, as the socially undesirable and
personally expensive reactions of an individual to the consequences
of a normal, expected physiological decline in general adequacy
and effectiveness. Cultural restrictions and personal factors also
enter into every one of these neurotic developments; but these will
be taken up later.

All who work with the aging and the aged are impressed by their
prevailing traits of general conservatism and resistance to change,
whether of routine, of arrangement, of manners and morals, or of
opinion. These trends are usually dismissed as simply "character
change" or are explained as the result of inadequately repressed
antisocial urges (17). The likelihood should not be overlooked,
however, that they may also represent a genuine disability resulting from irreversible organismic decline. Ruch (40) has concluded, on the basis of experimental evidence, that normal senile
and senescent persons find most difficulty with learning which demands a reorganization of old habits into new combinations. The
impersonal character of the problems he used indicates clearly
that this fairly specific difficulty appears in situations which can
hardly be suspected of arousing anxiety from inadequate repression.

In real life situations it seems more probable that many older
persons are biologically incapable of building up the new arrangements of their old habits which their changed circumstances demand, or are able to do so only with much greater effort and lessened gratification, which in turn engender irritability, bitterness,
dejection, and a sense of being ill-treated and unloved. The practical importance of the origin of conservatism and resistance to
change, in later maturity, lies in the decision as to what direction
one's therapeutic efforts shall take and how far they shall be carried. If a large proportion of older persons are biologically incapable of adapting successfully to certain kinds of novelty, and
this can be determined for the individual case, it is of little use to
attack the problem as primarily one of anxiety and inadequate repression. More of the attention and effort of the patient, the relatives, the social worker, and the therapist can then be focused upon
the development of greater tolerance toward such incapacity on all

sides and particularly on the part of the patient himself, and upon
exploring the possibilities of ameliorating its effects through introducing more flexibility into the environmental arrangements.
Malamud (31) questions the justice of regarding senescent changes
entirely as liabilities, and suggests that senescence might also be
able to provide useful assets if the prevailing social organization
were ready to utilize them.

In the clinical literature it is also usually taken for granted that
senescence is inescapably associated with a reduction in initiative
and a narrowing of interests, and that these are influential in neurotic developments. Such decrease in initiative and interests has
been attributed to fatigue, lost vigor, inadequate comprehension,
impaired learning, and forgetfulness on the basis of cerebral incompetence, or has been linked with inevitable egocentrism, selfishness, anxiety over perverse trends, and regression to pregenital
gratifications. There seems, however, to be some doubt as to the
presence of a genuine reduction in the range of interests with age.
Miles's report of Strong's study of interests in the aging and aged
(41) fails to support such an assumption; for, although interests
do shift with age, they do not seem to show a significant narrowing
in normal persons. It should be remembered that Strong's conclusions are based upon formal testing and that it is always possible
for a test to miss defects which show up unmistakably in real life
situations. The problem of interest and initiative is a very complex
one. Its clarification must await the accumulation of more objective evidence before we can decide how much of what we see clinically comes from biological decline and how much from cultural
restrictions and personal reactions.

II. CULTURAL FACTORS

Artificial as any distinction between organism and cultural
environment must always be, it serves here the useful purpose
of marking off (*a*) certain factors in the dynamics of neurotic development that depend more directly upon cultural attitudes and
social organization (*b*) from those already discussed, which arise
largely from the biological changes of involution. The process of
human aging is a matter not only of organismic decline but also of
change in social, economic, and dominance status. These latter can

be every bit as influential as involution in precipitating and sustaining maladaptive reactions, and very often they are even more so. In some respects the cultural sources of later-life neuroses offer greater hope for improvement than those based on involution. Biological decline can sometimes be delayed and often modified; but it is finally inescapable, and usually the best we can do is to work on the individual's personal attitudes toward it. Culturally determined restrictions and expectations, on the other hand, are at least potentially remediable. In practice, of course, they do not always turn out to be as modifiable as one might expect. Many cultural patterns that have to do with later maturity, including some of the most unreasonable and anachronistic ones, are extraordinarily resistant to change. They are very often quite oblivious to the wide differences one finds in individual needs and capacities, and particularly so to the vast majority of aging persons who happen to be neither rich nor highly talented.

Economic and social dependence.—The changes which the average senescent seems to dread most of all are the loss of independence and the loss of significance. It is quite inevitable that sooner or later one generation shall be superseded or displaced by the next in the active control and direction of affairs. For the large majority of older persons this carries with it the practical certainty of drastically reduced circumstances, and at least a threat of complete social and economic dependence upon others which, according to Piersol (35), is feared more than death itself. When such a prospect looms on the horizon of a habitually rather insecure individual it may initiate exaggerated reactions of anxiety, tension, fatigue, and dejection. His inner insecurity, as Kaufman (22) puts it, contributes to the threatening economic reality. The anticipation of a forced move from one's own home, for instance, to that of one's married offspring can scarcely be expected to have a reassuring effect. Kardiner (21) points out that the reversal of the former relationship between parent and child now gives the adult offspring his chance to gain revenge for the years of submission. Kardiner believes that his having to give up the role of dependent child and assume that of protector and provider increases the unemancipated adult offspring's resentment against his parent when the latter comes under his jurisdiction.

Neurotic reactions to the threat of social and economic dependence, or to its materialization, are not difficult to understand if one appreciates what this implies. It always means restriction and it often means distortion. The elderly person can no longer choose freely, make decisions and act, or decline to act. He must seek permissions, accept new distasteful compromises and experience reductions in gratification that often seem unnecessary as well as frustrating. A particularly serious consequence of dependence is that of involuntary relocation. Because of reduced circumstances and perhaps the loss of a marital partner, the aging person faces the necessity of stepping out of the established pattern of his own life and taking up an insecure position on the fringe of someone else's pattern in which he has no genuine part.

Older people have usually come to depend very much upon the design of their familiar surroundings for the organization of their own daily living. Objects and persons, however trivial and unimportant they may seem in themselves, may call out habitual response patterns in the elderly which help to stabilize their basic routine and to support it. To be lifted out of a particular home, a neighborhood, a circle of acquaintances, and the banal round of daily activities is to be separated from the behavior nucleus of one's existence. For many persons it is quite impossible to form adequate attachments to new and unfamiliar things or to develop a new routine that will rebuild their security under the altered conditions.

The immediate reaction to such uprooting, or to its anticipation, is often one of tense anxiety which may develop into pathological agitation. Reactive neurotic depressions appear in such a setting, often with strong elements of aversion and resentment that are easy to understand but hard to handle. Some relocated senescents and seniles mistake their own dejection and lost gratifications for a general decline and develop symptoms of fatigue and incompetence that yield to adequate therapy, provided they have not been allowed to grow into fixed habit patterns. Others take refuge in fantasy and reminiscence, neither of which is socially adaptive; and many devote themselves to the one right they have left, the right to be hypochondriacal, to watch and worry over their body's functions.

Loss of significance.—Hardly less serious than the loss of the familiar objects, persons, and routines upon which one's orientation depends, is the reduction in personal significance which must almost inevitably come with advancing age. Lawton attributes some of the anxiety that appears with economic dependence to the associated loss of prestige. He considers the "battle to retain the social usefulness and significance of maturity" as basic in the conflicts of older people (23). For men this usually means retaining prestige and power on the job, whether the job is professional or industrial. For women it more often means keeping the direction and control of domestic arrangements and the children. For both men and women it also means holding their accustomed place in the affairs of the home, the neighborhood, and their circle of relatives and friends.

As the average person passes his prime, he finds the younger generation, in the home and out of it, gradually superseding him, usurping one by one his positions and his prerogatives, edging him away from the center of the floor to the sidelines, and expecting him to accept the change without protest or ill-humor. Older men and women find themselves called upon to approve and admire the leadership of persons whom they can remember in the romper and diaper stages. Women hear the attractiveness of younger women discussed but no longer their own. Their sons and daughters become parents in their turn and wield authority instead of yielding to it, at first over the grandchildren but eventually over themselves also. For many senescents and seniles it is no easier to have to sit on the sidelines, unnoticed or patronized by others, than it is for the average adolescent wallflower. It is no easier for them to be under the thumb of their offspring than it was for their children to be under theirs in adolescence.

Frank (15) relates the distressing conflicts that arise between aging parents and their adult offspring to the former's continued preoccupation with the unresolved acute anxieties, guilt, and hostilities of their own childhood and youth, as well as to the humiliations they may have earlier inflicted upon their offspring in the name of education and discipline. Hamilton (17) has pointed out similarities between the neurotic maladjustment in the adolescent and in the senescent, both of whom in his clinical experience tend to develop an uneasy, vague, perplexed sense of personal disorientation. This he attributes in both to endocrinological changes, particularly gonadal, and to a reduction in the repressive strength of the ego. It should be realized, however, that similar deep anxieties may also arise in adolescence and senescence, because in both their status is undergoing a comparable change, i.e., from known relative security to unknown insecurity. The maladapted adolescent and the maladjusted senescent are both made to feel unwanted, inferior, unattractive, unnecessary, and perpetually out of place; and this situation in both can no more be chalked up entirely to internal factors than it can exclusively to external ones.

Leaving out for the time being the more personal factors, the appearance of neurotic behavior under conditions of decreasing influence and authority seems to depend somewhat upon how suddenly the change in prestige status takes place, upon the habitual level of domination to which the aging man or woman has been accustomed in the past, and upon the degree of residual prestige and power conceded him or her in the present. The very personality trends that have enabled one to dominate successfully and to gain prestige in early and middle maturity may now stand in the way of one's accepting the altered conditions of later maturity (8). Lost authority and influence, or suddenly lowered prestige, in persons who for a long time have taken them for granted as their due, are known to give rise to substitute neurotic aggressions, such as hypochondriacal complaints, attitudes of silent martyrdom, demands for constant care and reassurance that place a heavy burden on others and arouse guilt and resentment in the adult offspring, verbal attacks upon the alleged inferiority, ingratitude, or immorality of the younger generations, and stubborn refusals to acknowledge their own changed status when it is already an established fact. Anxiety, negation, rejection, and revenge enter into the dynamics of these patterns.

Retirement.—The ultimate problem, short of terminal invalidism and death, is that of retirement from active service, whether this be from skilled or unskilled labor, from business, professional work, or home management. Retirement is most hazardous when it comes too early or too suddenly. In practice such enforced deprivation of work is usually made to depend upon an arbitrary "age of incompetence" (26) which is related rather to economic, political, and military traditions than to modern age studies. Although it has been established for some time that very great individual differences in abilities exist within any given age decade, and that the test scores made by many persons in a given decade equal or exceed the average for those of a decade or two earlier (32), these facts seem to have had no noticeable effect upon the regulations of industrial employment agencies, academic institutions, or civil service codes (4), and relatively little official use is being made of the newer techniques for evaluating the aging individual's residual capacities which have been developed in recent years.

The abrupt termination of one's active interests and occupation, unless carefully handled, can have disastrous personal effects. Unemployment aggravates existing neuroses and tends to reactivate dormant ones (23). What has already been said about the effects of relocation upon an elderly person applies equally well to retirement. The retired worker, businessman, professional man, or homemaker misses the externally imposed routine (25). He loses his familiar landmarks, his points of reference, and with them his sense of personal identity. Piersol (35) believes the loss of sustaining habits and motives to be capable of turning anyone, even a young person, into a confirmed neurotic within six months. The experience of being all at once unnecessary and unwanted, with the deprivation of incentive and of an opportunity to continue one's accustomed work, may precipitate restlessness, weariness, and dejection that lead over into hypochondria, chronic fatigue states, or neurotic depression with resentment and self-depreciation. The development, in this setting, of compulsive doubt, indecision, and rumination grows out of the disorganization of habitual solutions and the resulting insecurity. Rituals are sometimes substituted for new solutions in an attempt to simplify and control the situation. Women as a rule are less subject to retirement neuroses than men are because domestic affairs allow much more latitude than men's work and there is much less danger of being displaced.

The treatment of this situation is obviously first that of preparing the individual for a shift in his activities and interests long in advance. It is sometimes possible to arrange for retirement to be a step-wise affair instead of a leap. Education of the general public to a more civilized attitude toward decline in ability might be more successful if younger generations could be made to realize that happy, contented oldsters are far less troublesome and expensive, and less likely to induce guilt, anxiety, and hostility in themselves, than are the discontented, resentful, and often vengeful ones who have been thrust into a corner and then punished whenever they tried to leave it. Retirement has its genuine compensations. It brings a certain freedom from responsibility and competition, although not necessarily in one's personal affairs; and it gives one leisure for activities formerly crowded out by work, provided one has means and personal liberty to facilitate them (35).

Social restrictions.—Biological regression, economic and social dependence, and enforced retirement are not the only restrictive influences that lead toward neurotic manifestations in later life. Our culture, in spite of many changes, still has some rather rigid conventions to which the oldster is expected to conform (20). These conventions are to a large extent the remnants of ancient codes of conduct. According to them, the elderly man or woman was supposed to live in a hazy twilight state, without any impelling hopes or desires and to need little more than warmth, and simple comfort. It was a resting phase that preceded the final great silence. This picture of the elderly person that we have inherited belongs, culturally, to a period in which the family unit consisted of three or four generations living under a single roof. Biologically, it is derived from a relatively recent era when few men lived beyond fifty and those who did were apparently on the average physiologically and psychologically older than those of corresponding age today. It does not fit our era, because old people can no longer count on a place of honor at the family hearth and because they are apt to be in far better all-round condition than they were even a century ago.

Lawton says that the way in which society treats aging and the consequent fear of aging raises more difficulties than the aging process itself (25, 26). Sweeping changes in family organization have deprived older people of their security, and have eliminated the small gratifications which once were accessible to them through whatever services they could still render to others in the home. In industry, quantity production by precision machines has minimized the worth of personal accuracy and experience, in which the older master craftsman excelled, and has maximized that of speed and endurance, in which he is sure to be inferior. Stream-lined business methods and business machines have tended likewise to reduce the value of caution and of slowly acquired skills. The mass production of household goods and appliances has similarly reduced the value of handicraft and experience in the older housewife, although the lack of other competition in her own household protects her from forfeiting her life work when she begins to falter and slow down.

The senile or late senescent male finds the doors of opportunity closing behind him and none opening in front of him. He exchanges the economic pressures of youth and maturity for the social restrictions of age. Without any special place in life, he is nevertheless expected to accept the role of the functionless oldster, with unruffled calm, expecting no rewards, needing few gratifications, and experiencing neither hope, regret, desire, nor envy. It is obvious that for many persons the anticipation or the presence of such demands must bring severe conflict and tension and in some may lead to neurotic maladaptations. These maladaptations may be in the form of anxiety states, neurotic depressions, complaints of fatigability and ill-health, or some other form of self-vindication, exemption, substitute gratification, or revenge. The way to avoid such developments is, of course, to eliminate their sources; but this is no easy task if one faces economic realities— unemployment, for example, and the prospect of still greater and greater speed and efficiency in work. Lawton (24) proposes that efficiency be considered only a secondary aim, and that the primary one be made the constructive use of human beings for human values, rather than for productive efficiency. Bortz (6) considers the question of finances a minor factor in the maladaptations of old age as compared with their need for self-expression, for some genuine interest, and for continued opportunities to make contributions to the life around them. According to Folsom (14), the oft-heard demand that old persons be given gainful employment represents an overevaluation in our culture of work per se, and of the importance of personal independence.

At this point some questions are worth raising, even though they cannot be answered without further data. How much of what we call emotional over-reaction in elderly persons is actually provoked by these unwelcome and seemingly unnecessary social restrictions upon later life? Their lability of mood is certainly related to their biological aging; but to what extent are frustrations and denials, imposed by tradition and the convenience of others, responsible for provoking the emotional behavior which organic

impairment then makes it so difficult to control? How much neurotic behavior in the aging and the aged is really just undesirable
dependent behavior which is the natural outcome of their dependent
and insecure social status? Do some of them, without evidence of
serious cerebral damage, seem childish mainly because they have
been placed in a position that actually calls for regressive behavior? It goes without saying that the more habitually insecure
an individual has been during childhood, adolescence, or maturity
the more likely he is to show insecurity under these circumstances.
But is it also true that the more objectively dependent his condition is upon the good will of others the more likely he is to grow
neurotic?

III. PERSONAL FACTORS

In adult human beings it is, of course, impossible to separate
personal factors completely from cultural and biological ones,
since personality is itself a product of cultural influences acting
upon a growing biological organism. It is, however, of great practical convenience to be able to consider separately the particular
reactions and attitudes of the individual which contribute to the
dynamics of neurotic developments. Among these are the person's
own habitual reactions to change, frustration, conflict, and neglect,
his usual modes of aggression, submission, and evasion, his dominant needs, wishes, fears, fantasies, and anxieties, and the protective or tension-reducing mechanisms with which he meets them—in
fact, all of the active ingredients of his premorbid personality,
whether recognized and understood by him or not. For example,
one individual may show relatively little biological decline but
may react excessively to that little with anxiety or depression, or
with some overcompensation. Another may preserve equanimity
in the presence of unmistakable biological waning, even though he
indicates clearly his recognition of its implications for him. Similarly, we can make a useful distinction between the actual social
restrictions and denials imposed upon an individual by convention
and his personal reactions to them, which latter may be moderate,
excessive, or decidedly inappropriate, and may follow any one of
several neurotic patterns. Discussion of some personal factors has
been unavoidably included in the foregoing material. These will

be reintroduced in what follows only if there is something new to be added.

Personal reactions to bodily change.—The degree and mode of acceptance of involution, when it comes, will to a considerable extent depend upon one's habitual premorbid attitude toward the body's competence and appearance. Atkin (2) has pointed out that the skin and its appendages, which possess very high narcissistic value, are also among the first systems to show the effects of aging. The great importance of this factor in the average woman's life, the important role it plays in her gaining and holding attention and prestige, has already been mentioned. But in later maturity men as well as women may become keenly sensitive over their progressive loss of attractiveness, and both may begin to look for signs that others care less for them or dislike them on this account. This can strike at the roots of personal security in those many individuals who have always depended upon strong emotional attachments and signs of acceptance by others. To persons who have habitually demanded of themselves perfect health and endurance, the signs of involution may seem very threatening and may succeed in arousing anxieties, compulsive rituals, or hypochondriacal preoccupation with health and disease. Personal reorientation toward biological involution usually involves a recognition and an understanding of the part played in one's economy by an overevaluation of good looks, strength, endurance, and sexual attractiveness, and the ability progressively to modify one's attitude toward and one's demands upon his organism as it grows progressively less attractive, strong, and perfect.

Personal reactions to social change.—The aging person of our time is faced with a difficult paradox. For, although he has for one reason or another become less adaptable than ever to change, he is more likely than ever to be called upon to adjust to sweeping alterations in his living conditions, his occupation, his place in society, and, nowadays, the very structure of that society itself. The comparative inflexibility, conservatism, and intolerance of social change that most elderly persons show undoubtedly have more than one determinant. Hamilton (17) emphasizes the need for the security and support which long-established beliefs and practices furnish. He maintains that older people are hostile toward any liberalization of social sanctions because they themselves are experiencing greater difficulty in repressing impulses of a forbidden, antisocial, or perverse character. Kaufman (22) thinks that the elderly individual's rigidity "really expresses a deeper repression of the anxieties with an increasing fixity of the reaction formations originally laid down as character traits." Lawton (26) raises the question of a possible relationship between conservatism in old age, on the one hand, and habitual intellectual plasticity, educational background, and emotional adjustment on the other.

While this widespread emphasis upon personal defensive and adjustive factors in the aging individual's attitude toward social change is thoroughly justified, it must not be allowed to obscure the fact that other less controllable and less remediable factors may also be operative. Ruch's experiments and other evidence collected by Miles (32) have already been cited to indicate that, quite apart from personal and emotional involvement, there are certain inevitable deficiencies in performance with age which are dependent upon cellular and humoral changes. These have been shown to affect impersonal as well as personal activities, unemotional attitudes as well as emotional. Older persons often place greater reliance upon already fixed habitual attitudes and routines for the simple reason that they are incapable of learning, retaining, and utilizing new ones without considerable effort, and even then only to a limited degree.

Impersonal as well as personal factors may operate also in relation to changes in one's own social status; but the elderly individual's reactions to these are likely to be more intense and uncontrolled because they strike at such very fundamental needs. For example, when his changed social status means that the most private and protected areas of his life are invaded, those into which the hard-pressed adult can ordinarily retire and mend his fences, the aging person finds himself deprived of his last refuge. He cannot any longer escape the increasing pressures of his environment by a further retreat, because there is nowhere left for him to go. He has the unhappy choice then of either fighting back or refusing to meet the situation. If he chooses the former he may resort to direct or substitute aggressions. These are unlikely to succeed because of his lost prestige and independence, just as a dependent child's aggressions are not likely to succeed in the end. If he declines to cope with conflict situations as they arise, he may withdraw

and fall back upon fantasy and other more passive modes of gratification, which do not precipitate clashes with the environment but
also fail to clear up his predicament.

Conflict and aggression in later life.—The aged are often pic-
tured as living in a state of suspended animation, in which neither
conflict nor aggression plays a serious part. But conflict is normal
to every age, and aggression is one of its most common products.
One difficulty is that, as age advances, the disabling effects of biological decline seem rarely to be quite compensated for by the decreases in need and desire. To this disequilibrium must be added
the burden of social restraints and denials imposed by anachronistic conventions. Thus society seems to conspire with biology to
reduce the aging person's resources and to build up his tensions
and frustrations. He also begins to realize that some of his lifelong
hopes and wishes will after all never be gratified; and yet they may
be too deeply ingrained in him to be wholly given up. Sometimes
they grow even more intense in later life. Old conflicts reappear
which for decades have been balanced by absorbing activities now
denied to one, by gratifications now disappearing, by recognition
and appreciation one can no longer command, or by emotional
attachments that are waning or have vanished.

Hamilton (17), stressing the continuity of personality difficulties through one's life, maintains that conflicts are carried over
from infancy and childhood, accentuated in adolescence, remain
still unresolved in maturity, and are finally reactivated in old age.
According to Kaufman (22), the neuroses of older persons show
that the conflicts of earlier childhood and adolescence have not lost
their intensity with age. Atkin (2), on the other hand, points out
that conflicts may also undergo marked reduction in old age.

The neurotic aggressions resorted to by nonpsychotic seniles
and senescents do not differ essentially in pattern from those employed by younger persons. One encounters active and passive
resistance, spite reactions and threats of all kinds, sulks, temper
tantrums, and accusations. The aggression may be directed toward
an offender, real or supposed, or toward a recognizable surrogate,
or may be worked off along less personal and less troublesome
channels. Because the old are also experienced, their aggressive
mechanisms are sure to include devices that fall within or border
upon what is socially acceptable. For them the most readily avail-

able and often the most potent are those relating to health and bodily comfort. They can make of fatigue, lameness, pain, nausea, and discomfort a bundle of stout rods with which to castigate their now dominant adult offspring. By complaint and accusation they arouse anxiety and guilt in their grown children and thus regain some measure of the control over them which they had lost. For many old persons hypochondriacal complaining becomes a major preoccupation which fills in time, gains sympathy and attention, and occasionally arouses strong emotional attachments.

The routines of many older persons grow very rigid, and sometimes they become more ritualistic than functional. Where they come into conflict with younger generations they may succeed in forcing others to give up whatever interferes with their inflexible and ritualistic patterns by raising a storm, sulking, or complaining of heartless and ungrateful treatment whenever objections are offered. The aggressive character of many neurotic depressions has long been recognized. Even those depressed persons who punish themselves unmercifully do not, as a rule, leave others out of their aggressive designs. In fact, the suffering and the chastening which one's neurotic depression may visit upon others seems to be a factor in prolonging the reaction.

Withdrawal and fantasy.—The late senescent or senile person may also react to his declining abilities by withdrawing from the struggle. He restricts his activities and interests progressively as his frustrations increase, or he suddenly gives up after an unsuccessful attempt at continued domination. The effect in either case is to reduce the anxieties and the painful sense of inadequacy which a growing loss in competence is apt to produce. This is another important source of the rather inflexible routines in old age. The more routinized and automatic one's behavior is made, the less danger there is of running into new situations which may force one to face the fact of reduced competence and make it obvious to others. The restriction and simplification of life in old persons, although seldom planned or recognized as such by them, often represent a protective device that eliminates some of the sources of tension and anxiety. Withdrawal may also be determined by the realization or the belief that one is no longer useful, attractive, or welcome to others.

Whatever its origins, withdrawal is an important source of neurotic behavior in old age. Excessive routinization leads easily over into rigid compulsive behavior in which painful anxiety is provoked the moment interference with completion of the ritual is attempted. The reduction in one's interest in the environment and in activity also may encourage interest in the body's machinery to increase; and, since aging persons function somewhat less well than persons in their prime, it is easy then to develop troublesome hypochondriacal complaints and preoccupations with fatigue. These reactions can secondarily arouse anxieties which nullify the original tension-reducing effects of withdrawal from competition, leaving the patient worse off than when he started.

Flight into fantasy is a mechanism that follows naturally upon withdrawal at any age. In old persons this is most apt to consist of reminiscences in which former gratifications under other circumstances are recalled and elaborated upon. To some degree this is so because the recall of recent events becomes more difficult in the later years; but it is also a result of the fact that the present is relatively empty and insecure and the future outlook gloomy (26). The reminiscences of old age are not all gratifying. The memories of disillusionments, losses, failures, and errors appear too. They lead in some persons to self-accusation, anxiety, and protective or penitent ritual. In therapy it is essential to recognize that all reminiscences, whether gratifying or the reverse, involve a great deal of fantasy as well as recall. It is too often tacitly assumed that elderly persons should not, and therefore usually do not, indulge in erotic fantasies. This assumption is quite unwarranted. Even though sexual drives are reduced, the progressive loss of other gratifications may raise them to a position of relative prominence in the life of aging men and women. In the past it has generally been concluded that increased autoerotism and sexual adventures and deviations were necessarily symptoms of degeneration; but they may just as well be merely over-reactions to deprivation, loneliness, and neglect.

B. PATTERNS OF NEUROSIS IN LATER MATURITY

Neurotic patterns of behavior are pathological at any age; they are no more normal or inevitable to old age than to adolescence. In both phases of life the individual is undergoing important changes in his biological and his social status which often call for sweeping reorientations. When such demands arise, some individuals are unsuccessful in meeting them and instead develop complaints of fatigue and somatic disorder without adequate physiological foundation, or anxieties and fears that seem unjustifiable to others. Others fall back upon protective and penitential rituals, hysterical disabilities, or neurotic depressions. The patterns of neurosis which one finds in nonpsychotic later maturity are not essentially different from those occurring in childhood, adolescence, and earlier maturity. In fact, Woltmann (43) reports that the complaints of aged neurotics often refer to the same organ or system about which they have been complaining for years.

If our information as to the incidence of neuroses in earlier maturity is uncertain and inadequate, it is probably even more so with regard to those of later maturity. The great majority of neurotic persons are treated by the general practitioner who is not primarily concerned either with exact diagnosis or with the collection and publication of tabulated data. Barker (5) reports that 43 of a group of 240 patients (17.9 per cent) between the ages of 60 and 70 years were diagnosed in his private medical clinic as suffering from neuroses or affective disorders. This enumeration is not broken down further. Barker's group cannot, of course, be regarded as a representative sample of the public, or even of the sick public, since socio-economic factors of a highly selective character were present. Woltmann (43) found psychiatric disorders in 40 of a group of 200 geriatric patients, of whom 11 were diagnosed as neurotic (5.5 per cent of total, 27.5 per cent of psychiatric cases). Prout and Bourcier (36), in a review of 100 cases between the ages of 40 and 60 years admitted to a private psychiatric institution, state that 16 were diagnosed as neurotic, most of whom had had neurotic episodes earlier in their lives. Their present attacks were regarded as having been precipitated by mid-life stresses and strains. Robinson (38) reported 11 diagnoses of neurosis in a group of 119 psychiatric cases (9.3 per cent) in old age.

In these reports the breakdown into specific neurotic patterns is indicated only in a very general way. Barker (5) lists many complaints that might point to neurotic developments; but he does not state what percentage of each was found upon diagnosis to be attributable to somatic pathology, what percentage to normal physiological aging, and what to disturbances incident to personal stress

and strain. Woltmann (43) lists, as common patterns of psychiatric disorder in old age, those of hypochondriacal concern, chronic
fatigue states, anxieties, and depressions. Watters (42) mentions
hypochondriases, anxiety states, and "minor disorders" as prevalent geriatric patterns of neurosis. Of 50 consecutive out-patient
psychiatric cases between the ages of 40 and 69 years, referred to
the writer in the Diagnostic Clinic of the Johns Hopkins Hospital,
23 were diagnosed hypochondriasis, 2 neurasthenia, 14 anxiety
states, 1 neurotic depression, 1 paranoid state, and 9 structural
disease of the central nervous system. These patients, however,
were also a selected group, consisting of middle-class persons who
were able to pay the hospital a fixed twenty-five-dollar fee but unable to defray the total cost of the diagnostic services rendered
them.

Hypochondriasis.—In our culture, preoccupations with one's
bodily functions seem to belong to normal senility (43). These are
most often directed at ingestion, digestion, and evacuation; but the
reproductive, excretory, cardiovascular, respiratory, and skeletal
systems, or the functioning of one or more receptor systems, are
also often implicated. In order to understand the appearance or
increase of hypochondriacal overconcern in later maturity one
should ask, not merely why old people are hypochondriacal but
why anyone, regardless of chronological age, might develop an
exaggerated concern over somatic functions under the circumstances
of biological and social aging. For one thing, of course, there is a
reduction in the range of activities permitted by one's physiology,
by social convention, and by one's economic status. There are
fewer worth-while things to hold one's attention and divert one from
incipient self-concern. It is easier to notice and talk about minor
biological incidents when the major affairs of life have been taken
away. In general, the older a person grows, the more direct and
indirect experience with illnesses, accidents, and operations he is
likely to have accumulated, and the easier it is for him to imagine
himself ill and in danger. The advantages and privileges of illness
have already been discussed in their relation to neurotic developments. These apply with especial force to hypochondriasis.

The fact that gastrointestinal preoccupations seem to be much
the commonest form in senescence and senility (33) cannot be
accounted for in terms of direct gastrointestinal morbidity or mor-

tality data, in both of which the digestive system is greatly exceeded
in incidence by the cardiovascular-renal group (13). Certain writers, influenced perhaps by the ancient characterization of old age
as a return to childhood, maintain that a senile interest in eating,
digestion, and bowel function represents a return to infantile levels
of libidinal gratification (17). It would be instructive in this connection to determine whether or not elderly persons who have kept
up their sexual interests pay relatively little attention to their gastrointestinal performance as compared with those who have abandoned sexual interests, and whether this is equally true of those
without opportunity for adequate sexual gratification as for those
with it.

In any case it must not be forgotten that the aging organism calls
attention to itself by its relatively poorer level of performance, and
that symptoms of gastrointestinal disturbance may be secondary
to deficiencies and diseases in other systems as well as to general
malnutrition (18). Bortz (6) calls attention to the fact that digestion is strongly influenced by fatigue at any age, and particularly
so in later maturity when the expenditure of energy is more apt to
be relatively excessive. Unnecessary or poorly conceived diets and
food indulgences often contribute to these difficulties in old age
(Robbins, 37). The responsiveness of the gastrointestinal system
in emotional disturbances, conflict, frustration, unhappiness, and
apprehension at all ages is now universally recognized. The dynamics of these reactions in later maturity and their utilization as
instruments for regaining attention, affection, domination, etc.,
from others have already been taken up.

Chronic fatigue states (neurasthenia).—At all ages there is an
inverse relationship between chronic complaints of fatigue or easy
fatigability and the presence of adequate motivation. Whenever
the prospect of gratification is small, one is apt to fatigue quickly,
and to remain fatigued until something interesting turns up. In
aging there is often a gradual, sometimes a sudden, reduction in
the opportunities for rewarding types of activity and in the available sources of gratification. The onset of neurasthenia or neurotic fatigue states is difficult to detect in later maturity, because it
is normal for elderly persons to tire more quickly and recover more
slowly and incompletely than when they were mature adults. The
sleep of older persons is also shorter and less sound, as a rule, and

they awaken from it feeling less refreshed and a bit irritable. So the diagnosis must rest upon comparisons between complaints and biological age, previous energy levels, reactions to remedial therapy, and, finally, upon the presence or absence of serious personal and environmental stress. Neurasthenic fatigue states in the aging and aged are no more to be met by old-fashioned rest cures and isolation than they are earlier in life. A wholesome balance between rest, recreation, and occupation, which need not necessarily be gainful to be beneficial, gives a starting point from which therapy may then proceed to explore the personal problems and attitudes with a view to constructive reorientation. Lawton's point deserves re-emphasis here—that normal old age should not be considered as a period of mere rest, contemplation, and consuming but as one in which there is still definitely present the need for some kind of satisfying accomplishment (26).

Anxiety states.—The anxiety neuroses of later maturity, like those earlier in life, are characterized by the physiological derivatives of strong emotional reactions. There may be increased skeletal tensions with marked difficulty in relaxing and sleeping, visceral disturbances, especially in the cardiovascular, gastrointestinal and genito-urinary systems, tremors, headaches, perspiring, increased irritability, and a vague or acute sense of impending danger. The individual is unlikely to recognize the source of his anxiety and usually focuses upon his symptoms. Anxiety states in older people are not, as a rule, entirely new to them. They have generally experienced similar episodes earlier in life when their security has been threatened, when severe conflicts have arisen, and when they have met with emotional deprivation. Enough has already been said about the innumerable sources of insecurity during the aging process; any of them is capable of provoking anxiety states in a sufficiently susceptible person. Sometimes rather acute anxiety crops up in an elderly person as a guilt reaction coming in the wake of hostile and vengeful fantasies involving their adult offspring, a mate, or others who seem to be dominating, belittling, or frustrating them. Sexual fantasies, autoerotism, and conflicts are also effective in precipitating anxiety, just as they are at other ages. The lack of other sources of gratification may lift sexual urges to an uncomfortably prominent place in the elderly person's behavior.

The circumstances of life in later maturity which provoke anxiety also provide fewer opportunities for regaining one's security and less likelihood of replacing the lost sources of gratification with new ones. The older person is usually less useful, less valued, less welcome, and less depended upon by anyone than formerly. However, a decreased drive for recognition, approval, and domination may help to compensate for the fewer available outlets, and may result in lessened tension. Access to a competently trained therapist, with whom the anxious patient can work his emotional problems through, holds out the greatest promise. Personal conflicts can be somewhat reduced through genuine acceptance by the aging person of his decreased potentialities, through the development of greater tolerance toward himself, and through improvement of his personal relationships with his associates. In addition, the objective conditions of living can nearly always stand some improvement.

Compulsive disorders.—While compulsions are perhaps commoner in persons developing involutional and senile psychoses, they also appear in later maturity alone or in conjunction with anxiety states. As a rule the patient has already exhibited compulsive trends earlier in life or has at least been overconscientious, perfectionistic, too orderly, or a stickler for details, given to doubts, rituals, and rumination, or tending easily to feel inadequate, anxious, and insecure. Compulsive patterns in later maturity are similar to those occurring earlier in life. There may be excessive cleanliness and orderliness, inflexible or perfunctory rituals to guard against error, danger, or contamination by thought or deed and to fend off evil and retaliation. One finds counting, set phrases or gestures, complaints of feeling compelled to do or not to do or say certain things, and the familiar checking and rechecking of safeguards and sources of danger such as door locks, gas jets, water faucets, etc. The preparation of food, eating and drinking, cleansing, dressing and undressing, excreting and evacuating—all may become entangled in irresistible compulsive behavior, any interference with which is likely to provoke acute, intolerable anxiety.

The appearance or reappearance of compulsive behavior in later maturity may amount to no more than a reversion to older routines and rituals in the face of mounting anxiety, insecurity, or inadequacy. Sometimes it represents an ineffectual attempt to simplify the environment by restricting and stereotyping one's reactions to it. The aging person may find himself unable to keep up his usual level of competence or unable to make the adjustments which new conditions of living impose. The resulting anxiety may then be misinterpreted by him as a sign of some impending danger and may lead to preoccupation with whatever he associates with safety and security. Compulsions of a protective, penitential, or conciliatory character also appear in elderly persons as a result of erotic, aggressive, or vindictive fantasies which arouse guilt and acute anxiety.

The treatment of compulsions is never a simple matter. In later maturity any frontal attack should be directed against the environment and not against the compulsive behavior itself, since the latter may well be the patient's last-ditch stand against acute anxiety. The therapist's goal must be the same as that of the patient, namely, the reduction of the anxiety. Only his methods are different. Except in the simplest cases, reduction in anxiety requires analysis of the total situation, including a detailed study of the patient's needs, wishes, fears, and conflicts. The outlook for improvement will depend upon the same general factors as in earlier life periods. In elderly persons with a long history of compulsive trends, amelioration is usually the most one can expect.

Hysterical disorders.—Hysteria, in the more exact sense of an exaggerated loss of function, or autonomous functioning, in the presence of physiologically normal equipment is very uncommon in later maturity (7). As Diethelm and Rockwell point out, most of the symptoms described in the literature as "hysterical," in patients over forty-five, are dramatic emotional reactions but not true dissociative-dysmnesic reactions (12). What one very often does see is an exaggeration of some partial defect in older persons, such as lameness, arthritic dyskineses, and even memory difficulties, the function of which is that of gaining attention, sympathy, and affection or of punishing and arousing guilt in others. Lewis (28) cites the exaggeration of partial defects in vision and hearing which, if persisted in until the attitude becomes habitual, may greatly impair the elderly person's social effectiveness. When such developments are not recognized as exaggerations by the patient, but are believed in by him, they may be regarded as quasi-hys-

terical phenomena. If they are successful in restoring some measure of security, in gaining attention, prestige, or sympathy, or
merely in justifying a complaining attitude, they are likely to
become fixed.

There are the usual difficulties in distinguishing hysterical exaggerations from the symptoms of structural defect and from malin-
gering. The elderly hard-of-hearing person, for example, is often
with justice accused of hearing only things that touch upon his
interests, and of shutting out a difficult and painful experience by
not hearing or seeing it, at the same time gaining a certain amount
of revenge upon others by the effort and irritation such behavior
provokes (27). This in itself, however, can be considered neither
very pathological nor wholly an old-age problem, since throughout
life, and for very similar reasons, what normal persons see and
what they hear very often shows a highly selective, and sometimes
a quite irritating, character.

Neurotic depressions.—Although there are no really satisfactory distinctions between neurotic and psychotic depressions, other
than those of severity and duration, the term *neurotic depression*
conveniently designates relatively mild, shallow, and usually brief
or fluctuating depressive episodes. In senescent and senile persons
they seem to be precipitated, as a rule, by some aspect or some
consequence of the aging process, by reductions in freedom of
activity and in gratifications as a result of changes in one's biological and socio-economic status. The death or serious illness of close
relatives, friends, or business associates may also be influential,
directly, on the basis of deprivation and sorrow and, indirectly,
through the anxieties and reflections such an event may induce
with respect to one's own safety. The elderly person then grows
unhappy, discouraged, pessimistic, and self-depreciatory. He may
become very self-centered, may lose his interest in others and his
appetite, and may complain of fatigue, malaise, and perhaps sexual
impotence (or frigidity). In some a more anxious, restless unhappiness appears, with irritability, mild aversion, insomnia, tension
symptoms, and digestive and other visceral disorders. Many be-
wail their lot and regret all the things that might have been and
the things they might have done or might better have left undone.

The net result to the patient of a neurotic depression is to make
him less acceptable than ever to others and less valued because of

his lowered social effectiveness. The very reasons for his having felt unhappy and neglected in the first place are in this way reinforced; and the situation therefore tends to be self-perpetuating unless broken into. The individual who earlier in maturity has developed adequate personal and social resources, upon which he can now fall back, may benefit considerably from reorientation and guidance on a fairly superficial level. Rigid, anxious, or limited personalities will require more detailed and thoroughgoing therapy. The advent of a neurotic depression in aging persons should never go unheeded. Sometimes it turns out later to have been a warning signal of a more sweeping depression that is not nearly so responsive to treatment; and this in turn may help to open the door to senile deterioration, from which relatively little improvement can be expected.

Sex deviation.—Deviations in conduct from the culturally acceptable, adult heterosexual norm appear in later maturity for a variety of reasons. The problem used to be dismissed with the simple statement that sex perversions in elderly persons were evidence of ethical deterioration on the basis of brain degeneration. The reality is not so simple. Most cases fail to show clear-cut evidence of cerebral pathology; and cerebral pathology, even when unmistakably present, is not necessarily associated with sexual deviations. One has always to look for the personal and cultural determinants as well.

Perhaps the simplest situation is that of the elderly man who is deprived of his usual opportunities for normal heterosexual relations by illness, separation, or death, and who then turns under sexual stress to other available sources of gratification. Aside from specific problems which biological waning may raise, the situation is not essentially different from that which younger heterosexual men face when deprived of their accustomed sexual outlets for any considerable time. In a certain percentage the solution involves autoerotism, homosexuality, rape, or attacks on children. It is usually assumed, in both young and old, that some degree of latent deviant trend has been previously present which, in combination with factors of temptation and opportunity, help to determine the particular pattern of sex behavior which appears.

The matter of latent trends has received considerable attention in discussions of deviant sex behavior in later maturity. Freud, who long ago observed that sexual impulses in some aged persons enter biologically or socially forbidden channels, regarded them as regressions to infantile levels of gratification (16). Hamilton compares them with similar adolescent upheavals and attributes both phenomena to a reduction in the repressive strength of the ego (17). But one must also consider individual differences in sexual interest and sexual stress, which may apparently be very considerable in all age groups; and the available sources of gratification and opportunities for activity must also be taken into account, nonsexual as well as sexual. If latent sex deviation is as widespread as many psychiatrists believe, it might be possible ultimately to reduce the question almost entirely to one of the balance between sex tension and inhibition, in the presence of opportunity and in conformity with pre-established trends. The basic assumption, however, has not yet passed beyond the hypothetical stage.

Sex tension in the senescent depends upon several factors which provide bases for the known wide individual differences. Biological aging may exceed or fall below the expectation based on chronology, and in a given person all systems are not as a rule equally affected (29). One's habitual level is of great importance. Under this must be included not only overt sex activities but also erotic fantasy, which has the disadvantages of stimulating sex tension without relieving it and of thriving upon enforced idleness. In many individuals anxiety, worry, or active frustration over almost anything have sexual repercussions. In aging men the challenge of impotence sometimes leads to erotic attempts at self-reassurance and, failing that, to compensatory and substitute sex gratifications. In both men and women sex gratification of any sort can offer a comforting relief from the cheerless and lonely pattern of their existence, in the same way that genital manipulation and masturbation are often resorted to by unhappy children and adolescents under comparable conditions.

Just because so many good reasons can be found to account for the eruption of deviant sexual behavior in an elderly person, one should not make the mistake of overlooking the possibility that some cerebral incompetence may also be present and effective. The biological, the cultural, and the personal are by no means mutually exclusive categories; they are only different aspects of a single organism. Unfortunately, even our best-standardized tests are not always adequate in detecting deficits that life situations succeed in uncovering; and of course routine neurological examinations often fail to establish the existence of brain damage which is later determined at autopsy. The deviant sex behavior of elderly persons frequently shows evidence of impaired judgment—in methods used, in a failure to seek privacy, or in choice of the love object—which it is quite impossible to account for simply in terms of desire, loneliness, or deprivation. It is fair to assume in these cases that, in the presence of strong sexual stimulation and the opportunity, an individual acts out urges that are often tragically antisocial, because his aging cerebrum has left him socially incompetent under the conditions of heavy stress.

Sexual problems in later maturity present certain special difficulties for the therapist. Old age is sexually a blind alley. No reorientation in terms of family formation is relevant, nor in terms of a sex partner in a large proportion of cases. Ethical standards, both verbal and actual, and customary sex gratifications have long been established. Life ordinarily promises fewer and fewer other outlets and sources of satisfaction. The elderly person is held strictly accountable by society in this sphere of action, where his knowledge is supposed to hold in check whatever desire he may still be harboring. If cerebral incompetence becomes prominent, his behavior may grow much less predictable and his co-operation much more uncertain. If predictability and co-operation are moderately good, however, there seems to be no reason why the trained therapist should not attempt detailed and sometimes analytic therapy in selected cases.

C. THERAPY

The generally pessimistic and indifferent attitude that has in the past prevailed toward the neuroses of later maturity is now being replaced by a more hopeful and constructive one. Maladaptation to the conditions of senescence and senility is not an inevitable product of aging. Our society must assume some of the responsibility for its occurrence and must develop a more aggressive interest in its amelioration and prevention. If due allowance be made for reduced vigor, agility, and educability in older per-

sons, it can be said that most of the procedures already in use for
the treatment of neuroses in earlier maturity are appropriate also
for those in later maturity. This is equally true of therapy carried
on at the level of personal conflict, insecurity, and revolt as it is of
therapy directed primarily at one's attitudes, at manipulation of
the environment, at social rehabilitation, or at one's general health.

It is always worth while to investigate the possibility of improving an aging person's health. It will be recalled that elderly persons generally place fear of invalidism and dependence at the top
of the list. If one expresses hypochondriacal worries and fears, it
is imperative first to make sure that they are not this time justified.
There are few elderly persons whose general hygiene or comfort
cannot be improved in some respect; and this approach frequently
affords a means of establishing a helpful relationship between the
therapist and a discouraged or averse patient. The problem of
social rehabilitation is somewhat more difficult. In some of the
larger communities clubs, workshops, guidance clinics, and recreation centers have been started where elderly men and women can
congregate and mingle socially on an equal footing. These facilities are designed primarily to help the lonely, functionless, unhappy normal senescent or senile person; but they are fully adaptable to the needs of the elderly neurotic, provided he is at the same
time undergoing some form of active therapy and environmental
reorientation, and provided he does not impose his own personality
difficulties upon the social group. The great majority of American
communities have as yet developed no such social provisions for
their aging and aged members. Until they recognize the need, and
get around to doing something about it, both normal and neurotic
men and women in their later years must depend upon finding
some function in whatever general community facilities there are—
clubs, churches, neighborhood affairs, gatherings, etc. The difficulty always remains, however, that older people are seldom very
welcome as active participants where younger ones are available;
and so they get pushed to the wall in clubs, in recreation centers,
and even in places of worship. They need their own organizations,
where they can regain their lost significance and rebuild their self-
respect among contemporaries.

Therapy in the neuroses can, of course, be carried on in spite
of adverse environmental conditions; but one should attempt, with

the aid of competent social workers, some manipulation of the older person's living conditions, if these seem to be in any way contributory to his maladaptation. Life with adult offspring and their children, for example, very often raises insoluble difficulties for the neurotic individual. Frictions develop over the competition of interests and affections between members of the three generations. These are often impossible to reduce because they are so deeply rooted and involve such an intricate tangle of unrecognized, unanalyzed, and even contradictory trends. Where a couple or an individual is able to care for a separate establishment, and funds can be raised from family contributions, pensions, social security, or community care, such an arrangement is apt to prove more economical in terms of final results, even though the immediate dollars-and-cents cost is appreciably higher. Lawton (26) predicts the greater use of private homes, villages, and apartment houses for the placement of normal persons in later maturity; and there is no reason why a majority of neurotic persons should not benefit from similar provisions. The same may be said in certain cases for the alternative of placement in a modern home-for-the-aged which would in no way preclude active personal therapy.

But whatever the living arrangements entered upon, the prime consideration for the elderly neurotic is that of a healthful routine to give him a behavior framework, and to prevent his level of general activity from unnecessary reduction and disorganization. The aim here should be that of preserving continuity between his earlier mode of living, if that has been reasonably satisfactory, and his present life. Habit deterioration in approaching old age can be fatal to an individual's personality organization. The prominent place given to economic insecurity in the fears of normal elderly persons should not be forgotten in dealing with the generally less secure neurotic; neither should the need for privacy, as well as that for companionship.

It is unquestionably true that we could reduce the neurotic developments of later life by preparing people for it, as Barker (5) suggests, while they are still in their prime. For a person's own habitual attitude toward old age and old people is often one of the most important factors in determining his adjustment to it when it begins to come on. Unfortunately, men and women in their prime are almost certain to share the general attitude of contempt and dread in which senility is held in our culture. They are unwilling or even unable to face the prospect of it for themselves until it is thrust upon them. The most promising approach to this phase of the problem seems to be that of first improving the lot of the aged and then on this firm basis raising their morale. After progress in the actual condition of old people warrants it, a program of re-education, supported by demonstration, may be successful in changing the general attitude toward old age in our society to one that does not encourage neurotic rebellion, fear, and surrender.

In reorienting the neurotic individual to his oncoming or already present old age, the therapeutic goal must be that of developing attitudes of acceptance but not of resignation. Resignation too often means a passive surrender to old age, whereas genuine acceptance means having an attitude of active participation in its terms. The first step toward active participation for the elderly neurotic should be that of exploring his potentialities. In addition to the medical and psychiatric studies, a psychological appraisal should be made by qualified psychological personnel on the basis of tests that include verbal ability, perceptual speed and precision, manipulative skill, problem solving, interest scales, vocational-aptitude scores, and personality evaluation, such as, for example, the thematic apperception test and the Rorschach. It is obvious that in dealing with elderly men and women the tester must make special provision for their greater fatigability, attitudes of discouragement and self-disparagement, possibly impaired recent memory, and slowness, imprecision, and weakness of perceptual and co-ordinative responses.

In themselves, these tests and measures provide neither psychiatric diagnosis nor therapy; but in the hands of the well-trained and alert clinical psychologist they can yield information of considerable value to the person planning a therapeutic program. By understanding and using this information a therapist can avoid the serious mistake of advising activity in which the patient is almost sure to fail because of some unrecognized deficit or an otherwise unimportant aversion of which both patient and therapist may have been unaware. It will very often be the case that aptitudes and interests will emerge from such studies that would otherwise remain unsuspected, at least until a therapeutic program had already been well under way that left them out. Some leads in the direction of personal problems and difficulties may also crop up in the testing results.

If a psychological appraisal of a person's latent and manifest abilities and interests requires the services of a qualified psychologist, it is also true that any far-reaching exploration of personal conflicts and trends calls for the services of a psychiatrist specifically trained in the treatment of neuroses. Either can, of course, do some of the work of the other, but only as an intelligent amateur, not as an expert. The question as to how far individual therapy shall be carried may be settled on the same general basis for patients in later maturity as for those earlier in life. One factor deserving special consideration is that of the general health of the elderly patient, with special reference to his cardiovascular-renal and gastrointestinal status, so that emotional disturbances may be properly evaluated and confined within the limits of what the organism can safely handle. This requires that the person carrying on therapy must also be competent in sizing up the situation and in taking prompt measures alone in an emergency. Other factors to be considered in deciding upon prolonged analytic therapy, whether Freudian or non-Freudian, are the suitability of the individual for such treatment from all angles, including that of his previous adaptations and maladjustments, and the degree to which a preliminary study indicates his modifiability and his capacity for establishing a workable therapeutic relationship. It is naturally essential also to know whether the neurotic reaction in general is something brand new in the patient's life history, a lighting up of earlier difficulties, or simply the continuation of a long-standing neurosis.

The personality difficulties that interfere with adaptation have already been outlined in discussing the dynamics of neuroses in later maturity. These differ in no fundamental way from the characteristics that stand in the way of adaptation during other phases of life. It has been pointed out that certain special circumstances are more likely to be operative in aging than in the younger years, such as biological waning, including sexual incompetence, reduction in social prestige, threats to one's security and one's life, losses in affection, in usefulness to others, and, finally, in the control of one's own life. However, it must never be forgotten that, no matter how favorable the aging person's environment, how highly developed the facilities available for social rehabilitation, how objectively adequate his economic and affectional security, and how considerate his family and friends, the personality characteristics with which he enters upon late senescence and senility may be enough in themselves to produce or to reproduce a neurosis.

REFERENCES

1. Allen, E. "Changes in Psychology Necessitated by Involution," *Jour. So. Med. & Surg.*, 1942, 104: 443–47
2. Atkin, S. "Old Age and Ageing: the Psychoanalytic Point of View (Discussion)," *Amer. Jour. Orthopsychiatry*, 1940, 10: 79–83
3. Barker, L. "The Senile Patient," *Annals Internal Med.*, 1933, 6: 1125–35
4. ———. "Convalescence of Old Age Patients," *Bull. New York Acad. Med.*, 1940, 16: 105–16
5. ———. "Ageing from the Point of View of the Clinician," in E. V. Cowdry, *Problems of Ageing* (2d edition) (Baltimore: Williams & Wilkins, 1942), pp. 832–54
6. Bortz, E. "Geriatrics: New Light on Old Folks," *Clinics*, 1942, I: 386–405
7. Bowman, K. "Types and Special Factors of Mental Illness of Old Age," in *Mental Hygiene in Old Age* (New York: Family Welfare Association of America, 1937), pp. 32–38
8. Brew, M., and Davidoff, E. "Involutional Psychoses, Prepsychotic Personality and Prognosis," *Psychiatric Quart.*, 1940, 14: 412–34
9. Cameron, N. "A Study of Thinking in Senile Deterioration and Schizophrenic Disorganization," *Amer. Jour. Psychol.*, 1938, 51: 650–65
10. ———. "Deterioration and Regression in Schizophrenic Thinking," *Jour. Abn. Soc. Psychol.*, 1939, 34: 265–70
11. ———. "The Functional Psychoses," in J. Hunt, *Personality and the Behavior Disorders* (New York: Ronald Press, 1944), pp. 861–921
12. Diethelm, O., and Rockwell, F. "Psychopathology of Ageing," *Amer. Jour. Psychiatry*, 1943, 99: 553–56
13. Dublin, L. "Longevity in Retrospect and in Prospect," in E. V. Cowdry, *Problems of Ageing* (2d edition) (Baltimore: Williams & Wilkins, 1942), pp. 91–110
14. Folsom, J. "Old Age as a Sociological Problem," *Amer. Jour. Orthopsychiatry*, 1940, 10: 30–39
15. Frank, L. "Old Age and Ageing: Old Age as a Sociological Problem (Discussion)," *Amer. Jour. Orthopsychiatry*, 1940, 10: 39–42
16. Freud, S. *The Ego and the Id.* London: Hogarth, 1927
17. Hamilton, G. "Changes in Personality and Psychosexual Phenomena with Age," in E. V. Cowdry, *Problems of Ageing* (2d edition) (Baltimore: Williams & Wilkins, 1942), pp. 810–31
18. Ivy, A. "Digestive System," in E. V. Cowdry, *Problems of Ageing* (2d edition) (Baltimore: Williams & Wilkins, 1942), pp. 254–301
19. Kahn, E. "Old Age and Ageing: Psychiatric Aspects (Discussion)," *Amer. Jour. Orthopsychiatry*, 1940, 10: 69–72
20. Kahn, E., and Simmons, L. "Problems of Middle Age," *Yale Rev.*, 1940, 29: 349–63

21. Kardiner, A. "Psychological Factors in Old Age," in *Mental Hygiene in Old Age* (New York: Family Welfare Association of America, 1937), pp. 14–26
22. Kaufman, M. "Old Age and Ageing: the Psychoanalytic Point of View," *Amer. Jour. Orthopsychiatry*, 1940, 10: 73–79
23. Lawton, G. "Mental Hygiene at Senescence," *Mental Hyg.*, 1939, 23: 257–67
24. ———. "Old Age and Ageing: Concluding Remarks," *Amer. Jour. Orthopsychiatry*, 1940, 10: 85–87
25. ———. "After Sixty-five?" *Mental Hyg.*, 1941, 25: 414–19
26. ———. "Psychological Guidance for Older Persons," in E. V. Cowdry, *Problems of Ageing* (2d edition) (Baltimore: Williams & Wilkins, 1942), pp. 785–809
27. ———. "Ageing Mental Abilities and Their Preservation," in G. Lawton (ed.), *New Goals for Old Age* (New York: Columbia University Press, 1943), pp. 11–33
28. Lewis, N. "Mental Hygiene of the Senium," *Mental Hyg.*, 1940, 24: 434–44
29. ———. "Applying Mental Health Principles to Problems of the Ageing," in G. Lawton (ed.), *New Goals for Old Age* (New York: Columbia University Press, 1943), pp. 91–105
30. Lorge, I. "Old Age and Ageing: Psychometry, the Evaluation of Mental Status as a Function of the Mental Test," *Amer. Jour. Orthopsychiatry*, 1940, 10: 56–61
31. Malamud, W. "Current Trends and Needs in Research on Problems of the Aged," *Dis. Nerv. System*, 1941, 2: 37–43
32. Miles, W. "Psychological Effects of Ageing," in E. V. Cowdry, *Problems of Ageing* (2d edition) (Baltimore: Williams & Wilkins, 1942), pp. 756–84
33. Overholser, W. "Mental Problems and Their Management," *Med. Annals of the District of Columbia*, 1941, 10: 212–17
34. Pearl, R. *Biology of Population Growth.* New York: Knopf, 1925
35. Piersol, G. "The Problem of Ageing," *Bull. New York Acad. Med.*, 1940, 16: 555–69
36. Prout, C., and Bourcier, A. "Mental Health Problems of Mid-Life," *New England Med. Jour.*, 1940, 223: 576–81
37. Robbins, I. "A General Discussion of the Problems of Old Age," *New Orleans Med. & Surg. Jour.*, 1940, 93: 184–87
38. Robinson, G. "The Abnormal Mental Reactions of Old Age," *Jour. Missouri Med. Assoc.*, 1942, 39: 36–40
39. Rothschild, D. "Pathological Changes in Senile Psychoses and Their Psychobiologic Significance," *Amer. Jour. Psychiatry*, 1937, 93: 757–88
40. Ruch, F. "The Differentiative Effects of Age upon Human Learning," *Jour. Gen. Psychol.*, 1934, 11: 261–86
41. Strong, E. *Changes of Interests with Age.* Stanford, Calif.: Stanford University Press, 1931
42. Watters, T. "Nervous and Mental Aspects of Old Age," *New Orleans Med. & Surg. Jour.*, 1940, 93: 187–93
43. Woltmann, H. "Neuropsychiatric Geriatrics," *Arch. Ophthal.*, 1942, 28: 790–801

Chapter IX

THE INVOLUTIONAL PSYCHOSES

Eugene Davidoff

Owing to the increase in the span of human life, renewed interest has been directed recently toward the climacteric syndrome in general and the involutional psychoses in particular. The latter term, involutional psychoses, has generally superseded the older designation of involutional melancholia.

I. THE INVOLUTIONAL SYNDROME WITHOUT PSYCHOSIS

Involutional manifestations are more often evident in females than in males. The symptoms of the climacteric are experienced by most women to a lesser or greater degree.

In this group are found individuals who manifest, in exaggerated but temporary form, physiologic and psychologic symptoms of estrogenic deficiency usually present to a greater or less degree in most individuals during the menopause. Menstrual disturbances, hot flashes, vasomotor instability, transitory crying spells, feelings of discomfort, restlessness, fatigability, and somatic complaints are observed.

Hawkinson (14) has listed in order of frequency the following phenomena occurring in the female involutional syndrome without psychosis: "Nervousness" (subjective), menstrual disturbances, flushes and chills, excitability, fatigability and lassitude, depression and crying, irritability, disturbed sleep, tachycardia palpitation and dyspnoea, vertigo and scotomata, "decreased memory" and concentration, headache, frigidity, numbness and tingling, occipitocervical aching, vague and indefinite pains, excessive sweating, and formication.

Werner (36) in discussing the male climacterium, listed the following symptoms: vasomotor disturbances, hot flushes, emotional instability with sudden uncontrollable shifts in mood, tendency to break into tears, periods of irritability, and sudden anger. He found men at this period to exhibit a moderate degree of physical and mental fatigability, to complain of difficulties in concentration, to show general apathy, to have somatic complaints, and

244

to be impotent. Werner (36) stated that 52 per cent of these individuals developed a psychosis.

The involutional syndrome in the male which is associated with androgenic hormone (testosterone) deficiency differs in certain respects from the symptom complex in the female. Psychologic manifestations in the involutional period with or without the presence of a definite psychosis occur more frequently among women. Mild involutional neuroses which resemble the normal menopausal symptoms and appear to have a rather intimate association with the climacterium are encountered more often in females.

Among males, apathy or emotional instability associated with impotence, early organic changes in the central nervous system, or arteriosclerosis is more often found.

The influence of the progesterone factor as well as general endocrine and autonomic imbalance have to be considered as causative factors of the mild emotional instability noted in females. Since many women exhibit these psychologic signs, which may wane after a time or after estrogenic therapy, the previous personality only indirectly or to a slight degree affects the emotional manifestations.

Premenopausal tensions have been found to exist in some women and a few undergo climacteric changes at a younger age than the average. Postmenopausal emotional symptoms associated with vasomotor instability and some degrees of essential hypertension or early arteriosclerosis are also encountered. In these, autonomic factors as well as other endocrine influences have to be considered.

From the endocrinologic viewpoint, the situation in females might be summarized as follows: At the time of involution, ovarian function decreases. This results in cessation of ovulation and a decrease in the production, by the follicle, of estrogen. As a result the uterus no longer receives sufficient hormone to produce endometrial changes, and catamenia ceases. Furthermore, the lack of estrogen (which normally inhibits the anterior pituitary follicle-stimulating hormone) results in an excessive amount of follicle-stimulating hormone, which can be found in the menopausal urine. The level runs from 52 mouse units per 24 hours up to 500 or 600 or more mouse units per 24 hours, while normal levels range from 13 to 52 mouse units per 24 hours. There is, therefore, an imbalance between the estrogen (which is decreased) and the follicle-stimulating hormone (which is increased). In some women this

produces no symptoms; in others it upsets the vegetative nervous system so that there are periodic attacks of warmth and flushing of the body, particularly of the face, of short duration, which are called "hot flushes." During a period of years the patient gradually readjusts her nervous system and the hot flushes disappear or the hormone imbalance persists [Reifenstein (28) and Albright (1)—personal communication of Dr. Reifenstein]. It has not been definitely established that there is an alteration in other pituitary gonadotropins or the adrenal function following menopause.

It is the consensus of opinion that these involutional syndromes which manifest no signs of psychosis respond exceedingly well to larger doses of estrogenic therapy of the substitutive type.

For further discussion of the involutional syndrome without psychosis the reader is referred to the contributions of Sevringhaus (31), Burlingame and Patterson (4), Hawkinson (14), Werner (36), Douglas (10), Albright (1), and Shorr, Robinson, and Papanicolaou (32).

II. THE INVOLUTIONAL PSYCHOSES

Frequently in the writer's experience there may be a qualitative as well as a quantitative difference between the nonpsychotic involutional syndrome and the involutional psychosis. In nonpsychotic individuals undergoing involutional changes, a restricted range of interests, hypochondriasis, and uneasiness may be present. Their attitude, however, is never so hopeless. There are compensations. These persons may become intolerant, irritable, and difficult to live with; but generally they express their algolagnia sadistically rather than masochistically. The feeling of being wronged or discarded does not develop into a delusion of sin or unworthiness, and there is better preservation of the individual personality.

In the involutional psychotics there is more marked, more constant, and more prolonged expression of agitated depression or disillusioned apathy. The anxiety has taken more complete hold, and one is dealing with a continuous anxiety state. Objects of pity, these patients develop feelings of unreality and their ideas are further divorced from reality. Superficially the endocrine and autonomic symptoms do not appear as severe and are outweighed by the mental signs. The somatic factors are not as evident on the surface and are overshadowed by the individual's hypochondriacal

complaints, which are out of proportion to the physical findings. The emotions are more rigid, stereotyped, and circumscribed; and there is no daily fluctuation. Evidences of regression are present.

In the nomenclature approved by the American Psychiatric Association, this group is designated "involutional psychoses." It is listed as a subdivision of psychoses due to disturbance of metabolism, nutrition, or endocrine function. Two subtypes are mentioned —the melancholic and the paranoid.

The involution psychoses usually are described as those depressions occurring in middle life and later years without evidence of organic intellectual defects or without a history of previous depression. The symptoms manifested are those of agitation, uneasiness, insomnia, or self-condemnatory trends (the so-called melancholia type, formerly called "involutional" melancholia). In this type of psychosis are also included those cases who during the involutional period and without any previous indication of paranoid reactions show transitory or prolonged paranoid trends, with delusions of persecution, suspicion, and misinterpretation.

However, in females, involutional psychoses may also be regarded as mental disorders which occur coincident with, or soon after, the phenomenon called the menopause. According to Albright (1), the female menopause is associated with the cessation or diminution of ovarian function and the lack of production of ovarian hormones.

The clinical features of the "involutional melancholias" have been described by Dreyfus (cited by Kraepelin) (22), who considered them as mixed manic or agitated depressions. Kraepelin (22) considered this psychosis as more nearly allied to schizophrenia but later agreed with some of the concepts of Dreyfus (22), although only partially. Psychiatric opinions still are divided as to whether the involutional psychosis may properly be classified with the agitated depressions or is a separate entity or group of entities. Titley (35) has stated that the agitated depressions and involutional psychoses are identical with respect to prepsychotic personality and clinical features. He describes the narrowed interests, the difficulty in reacting to change, and the unfriendly attitudes observed. He suggests separation of the agitated depressions from the clear-cut manic-depressive depressions.

On the other hand, Strecker and Palmer (33) and Palmer and

Sherman (26) stress the rigidity of persons developing involutional melancholia. However, they state that this psychosis differs from the agitated depressions and insist that there is a definite prepsychotic type of involutional personality.

McCurdy (23) stressed the psychologic concomitants of this period and described the emotional and total personality characteristics encountered in these psychoses. He further attempted to align those cases exhibiting ridiculous delusions with the schizophrenic group. Others he considered as belonging to the manic-depressive reaction type or as a recurrence of a manic-depressive psychosis. He mentioned two other types, one with apathy and hypochondriasis and the other with fear of impending death or poverty.

Kirby (15) distinguished four main groups: (*a*) cases of simple anxiety; (*b*) cases of anxiety with fear, perplexity, and allopsychic "concepts"; (*c*) cases with a somatic complex and feelings of unreality; and (*d*) cases developing arteriosclerosis. White (37) included the involutional psychoses in the presenile group. Manifestations observed in early Alzheimer's disease or cerebral arteriosclerosis do seem to parallel the symptoms seen in involutional psychoses.

Jelliffe and White (19) have stated that the mechanisms associated with involutional melancholia are acute loss or disappointment, narcissistic fixation on the love object, with identification and marked ambivalence. The psychoanalytic school seems to regard involutional melancholia as essentially a narcissistic disorder. Regression, "genital loss," relinquishment of all adult strivings, turning to the loving parent, liberation of the early instinctive drives, as well as anal and obsessive tendencies, have been stressed. Alexander (23) mentions the strife between the ego and the harsh superego. However, in the evolution of the psychosis, we are impressed by the fluctuations in the superego and the id, together with ego's attempt to maintain itself between these two changing forces. The id forces frequently flare up before they wane. The superego power is frequently lessened as the process continues. These two forces, derived as they are largely from the unconscious, are more under the influence of the restrictive catabolic and conditioned reflex alterations occurring in this period.

For a further survey of the literature on this subject the

reader is referred to the contributions of Kraepelin (22), Henderson (15), Henderson and Gillespie (16), McCurdy (23), and
Strecker and Palmer (33).

The controversial points raised in regard to this psychosis
center about the influence of the prepsychotic personality, the endocrinological (especially estrogenic) factors, and the effects of the
involutional period per se with special reference to the psychologic
changes occurring in this period. Do these psychoses appear exclusively in rigid personalities? Are they due entirely to hormonic
alterations? Are they peculiar to the involutional period? Is
there a single entity in the involutional psychosis? Are there groups
of symptoms referable to the involutional period? Are they delayed or latent schizophrenias? Are they recurrent to late-appearing manic-depressive reactions, or are they prolongations of severe
psychoneurotic reactions? It is doubtful if these questions can always be answered satisfactorily, particularly in regard to the
schizophrenic reaction types.

Sevringhaus (31) has stated that the manifestations in the
menopause are so varied in type that one is tempted to attribute
to the climacterium any complaint without obvious cause which is
made by a woman in the fifth or sixth decade of life. He has also
advised the use of large doses of estrogens but recognizes the importance of psychotherapy.

Gynecologists have been divided in their opinions concerning
the influence of the personality in the mild symptoms manifested
in the menopause. Some texts state that the mild as well as the
malignant symptoms occur in predisposed individuals. Others
believe that the atrophic gonadal changes, the pituitary, adrenal,
and thyroid influence, and the autonomic functions are responsible.
The artificial menopause and castration syndrome is thought by
some to exhibit symptoms more or less identical with the real menopause, although this has not always been the experience of the
writer.

It would seem, from the scant mention which the involutional
syndrome has received in gynecological and medical tests, that
until recently the approach to these early cases has been almost
entirely gynecological or endocrinologic and that the psychiatric
aspects have been more or less disregarded. This attitude is
epitomized in Hawkinson's (14) contribution in 1938: One thou-

sand consecutive patients were treated by him with concentrated estrogens. He admits that the precise mechanisms by which symptoms are produced is not fully known, but mentions as etiological factors the endocrine imbalance in this period and its effect on the autonomic nervous system. He used as much as 10,000 international units of estrogen in oil daily in 14 cases of involutional melancholia, which he characterizes as a condition associated with menopause. Twelve cases are reported to have made complete recovery. One of the patients who did not respond was considered to have schizophrenia. Hawkinson (14) further states: "There is no question that psychotherapy and sedatives are of some value in the treatment of the menopausal syndrome. However, their value has been too highly regarded. Few patients were given psychotherapy. The limited value of psychotherapy and sedatives is demonstrated when estrogen is discontinued."

He continues with the statement that insufficient therapy is often worse than no therapy at all and accounts for the failure reported. The work of Sevringhaus (31), Werner (36), Mazer and Israel (14), and Frank and his associates (13) is reviewed to support this contention. According to this résumé, many internists seem to believe that the involutional syndrome can be explained and treated on a purely endocrinologic basis. Small doses of estrogens are condemned because of their stimulative effect. Large doses are recommended because of their value as substitution therapy.

III. DELIMITATION OF THE PSYCHOSES

The involutional psychoses in males differ in certain respects from the symptom complex in the female. Psychologic manifestations in the involutional period occur more frequently among women. The number of female patients exceeds the number of male patients with involutional psychoses in the ratio of 8:3. Mild or involutional psychoses which resemble the normal menopausal symptoms and appear to have a rather intimate association with the climacterium are encountered more often in females. Because of the complex pelvic, endocrine, and autonomic organization, some of the psychologic concomitants may be recognized earlier, and milder agitated depressions arising from the emotional tensions in this period of life are more frequent among women.

A smaller percentage of the mild forms of this psychosis are observed among men. Severe apathy or more general emotional unstable behavior is found more often than the typical agitated depressions manifested by the women. Impotence and early organic changes in the central nervous system are more often encountered. Since the male patients exhibiting symptoms of the involutional period are on the average older by ten years than the women, accompanying arteriosclerotic, senile, or presenile changes occur more often.

The involutional psychoses usually occur in women after 40 years and are found in the pre-, intra-, and postclimacteric stages but are more often closely associated with the menopause. Although a depression without retardation has been considered characteristic, the psychosis may begin as a simple or clear-cut depression with retardation or apathy, or at times as an excitement. True depressive retardation may appear in its course, or as a terminal reaction, or in the prodrome. The typical agitated depression appears frequently at some time in the course of the psychosis. However, depression with overproductivity and hypomotility or depression with hypermotility and restricted ideation or underproductivity are often found. Continual repetition of the same depressive ideation and a pseudostereotypy of rhythmic to-and-fro movement accompanied by hand-wringing, hand-clasping, or other manual manifestations are often present. A certain tenseness of mood and increased muscle tonus is often observed. Indecision also is frequently observed.

Superficially, there is a slow, gradual, "restrictive" alteration in the personality; however, certain repressed, poorly utilized conflicts and guilt feelings, maladaptations, and "castration" mechanisms often come to the fore. Thus the change may be more apparent than real. A restricted range of interests occurs noticeably prior to the psychosis. There is a tendency to withdraw from "outside objects" or persons. This appears deliberate and emotionally conditioned, rather than instinctive or impulsive as is the case of patients with dementia praecox. The shrinkage is accompanied by a "horrified" emotional reaction as if the person touching the patient is polluting or being polluted. The self-interest and self-preoccupation must be differentiated from self-absorption. The individuals are quite aware of the external surroundings, but do not deign to notice them. A painful, perverse narcissism is present, with an attempt, often unsuccessful, to annoy and punish the persons about them as well as themselves. Regressive phenomena are not as obvious in the early states of this psychosis when compared with those observed in schizophrenia.

The anxiety is more marked, more constant, and more prolonged than that found in the anxiety neurosis. It has taken more complete hold of the personality. There is less hope, more depression, and greater agitation.

The anxious, agitated depression occurs more frequently here than in the mixed manic reactions seen in the earlier periods of life. It is less frequently a transitional, changing phase, as in the cyclothymic reaction type. Elation or elevation of mood does not appear with the irritability seen in young manics. The expression of their irritability is rarely so destructive to the object or to the world about them as it is in the younger mixed manics, although the tendency is there. Self-destruction and self-destruction ideation are more common. In studies of mentally ill patients who had attempted suicide, it was found that about one-third of the attempts were made by individuals in the involutional period and that the greater percentage of these were women.

At the same time one notes a certain attitude of martyrdom in regard to those about them. Although they are wronged, they are willing to take the blame; although they are not worthy of the world, the world is not worthy of them and does not appreciate their sacrifice. They figuratively "disembowel themselves on their neighbor's doorstep." They may beg to be saved but "know" no one will or can save them. A whining, disgusted, nagging attitude toward the marital partner, relatives, or physicians is frequently observed. There is more rigidity and a greater tendency to regress than is observed in manic-depressive states. Manic-depressive or other psychotic manifestations are not as often observed in the family history. The mood is more appropriate to ideas expressed than in schizophrenia, but affect is a trifle less labile and is more circumscribed than that observed in manic-depressive psychoses. Marked fear, hypochondriacal delusions, ideas of sin and unworthiness, hallucinations, and paranoid manifestations are common.

The development and course of the psychosis is dependent upon the precipitating catabolic, physicoendocrine, and other complicating factors and the severity of the repressed conflicts which come to the fore, as well as the personality. The satisfactions, bolstering, hope, or compensations that can be obtained from the environment are often important in the prevention of the more serious symptoms.

Those who have had previous manic-depressive or mixed attacks are excluded from this group of involutional psychoses. Such cases, however, should be further investigated with respect to their contrast or similarity to the involutional picture.

In only a few cases did we find psychoneuroses early in life of sufficient intensity to be considered as such, although psychoneurotic traits were present in many. If the involutional psychoses were to be considered as a continuation of prolonged psychoneuroses, their validity as an entity in these cases might be as seriously questioned as are the involutional symptoms occurring in persons who have had previous attacks of manic-depressive psychosis. The same differentiation must be made in regard to the schizophrenias appearing later in life, or masked schizophrenias, where involutional symptoms may appear superimposed on a pre-existing schizophrenic process.

A minimum of organic cerebral manifestations is present, although arteriosclerosis or early senility may at times mask the picture, be masked by it, or be associated therewith. Somatic disorders, including pelvic and thyroid disease, however, are a precipitating or accompanying factor in about half the cases.

IV. CLASSIFICATION OF INVOLUTIONAL PSYCHOSES

While poor integration of the prepsychotic personality may more or less influence the occurrence of involutional psychoses, this factor in itself seemed to have less bearing on the course and prognosis in some of the patients who apparently suffered from what appeared to be less severe syndromes. Therefore, Brew and Davidoff (3) attempted to subdivide the various types of involutional states encountered, not only according to the severity of presenting symptoms at a given time in the psychosis or the personality factors alone but also on a prognostic basis.

This classification is briefly summarized as follows:

1. *Simple or mild type.*—In this subdivision are placed those patients with more than transitory depressed and agitated states which are apparently caused by the estrogenic deficiency compo-

nent of the climacterium. In general, only a quantitative difference
exists between the psychotic patients of this subgroup and the nonpsychotic individuals mentioned in I. The psychogenic and the
personality factors do not appear as important in these patients as
in other cases classified as having involutional psychoses. This subgroup, therefore, may be considered as manifesting a psychosis due
mainly to an endocrine dyscrasia (estrogenic deficiency). These
patients respond well to estrogenic therapy (Shorr, 17, 29).

2. *The moderate type or mixed type.*—In this subdivision the
symptoms appear to be precipitated to a large extent by the climacterium; but other factors are present. In many of these cases we
are not dealing with one component but with a constellation of factors of psychogenic origin, including personality development, and
of organic origin, including somatic, autonomic, and other endocrine and gonadal influences which may be associated with the
menopause or independent of it. Because of these several factors
involved it may be difficult to decide which element predominates
in the production of symptoms. However, these patients respond
moderately well to therapy, although their improvement tends to
be more temporary and less in degree than that observed in the
mild type. In this group, estrogenic therapy is of value as an adjunct to other procedures, particularly since the reaction is often
reversible. Persons with depressive or cyclothymic tendencies
may be found in this subdivision.

Some of the symptoms found in these patients may be similar
to those observed in the mild type but are generally more severe
or protracted. Somatic complaints which seem out of proportion
to the physical findings, prolonged hypochondriasis, ideas of unworthiness, delusions of sin, an attitude of hopelessness, and some
suicidal tendencies may exist; and a continuous, agitated, anxious,
indecisive state may be present for a considerable space of time.
However, a few of the manifestations are similar to those observed
in the severe type, and the prepsychotic personality factors are observed to influence the course of the psychosis to some extent.

3. *The severe type.*—In this subdivision the involutional symptoms color and are superimposed upon pre-existing severe personality deviations or abnormal mental states. The climacterium per
se is relatively unimportant in comparison with other factors involved. A largely qualitative difference exists between this type

and the involutional syndrome without psychosis. In this group the involutional state is the manifestation of an irreversible ontogenic catabolic process. These patients respond poorly to estrogenic therapy or other forms of treatment.

This group includes among others the individuals described by Palmer (25) as possessing rigid or poorly integrated personalities. They are frequently, in our opinion, predominantly schizoid but not always schizophrenics, although many may be late-appearing or latent cases of dementia praecox. It is often difficult to decide whether these should be grouped as involutional psychoses or as schizophrenics. The paranoid types for the most part appear to be more satisfactorily classified as cases of dementia praecox.

Others found in this subdivision are those resembling manic-depressive, mixed, or severely depressed types, those with previously prolonged somatic or endocrine disturbance including pelvic disease, and those in whom the involutional symptoms are merely early signs of organic brain disease such as arteriosclerosis or presenile psychoses.

These patients frequently manifest marked feelings of unreality and express ideas divorced from reality. Their emotions are more rigid, their actions more stereotyped, their attitude more hopeless and preoccupied. Their behavior is more peculiar and atypical than that usually associated with milder agitated depressions. Bizarre delusions and hallucinations are more in evidence. Repeated suicidal attempts may be noted. Marked tensions, indecisive, compulsive behavior, and a tendency to regression are present. However, many of these symptoms except the most atypical may be observed in the moderate forms and for a time in the mild type, so that severity of symptoms alone cannot be used as a criterion. Another point of view concerning this psychosis has been presented by Palmer (25).

4. *The involutional state complicating other psychoses.*—In this group are placed those cases in whom the involutional disturbance exists concomitantly with well-established or long-standing, definite, functional or organic mental illness. In those patients the onset of the climacterium may intensify or reactivate the psychosis.

It is apparent that estrogenic dyscrasia may exist concomitantly with well-established and long-standing cases of functional or organic mental illness occurring during the involutional period and prior or subsequent to it.

A correlation of the influence of the personality and type of involutional psychosis with respect to prognosis and therapy is in order. Apart from the group as a whole there were distinct differences in the influence of the early personality with respect to prognosis in the three subdivisions outlined by Brew and Davidoff (3). In the mild types the early personality traits had less bearing on the outcome, while in the severe types the personality exercised a more profound influence on the prognosis. In the moderate types somatic and other endocrine influences associated with the menopause or independent of it shared importance with the personality. However, the previous make-up of the individual has more bearing on the outcome in the moderate group than in the mild group.

Furthermore, the prognosis in the severe cases further depended on age of the patient, duration of illness, presence of arteriosclerotic or other organic findings, and paranoid trends, as well as type of personality malintegration.

One of the important pitfalls to avoid in the specific personality estimation of these patients is the inclusion, in the biographical description, of the prepsychotic symptoms occurring in the long prodromal period preceding these psychoses. In this period, compulsive and anxiety states, rigidity, and a restricted range of interests frequently occur with depression. Each case must be carefully evaluated individually.

Almost all the patients in group 1 who exhibited mild symptoms associated with androgenic or estrogenic deficiency showed marked improvement following hormonal-replacement therapy. Adequate estrogenic or androgenic therapy has a definite value in the treatment of involutional psychoses of the mild or simple type. For further discussion of the method of treatment and the gonadal-hormone preparations employed, the reader is referred to papers by Davidoff and Goodstone (6), Davidoff, Reifenstein, and Goodstone (8), Davidoff and Raffaele (9) and Brew and Davidoff (3).

In the second group other etiologic factors were present in addition to gonadal deficiency. About 30 per cent of this moderate type responded very favorably to estrogens or androgens. Approximately 50 per cent were slightly improved. Their improvement was more temporary in nature and required the use of other therapeutic procedures; about 20 per cent were unimproved.

In the severe group we included those patients who failed to show appreciable response to estrogenic or androgenic therapy, those individuals in whom the involutional symptoms colored or were superimposed upon pre-existing severe personality deviations which were frequently schizoid in nature, those in whom long-standing endocrine or somatic disturbances (including pelvic disease) were present, and others in whom the symptoms manifested were similar to the early signs of organic brain disease such as cerebral arteriosclerosis. Patients with paranoid trends belong in this group.

Furthermore, all those patients at times resembled individuals in whom the involutional manifestations obviously occurred subsequent to or concomitant with the symptoms of other well-established functional or organic psychoses. Properly speaking, a majority of this last-mentioned type cannot be allocated with the involutional psychoses. Frequently it is difficult to decide whether a patient should be classified in the severe group of involutional psychoses or should be considered as exhibiting involutional symptoms which complicate paranoid schizophrenic or arteriosclerotic psychoses.

Subsequently it was brought to our attention that some of the female patients in the mixed or moderate group who failed to show appreciable improvement, or who had regressed after initial improvement following estrogenic therapy, responded much more favorably to the administration of electric-shock therapy at the Willard State Hospital and other institutions. Kalinowski (20) and Impastato and Almansi (18) reported marked improvement following electric shock in those who appeared to be moderately severe types but failed to observe any significant changes in patients of the paranoid group. Palmer reported encouraging results following the use of metrazol in patients who apparently manifested symptoms of the protracted type of involutional psychosis.

Electric shock appears to be the treatment of choice in the severe forms and in many of the moderately protracted types. According to Davidoff and Raffaele (9), the results with electric-shock therapy in involutional psychoses of the moderate type and of the severe form may be summarized as follows: Cases of the more severe type of involutional psychosis who had previously received hormonal therapy without much response are best treated with electric shock. Almost all the patients who manifested symptoms of relatively recent onset, symptoms which were more or less allied to typical involutional agitations, and in whom paranoid trends were relatively minimal or less severe or whose personalities were not as markedly schizoid, responded well. Those in whom the atypical features predominated did not react as favorably. The presence of suicidal trends did not affect the prognosis adversely.

Among the female patients those under 50 years of age, the duration of whose illness was generally less than 3 years and who were described as dependent or depressive personalities, reacted best. Women approaching 60 years of age who manifested markedly aggressive schizoid personalities, severe paranoid trends, and arteriosclerotic features and who were ill for more than 5 years did not respond favorably.

In men the presence of advancing years and arteriosclerosis did not necessarily affect the results as adversely. Aggressive personality make-up, which was less commonly found in men, exercised a more favorable influence on their prognosis.

Preliminary administration of sex hormones plus subsequent application of electric shock may serve to differentiate the more typical involutional manifestations from the atypical psychoses which are most likely schizophrenic or arteriosclerotic in nature. Allowing for the exceptions mentioned in the discussion these procedures may be regarded as therapeutic tests.

Preliminary or subsequent treatment with endocrines may also be a useful therapeutic adjunct in obtaining a favorable prognosis in some instances. In addition, the prior administration of hormonal therapy lessens the possibility of vertebral fractures, particularly in females.

Electric shock is a valuable adjunct to the total treatment of patients with severe involutional psychoses, in that it renders them more accessible to psychotherapeutic procedures.

In conclusion, in comparison with other methods of treatment thus far employed, electric shock is the most useful form of therapy in the severe types of involutional psychoses.

For further consideration of treatment with electric shock the reader is referred to the contributions of Kalinowski (20), Impastato (18), Bennett and Wilbur (2), and Davidoff and Raffaele (9). In addition, other procedures employed involved the use of metrazol and insulin. Metrazol is slightly less effective than electric shock and is somewhat more dangerous and unpredictable. Insulin is not nearly as effective as either metrazol or electric shock. Miscellaneous and routine hospital procedures are also of value, including adequate nursing care, sedation or stimulation or a combination of both, hydrotherapy and occupational therapy, adequate medical treatment, including the use of tonic, vitamins, etc. Measures to stimulate appetite and prevent loss of weight also are indicated. At times it is necessary to resort to adjutant endocrine therapy, including the use of thyroid, pituitary, and adrenal preparations. The social-service department of the hospital can be of great aid in the rehabilitation of a patient in the community by attention to familial, economic, and other factors in the patient's environment by making community resources available to the individual, and by assisting in the formation of a program of practical mental hygiene.

REFERENCES

1. Albright, F. "Studies on Ovarian Dysfunction. III. The Menopause," *Endocrinology*, 1936, 20: 24–39
2. Bennett, A. E., and Wilbur, C. B. "Convulsive Shock Therapy in Involutional States after Complete Failure with Previous Estrogenic Treatment" (Read at the 99th Annual Meeting of the American Psychiatric Association, May 1943)
3. Brew, M. F., and Davidoff, E. "The Involutional Psychoses," *Psychiatric Quart.*, 1940, 14: 412–34
4. Burlingame, C. C., and Patterson, M. B. "Involutional Psychoses," *Jour. Nerv. Mental Dis.*, 1941, Vol. 94, No. 3
5. Cohen, L. A. "Involutional Melancholia and Depressive States: Results of Treatment Over a 5-Year Period," *Jour. Arkansas Med. Soc.*, 1951, 48: 123–24
6. Davidoff, E., and Goodstone, G. L. "Use of Testosterone Propionate in Treatment of Involutional Psychosis in the Male,'" *Arch. Neurol. & Psychiatry*, 1942, 48: 811–17
7. ———. "The Treatment of Involutional Psychoses with Diethyl Stilbestrol and Estradiol," *Dis. Nerv. System*, 1942, Vol. 3, No. 11
8. Davidoff, E., Reifenstein, E. C., Jr., and Goodstone, G. L. "The Treatment of Involutional Psychoses with Diethyl Stilbestrol," *Amer. Jour. Psychiatry*, 1943, 99: 557
9. Davidoff, E., and Raffaele, A. "Electric Shock Therapy in Involutional

Psychoses" (Read at the 99th Annual Meeting of the American Psychiatric Association, May 1943), *Jour. Nerv. Mental Dis.*, April 1944, Vol. 99, No. 4

10. Douglas, R. J. "The Male Climacteric: Its Diagnosis and Treatment," *Jour. Urology*, 1941, Vol. 45, No. 3
11. Enelow, A. J. "Psychosomatic Problems of the Involutional Period," *Jour. Kansas Med. Soc.*, 1951, 52: 486–89
12. Fessler, L. "Psychopathology of Climacteric Depression," *Psychoanalyst. Quart.*, 1950, 19: 28–42
13. Frank, R. T., Goldberger, M. A., and Salmon, U. J. "The Menopause Symptoms, Hormonal Status and Treatment," *New York State Jour. Med.*, 1936, 36: 19, 1363, 1371
14. Hawkinson, L. F. "The Menopausal Syndrome: Treatment with Estrogen," *Jour. Amer. Med. Assoc.*, 1938, 115: 390–93
15. Henderson, D. K. *Oxford Medicine* (New York: Oxford University Press, 1936), Vol. 7, chap. i
16. Henderson, D. K., and Gillespie, R. B. *Textbook of Psychiatry.* New York: Oxford University Press, 1932
17. Henry, G. W., and Shorr, E. "Problems of Mental Adjustment at the Climacteric," *U.S. Pub. Health Service*, 168: 125–37
18. Impastato, D. J., and Almansi, R. "A Study of Over Two Thousand Cases of Electrofit-treated Patients," *New York State Jour. Med.*, 1943, 43: 2057–64
19. Jelliffe, S. E., and White, W. A. *Diseases of the Nervous System* (5th edition). Philadelphia: Lea and Febiger, 1929
20. Kalinowski, L., Bigelow, N., and Brikates, P. "Electric Shock Therapy in State Hospital Practice," *Psychiatry*, 1941, 15: 450–59
21. Knoll, H. "Delusional Psychoses During the Period of Climacterium and Involution: Clinical and Genealogic Aspects," *Arch. Psychiatry*, 1952, 189: 59–92
22. Kraepelin, E. *Manic-depressive Insanity and Paranoia.* Trans. by M. Barclay and G. M. Robertson. Edinburgh: Livingstone, 1921
23. McCurdy, J. T. *The Psychology of Emotion.* New York: Harcourt, Brace & Co., 1925
24. Milici, P. S. "Involutional Death Reaction," *Psychiatric Quart.*, 1950, 24: 775–81
25. Palmer, H. D. "Involutional Psychoses," in *Mental Health in Later Maturity*, Suppl. No. 168, *U.S. Pub. Health Repts.*, 1942, 168: 118–24
26. Palmer, H. D., and Sherman, S. H. "The Involutional Melancholia Process," *Arch. Neurol. & Psychiatry*, 1939, 40: 762–88
27. Polatin, P., and McDonald, J. F. "Symposium on Geriatric Gynecology: Involutional Psychoses," *Geriatrics*, 1951, 6: 391–98
28. Reifenstein, E. C., Jr. Personal communication
29. Ripley, H. S., Shorr, E., and Papanicolaou, G. N. "The Effect of Treatment of Depression in the Menopause with Estrogenic Hormone," *Amer. Jour. Psychiatry*, 1940, 96: 905–10
30. Rusch, K. H. "Involutional Melancholia," *Hawaii Med. Jour.*, 1952, 11: 152–54
31. Sevringhaus, E. L. *Endocrine Therapy in General Practice.* Chicago: Year Book Publishing Co., 1938

32. Shorr, E., Robinson, F. H., and Papanicolaou, G. N. "Clinical Studies of the Synthetic Estrogen Stilbestrol," *Jour. Amer. Med. Assoc.*, 1939, 113: 2312–18
33. Strecker, E. A., and Palmer, H. D. *Oxford Medicine* (New York: Oxford University Press, 1936), Vol. 7, chap. i
34. Tait, C. D., Jr., and Burns, G. C. "Involutional Illnesses; Survey of 397 Patients, Including Follow-up of 114," *Amer. Jour. Psychiatry*, 1951, 108: 27–36
35. Titley, W. "Prepsychotic Personality of Patients with Involutional Melancholia," *Arch. Neurol. & Psychiatry*, 1936, 36: 19
36. Werner, A. A. "The Male Climacteric," *Jour. Amer. Med. Assoc.*, 1939, 112: 1441–43
37. White, W. A. *Outline of Psychiatry.* Washington, D.C.: Nervous and Mental Disease Publishing Co., 1929
38. Young, R. J. "Rorschach Diagnosis and Interpretation of Involutional Melancholia," *Amer. Jour. Psychiatry*, 1950, 106: 748–49

Chapter X

THE PRESENILE DEMENTIAS

George A. Jervis

THE TERM "presenium" is conventionally applied to that period of life preceding senility and is arbitrarily understood to include the years from 45 (or 40) to 60. The occurrence of forms of dementia during this period of life has been known for many a year, but only toward the end of the last century was the concept of presenile dementia introduced in psychiatry by Biswanger and shortly after clarified and expanded by Kraepelin (57) and his school.

Originally, the term presenile dementia was meant to characterize an early and rapid senility or, more correctly, a type of organic intellectual deterioration in which the processes of senescence play an important, if not the exclusive, role. Of late, however, the term has been increasingly used as a purely temporal notion, to indicate any type of organic dementia occurring in the presenium irrespective of its relationship to senility.

Classifications of presenile dementias, in this broad sense, include two main groups:

a) The primary (or essential or specific) presenile dementias.—With some exceptions, these are diseases peculiar to the presenium, occurring almost exclusively in this age period. Moreover, each type shows a characteristic clinicopathologic picture which may be considered to a certain extent "specific" of that particular type. Finally, these diseases are "primary" or "essential" in the sense that little is known of the etiologic factors operating in the determination of the pathologic process, although it is generally conceded that the incidence of the disease in the presenium is of some etiologic significance.

b) The secondary presenile dementias.—These are observed at various age periods and their occurrence in the presenium is usually fortuitous. As the designation "secondary" implies, the dementia is caused by a known etiologic agent. In the secondary group are included arteriosclerotic, syphilitic, neoplastic, toxic, and traumatic presenile dementias. In each secondary type the

262

clinicopathologic picture is that of the original condition which is at the basis of the morbid process, the age factor contributing only unimportant features.

In the present chapter, the primary presenile dementias only will be considered. This group includes two well-established clinicopathologic entities associated with the names of Alzheimer and Pick; two conditions, the so-called Jakob's disease and Kraepelin's disease, the distinctive traits of which are not yet completely known; and a certain number of sporadic cases whose classification in this group remains open to question.

I. ALZHEIMER'S DISEASE

Definition.—Alzheimer's disease is a presenile dementia, of unknown etiology, characterized clinically by rapidly progressing mental deterioration and multiple neurologic symptoms and pathologically by severe brain changes of the senile type.

History.—Alzheimer (4) in 1907 published the first clinical and pathological description of the disease. To Kraepelin (57) are due the recognition of the disease as a well-defined clinicopathologic entity and the basic criteria for its differentiation from other psychoses. In this country the disease was recognized as early as 1912 (Fuller, 33) and has been the object of numerous studies. These will be mentioned in the course of the discussion.

Incidence.—Although the commonest of all primary types of presenile dementias, Alzheimer's disease is still considered of infrequent occurrence. However, comprehensive statistics on the incidence of the disease are not available, and on the basis of limited surveys there is the distinct possibility that the condition is more frequent than commonly thought. For instance, a 4 per cent incidence in a series of necropsies performed in a psychiatric institution is reported in America (88) and in Italy (8). In England, 1.2 per cent was found in comparable material (63). In Sweden (93), 7 per cent of all cases of psychoses of later life were found to be instances of Alzheimer's disease.

The incidence among women is larger than among men, in the proportion of 3:2.

Etiology.—It was Kraepelin's original opinion (57) that Alzheimer's disease is a severe and early variety of senile dementia—the "praecocious senium" of Fuller (33)—which is determined by the same constitutional factors operating in senility and in senile dementia. As a matter of fact, the type of pathologic changes and, to a lesser degree, the clinical picture of Alzheimer's disease may be regarded as fundamentally similar to those of senile dementia. Differences may be found only in the earlier onset of Alzheimer's disease, its more rapid course, the peculiarity of some of its clinical features, and the greater intensity of its pathologic lesions.

That endogenous factors are of significance in the etiology of the disease was recently confirmed by several authors (10, 28, 41), who published interesting instances, verified histologically, of Alzheimer's disease occurring in siblings. Similar cases, lacking, however, pathologic confirmation, were previously recorded (8, 27, 62, 64, 92). Sufficient data are thus available indicating that in a certain number of cases genetic factors play a role in the causation of Alzheimer's disease.

However, the classical opinion which considers Alzheimer's disease a form of precocious senility is hardly consistent with the observation that occasionally the disease occurs at an earlier age than presenium. These "early" cases may be divided into two groups, the adult and the juvenile (30). The adult variety of Alzheimer's disease occurs in the fourth decade of life and includes no more than ten published cases which show typical clinical picture and characteristic pathology. The juvenile variety occurs before the fourth decade. Here are included a few cases showing the pathologic lesions of Alzheimer's disease and a symptomatology which is more akin to that of a toxic psychosis than to the clinical picture originally described by Kraepelin (57). Most significant among these juvenile cases is the patient described by Malamud and Löwenberg (66), a boy of 15 years of age who showed excitement, confusion, and compulsive and negativistic behavior. After a remission of about four years he developed progressive mental deterioration, and died at 24 years of age. At post-mortem there were numerous senile plaques and Alzheimer's neurofibrillary changes diffuse throughout the cerebral cortex. The nosological position of the juvenile variety is still in doubt (54); in fact, the clinical features are very atypical, and the finding of senile plaques and Alzheimer's neurofibrillary degeneration is not exclusive of other diseases of the brain. In any event, the occurrence of "early" cases of Alzheimer's disease is highly significant for the etiologic problem, suggesting the action of factors other than that of senescence.

In conclusion, although definite deductions as to the etiology of Alzheimer's disease are not possible in the present state of our knowledge, the available data permit tentative assumptions and indicate the lines along which further research may be prosecuted. It appears well founded, first, that the process of senescence plays an important role in the causation of the disease, as indicated by the age of the majority of patients and the senile type of pathology; second, that constitutional and probably genetic factors are operative in determining premature pathologic aging of the brain, as evidenced by the occasional familial incidence of the disease; third, that the role of senescence is not exclusive, being supplemented by contributing pathogenic factors, exogenous and probably toxic or infectious in nature (61).

The assumption of this variety of factors will make it reasonable to conceive of numerous gradations, from the classical endogenous case in which constitutional factors are conspicuous and exogenous agencies minimal, to the "early" atypical juvenile case resembling toxic psychosis in which exogenous factors predominate over endogenous ones.

Morbid anatomy.—On gross examination, the brain as a whole shows usually marked atrophy; the sulci are wide and shallow, the convolutions are narrow, the white matter is shrunken, and the ventricles are enlarged. Grossly, the atrophic process involves more markedly the cerebral cortex than any other portion of the brain. Of the cortex, the prefrontal and temporal areas are not infrequently more atrophic than other cortical zones. In some instances the parietal convolutions appear most affected; however, clear-cut circumscribed atrophies of the brain, as seen in Pick's disease, are absent.

On microscopic examination, the atrophic cerebral cortex shows a conspicuous diminution in the number of nerve cells, resulting in a disorganization of the normal cytoarchitecture. This numerical loss is usually diffuse throughout all cellular layers of the cortex, although not infrequently the superficial layers, from first to third, are more affected than the deep ones. Occasionally, a selective involvement of the third layer or of the third and fifth may be observed. The nerve cells still remaining in the atrophic cortex frequently show degenerative changes; among these, the most commonly found is a process of cellular atrophy whereby the cytoplasm of the nerve cell decreases in volume, the nucleus shows incipient degeneration, and the whole cell appears shrunken. Intracellular pigment is often increased. A peculiar type of neurocellular change may be found which is characterized by the presence of cytoplasmic vacuoles containing small granules ("granulovacuolar degeneration").

Following the loss of neurons, the glia tissue proliferates, filling up the space left vacant by the destruction of the nerve cells. This glial hyperplasia, however, is usually inconspicuous. Not infrequently the proliferated glia cells show evidence of degenerative changes. Diminution in number and atrophic changes of the myelin sheath also are observed in association with and depending upon the alterations of the nerve cells. Such various pathologic changes are not limited to the cerebral cortex; to a lesser degree, similar features are observed in the basal ganglia, the thalamus, and the cerebellum.

In addition to this unspecific pathologic picture, two distinctive types of histologic alterations are present which may be considered characteristic, although not exclusive, of Alzheimer's disease, i.e., senile plaques and so-called Alzheimer's neurofibrillary changes. Senile plaques are minute areas of tissue degeneration measuring from 5 to 150 micra in diameter, more or less spherical in configuration, and consisting of a granular or filamentous detritus which shows strong affinity for silver. The argentophil material is often mingled with degenerated fragments of glia cells, neurofibrils, and nerve cells. Not infrequently, at the periphery of the plaque, glia cells of various types are observed exhibiting varying proliferative and regressive changes. A large variety of forms results from the different arrangement of the various constituent elements. Thus plaques may appear as a small deposit of dust-like argentophil substance ("primitive plaques") or may show complicated ring-shaped, star-shaped, or radial figures with or without a central amorphous core. Small plaques may fuse together to form large plaques, often of bizarre configuration. Senile plaques are present throughout the gray matter of the cerebral cortex and, to less extent, of the basal ganglia, the cerebellum, and the brain stem.

Only occasionally are plaques present in the white matter. The histogenesis of the senile plaques is obscure. It is probable that a circumscribed necrotic process occurs following local metabolic alteration—whether in the intercellular tissue or in the cellular elements it is difficult to determine. Subsequently, a reaction of microglia develops about the necrotic tissue, followed by a stage of astroglia proliferation. There is some histological evidence indicating that the microglia reaction is very conspicuous in Alzheimer's disease; this feature would differentiate the senile plaques occurring in this condition from those observed in other diseases, particularly in senile dementia, where microglia proliferation is scanty (52).

So-called Alzheimer's neurofibrillary changes consist of an irregular thickening, conglutination, and alteration of alignment of the intracellular neurofibrils. The fibrils thus altered show strong affinity for silver and acquire characteristically bizarre aspects shaping variously as spirals, loops, strands, baskets, etc. The nucleus of the affected cells usually undergoes degenerative changes and eventually disappears. This type of change is found usually throughout the entire cortex and involves all forms of nerve cells, although it is observed most conspicuously in the large pyramidal cells. Its distribution is irregular. In certain regions the proportion of cells thus altered to normal cells may be as high as 1 to 4.

Senile plaques and neurofibrillary changes are present in almost every case of Alzheimer's disease. However, Alzheimer (4) himself reported an instance without neurofibrillary changes and, recently, Grünthal and Wegner (41) described a typical case without senile plaques. Although in no other condition are senile plaques and neurofibrillary changes found in such abundance as in Alzheimer's disease, they are by no means pathognomonic of this condition, being present also in senile dementia. They are found, occasionally, in normal senility and in a variety of brain diseases, including, among others, amyotrophic lateral sclerosis, chronic encephalitis, and certain types of cerebellar ataxia.

The blood vessels of the brain show no significant alteration, as a rule. Some fibrosis of small vessels may be present, but arteriosclerotic changes are absent.

Examination of viscera and tissues other than the central nervous system shows no constant pathologic changes which might be considered characteristic of the disease.

Symptoms and signs.—The clinical picture of Alzheimer's disease is characterized by the occurrence of mental changes and neurological symptoms and signs.

The course of the disease may be conveniently divided into three stages. In the first stage the outstanding symptom is usually an incipient intellectual deterioration which first becomes apparent in an impairment in the field of calculation and logical reasoning; in a defective perception and comprehension, particularly of abstract material; in a loss of co-ordinating function and a narrowing of the ability to perform in several fields at once (14). Loss of memory for recent events is often one of the first symptoms which indicate the oncoming dementia. Spatial disorientation is frequently observed (26). Alterations of emotional reactions develop concomitantly with the intellectual deficit. Although the character of the change depends to a certain extent upon the emotional pattern of the prepsychotic personality, it is a matter of observation that depression of mood, anxiety, and irritability are much more frequent than elation, euphoria, or apathy. Changes in personality and general behavior, such as disregard of property, callousness, and antisocial or immoral acts, are observed not infrequently. If paranoid patterns were present before the disease develops, paranoid trends may characterize the onset of the disease, although fixed and systematized paranoid delusions are rare. Insight is often preserved at this time, at least, as a certain distressing awareness of impending insanity.

In this first stage, alterations of the speech mechanism are not infrequent. Words are forgotten, pronunciation is difficult and faulty, comprehension of spoken language is poor, and errors are committed in writing and reading. Epileptic attacks occur occasionally at this time.

In the second stage the clinical picture becomes more characteristic. The intellectual impairment is now obvious in every mental performance. Memory appears to be particularly involved. Confabulations and vague delusions may be present. Hallucinations are rare and usually fleeting in character. Mood is deeply altered; the patients are depressed, apprehensive, and even distressed. Apathetic and euphoric states are infrequent. Compulsive crying and laughing may be present. The observation of the general behavior of these patients shows consistently some hyperactivity, continuous or sporadic in character. This manifests itself in various forms—a general restlessness, an aimless wandering around, a tendency to repetition of the same acts or the same occupation in a stereotyped manner, etc. (46). The overactivity tends to become more futile and less purposeful with the advance of the dementia. The general behavior and emotional reaction of patients affected with Alzheimer's disease occasionally show striking similarities to those of patients suffering from involutional melancholia (96).

Outstanding among the neurological manifestations of the second stage are alterations in the speech mechanism. The articulation of words is defective, speech is slurred, names are mixed up, sentences contain grammatical errors or are often incomplete and poor in substantives (96). Understanding of spoken words is gravely impaired. Other speech disturbances often encountered are "clang" association of words, tendency to senseless rhyming, repetition as an echo of a sentence or part of a sentence (echolalia), automatic reiteration of the last words of a sentence (palilalia), and stereotyped repetition of distorted and meaningless parts of words (logoclonia). The functions of writing and reading are always disturbed earlier and more severely than speech. The profound alteration of speech mechanism is of a complex nature; it appears to be the result of the interaction of cortical focal lesions and diffuse cortical damage, the former resulting in various aphasic symptoms, the latter conducive to intellectual deterioration. As a matter of fact, it is usually difficult in the single patient to assess the element of speech impairment due to aphasia and that due to dementia, the two components being almost inseparable from each other.

Other neurological manifestations observed at this stage are various types of agnosia and apraxia, tremors of different varieties, and paresis and rigidities of both extrapyramidal and pyramidal nature. Epileptic seizures of the grand mal type occur in a large percentage of cases. Usually, following each epileptic attack, there is noted a more rapid progress of the mental deterioration.

The third stage of the disease shows little that is characteristic. The patients are deeply demented and reduced to a purely vegetative existence. Speech is limited to a few automatic utterances without sentence formation. Contractures of extremities are frequent. Death intervenes usually from intercurrent infection.

Laboratory examination.—The air encephalogram is characteristic, showing generalized cortical atrophy with enlargement of the lateral ventricles and of the basal cisterns (68, 87).

Electroencephalogram in advanced cases shows small irregular changes of potential and absence of rhythmic activity (96).

There are no significant changes of the spinal fluid.

Differential diagnosis.—Aside from the characters of the clinical picture, Alzheimer's disease is differentiated from the secondary types of presenile dementia by routine methods which are used to rule out known etiologic factors such as brain tumors, syphilis, or other specific infection, arteriosclerosis, etc. Not infrequently, difficulties arise in the differential diagnosis from arteriosclerotic dementia. Helpful points in favor of arteriosclerosis are, aside from physical signs of arterial involvement, a sudden appearance of symptoms and their frequent conspicuous remission, a lacunar instead of a global type of intellectual deterioration, unevenness of the memory defect, preservation of a certain insight even in advanced stages, and lack of emotional control.

Senile dementia can be differentiated on the basis of the more advanced age, the slower evolution, and the absence of evidence of focal cortical lesions, particularly of speech defects.

The most difficult diagnostic problem of Alzheimer's disease is its differentiation from Pick's disease. The age of onset, the progressive organic dementia, and the presence of focal cortical signs are common to both conditions. However, the observation of the general behavior will usually show overactivity in Alzheimer's and loss of initiative in Pick's disease; emotional distress and agitation in the former and apathy in the latter. In Pick's disease, memory defect occurs later and is less pronounced. Preservation of insight at the onset is more consistent with the diagnosis of Alzheimer's disease. Signs of cortical focal lesions are usually clearer in Pick's than in Alzheimer's disease, where they are concealed in a more global and more rapid intellectual deterioration. The air encephalogram is of great diagnostic value, showing circumscribed cortical atrophy in Pick's disease in contrast to the diffuse type of atrophy in Alzheimer's disease. In exceptional cases, the diagnostic problem may be solved by performing a biopsy of the brain cortex.

Prognosis is invariably fatal. The duration of the disease is from 2 to 10 years, the average being about 4 years. The course is steadily progressive, although remissions have been occasionally recorded in atypical cases.

Treatment is limited to routine symptomatic measures.

II. PICK'S DISEASE

Definition.—Pick's disease is a presenile psychosis of unknown etiology, characterized clinically by a combination of progressive dementia and focal cortical signs and pathologically by circumscribed atrophy of the brain.

History.—The condition was first described by A. Pick (76, 82) in a series of papers, the first of which was published in 1892. Pick's original purpose was to illustrate the different aphasic manifestations occurring in senility. Subsequent contributions dealt mainly with the aphasic and apraxic sides of the disease. Since 1926 the Munich School of Psychiatry published a series of remarkable papers (15, 16, 74, 91, 94, 99), which have definitely established Pick's disease as a distinct clinicopathologic entity. A similar concept had been previously advanced by Reich (83, 84, 85) and Gans (34).

Incidence.—Pick's disease is a rare condition. Some two hundred cases have been published in the literature. It is undoubtedly rarer than Alzheimer's disease, the ratio being variously assessed as 1 to 10 or 1 to 15. An incidence of 0.2 per cent in the autopsy material of a mental hospital is reported by Neuman (71).

Women are more frequently affected than men, in a proportion of 2 to 1.

Etiology.—Pick's original contention was that the condition he described is closely related to, if not a variety of, senile dementia. In favor of this concept is the age of the patients, which ranges, as a rule, within the limits of the presenium, with not infrequent exceptions in older age; thus one of Pick's cases was 72, Braunmühl's patient (15) was 79, Bonfiglio's (13) was 80, and Moyano's (70) was 91 years old. Furthermore, in both senility and Pick's disease the pathologic changes of the neuron cells consist primarily of a slow process of cellular atrophy which is diffuse in distribution in the former, circumscribed in the latter.

In opposition to Pick's contention is the concept that the etiology of the disease is to be found in a specific heredo-degenerative process independent of senescence. The following significant data seem to corroborate this concept.

First, repeated observations show that genetic factors play an important role in the determination of the disease. Clinical and genealogic reports suggesting that Pick's disease may affect several members of a family have been published (43, 60, 90, 101). This suggestion was verified by the reports of complete clinicopathologic studies of sibs suffering from Pick's disease (17, 24, 39, 40). Moreover, Sanders *et al.* (89) commented on a family in which seventeen members were presumably affected by the disease in the course of four generations; the diagnosis was confirmed at autopsy in four members. A similar family was reported by Malamud and Wagoner (65), having fifteen affected members in four generations. In a family reported by Friedreich (31), the disease was present in two generations and the clinical diagnosis was confirmed by pathological findings. There is little doubt that in these three families the condition behaves as a Mendelian dominant character.

Second, the pathologic similarities between Pick's disease and senility are confined to the characters of the neurocellular atrophic process; other characteristic traits of the senile brain such as senile plaques and neurofibrillary degeneration do not belong, as a rule, to the pathologic picture of Pick's disease.

Third, typical cases of Pick's disease are known to occur in the fourth decade of life (8, 13, 25, 86) and even earlier (17, 31, 42, 60, 89).

Finally, additional evidence, though of a speculative and controversial nature, may be found in alleged localizations of the atrophic process to functionally differentiated layers of the cerebral cortex (3, 102) or to phylogenetically recent cortical areas (34, 65), these localizations following hypothetical rules which govern the pathologic picture of degenerative diseases of the nervous system.

Any final statement as to the etiology of Pick's disease seems premature. It may be said, however, that the two apparently conflicting etiologic theories, referred to above, are not of necessity mutually exclusive (29). One may conceive, in fact, of a slowly progressive atrophic process, essentially senile in type, involving certain areas of the brain which constitutionally or hereditarily are prone to precocious and rapid aging. This concept will be commented upon further in the final remarks of this chapter.

Morbid anatomy.—Macroscopically, the characteristic pathologic lesion of Pick's disease consists of a striking atrophy involving both gray and white matter, circumscribed to one or more lobes or parts of a lobe of the brain. The atrophic convolutions appear shrunken, often rough in their surface, and sometimes brownish-yellow in color. The underlying white matter is harder than normal in consistency. The demarkation of atrophic area from the remaining parts of the brain is usually clear-cut.

The localization of the atrophic areas varies considerably from case to case. Consequently, different pathologic types have been recognized according to the lobe or lobes involved. Perhaps the most frequent is the bilateral frontal type, in which the atrophy is circumscribed to the frontal lobes; the pole, the anterior third, and the orbital surface (94) are usually most involved, while the precentral convolutions are grossly intact and the inferior frontal gyrus is less atrophic than the first and second. The anterior portion of the insula and the corpus callosum also are involved. The atrophy is usually more pronounced in the left than in the right lobe. Unilateral frontal atrophies are rare. Next in frequency is the bilateral temporal type, in which the second and third temporal convolutions and the fusiform gyrus are most affected. Combinations of frontal and temporal atrophies are frequently observed.

The frontal or temporal atrophic process may spread to involve the parietal lobe (especially the angular and supramarginal convolutions), the occipital lobe, and the basal ganglia, resulting in a wide variety of types and combination of types. Exclusive localizations to the occipital lobe (47), to parietal areas (58), and to the corpus striatum (11) have been described but are the exception.

Microscopic examination of the atrophic areas of the cortex shows considerable loss of nerve cells resulting in a profound disorganization of the normal cellular lamination. At times all layers are involved; at other times only the superficial layers or the third and fifth are more damaged than the remaining ones. The neuron cells, which are still present in the diseased areas, exhibit marked alterations consisting of atrophy of the cell body with pyknosis of the nucleus. In addition, two distinct types of neurocellular degeneration which may be considered characteristic of Pick's disease are frequently found. The first consists of a peculiar "swelling" of the nerve cell; the cell body appears enlarged and round in shape, the Nissl bodies disintegrate, the cytoplasm acquiring a homogeneous structure, and the nucleus is displaced toward the periphery. These pathologic features are somewhat similar to those of the "primary reaction" of Nissl. The second type consists of peculiar inclusions within the cytoplasm of the nerve cells, the size of a nucleus or larger, round in shape, homogeneous or finely granular in texture and showing strong affinities for silver. They are known as "argentophil cytoplasmic inclusions of Alzheimer." Cellular swellings and cytoplasmic inclusions are found frequently but not regularly in Pick's disease. Their distribution is uneven throughout the atrophic cortex; little-involved areas often contain a larger number of swellings and inclusions than severely atrophic convolutions. The nature and significance of these changes are obscure. It is known, however, that cellular swellings similar to those described in Pick's disease may be found in several other pathologic conditions and that cytoplasmic inclusions are occasionally seen in a few other diseases.

Nerve fibers partake of the atrophic process in the affected lobes. Occasionally, in cases of rapid evolution, extensive destruction of myelinated fibers is found which appears to be independent of cellular loss (17, 91).

Protoplasmic and fibrous glia proliferate in the atrophic areas. There are observed cases in which the glia proliferation is so conspicuous that the condition has been considered a primary alteration of the glia (18, 44); however, in other instances even the proliferated glia undergoes in time atrophic changes. The other types of glia (oligo- and microglia) have little part, if any, in the pathologic process.

Iron pigment is found in abnormal amount in the atrophic areas and in other parts of the brain. Morphological alterations of the blood vessels are usually absent. Senile plaques and Alzheimer's neurofibrillary changes do not belong, as a rule, to the pathologic picture of Pick's disease.

Incipient microscopic pathologic changes of the type described above may be found also in cortical areas which grossly show no atrophy. Similar changes are often present in the basal ganglia (1, 16).

Symptoms and signs.—Characteristic of the clinical picture of Pick's disease are a slowly progressive dementia, organic in type, and symptoms of focal cortical lesion, mainly aphasia, apraxia, and agnosia. These vary in accordance with the type of localization of the atrophic process.

The clinical course of the disease may be conveniently divided into three stages (91). In the initial stage, intellectual impairment develops insidiously; the patients show some difficulty in thinking and concentration, are easily fatigued and distractible, and reveal a peculiar inability to elaborate new mental material, to deal with unaccustomed problems, or to adapt themselves to new situations (91, 99). Memory is little involved. In successive performances, interest, attention, and intellectual ability often show marked fluctuations. These are best explained by the hypothesis of Goldstein and Katz (36) that the patients have lost the "abstract attitude," whereas the "concrete attitude" is well preserved. In other words, as long as the patients are able to utilize objects or situations from a concrete approach, performances are remarkably correct; but when an abstract approach is necessary, for instance when abstract spatial or temporal relations are used, conspicuous failures become apparent. In the initial stage, emotional changes usually occur: narrowing and blunting of emotional reactions with or without euphoria are the rule, depressive states the exception. As in other types of organic dementias, moral and social values suffer early. In a minority of cases, aphasic and apraxic symptoms are conspicuous in early stages of the disease.

In the second stage, with the increasing of the intellectual deterioration and the appearance of aphasia the symptomatology becomes more characteristic. Two types of general behavior may be observed: the first and more frequent type is characterized by limitation and slowness of motor activity, intellectual inertia, loss of initiative and spontaneity, and refusal to talk; the second variety is characterized by restlessness, aimless activity, and talkativeness. It has been maintained that the former is observed in the frontal atrophy, the latter in the temporal atrophy; but exceptions are frequent. Moreover, the two types are not mutually exclusive, the same patient exhibiting at different times inertia and hyper-activity. At this stage, intellectual deficit is readily brought out by usual tests. It should be noted, however, that the memory function may be comparatively well preserved, its use being defective only in the free formation of new ideational material (72). This is in contrast to other forms of organic dementia where memory is usually early and severely involved. The emotional reaction deteriorates usually in the direction of apathy and mild euphoria, rarely of depression and anxiety. This striking emotional bluntness may depend upon the lack of conceptual grasping of a determined situation and, consequently, the inability to attach a definite affective coloring to the situation as a whole (20). Hallucinations, delusions, and confabulations do not belong as a rule to the clinical picture of Pick's disease.

The occurrence of focal signs completes the symptomatology of the second stage. Aphasia may be of any type or combination of types, depending upon the area or areas involved in the atrophic process. The most frequent type of aphasia is of the amnestic variety with frequent paraphasiae and agrammatisms; next in frequency is a sensory aphasia, while pure motor forms are rare. Intellectual deterioration usually complicates the aphasic syndrome so that only in a small number of cases can the type of aphasia be correctly evaluated in all the necessary details. Writing and reading may be affected independently of intellectual deficit, resulting in various types of agraphia, dysgraphia, alexia, paralexia, etc. Apractic manifestations, generally of the ideomotor type, often coexist with aphasic symptoms; but pure apraxia may also occur (58). Agnosia in the tactile and visual spheres is less commonly observed. A remarkable case of psychic blindness is described by Horn and Stengel (47). Often all these manifestations of cortical lesions are blended, resulting in complex syndromes which are further complicated by one or another form of perseveration.

At this stage the air encephalogram may be characteristic and almost pathognomonic, showing the distribution and intensity of the atrophic area of the brain. Electroencephalographic studies have been thus far inconclusive (5, 23). Other laboratory procedures, including examination of spinal fluid, are negative.

In the final stage the symptomatology becomes less characteristic. The patient gradually sinks into a state of hebetude and inert vegetative existence. Speech, if present, is reduced to meaningless and automatic repetition of simple words. Paralyses and contracture of limbs often occur. At this time epileptiform seizures are not infrequently observed, while they are rare in earlier stages.

Diagnosis.—In a typical case, the age of onset, the peculiar mental symptoms, the presence of focal signs, and the encephalographic findings make the diagnosis possible on clinical grounds. In the absence of focal signs, and when the onset is late, clinical distinction from senile dementia may be difficult. The criteria by which Pick's disease may be differentiated from the secondary forms of presenile dementias are essentially those described for Alzheimer's disease. The problem of differential diagnosis between Pick's and Alzheimer's disease already has been outlined.

Prognosis.—The disease is invariably fatal. The course is progressive. The duration varies from 2 to 15 years. Acute and chronic forms are recognized; intermediate forms are, however, in the majority.

Treatment.—There is no adequate treatment.

III. JAKOB'S DISEASE

Definition.—Jakob's disease is a presenile psychosis of unknown etiology, characterized clinically by a progressive dementia associated with symptoms of motor deficit, pyramidal and extrapyramidal in type, and, pathologically, by diffuse degenerative lesions involving cerebral cortex, basal ganglia, and spinal cord.

History.—The first cases of the disease were described in 1921 by Creutzfeldt (19) and Jakob (48, 49). The disease is known by several other names—cortico-striato-spinal degeneration, Jakob-Creutzfeldt disease, presenile dementia with spastic paralysis, disseminated encephalopathy, spastic pseudosclerosis. Published records of patients presumably belonging to this group are still scanty, and variations in both clinical and pathologic features have been observed from case to case. Some doubt may be expressed, therefore, whether one is dealing with a distinct clinicopathologic entity.

Etiology.—Although a few recorded patients (21, 22, 48, 104) were in the fourth decade of life, and two patients were in their twenties (19, 95), in the majority of cases the disease occurs in the presenium, thus indicating the possibility of etiologic factors, endogenous in type, connected with the process of senescence. The occasional occurrence of familial cases (22, 50, 67, 103) offers additional evidence of this contention.

The possibility of exogenous factors seems worthy of consideration. Some weight has been given to the hypothesis that an encephalitic process is the basis of the disease; however, the pathologic findings which show no involvement of the mesodermic elements are hardly consistent with this hypothesis. There are some similarities between Jakob's disease and pellagra, suggesting that deficiency factors may play a role in the etiology of this type of presenile dementia (97). Both Jakob's disease and pellagra show clinically a combination of mental changes and spinal cord symptoms. In both conditions, there are, pathologically, diffuse degeneration of neuron cells, nonsystemic destruction of myelin, and progressive microglia reaction (53).

An etiologic hypothesis which would consider the role of deficiency factors operating upon an aging brain constitutionally (or genetically) predisposed to degeneration appears to be the most satisfactory tentative explanation of the problem of the nature of the disease, on the basis of the scanty evidence thus far available.

Morbid anatomy.—No gross changes are observed in the brain of patients suffering from Jakob's disease.

The histological lesions involve neuron cells, myelin, and glia. The changes of the neuron cells are of the degenerative type— atrophy, shrinkage, fatty infiltration, and at times swelling. They are widespread, involving the cerebral cortex, especially the frontal (including the motor region) and temporal areas, the basal ganglia, and the spinal cord, particularly the anterior horns.

The lesions of the myelin sheaths consist of a degenerative and destructive process which involves several tracts of spinal cord in unsystematic manner, somewhat similar to what occurs in pernicious anemia. The motor tracts are more frequently affected than other pathways. Diffuse degeneration of the centrum semiovale has been observed occasionally (48, 50).

The pathological lesions of the glia consist of proliferation of both protoplasmic and fibrotic macroglia, together with hypertrophy and hyperplasia of microgliacytes. Senile plaques and Alzheimer's neurofibrillary changes are usually absent.

The distribution of the pathologic lesions and their intensity in the various locations show considerable variations. In typical cases, changes are evenly distributed in the cerebral cortex, basal ganglia, and spinal cord; at times, however, cortical lesions are preponderant and spinal involvement minimal (56, 95, 104); at other times, spinal changes are more pronounced than cortical ones (69, 100).

Symptoms and signs.—Following Jansen and Monrad-Krohn (51) three stages of the disease may be distinguished. The prodromal stage, of a few months' duration, is characterized by slight mental changes such as fatigability, loss of interest, memory impairment, and episodes of inconsistent behavior. Unsteadiness of gait, some motor impairment, and speech defect are often present. Occasionally severe muscular wasting with fibrillation and spasticity are observed in this first stage, the patients showing the neurological picture of amyotrophic lateral sclerosis.

The second stage is characterized by psychotic manifestations and neurological symptoms. The mental reaction is that of a progressive dementia, organic in type, with narrowing of interest, memory impairment, intellectual deterioration, and apathy. Confabulations, delusions, and hallucinations occur frequently. The neurological picture is manifold, signs of damage of the upper and lower motor neuron being usually associated with extrapyramidal manifestations such as tremors, athetosis, and disturbances of muscular tone. Dysarthria is usually present. Involvement of various cranial nerves has occasionally been reported.

In the third or terminal stage there are extreme dementia, generalized spasticity, and motor paralyses.

Clinical varieties are observed, depending upon the variations in distribution and intensity of pathologic lesions mentioned above. Thus cortical, striatal, and spinal varieties occur, in which predominant symptoms are, respectively, mental, extrapyramidal, or pyramidal in type. Combinations of these varieties are the rule rather than the exception.

The course of the disease is rapid, from six months to two or three years, the average being about one year.

The diagnosis offers some difficulty except in the cortico-striato-spinal clinical variety. The spinal variety is differentiated from amyotrophic lateral sclerosis mainly on the basis of mental changes. In the cortical variety the clinical differentiation from other types of primary presenile dementia may offer considerable difficulty.

The prognosis of the disease is invariably fatal and the treatment purely symptomatic.

IV. KRAEPELIN'S DISEASE

History.—Kraepelin (57) first described the clinical picture of this disease in 1912. Some years later, Oksala (73) reported on the pathologic lesions. Grünthal (38) and Best (7) published additional cases, and the former proposed the term of Kraepelin's disease. Perhaps some of the patients recorded by Fünfgeld (32) in his clinicopathologic study of involutional psychoses had this disease. Whether the condition represents a clinicopathologic entity is still open to question.

The *etiology* is unknown. Since the disease occurs in the presenium or shortly before it, some etiologic relationship to the process of senescence is usually assumed.

Pathologic changes consist of severe diffuse degenerative changes, mainly so-called "liquefaction," of the neuron cells. Some reactive changes of macroglia and some swelling of endothelial cells of the brain capillaries may be present; but the neurocellular lesions are preponderant and may be considered characteristically selective in type (38). Senile plaques are usually absent. These changes, presumably toxic in nature, are diffusely distributed throughout the gray matter of the brain.

Clinically the disease is characterized by a rapidly progressive intellectual deterioration with anxiety, depression, and psychomotor restlessness. Speech defect of the organic type is frequent. Peculiar motor symptoms, catatonic-like in type, are present. These can be differentiated from true catatonia because of their fleeting character and the absence of schizophrenic withdrawal (57).

The course of the disease is rapid, from one to two years, or less; and the outcome is invariably fatal.

V. OTHER TYPES OF PRESENILE DEMENTIA

Clinical and pathologic observation indicates that other types of primary presenile dementias occur in addition to the four above described. However, the information available is still too scanty to justify more than passing mention. Intermediary forms between Alzheimer's and Pick's disease have been reported occasionally (6, 59). Other types are the following:

1. *Presenile dementia with cerebellar atrophy.*—This group may be subdivided into three varieties: (*a*) *With parenchymatous atrophy of cerebellum.* Remarkable in this variety are the five familial cases described by Akelaitis (2), showing progressive and severe mental deterioration of two years' duration, accompanied by cerebellar symptoms. (*b*) *With olivo-cerebellar atrophy.* Typical instance is the patient described by Bogaert and Bertrand (9) who developed mental and cerebellar symptoms at the age of 46 and died two years later in a state of deep dementia. (*c*) With *spino-cerebellar atrophy.* In this variety are the patients recorded by Greenfield (37), in which dementia, ataxia, and dysarthria rapidly developed. Death ensued within a few months.

2. *Presenile dementia with degeneration of the thalami.*—The remarkable case of a man 41 years of age who showed severe dementia with inertia is described by Stern (98). The pupillary reflexes were absent. Post-mortem, there was parenchymatous atrophy and degeneration, with glia reaction most marked in the thalami. Some similarities may be found in the nature of the pathologic process between this type and Pick's disease.

3. *Simple presenile dementia of Gillespie* (35).—This author describes a form of presenile dementia characterized by gradual failure of intellectual function with progressive diminution of energy and initiative but without neurological signs of focal type. Gillespie reports no post-mortem findings. It would appear impossible to differentiate clinically this form from certain cases of Pick's disease.[1]

A few additional comments on the general nature and significance of the presenile dementias appear pertinent at the close of this chapter.

On cursory examination the various diseases which have been grouped under the common heading of presenile dementias seem to show considerable variations. Etiologically the most diverse agencies are apparently responsible for determining the morbid condition—genetic factors in certain cases of Pick's disease, constitutional factors in many forms of Alzheimer's disease, and ex-

[1]Presbyophrenia is regarded by a few authors as a form of presenile dementia. In fact, following Henderson and MacLachlan (45), presbyophrenia is indistinguishable from Alzheimer's disease. However, since presbyophrenia is more commonly considered as a variety of senile dementia, it is not discussed in this chapter.

ogenous toxic agencies in the "early" Alzheimer's type and in the majority of cases of Jakob's and Kraepelin's diseases. Diversity in morbid anatomy may be pointed out: the pathologic picture of Alzheimer's disease, with its numerous senile plaques and neurofibrillary degeneration, is apparently different from that of Pick's disease, in which these characteristic senile features are conspicuous by their absence. Finally, from a clinical point of view, the simple dementia slowly developing over a period of some ten years of certain cases of Pick's disease seems to have little in common with the complex and rapidly unfolding symptomatology of many cases of Alzheimer's and Jakob's diseases.

In consideration of these differences it has been proposed recently by such an experienced investigator as Kehrer (55) that the whole nosological group of presenile dementia be done away with and each disease be classified separately as a distinct entity.

However, the fact which was emphasized by Kraepelin (57), and clearly indicated in the term presenile dementia, still remains: these diseases possess two common characteristics, that is, organic mental deterioration and occurrence in the presenile age. The question may be raised at this point whether other distinctive features are common to the group.

The pathologic aspect may be considered first. The essential pathologic feature in Pick's disease, in the presenile dementias associated with cerebellar atrophies, and in the type described by Stern, is a process of atrophy of the nerve cells and nerve fibers, with consequent reaction of glia but without involvement of mesodermic elements. This process is confined to certain regions or systems. In Alzheimer's disease the same atrophic process can be detected throughout the brain; it is diffuse in distribution and, to be sure, concomitant with more conspicuous features such as senile plaques. In Jakob's disease similar cellular atrophy also is present, although more acute degenerative changes predominate.

There is some justification, therefore, for considering the process of atrophy of the neurons as the distinctive pathologic feature common to all forms of presenile dementias.

This finding suggests that common pathogenic factors are present, although etiologic deductions based on pathologic features should be accepted with caution. If the fact is considered that this very same pathologic process, i.e., progressive atrophy of the parenchymatous elements, characterizes in general aging of all organs, one is tempted to see in the process of senescence the common pathogenic factor which plays a significant role in the etiology of all forms of presenile dementia. A series forming successive grades may then be conceived which will include: (*a*) senescence affecting all tissues (senility); (*b*) senescence affecting all organs but particularly the brain (senile dementia); (*c*) premature senescence affecting only the brain (Alzheimer's disease); (*d*) premature senescence singling out lobes of the brain (Pick's disease); or (*e*) certain cerebellar systems (cerebellar types of presenile dementia); or the thalami (Stern's type of presenile dementia).

With respect, next, to the genetic aspect of presenile dementias, it was shown that in each type, with the exception of the little-known Kraepelin's disease, cases are known in which genetic factors play the dominant role in determining the pathologic process. The possibility of familial occurrence may be considered, indeed, a common characteristic of presenile dementias. Although the precise nature of these genetic factors remains undetermined, their significance may be better understood when presenile dementias are regarded as the expression of limited viability and premature aging of the brain or certain parts of it. There is, in fact, convincing experimental and statistical evidence indicating that the decay of particular organ systems occurs in an orderly manner, their longevity being determined mainly by inherent physicochemical constitution. That this constitution is largely determined by genetic factors has been proved in a variety of ways: directly, for man and lower animals, by measuring the degree of hereditary transmission of duration of life; and, indirectly, by showing that the death rate is selective and has been so since nearly the beginning of recorded history (Pearl, 75).

This same concept of premature senescence may be of assistance in explaining the role of exogenous factors, toxic, infectious, or deficitary in nature, which were mentioned in the discussion of the etiology of Alzheimer's and Jakob's diseases. Premature aging implies defective resistance to involutional processes, which, although largely inherited, is capable of modification within certain limits, as a result of the impact of environmental forces (Pearl, 75). Thus, in inferior animals, changes in viability, resulting in precocious senescence and death, can be brought about experimentally by modifications of physical or chemical milieu. One is tempted to postulate that in presenile dementia, given a limited viability inherent to certain tissues, exogenous factors may contribute to early decay. This impinging of exogenous agencies upon the pathologic process of Alzheimer's and Jakob's diseases may explain also the more rapid course of these conditions when compared with Pick's disease. Perhaps certain differences in the pathologic picture of presenile dementias are also susceptible of explanation on this basis: acute degenerative changes as seen in rapidly evolving cases and, possibly, also senile plaques may be accounted for by the action of exogenous factors superimposed upon the fundamental pathologic process of senescent atrophy.

In conclusion, on the basis of the concept of localized premature senescence, which is derived from histopathologic evidence, the various types of presenile dementia may be grouped together and their complex etiologic problems may be interpreted and investigated as part of the biological problem of aging.

REFERENCES

1. Akelaitis, A. J. "Atrophy of the Basal Ganglia in Pick's Disease," *Arch. Neurol. Psychiatry*, 1944, 51: 27
2. ———. "Hereditary Form of Primary Parenchymatous Atrophy of the Cerebellar Cortex Associated with Mental Deterioration," *Amer. Jour. Psychiatry*, 1938, 94: 1115
3. Altmann, E. "Ueber umschriebene Gehirnatrophie des späteren Alters," *Ztschr. f. ges. Neurol. Psychiatrie*, 1923, 83: 610
4. Alzheimer, A. "Ueber eine eigenartige Erkrankung der Hirnrinde," *Allgem. Ztschr. f. Psychiatrie*, 1907, 64: 146
5. Berger, H. "Ueber das Elektroencephalogramm des Menschen," *Arch. f. Psychiatrie*, 1938, 108: 407
6. Berlin, L. "Presenile Sclerosis (Alzheimer's Disease) with Features Resembling Pick's Disease," *Arch. Neurol. Psychiatry*, 1949, 61: 369
7. Best, C. R. "Klinische-anatomische Beiträge zur Kenntnis der präsenilen Psychosen," *Monatsschr. f. Neurol. Psychiatrie*, 1941, 103: 308
8. Bini, L. *Le demenze presenili*, Edizioni Italiane Ed. Rome, 1948
9. Bogaert, L. van, and Bertrand, I. "Une variété d'atrophie olivopontine à évolution subague avec troubles dementielles," *Rev. Neurologique*, 1929, Vol. 165, Part 2
10. Bogaert, L. van, Maere, M., and De Smedt, E. "Sur les formes familiales précoces de la maladie d'Alzheimer," *Monatsschr. f. Neurol. Psychiatrie*, 1940, 102: 249
11. Bonfiglio, F. "Die umschriebene Atrophie der Basalganglien," *Ztschr. f. ges. Neurol. Psychiatrie*, 1937, 160: 306
12. ———. "La patoarchitettonica corticale nello studio della malattia di Pick," *Ann. di Nevrol.*, 1927, 41: 146

13. ———. "Clinica e anatomia patologica dell'atrofia circoscritta del cervello," *Osped. Psichiat.*, 1937, 4: 1
14. Boyd, D. A. "A Contribution to the Psychopathology of Alzheimer's Disease," *Amer. Jour. Psychiatry*, 1936, 93: 155
15. Braunmühl, A. von. "Zur Histopathologie der umschriebenen Grosshirnrindenatrophie," *Virchov's Arch. f. Path. Anat.*, 1928, 270: 448
16. ———. "Ueber Stammganglienveränderungen bei Pickscher Krankheit," *Ztschr. f. ges. Neurol. Psychiatrie*, 1930, 124: 214
17. Braunmühl, A. von, and Leonhard, K. "Ueber ein Schwesternpaar mit Pickscher Krankheit," *Ztschr. f. ges. Neurol. Psychiatrie*, 1934, 150: 209
18. Cardona, F. "Sull'atrofia circoscritta di Pick," *Riv. Pat. Nerv. e Ment.*, 1946, 67: 70
19. Creutzfeldt, H. F. "Ueber eigenartige herdförmige Erkrankungen des Zentralnervensystems," *Nissl-Alzheimer Arb. Ergänzungband (1921)*, p. 1
20. Critchley, MacD. "Discussion on Presenile Psychoses," *Proc. Roy. Soc. Med.*, 1938, 31: 1443
21. Davison, C. "Spastic Pseudo-Sclerosis (Cortico-Pallido-Spinal Degeneration)," *Brain*, 1932, 55: 247
22. Davison, C., and Rabiner, A. M. "Spastic Pseudo-Sclerosis (Disseminated Encephalopathy: Cortico-Pallido-Spinal Degeneration)," *Arch. Neurol. Psychiatry*, 1940, 44: 578
23. Delay, J., and Desclaux, P. "L'encephalographie dans les démences degeneratives," *Rev. Neur.*, 1945, 77: 213
24. Delay, J., Desclaux, P., Perrin, J., and Buvat, J. F. "La maladie de Pick familiale," *ibid.*, 1945, 77: 85
25. DeWulf, A. "Un cas de maladie de Pick avec lesions predominantes dans les noyaux gris de la base du cerveau," *J. Belge Neur.*, 1935, 35: 508
26. Eiden, H. F., and Lechner, H. "Psychotische Zustandsbilder der Pick- und Alzheimerschen Krankheit," *Arch. f. Psychiatrie*, 1950, 184: 393
27. English, H. W. "Alzheimer's Disease," *Psychiatric Quart.*, 1940, 14: 583
28. Essen-Möller, E. "Alzheimer's Disease," *Acta Psychiat. et Neur.*, 1946, 21: 232
29. Ferraro, A., and Jervis, G. A. "Pick's Disease," *Arch. Neurol. Psychiatry*, 1936, 36: 739; "Pick's Disease," *Psychiatric Quart.*, 1940, 14: 17
30. ———. "Alzheimer's Disease. An Attempt at Establishing the Adult Type of the Disease," *ibid.*, 1941, 15: 3
31. Friedreich, G. "Pathologisch anatomischer Nachweis der Vorkommen der Pickschen Krankheit in zwei Generationen," *Ztschr. f. ges. Neurol. Psychiatrie*, 1940, 170: 31
32. Fünfgeld, E. "Klinisch-anatomische Untersuchungen über die depressiven Psychosen des Rückbildungsalters," *Jour. f. Psychol. Neurol.*, 1933, 45: 1
33. Fuller, S. C. "Alzheimer's Disease (Senium Praecox)," *Jour. Nerv. Ment. Dis.*, 1912, 39: 440
34. Gans, A. "Betrachtungen über Art und Ausbreitung des krankhaften Prozesses in einem Fall von Pickscher Atrophie des Stirnhirns," *Ztschr. f. ges. Neurol. Psychiatrie*, 1922, 80: 10
35. Gillespie, R. D. "Mental and Physical Symptoms of Presenile Dementia," *Proc. Roy. Soc. Med.*, 1933, 26: 1077

36. Goldstein, K., and Katz, S. E. "The Psychopathology of Pick's Disease," *Arch. Neurol. Psychiatry*, 1937, 38: 473
37. Greenfield, J. G. "Subacute Spino-cerebellar Degeneration Occurring in Elderly Patients," *Brain*, 1934, 57: 161
38. Grünthal, E. In O. Bumke and O. Forster, *Handbuch der Neurologie* (Berlin: Springer, 1936), 11: 497
39. ———. "Ueber ein Brüderpaar mit Pickscher Krankheit," *Ztschr. f. ges. Neurol. Psychiatrie*, 1930, 129: 350
40. ———. "Klinisch-genealogischer Nachweis von Erblichkeit bei Pickscher Krankheit," *ibid.*, 1931, 136: 464
41. Grünthal, E., and Wegner, O. "Nachweis von Erblichkeit der Alzheimerschen Krankheit," *Monatsschr. f. Neurol. Psychiatrie*, 1939, 101: 8, and 1940, 102: 302
42. Guillain, G., Bertrand, I., and Mollaret, P. "Considerations anatomocliniques sur un cas de maladie de Pick," *Ann. de méd.*, 1934, 36: 249
43. Hackovec, V. "Picksche Krankheit," *Zentralbl. f. ges. Neurol. Psychiatrie*, 1934, 73: 345
44. Hassin, G. B., and Levitin, D. "Pick's Disease," *Arch. Neurol. Psychiatry*, 1941, 45: 814
45. Henderson, D. K., and MacLachlan, S. H. "Alzheimer's Disease," *Jour. Ment. Sci.*, 1930, 76: 646
46. Herz, E., and Fünfgeld, E. "Zur Klinik und Pathologie der Alzheimer Krankheit," *Arch. f. Psychiatrie*, 1928, 84: 633
47. Horn, L., and Stengel, E. "Zur Klinik und Pathologie der Pickschen Atrophie," *Ztschr. f. ges. Neurol. Psychiatrie*, 1930, 128: 673
48. Jakob, A. "Ueber eigenartige Erkrankungen des Zentralnervensystems mit bemerkenswertem anatomischem Befunde," *ibid.*, 1921, 64: 147
49. ———. *Die extrapyramidalen Erkrankungen* (Berlin: Springer, 1923), pp. 215–56
50. Jakob, H., Pirkosch, W., and Strube, H. "Die erbliche Form der Creutzfeldt-Jakobschen Krankheit," *Arch. f. Psychiatrie*, 1950, 184: 653
51. Jansen, J., and Monrad-Krohn, G. H. "Ueber die Creutzfeldt-Jakobsche Krankheit," *Ztschr. f. ges. Neurol. Psychiatrie*, 1938, 163: 670
52. Jervis, G. A. "Alzheimer's Disease," *Psychiatric Quart.*, 1937, 11: 5
53. Jervis, G. A., Hurdum, H. M., and O'Neill, F. J. "Presenile Psychosis of the Jakob's Type," *Amer. Jour. Psychiatry*, 1942, 99: 101
54. Jervis, G. A., and Soltz, S. E. "Alzheimer's Disease. The So-called Juvenile Type," *ibid.*, 1936, 93: 39
55. Kehrer, F. "Die krankhaften psychischen Störungen der Rückwandlungsjahre vom klinischen Standpunkt," *Ztschr. f. ges. Neurol. Psychiatrie*, 1939, 167: 35
56. Kirschbaum, W. "Zwei eigenartige Erkrankungen des Zentralnervensystems nach Art der spastischen Pseudosklerose Jakobs," *ibid.*, 1924, 92: 175
57. Kraepelin, E. *Lehrbuch der Psychiatrie* (Leipzig: Barth, 1912), Vol. 2, 8th edition
58. Lhermitte, J., and Trelles, J. O. "Sur l'apraxie pure constructive," *Encéphale*, 1933, 28: 413
59. Liebers, M. "Alzheimersche Krankheit mit Pickscher Atrophie der Stirnlappen," *Arch. f. Psychiatrie*, 1939, 109: 363

60. Lowenberg, K., Boyd, D. A., and Salon, D. D. "Occurrence of Pick's Disease in Early Adult Years," *Arch. Neurol. Psychiatry*, 1939, 41: 1004

61. Lowenberg, K., and Rothschild, D. "Alzheimer's Disease. Its Occurrence on the Basis of a Variety of Etiologic Factors," *Amer. Jour. Psychiatry*, 1931, 11: 269

62. Lowenberg, K., and Waggoner, R. W. "Familial Organic Psychoses (Alzheimer's Type)," *Arch. Neurol. Psychiatry*, 1934, 31: 737

63. McMenemey, W. H. "Alzheimer's Disease. A Report of Six Cases," *Jour. Neurol. Psychiatry*, 1940, 3: 211

64. McMenemey, W. H., Worster-Drought, C., Flynd, J., and Williams, H. G. "Familial Presenile Dementia: Report of Case with Clinical and Pathological Features of Alzheimer's Disease," *ibid.*, 1939, 2: 25

65. Malamud, N., and Waggoner, R. W. "Genealogic and Clinicopathologic Study of Pick's Disease," *Arch. Neurol. Psychiatry*, 1943, 50: 288

66. Malamud, W., and Lowenberg, K. "Alzheimer's Disease," *ibid.*, 1929, 21: 805

67. Meggendorfer, F. "Klinische und genealogische Beobachtungen bei einem Fall von spastischer Pseudosklerose Jakobs," *Ztschr. f. ges. Neurol. Psychiatrie*, 1930, 128: 337

68. Menninger, W. "Encephalography in Alzheimer's Disease," *Radiol.*, 1934, 23: 695

69. Meyer, A. "Ueber eine der amyotrophischen Lateralsklerose nahestehenden Erkrankung mit psychischen Störungen," *Ztschr. f. ges. Neurol. Psychiatrie*, 1929, 121: 107

70. Moyano, B. A. "Demencias preseniles: enfermidad de Alzheimer; atrofia de Pick," *Arch. Agr. de Neurol.*, 1932, 7: 231

71. Neuman, M. A. "Pick's Disease," *Jour. of Neuropath. and Exp. Neurol.*, 1949, 8: 255

72. Nichols, I. C., and Wegner, W. C. "Pick's Disease—A Specific Type of Dementia," *Brain*, 1938, 61: 237

73. Oksala, O. "Ein Beitrag zur Kenntnis der präsenilen Psychosen," *Ztschr. f. ges. Neurol. Psychiatrie*, 1923, 81: 1

74. Onari, K., and Spatz, H. "Anatomische Beiträge zur Lehre von der Pickschen umschriebenen Grosshirnrinden Atrophie," *ibid.*, 1926, 101: 470

75. Pearl, R. *The Biology of Death.* Philadelphia: Lippincott, 1922

76. Pick, A. "Ueber die Beziehungen der senilen Hirnatrophie zur Aphasia," *Prag. med. Wochschr.*, 1892, 17: 165

77. ———. *Die umschriebene Hirnatrophie als Gegenstand klinischer und anatomischer Forschung, in Arbeiten aus der deutschen psychiatrischen Universitäts-Klinik.* Berlin: S. Karger, 1908

78. ———. "Senile Hirnatrophie als Grundlage von Herderscheinungen," *Wien, klin. Wochschr.*, 1901, 14: 403

79. ———. "Ueber Symptomcomplex bedingt durch die Kombination subkortikaler Herdaffectionen mit seniler Hirnatrophie," *ibid.*, 1901, 14: 1121

80. ———. "Ueber eigentümliche Sehstörungen in senilen Dementen," *Jahrb. f. Neurol. Psychiatrie*, 1902, 22: 35

81. ———. "Zur Symptomatologie der linkseitigen Schläfenlappenatrophie," *Monatsschr. f. Neurol. Psychiatrie*, 1904, 16: 378

82. ———. "Ueber einer Symptomcomplex der Dementia senilis bedingt durch umschriebene Hirnatrophie," *ibid.*, 1907, 19: 97

83. Reich, F. "Ein Fall von alogischer Aphasie und Asymbolie," *Allg. Ztschr. f. Psychiatrie*, 1905, 62: 825, and 1906, 64: 380

84. ———. "Aphasie oder Alogie," *Arch. f. Psychiatrie*, 1910, 46: 1234

85. ———. "Zur Pathogenese der circumscripten systemartigen Hirnatrophie," *Ztschr. f. ges. Neurol. Psychiatrie*, 1927, 108: 803

86. Richter, M. "Eine Besondere Art von Stirnhirnschwund mit Verblödung," *ibid.*, 1917, 38: 127

87. Romano, J., and Miller, W. C. "Clinical and Pneumoencephalographic Studies in Presenile Dementias," *Radiol.*, 1940, 35: 131

88. Rothschild, D., and Kasanin, J. "Clinicopathologic Study of Alzheimer's Disease: Relationship to Senile Conditions," *Arch. Neurol. Psychiatry*, 1936, 36: 293

89. Sanders, J., Schenk, V. W. D., and Van Veen, P. "A Family with Pick's Disease," *Verh. Kon. Ned. Akademie van Wetenschappen* (1939), Sec. 2, D. 38, No. 3

90. Schmitz, H., and Meyer, A. "Ueber die Picksche Krankheit mit besonderer Berücksichtigung der Erblichkeit," *Arch. f. Psychiatrie*, 1933, 99: 747

91. Schneider, C. "Ueber die Picksche Krankheit," *Monatsschr. f. Neurol. Psychiatrie*, 1927, 65: 230

92. Schottky, J. "Ueber präsenile Verblödung," *Ztschr. f. ges. Neurol. Psychiatrie*, 1932, 140: 333

93. Sjögren, H. "Twenty-four cases of Alzheimer's Disease," *Acta Med. Scand.*, 1950, 138: 225

94. Spatz, H. "Über die Bedeutung der basalen Rinde. Auf Grund von Beobachtungen bei Pickscher Krankheit und bei gedeckten Hirnverletzungen," *Ztschr. f. ges. Neurol. Psychiatrie*, 1937, 158: 208

95. Stender, A. "Weitere Beiträge zum Kapitel 'Spastische Pseudosklerose Jakobs,'" *ibid.*, 1930, 128: 528

96. Stengel, E. "A Study on the Symptomatology and Differential Diagnosis of Alzheimer's and Pick's Disease," *Jour. Ment. Science*, 1943, 89: 1

97. Stengel, E. and Wilson, W. E. J. "Jakob-Creutzfeldt Disease," *ibid.*, 1946, 92: 370

98. Stern, K. "Severe Dementia Associated with Bilateral Degeneration of Thalami," *Brain*, 1939, 62: 167

99. Stertz, G. "Ueber die Picksche Atrophie," *Ztschr. f. ges. Neurol. Psychiatrie*, 1926, 101: 729

100. Teichmann, E. "Ueber einen der amyotropischen Lateralsklerose nahestehenden Krankheitsprozes mit psychischen Symptomen," *ibid.*, 1935, 154: 32

101. Verhaart, W. J. C. "Ueber die Picksche Krankheit," *Zentralbl. f. ges. Neurol. Psychiatrie*, 1931, 59: 485

102. Vogt, M. "Die Picksche Atrophie als Beispiel für die eumonische Form der Pathoclise," *Jour. Neurol. Psychol.*, 1928, 36: 124

103. Worster-Drought, C., Hill, T. R., and McMenemy, W. H. "Familial Presenile Dementia with Spastic Paralysis," *Jour. Neurol. Psychiatry*, 1933, 14: 27

104. Zimmerman, R. "Ein weiterer Fall von Pseudosklerosis spastica," *Ztschr. f. ges. Neurol. Psychiatrie*, 1928, 116: 1

Chapter XI

SENILE PSYCHOSES AND PSYCHOSES WITH CEREBRAL ARTERIOSCLEROSIS*

David Rothschild

S ENILE psychoses and psychoses with cerebral arteriosclerosis constitute the great bulk of mental illness in later life for which hospitalization is commonly required. They represent a heavy and increasing burden to state mental hospitals. Dayton (17) has pointed out that they are by far the most frequent of all psychoses, when one takes into consideration the size of the population from which each psychosis is drawn. At the Worcester State Hospital, 41.9 per cent of all first admissions during the year ending June 30, 1945 were patients 60 years of age or older, and 33.7 per cent of first admission during that year were classified as senile or arteriosclerotic psychoses (53). Kolb (30) has estimated that if present admission rates and population trends continue, these two disorders may be expected to show an increase of 200 per cent in the number of first admissions to state hospitals by the year 1980.

The two disorders resemble each other in many ways and differ in others, so that they may conveniently be studied side by side. They possess a common historical background, since they were not given separate consideration until relatively recent times. Clinically, they show many resemblances and it is often stated that they cannot be reliably distinguished from each other. However, the frequent confusion in their differentiation is probably due to a lack of precise information; an adequate history and good clinical observations will usually reveal differences which are clear-cut enough to establish the correct diagnosis. Furthermore, they present different anatomic processes, which will be described later. This distinction still requires emphasis, for it is not recognized even in some modern textbooks. It is true that, anatomically, admixtures of the two con-

---

* These disorders have been designated as "Chronic Brain Syndrome Associated with Senile Brain Disease" and "Chronic Brain Syndrome Associated with Cerebral Arteriosclerosis" in the new nomenclature published in the *Diagnostic and Statistical Manual, Mental Disorders* by the American Psychiatric Association, Mental Hospital Service, Washington, D.C., 1952.

ditions occur frequently, but just as frequently pure cases are observed. Many workers accept the view that both types of cerebral involvement owe their origin to the same basic factors, that is, processes of aging, which affect the parenchyma directly in senile psychoses and the blood vessels in arteriosclerotic disease, though this view is disputed by some investigators.

At the same time, newer conceptions suggest that personal and social factors contribute to the etiology of both disorders, which must therefore be considered within the broad framework of the life stresses associated with aging in our society.

A. HISTORICAL CONSIDERATIONS

Undoubtedly, senile dementia and arteriosclerotic psychoses have occurred since earliest times. Early scientific writings contain occasional references to mental disturbances of the aged and the more dramatic aspects of apoplexy; but these discussions were scanty and vague until the last part of the nineteenth century. Novelists and poets have provided graphic descriptions, particularly of senile dementia. To mention only a few, Shakespeare's *King Lear* has been regarded as an example of senile dementia, and Burton's *Anatomy of Melancholy* (1620) gives a concise picture of this condition. In *Gulliver's Travels* there is a famous passage depicting the progressive physical and mental failure of senility.

In medical literature of the last century, Griesinger's volume on psychiatry (English edition of 1861), regarded as a forerunner of modern textbooks, contains no mention of these conditions in any separate section. In a small paragraph, under the heading "Apathetic Dementia," he uses the term senile dementia, stating, "Those cases in which a primary state of mental weakness has for a long time preceded an attack of apoplexy or of encephalitis, generally depend upon disease of the cerebral arteries." Krafft-Ebing, in his book on psychiatry published in 1888, and later writers gave more attention to the topic. Yet even from textbooks by Bevan Lewis in 1899, Berkeley in 1900, and Clouston in 1904 it is evident that the whole subject was in a state of confusion; the term "senile psychoses" still included arteriosclerotic conditions and senile dementia, without any consistent distinction between them, except that postapoplectic dementia was given separate discussion. Furthermore, some of the observations indicated that a variety of miscellaneous mental disorders occurring by chance in elderly persons were included under the heading of senile psychoses. Different pathologic pictures, namely, brains with focal lesions and brains with diffuse atrophy, were recognized, but all of them were generally attributed to cerebral vascular disease.

Order was finally established by the neuropathologists, who separated arteriosclerotic vascular disease from neurosyphilis on the one hand and from senile psychoses on the other. The most important work was done by Alzheimer (1), whose earlier studies were amplified in a paper published in 1902, describing and clearly delineating the arteriosclerotic psychoses. Binswanger (3) contributed to the subject in 1894, when he reported, under the term "chronic progressive subcortical encephalitis," an uncommon form of arteriosclerotic disease with involvement confined to the white matter. Kraepelin's textbook in its seventh edition was apparently among the first to provide a well-rounded clinicopathologic differentiation between senile dementia and psychoses with cerebral arteriosclerosis. In 1910, Simchowicz (61) published a fundamental anatomic study of senile dementia, a work which is still one of the finest in the field. Fischer (19, 20) and Spielmeyer (63) also made important contributions. Fischer's efforts were chiefly directed toward proving that the presbyophrenic type of senile dementia differed anatomically from other forms of senile psychosis, a theory which was disproved by later writers. In the early American literature, Barrett (2) provided an excellent description of senile and arteriosclerotic disorders.

Among the numerous later publications, one might mention the detailed studies of senile dementia by Grünthal (27), those of arteriosclerotic disorders by Neubürger (43), and the exhaustive work by Gellerstedt (24) on senile changes in old persons without psychoses. Critchley (15) presented a broad survey of neurologic aspects of aging, but he did not deal to any great extent with psychiatric manifestations.

During the past few years there has been increasing interest in normal as well as pathologic phenomena associated with aging. Books of reference (13, 14), symposia (41, 68), and reviews (39, 46) have been published. No doubt, this interest has been due largely to the rapid rise in the proportion of old persons making up the general population and to the realization that old patients have become a growing burden to psychiatric hospitals. The practical importance of senile and arteriosclerotic psychoses has stimulated a search for broader and more hopeful viewpoints than those hitherto prevalent. These viewpoints have been advocated by Malamud (33, 34) and by the writer (53, 55), and they will be discussed in the succeeding sections.

B. GENERAL ETIOLOGIC CONSIDERATIONS

During its early scientific period psychiatry sought for demonstrable cerebral changes as the cause of mental disorder. Certain conditions, such as senile and arteriosclerotic psychoses, were associated with obvious damage to the brain, and the belief that such damage was the only factor of importance became traditional. In recent years, however, studies of senile psychoses (48, 55) and arteriosclerotic psychoses (47, 49) have suggested the need for revision of this belief. Numerous inconsistencies between the severity of the mental symptoms and the extent of the cerebral lesions were encountered. Some patients with mild mental alterations showed marked neuropathologic changes, and others with pronounced clinical disturbances displayed relatively slight anatomic involvement. Also, Gellerstedt (24) and others have demonstrated that elderly persons who are normal mentally may exhibit cerebral changes which are as severe as those observed in patients with outspoken senile or arteriosclerotic psychoses. There has been a tendency to forget the fact that the brain, like other organs, possesses reserve powers and within certain limits can compensate for damage to its structure.

When the anatomic changes are scrutinized without preconceived ideas as to their significance, it becomes apparent that they are but one element in the total picture and that factors of a more personal nature are of etiologic importance in some cases. Too exclusive preoccupation with the cerebral pathology has led to a tendency to forget that the changes are occurring in living, mentally functioning persons who may react to a given situation, including an organic one, in various ways. The same damage which produces a psychosis in one case may not do so in another. Evidently, different persons vary greatly in their ability to withstand cerebral damage, so that the factor of individual mental vulnerability must be taken into consideration. Thus, anything which lowers a per-

Fig. 16.—Section from the anterior frontal region of a senile brain showing diffuse loss of nerve cells without gross disturbance of the cortical architecture. The nerve cells are small; many of them are dark and shrunken, others are pale. The white matter exhibits neuroglial proliferation and several dilated perivascular spaces, which are probably due to shrinkage of the surrounding tissue. Nissl stain; ×35. (Rothschild, *Amer. Jour. Psychiatry*, 1937)

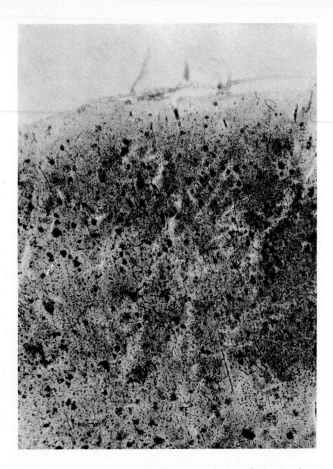

Fig. 17.—Section from the cerebral cortex of a senile brain showing many senile plaques. They appear as rounded, darkly stained, granular masses, which vary greatly in size. They occur in the intercellular substance. Dieterle-Neumann modification of the Hortega stain; ×30. (Rothschild, *Amer. Jour. Psychiatry*, 1937)

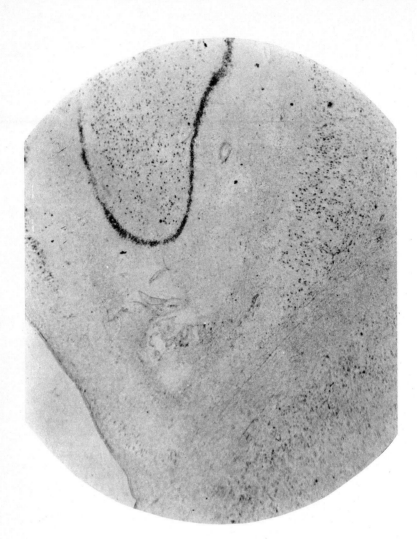

FIG. 21.—Acellular or devastated area in the cornu ammonis, affecting the nerve-cell band as it proceeds from the hippocampal gyrus on the upper right, swinging down and to the left and then bending sharply upward to the left. The lesion consists of a focal loss of nerve cells without disintegration of the tissues or noteworthy reactive phenomena. The adjacent white matter above the sharp bend in the devastated nerve-cell band shows a small area of softening characterized by complete disappearance of the tissues to form cystlike spaces. Nissl stain; ×26. (Rothschild, *Arch. Neurol. Psychiatry*, 1942)

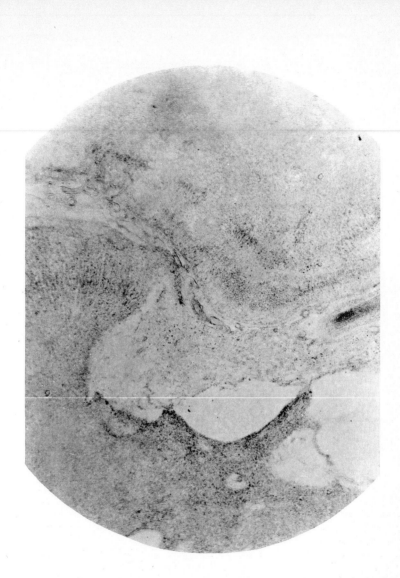

FIG. 20.—Section from an arteriosclerotic brain showing in the lower convolution an area of softening of recent origin with complete disappearance and
disintegration of the tissues and in the upper convolution an area of incomplete
destruction, which in places leaves intact the second, parts of the third, and the
fourth cortical layers. Nissl stain; ×26. (Rothschild, *Arch. Neurol. Psychiatry,*
1942)

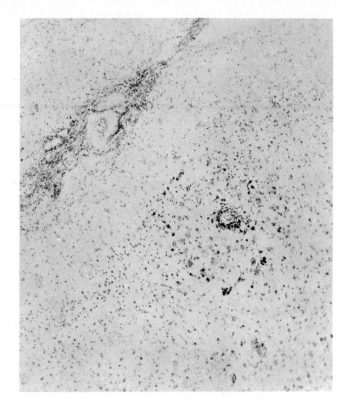

Fig. 19.—Section from an arteriosclerotic brain showing arteriolosclerosis of two meningeal vessels and the remains of an old, small hemorrhage in the cerebral cortex. The two vessels, located in the upper left of the figure, display thickening, hyaline changes, and endothelial proliferation. The hemorrhage is marked by blood pigment in the adventitial spaces of a thickened vessel and in the surrounding nerve tissue. Some of the pigment lies free in the tissues, and some is contained in cellular elements. There is proliferation of large neuroglial cells in the affected area, and the meninges exhibit reactive alterations. Nissl stain; ×65. (Rothschild, *Arch. Neurol. Psychiatry*, 1942)

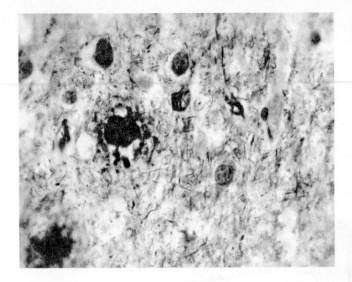

Fig. 18.—High-power view of the cerebral cortex of a senile brain. To the left of the center, the figure contains a senile plaque consisting of a large solid central mass, surrounded by an irregular clear area, a so-called halo, around which there is some granular material. Near the center and slightly to the right are two nerve cells showing neurofibril lesions of the Alzheimer type, with thickening and clumping of the intracellular neurofibrils. Near the left-hand margin of the figure a third cell not completely in focus exhibits neurofibril alterations. Bielschowsky stain; ×500. (Rothschild, *Amer. Jour. Psychiatry,* 1937)

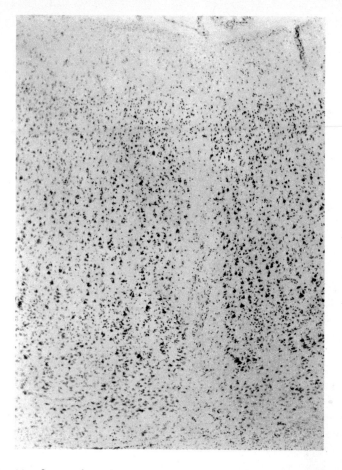

Fig. 22.—Section from the cerebral cortex of an arteriosclerotic brain presenting a focal lesion corresponding to Alzheimer's perivascular gliosis. There is a perivascular loss of cellular elements extending vertically through the cortex. Part of the blood vessel is visible in the lower half of the lesion. With appropriate stains, these foci usually show a perivascular increase of glia fibers. Nissl stain; ×65. (Rothschild, *Arch. Neurol. Psychiatry*, 1942)

son's adjustive capacities may be of significance in the causation of the psychosis. This opens up many fields for study—for example, unfavorable hereditary or constitutional tendencies, and unfavorable personality characteristics or situational stress.

In other words, patients with senile or arteriosclerotic psychoses should not be regarded merely as passive carriers of a morbid anatomic process. One should attempt to estimate to what extent anatomic factors and to what extent more personal factors are concerned in each case. In many cases, such a study suggests that the qualities of the living person and his life experiences are the most important factors in the origin of the mental breakdown. For example, Kral (31) reports an increased frequency of cases of senile dementia in a concentration camp, attributing the increase in part to the stressful conditions in the camp.

Thus, there emerges a more meaningful picture of the psychosis as an end state in a long process which has its roots not just in certain impersonal tissue alterations but in psychological stresses and in social problems which affect the aging population. This shift in emphasis may be noted in the work of Williams (75), Semrad (59), Goldschmidt (26), and others stressing the role of social factors in senile and arteriosclerotic psychoses. Also, Gitelson (25) pointed out that many of the symptoms commonly observed in old persons are understandable reactions to emotional disturbances and that even the impairment of memory is due not to organic changes alone but to psychologically determined mechanisms.

The idea that personal problems and social stresses are of importance brings up new therapeutic possibilities, since such factors are at least potentially susceptible of modification. As suggested in a recent paper (53), the therapeutic aim would be one of prevention rather than treatment of the well-established psychosis. This will be discussed further in the section dealing with the treatment of senile psychoses. The foregoing conceptions probably apply with greater force to senile psychoses than to arteriosclerotic psychoses. The former is an expression of general processes of aging and one would therefore expect it to reflect more adequately the sociopsychologic stresses of aging than arteriosclerotic disease, which is in a sense a localized condition. However, the belief of Williams (75) and others that such stresses can be virtually eliminated from considerations of arteriosclerotic psychoses is not borne out by clinical observations (47) which will be touched on later.

C. SENILE PSYCHOSES

The term senile psychosis or senile dementia is now properly restricted to those chronic mental disorders occurring in elderly individuals and presenting a variety of clinical pictures, which show in common progressively increasing signs of organic mental deficit in association with characteristic changes in the brain.

I. ANATOMIC CHANGES

The essential anatomic process consists of diffuse atrophic and degenerative alterations, which are independent of vascular disturbances. While any part of the body may be involved, attention will be devoted chiefly to the brain, and particularly the cerebral cortex, which displays the most striking damage. The process affects single nervous elements without producing any breakdown of the nervous tissue as a whole, and it presents certain special features which will be described below. Approximately half the cases are complicated by cerebral changes based on vascular disease; but in most instances these lesions are only a minor part of the total picture. A detailed study of the neuropathology was presented in 1937 (48).

General somatic changes.—The soft tissues usually exhibit atrophy and shrinkage. Such changes are occasionally inconspicuous, indicating that senile processes can affect the brain more severely than other parts of the body. As a rule, the heart and other inner organs are atrophic, though cardiac enlargement of a moderate degree is observed in about one-third of the cases. In the great majority of instances the aorta and coronary vessels show mild or moderate atheromatous alterations, but coronary occlusion is seldom noted in pure senile conditions. Carcinomatous growths are observed in a few cases. As terminal infections, bronchopneumonia and lobar pneumonia are frequent, pyogenic infections are not uncommon, and tuberculosis is by no means rare.

Gross neuropathologic changes.—Senile brains show all variations from very slight to very pronounced shrinkage of the cerebral convolutions and the white matter. In my material the brain weights ranged from 865 gm. to 1,425 gm., the average for the group being 1,159 gm. As a rule, the brain is firm and the sulci are somewhat widened, especially in the anterior frontal regions. Slight or moderate fibrous thickening of the pia-arachnoid is common. The large arteries usually exhibit mild or moderate atheromatous alterations; but focal lesions of the cerebral tissues do not occur in uncomplicated cases. In many instances the gross changes are no greater than those encountered in mentally normal persons of similar age.

Microscopic changes in the cerebral cortex.—There is usually shrinkage of the tissue as a whole. The nerve cells display a variety of changes of a nonspecific nature (Fig. 16). Shrinkage and atrophy of nerve cells is frequent. With the Nissl stain some cells are pale and shadowy; others become dark and shrunken, conforming to Nissl's cell sclerosis. Lipoid accumulations are commonly noted in the cells. Some neurones may show chromatolysis. There is a widespread dropping out of individual nerve cells, but as a rule the cortical architecture is relatively well preserved (Fig. 16). Mild to moderate proliferation of the microglia and macroglia is observed. Not infrequently, the microglial reaction is severe and pronounced astrocytic proliferation occurs immediately beneath the surface of the cortex (marginal gliosis). Regressive alterations are encountered in some of the neuroglial cells. The small blood vessels exhibit mild or moderate thickening, with regressive changes in the endothelial cells.

With silver stains the cerebral cortex displays characteristic lesions called senile plaques (Fig. 17). They are argentophil masses, usually round in shape, but sometimes irregular or even confluent, occurring between the cells, that is, in the intercellular substance. They vary greatly in size and number; they may be smaller than a medium-sized nerve cell or many times larger. As a rule, they are found in practically all low-power microscopic fields in numbers ranging from ten to twenty up to fifty or seventy or even more per low-power field. In most instances the lesions consist of amorphous threads, masses, or granular material. Sometimes they assume a peculiar form (Fig. 18), whereby the center of the plaque contains a solid mass like a nucleus, surrounded by a pale, clear area like a halo, around which there may be a ring of thready or granular material. In occasional cases, ring-like perivascular plaques are encountered. Glial elements, chiefly microglia, are often observed partially or completely within a plaque, but they do not form an essential component of the lesions. In very rare cases (55) senile plaques are completely lacking.

The origin of senile plaques is still a much disputed question.

Apparently they occur only in the central nervous system of the human species. At one time or another, they have been attributed to every component of the nervous tissue. The most widely accepted theory is that they are due primarily to alterations in the intercellular substance, which is composed of a complex network of neurofibril and neuroglial processes in the ground substance or matrix of the cerebrum. As to the nature of these alterations, von Braunmühl (5, 6) believes that they are manifestations of colloidal disturbances in the protoplasm leading to an increasing aggregation of colloidal particles, which finally precipitate and form argentophil masses.

A less common type of alteration affecting the nerve cells of the cerebral cortex is the Alzheimer type of neurofibril lesion (Fig. 18). These lesions, which are best demonstrated by Bielschowsky's silver stain, consist of peculiar changes of the intracellular neurofibrils, which become thickened, clumped together, or twisted into rope-like coils or other distorted forms. They are present in most cases of senile dementia but are usually infrequent, sometimes occurring only in the cornu ammonis.

While the cortical involvement is diffuse, it may vary considerably in severity even in closely adjacent spots, and it is often accentuated in certain areas. As a rule the anterior frontal regions are affected most severely and the occipital lobes least severely. In general, the phylogenetically older parts, such as the motor area, are less vulnerable than the parts developed later. The upper half of the cortex, particularly the third lamina, usually shows the greatest damage; but in most cases the changes do not produce any profound distortion of the cortical laminations.

Microscopic changes in other parts of the brain.—The pia-arachnoid exhibits moderate fibrosis. The small meningeal vessels show adventitial thickening. There is usually an increase of connective tissue in the choroid plexus. The basal ganglia present mild or moderate degenerative changes of the nerve cells, with neuroglial proliferation. Most cases exhibit an abundance of senile plaques in the amygdaloid nucleus and a small number in the putamen and candate nucleus. These lesions are observed less frequently in the thalamus, the substantia nigra, and the gray matter about the third ventricle and the aqueduct of Sylvius. In the white matter of the cerebral hemispheres the perivascular spaces are frequently dilated, possibly owing to shrinkage of the surrounding tissues, and the neuroglia show proliferation. As a rule, the cerebellum and the brain stem display only slight alterations. A slight paucity of Purkinje cells is common, but severe atrophic changes of the cerebellum have not been encountered in my material. Corpora amylacea are encountered in practically all cases, and calcareous-like material is frequently noted in the walls of blood vessels in the globus pallidus, the putamen, and occasionally elsewhere; but it is doubtful if these changes are of any pathologic significance.

II. SPECIAL ETIOLOGIC CONSIDERATIONS

While the foregoing neuropathologic picture is highly characteristic of senile dementia, it is by no means pathognomonic of that disorder. Similar changes are observed in Alzheimer's disease and in normal old age; in the former the damage is usually more pronounced and in the latter less pronounced than in senile psychoses, though exceptions to this rule are by no means rare. In a few cases (35), changes of the same type have been described at such an early age or in such obvious toxic states (54) that a senile etiology cannot be seriously considered. It is probable that the alterations under discussion represent, as claimed by von Braunmühl (5, 6), a general type of tissue reaction, which may result not only from aging but also from a variety of other etiologic factors.

For detailed studies of normal aging one may refer to the volume edited by Cowdry (14). Certain problems connected with the question as to why some persons age more rapidly or more severely than others have been discussed in a paper with Kasanin (54). There is no general agreement on the factors involved in pathologic aspects of aging processes nor on what constitutes the difference between normal and pathologic aging. Warthin (70) laid special stress on vascular changes in old age, yet the neuropathologic picture associated with senile psychoses cannot be attributed to damage to blood vessels. Recently Fisher (21) has suggested that some cases of senile dementia are due to occlusion of one or both carotid arteries, but clinically his cases were obviously examples of cerebral vascular disease and not of senile dementia. Simchowicz (61) believed that senile dementia was merely an exaggeration of the normal senium, but Gellerstedt (24) has shown that anatomically there is no simple quantitative difference between these two conditions. Grünthal (27) and Critchley (15) concluded that there is more than a quantitative difference between senile dementia and normal old age, and Grünthal thought that there must be some as yet unknown factor which determines the occurrence of the former. Some workers believe that heredity plays an important role in senile dementia. According to Kallmann and Sander (28), heredity and constitution play a basic role in determining the variable ability to maintain a state of physical and mental health until and through the period of senescence. Others have suspected alcohol as a factor; but such an idea is not substantiated by a scrutiny of the whole senile group. Tilney (69) expressed the idea that old age as shown in the brain is the result of life's successive and cumulative intoxications, the old brain being actually a diseased organ.

However, there is no concrete evidence that toxic factors play a role in the etiology of senile psychoses. A search for hypothetical somatic disorders modifying the normal aging process and leading to a senile psychosis has proved unproductive. In my experience many of the patients have been extraordinarily free from somatic disease prior to the onset of the mental disorder. On the other hand, there are good grounds for believing, as already pointed out, that tissue damage per se does not necessarily produce a psychosis but rather the person's capacity to compensate for the damage. In some cases it appears that personal factors, such as social and situational stresses (31, 48) and less frequently unfavorable traits of personality (55), may impair the individual's ability to withstand the cerebral damage. Apparently, such factors represent the essential difference between normal old age and a senile psychosis in certain cases. Illustrations of these points will be provided in the succeeding section.

III. CLINICAL FEATURES OF SENILE PSYCHOSES

In 1945 senile dementia accounted for 14 per cent of first admissions to state hospitals for mental diseases in Massachusetts (38).[1] Data obtained in anatomically verified cases indicate that

---

[1]Figures for the frequency of senile dementia and arteriosclerotic psychoses, considered separately, may show large variations from time to time owing to varying standards of diagnosis as well as to mistakes in distinguishing between the two conditions. Thus in 1938 the figure for first admissions of senile psychoses in Massachusetts was only 6.1 per cent (37). It is unlikely that a rise from 6.1 to 14 per cent has actually occurred in a span of seven years. It seems probable that such a rise has been due to less rigid application of the rule whereby preference is customarily given to a diagnosis

the disease is much commoner in women than in men, in the proportion of more than two to one, and that the age of onset ranges from the sixties to the nineties. The average was seventy-five years for the whole group.

Mental symptoms.—The onset is practically always gradual, except in occasional cases complicated by arteriosclerotic disease. As a rule, the illness is preceded by longer or shorter periods of normal physical and mental letdown associated with old age. There is usually an exaggeration of previous personality traits and of the conservative and egocentric tendencies commonly noted in the aged. A gradually increasing impairment of efficiency and memory occurs, and the patient may pass into a psychotic state so imperceptibly that it is impossible to date the onset with any degree of exactitude. In some instances, however, a minor physical ailment or some situational stress may appear as a landmark between normal old age and psychotic behavior. Errors of judgment and a deterioration of personal habits with a loss of moral inhibitions may be early features, though pronounced untidiness is usually a later manifestation. There is a lack of attention and impressibility. Irritable and jealous tendencies, which may lead to threatening or violent acts, are often prominent. Sleeplessness may be a persistent symptom. Restlessness is common, particularly at night. The patient may wander away from home and be unable to find his way back. In some cases there is an early outcropping of new and abnormal traits, for example, delusions, hallucinations, and paranoid tendencies. Anxious and agitated states occur frequently, but deep depressions are seldom noted. Loss of interest and apathy are features of certain cases. Behavior suggestive of manic or hypomanic states is occasionally encountered.

As the psychosis develops, symptoms of intellectual deficit dominate the picture except in certain forms to be described later. There is pronounced impairment of memory, which first tends to affect recall of recent events and immediate retention. When later

of arteriosclerotic psychosis when doubt arises in differentiating between senile and arteriosclerotic psychoses and when mixtures of the two conditions occur. This rule probably accounts for statistics indicating that admission rates of senile psychoses have remained largely stationary while those of arteriosclerotic psychoses have increased alarmingly. For statistical purposes it would seem more accurate to consider the two conditions together. In 1938 they accounted for 22.3 per cent of first admissions in Massachusetts as compared to 29.1 per cent in 1945.

happenings have been completely forgotten, the patient may
able to remember events of childhood and youth, though th
temporal relationships may not be preserved. Thus the senile
tient tends to live in the past, indulging in reminiscences conc
ing friends, relatives, and occurrences of long ago. Fabrica
may be noted. Orientation is defective for time and place,
loss of self-identity usually a much later development. Imp
ment of comprehension and a greater or lesser degree of confus
are observed. Single impressions may be adequately perceiv
but they cannot be properly related to each other, so that the to
situation is not adequately appreciated. The ability to perfo
concrete activities may be retained when abstract thinking is
longer possible. Hallucinations are common; sometimes they
cur in delirious episodes. Delirium is especially apt to occu   a
night (7). Speech becomes rambling and incoherent.

6 Senile psychoses have been customarily subdivided into the
following types: (*a*) simple deterioration; (*b*) depressed and agitated types; (*c*) delirious and confused type; (*d*) presbyophrenic
type; and (*e*) paranoid types.

This classification is of doubtful value. Only the last two forms
stand out from the others, and of these the presbyophrenic type is
not too well defined. The designations of the first three types are
self-explanatory, so that no special descriptions are needed; they
scarcely warrant consideration as separate forms, since transitions
and admixtures of all sorts are observed. The same patient may
present a picture of simple deterioration at one time, an agitated
state later, and a delirious condition at still another time. White
(73) believed that senile delirium was really due to some complicating toxic disease; and Wexberg (72) expressed a somewhat
similar idea, attributing it to neurometabolic deficiency. There is no
relation between the extent of the cerebral damage and the type of
senile psychosis. Clinical pictures in which symptoms of simple
deterioration predominate occur with greatest frequency; according to Strecker and Ebaugh (67) they constitute about 50 per cent
of the whole senile group.

The presbyophrenic type is characterized by marked impairment of memory, fabrications, and a jovial or amiable mood. The
patients usually present an appearance of alertness which is only
superficial. They are usually restless, displaying continual activ-

ity of an aimless nature. As a rule they are loquacious, talking volubly in a rambling, confused manner. Typical, full-fledged forms of this condition are infrequent, but partially developed ones are fairly common. Strecker and Ebaugh (67) state that the presbyophrenic type includes 8 per cent of the senile group. The picture is reminiscent of Korsakoff's psychosis of alcoholic origin. Some workers have claimed that alcohol is an etiologic factor, but in my experience presbyophrenia may occur in teetotalers.

The paranoid form of senile psychosis constitutes from 20 to 25 per cent of all psychoses in my material, though Strecker and Ebaugh (67) give a smaller figure—15.75 per cent—for this group. It differs from the other types by reason of florid delusional features and a relatively well-preserved personality. It tends to develop in persons who possess a suspicious and more or less paranoid make-up throughout their lives. In some cases the impression is obtained that the mental disturbances may have really begun before the senile period, perhaps in middle age or even earlier. Such cases may represent a paranoid state to which a senile condition has been subsequently added. But in other instances the paranoid symptoms occur only with the development of a senile process.

The picture is characterized by the gradual formation of delusions which are systematized to some extent, though illogically and loosely connected; they are of a persecutory, erotic, or grandiose nature, alone or in combination, and they are usually accompanied by hallucinations of a similar content. The content is often concerned with money or personal harm and sometimes with obvious wish-fulfilling tendencies. In the beginning, there is little evidence of the customary senile decay. The memory is relatively well retained, orientation is generally complete, or almost complete, and there may be little if any evidence of confusion. While indications of intellectual impairment gradually increase, they may not become pronounced for several years. Ultimately, however, patients with the paranoid form of senile dementia show advanced deterioration similar to that encountered in other types of the disorder. It should be added that there are transitional forms in which paranoid features are less well developed and signs of intellectual deficit more outspoken.

The following cases, which have been reported elsewhere (48),

may serve to illustrate some of the points mentioned in the foregoing paragraphs.

E.F., a married woman, age 80, was admitted to the Foxborough State Hospital on January 3, 1934. Her health had always
been excellent and apart from friction with her husband because
of his alcoholic habits there was nothing of note in her personal
history. In recent years there had been increasing financial difficulties, and in August 1933 the patient was obliged to sell her
house, which had been left to her by her father and in which she
had lived all her life. Her husband was sent to the town infirmary
and the patient stayed with relatives. She became very much upset over the breaking up of her home. Previous to that she had
appeared much younger than her actual age. She seemed to "go
to pieces" rapidly. She was unable to understand why she had to
leave her home. Her memory became very poor, and she became
feeble physically, falling on a number of occasions. She failed to
recognize her relatives, and grew very irritable, showing an obvious
dislike for her surroundings. She became somewhat restless and
shrieked a great deal, so that it was finally necessary to bring her
to the hospital. On examination the patient showed marked impairment of memory, disorientation, and an irritable and scolding
attitude. On one occasion, she stated that she was young and had
been recently married; but on the whole the picture was one of
intellectual deterioration. The patient rapidly grew weaker, developed bronchopneumonia, and died on March 3, 1934. The
brain showed typical senile changes of moderate severity.

Comment.—The clinical picture in this case was predominantly
that of simple deterioration, with short periods during which it took
on the appearance of a depressed and agitated type. Although the
neuropathologic changes were not pronounced, the course was unusually rapid, the intellectual impairment was very severe, and the
onset was more sudden than that observed in most cases of senile
dementia. However, it should be noted that the onset was related
to a series of disturbing experiences. There is no reason to suppose
that senile lesions were suddenly formed in the brain at the age of
80 when the psychosis began. On the contrary, all our knowledge
of such lesions indicates that they develop gradually over a period
of years. In other words, senile changes had been occurring for
years, but the patient had remained mentally normal until she was

obliged to cope with situational stresses which called for radical readjustments in her long-established patterns of living. It seems likely that these stresses were the crucial factor in the sense that they completely upset the equilibrium, which had hitherto been well maintained.

M.P., a woman, aged 75, was admitted to the Foxborough State Hospital on March 17, 1931. The patient had been married and divorced many years before. She was capable and intelligent, but of a suspicious nature. She had been able to support herself adequately by doing hairdressing until three years prior to admission, when her vision began to fail owing to a cataract in one eye. She had increasing financial difficulties in her business, partly owing to a natural physical letdown due to her age and partly to her visual disturbances. She started to worry about what would happen to her in her old age. An operation was performed on her eye, but it was unsuccessful. She became more alarmed about her future, and finally sold her business and belongings, collecting enough money to enter an old ladies' home in 1929. She soon began to show peculiarities of behavior. She tried to look youthful by bobbing her hair and adopting other beauty aids regarded as odd for a person of her age, and she tried to act in a manner calculated to impress people with her youthfulness. She became domineering and assumed an attitude of superiority toward the other women. She began to display delusions of persecution, mild grandiose traits, and a slight defect of memory. She thought the other women were in league against her, were trying to steal her belongings, and were entering her room at night. She grew increasingly irritable and aggressive in reaction to these ideas until it was necessary to commit her to the hospital. Examination disclosed a rather feeble woman, who presented a typical picture of a paranoid type of senile dementia, with outspoken delusions of a persecutory nature, moderate intellectual impairment, and a tendency to fabricate. The course of the illness was gradually progressive, with slowly increasing mental deterioration, physical enfeeblement, and diminishing paranoid features. Death occurred on February 6, 1933, after an illness of about four years' duration. The brain exhibited severe alterations of a senile nature.

Comment.—This case represents a paranoid form of senile psychosis. As in the foregoing case, the onset seemed related to a series of events which made great demands on her adaptive capacities, but in contrast to the first example, the patient reacted to the situation by developing paranoid features, which represent compensatory psychologic mechanisms. It has been shown (48) that persons who possess a strong compensatory capacity in psychologic fields tend to possess a similar capacity in somatic fields. They are apt to show cardiac hypertrophy and other tissue reactions indicative of compensatory somatic processes. It should be noted that the lack of pronounced intellectual impairment in paranoid forms of senile dementia is not due to a milder anatomic process. For example, in one case death from lobar pneumonia occurred in the early stages of the illness, when the patient had been well oriented and his memory had exhibited only slight disturbances. Yet the brain displayed extensive changes, which were actually more severe than those found in some patients with profound mental deterioration. Thus patients with a paranoid type of senile psychosis possess a strong capacity to compensate for cerebral damage, and as a result less deterioration occurs in such cases.

The picture presented above is not just that of an impersonal organic process. It is the picture of an individual who is struggling to adjust to some of the somatic handicaps and sociopsychologic problems which face many persons as they are growing old; and because of her special traits of personality her efforts to cope with these difficulties led to paranoid reactions. In attempting to understand a senile psychosis, the adequacy of the personality make-up and the environmental influences must be taken into consideration, as in other psychiatric disorders, with the added factor that the old patient must reckon with a variable degree of senile functional decline. In surveying the whole senile group, one can trace the interplay of these forces through all gradations from one extreme, at which the patients have little or no adaptive resources, to the other extreme, at which there is great capacity to compensate for the handicaps of situational stress as well as of structural damage to the brain. In this way one can explain the otherwise puzzling inconsistencies between cerebral damage and clinical features, including those cases in which marked neuropathologic changes are observed in old persons who remain normal mentally.

In view of the foregoing points it would seem useful to seek for groupings which would reveal the different forces at work and would therefore have more meaning than the grouping provided by the standard classification. One may think, for example, in terms of three groups—which may overlap or even combine but which present different sets of factors—as follows:

1. A group in which the psychosis is an understandable if not inevitable outgrowth of long-standing personality difficulties. These patients are able to make an adjustment of sorts as long as their physiological status is intact, but when processes of aging set in their resources are insufficient to maintain an adequate equilibrium. In many cases situational stresses may be an added factor.

2. Patients with apparently well-integrated personalities in whom the psychosis develops in relation to special stresses of a somatic or situational nature. The psychologic stresses are of the type which commonly afflict the aging population, such as separation from or death of a spouse, break-up of the home, lack of employment, and the like; the unusual traumatic effect may perhaps be due to the suddenness of the events or to the occurrence together of a number of these unfavorable factors.

3. A group in which there are no dramatic events and no obvious defects of personality. These cases form the largest group. They are apt to show a picture of simple deterioration, and the question may be raised whether the clinical picture is the expression of complete surrender to the appalling isolation and the completely meaningless existence which often constitute the setting for the psychosis. Although these patients display little evidence of personal factors in the psychosis, it should be noted that many of them come to psychiatric hospitals only after they have reached an advanced state of senile mental deterioration. As Cameron (8) has pointed out, such factors may have been present earlier but are now overshadowed by the senile deficit.

Most of the senile paranoid and depressive reactions occur in the first group. Reasons for the relatively high incidence of paranoid disorders have been discussed by Cameron (8). In recent years a number of writers (11, 22) have described paranoid and depressive reactions in elderly persons who show no evidence of cerebral incompetence. These cases are usually classed as late involutional psychoses, since a diagnosis of senile psychosis is not justified, according to our standard classification, unless signs of intellectual deficit are present. However, it is doubtful whether there is any sharp line of separation between such cases and those showing the accepted features of a senile psychosis. In this connection it has been observed (58) that many patients with senile dementia displayed in their premorbid make-up unfavorable traits of personality qualitatively similar to those described in patients with involutional psychoses (36). Furthermore, similar precipitating factors are often noted in the two disorders. Of course, this is not surprising, since both groups represent reactions to aging and both are subject to the same types of sociopsychologic pressures, but the resemblances have not been sufficiently stressed.

Physical changes in senile psychoses.—Changes customarily associated with old age, such as general wasting and shrinkage of the soft tissues, wrinkling and loss of elasticity of the skin, thinning and graying of hair, and the like, are usually observed. However, outspoken senile alterations are by no means always present early in the disease, and occasionally they may be inconspicuous even at the end. Arcus senilis is usually but not invariably present. In the great majority of instances the peripheral arteries show sclerotic changes, and the blood pressure is frequently raised; these disturbances are noted even in cases that are not complicated by arteriosclerotic brain disease. In a group of 31 anatomically verified cases (50) the systolic blood pressure was below 150 in 12 cases, between 150 and 200 in 13 cases, and above 200 in 6 cases. The average for the whole group was 165 systolic and 83 diastolic. In spite of such findings, marked cardiac hypertrophy is uncommon, and evidences of cardiac decompensation are seldom noted except as a terminal phenomenon.

Striking neurologic changes do not occur in uncomplicated cases. There is an increase of muscle tonus, which is apt to be variable rather than constant, and the gait is uncertain and unsteady. Tremors of an irregular type are common. In my experience, however, clear-cut parkinsonian syndromes occur in the arteriosclerotic rather than the senile group. Defects of hearing and visual impairment associated with cataracts are frequent. The pupillary reactions may be sluggish; occasionally there are disturbances of speech reminiscent of the impure aphasia often noted in Alzheimer's disease. Senile chorea, that is a chronic form of chorea based on senile lesions, has been described as a rare accompaniment of senile dementia, but a study of this problem

(51) suggests the possibility that such cases may be atypical forms of Huntington's chorea.

Electroencephalographic abnormalities, as indicated by a slowing of the predominant rhythm, are frequently observed, especially in cases with more severe intellectual deficits (32). The urine does not show marked changes unless extraneous infections of the urinary tract occur. The blood chemistry is usually within normal limits. The spinal fluid may present a mild or moderate increase of total protein but otherwise displays no abnormalities.

The course of the illness.—The disease is gradually progressive, with slowly but steadily increasing mental and physical decay. However, the rapidity of progression varies greatly from case to case. In my anatomically controlled material, the shortest illness lasted for 7 months and the longest 11 years, with an average duration of 4.7 years for the whole group; in a larger series probably a still wider range would be encountered. The patients become feebler and more uncertain on their feet. Falls are common and, as a result of senile bone changes, fractures readily occur, the neck of the femur being especially vulnerable. Certain symptoms, such as restlessness, agitation, or delirious conditions may come and go, but the general intellectual impairment continues on its downward course. Cameron (9) has pointed out that many senile patients show a remarkable preservation of general social function up to an advanced state of general deterioration, in that one may find the observance of the simpler social amenities of courtesy, considerateness, and deference. But unless the psychosis is terminated by intercurrent disease, all patients grow more and more deteriorated and oblivious of their surroundings, so that finally they all look alike, regardless of the type of senile psychosis noted earlier. Utterances are indistinct, often consisting of incoherent mumbling or meaningless noises. The patients become helpless, incontinent, and bedridden, leading a completely vegetative existence. In these far-advanced stages, sucking reflexes and grasp reflexes may be observed. Death usually occurs from pneumonia, infections from decubital ulcers, or other terminal infections.

IV. DIFFERENTIAL DIAGNOSIS

In the average case of senile psychosis, the insidious onset in later life and the slow but inexorable increase of mental and physical decay extending over a period of years provide a picture that can scarcely be mistaken for any other condition.[2] Nevertheless, the disorder is often confused with arteriosclerotic psychoses. Their differentiation from each other will be discussed in the section dealing with the latter condition.

A less frequent yet common mistake is to diagnose a toxic or symptomatic psychosis as senile dementia. This seems surprising, since a toxic psychosis usually begins acutely and runs a rapid and stormy course. Old persons are probably highly vulnerable to toxic influences, and the somatic process responsible for the disorder may not be conspicuous. Also, the mental symptoms are apt to last longer and are more likely to have a fatal outcome than in younger patients. However, the chief source of error is an uncritical attitude toward psychoses of old age, whereby one tends to forget the possibility that a mental disorder other than a senile condition may be present. As a result of this attitude, almost any form of mental disease, including such conditions as schizophrenia and manic-depressive psychosis, may be labeled senile dementia if it happens to occur in elderly persons.

Depressed and agitated forms of senile psychosis may be confused with late involutional depressions. In the former, however, the depression may be more superficial, and it is apt to consist largely of a state of apprehension without clear motivation. Also, senile paranoid psychoses may be difficult to distinguish from involutional paranoid reactions. In the latter the age of onset is apt to be earlier, but recent writers (22) have described cases well within the age range of senile dementia. Of course, according to standard practice the conclusive point is the presence of definite defects of intellectual activities in senile psychoses and their absence in depressive as well as paranoid involutional reactions. As indicated

---

[2]The differentiation of senile psychoses from normal senility may theoretically present considerable difficulty, depending to some degree on how one defines the term psychosis. It is sometimes stated (66) that many of the senile patients admitted to mental hospitals are merely confused and feeble but not psychotic. It is generally agreed (4, 16, 44) that there is the subtlest gradation between normal old age and the symptoms of a senile psychosis. Any decision as to where the line between normal senility and senile dementia should be drawn must often be an arbitrary one. As Bleuler (4) has pointed out, one must depend on practical considerations. The fact is, the patients in question are unable to care for themselves because of senile changes, and the psychiatric hospitals are as a rule the only places where facilities for their care are available.

previously, however, senile and late involutional psychoses show points of similarity which render it difficult to draw a sharp line of demarcation between them.

The presbyophrenic type of senile dementia may superficially resemble an alcoholic Korsakoff's psychosis. In addition to the frequent occurrence of polyneuritis in the latter, there are many differences between the two disorders. The presbyophrenic patient is usually happy, restless and very loquacious; the alcoholic patient is usually dull and deficient in spontaneous activities. Confusion is usually more severe in the former, except perhaps in the early acute phases of Korsakoff's psychosis. The alcoholic patient ordinarily shows less serious defects of judgment, less profound intellectual impairment, and less severe disorganization of behavior in general than the presbyophrenic patient. A Korsakoff syndrome may be associated with many other conditions, for example, cerebral trauma, toxic or deficiency states, and even cerebral arteriosclerosis, but in such cases the general setting of the illness should reveal its true nature.

General paresis occurs occasionally in elderly persons, and it may be mistaken for senile dementia. In some cases euphoric and grandiose traits or changes of pupillary reactions may provide clues pointing to the former, but in others the two conditions may be indistinguishable without serologic study of the blood and spinal fluid. Brain tumor may present a picture of general intellectual impairment as the leading feature (57); and if this occurs in elderly persons, it may be regarded as a senile psychosis, though confusion with arteriosclerotic disorders is commoner. In such cases electroencephalographic and roentgenologic studies may establish the correct diagnosis.

Senile psychoses resemble the so-called presenile disorders, Alzheimer's disease and Pick's lobar atrophy, in some ways, but in Alzheimer's disease the onset is earlier, usually in the forties or fifties, there is more profound intellectual impairment at a relatively early stage of the illness, and aphasic disturbances or other focal disturbances are commonly noted (52, 55). Also, in Pick's lobar atrophy the onset is usually earlier, in the same age range as Alzheimer's disease, but it has been observed in older persons. The intellectual impairment is more variable and less diffuse in the earlier stages of Pick's lobar atrophy than in senile psychoses; states of inertia or apathy are common and vivid hallucinatory episodes are usually lacking in the former, whereas the latter often display noisy and hallucinated states. Detailed descriptions of the presenile disorders are presented in another chapter.

V. TREATMENT

Since recent trends point to sociopsychologic stresses as etiologic factors in senile dementia, the question arises whether attempts to prevent such stresses or mitigate their traumatic effects might be of therapeutic benefit. There has been no adequate exploration of the possibility that the psychosis might be favorably influenced by intensive treatment in the earliest stages of the disorder, employing modern techniques and knowledge of the special problems of aging persons; for in my experience most of the cases are hospitalized at relatively advanced stages of the disease without having had even a minimal amount of psychiatric guidance. Bearing this in mind, it must be added that whatever group of factors may combine to produce a senile psychosis, the process appears to be irreversible once well started, so that all therapy of the well-established disorder is supportive and symptomatic. A more hopeful approach, though still a subject of speculation, is the prevention of senile psychoses. If the aforementioned trends are correct, it seems likely, as pointed out in recent papers (26, 53), that a broad program of mental hygiene for the older population groups should diminish the frequency of senile dementia. Encouraging observations in this connection have been reported by Rusk (56).

Many of the practical problems of treatment have been discussed by Simon and Kaufman (62). Measures should be taken to protect the patient from harm resulting from his bad judgment or other psychotic manifestations. Attention should be devoted to simple hygienic measures, such as proper clothing, an adequate diet, which should be nutritious and easily digestible, bodily cleanliness, regularity of bowel habits, and the like. The liability to physical injury from falls or from faulty handling of matches or other household appliances should be remembered. One must guard the patient from foolish financial transactions and difficulties due to laxity of moral standards.

Mild cases can be supervised at home, but if there are marked confusion, restlessness, violent and noisy behavior, depressive tendencies, or other more active disturbances, care in a hospital for mental diseases is indicated. For insomnia, restlessness, and excitement the newer drugs, serpasil and thorazine, appear to be more effective and less likely to produce toxic effects than the older forms of sedative medication. Hydrotherapy in the form of continuous baths may be useful in patients who are fairly robust physically. In general, the senile patient should be kept out of bed as long as possible; but in some cases severe agitated states respond well to complete bed rest as a temporary measure. In treating fractures, a moderately successful result allowing the patient to be up as soon as possible may be more desirable than more elaborate surgical procedures requiring prolonged immobilization in bed, which carries with it the danger of developing pneumonia. In confused and delirious states, vitamin therapy and nicotinic acid may be given in view of the belief of certain workers (72) that such conditions are due to nutritional or metabolic deficiency; in my experience this type of medication has not proved definitely beneficial. Garnett and Klingman reported improvement in presenile, senile, and arteriosclerotic states with cytochrome C (23). There has been increasing and successful use of electric shock treatment to combat depressive and paranoid reactions in elderly patients (22), and with caution in the number and frequency of the treatments, untoward results should not occur (40). Group therapy has been employed by Silver (60) with improvement in the patients' morale, cleanliness, and general behavior. Occupational therapy, including a good recreational program, is useful in many cases; it should be confined to relatively simple activities which do not tax the patient mentally or physically. The patients should be given as much latitude as is consistent with safety, and for their proper handling a judicious mixture of tact, firmness, and kindliness is essential.

Considerable attention has been given to better methods of handling senile patients who are now for the most part cared for in mental hospitals (56). Senile patients present somewhat different problems than younger ones, and hospitals which are geared for the more vigorous younger group are in many ways unsuited for the aged. To remedy this situation, plans for segregation within a suitable part of the mental hospital, or the construction of units specially designed for old patients, or attempts to develop resources for their care in the community have been proposed (53, 56).

D. PSYCHOSES WITH CEREBRAL ARTERIOSCLEROSIS

Arteriosclerotic psychoses include those mental disorders of middle-aged and elderly persons associated with damage due to arteriosclerotic involvement of the cerebral blood vessels.

I. ANATOMIC CHANGES

In accordance with general usage, the term arteriosclerosis is used in a broad sense to include the following: (*a*) atherosclerosis, which affects the larger arteries and is characterized chiefly by intimal changes; (*b*) arteriolosclerosis, in which the arterioles and precapillaries show thickening of their walls with hyaline changes, fatty deposits, and sometimes endothelial swelling; and (*c*) capillary or arteriocapillary fibrosis, which consists essentially of an increase of mesenchymal fibrils in the walls of the capillaries and precapillaries. These changes have been described in detail by Spielmeyer (64), Neubürger (43), Cobb and Blain (12), and many others. Monckeberg's type of arteriosclerosis, characterized by calcification of the media, is generally included under the term arteriosclerosis, but it rarely occurs in the cerebral vessels, being in fact completely lacking in my own material.

The neuropathologic picture is characterized by vascular changes and a variety of focal lesions, in which the cerebral structure is destroyed as a whole, partially or completely, with relatively good preservation of the rest of the tissues. Alzheimer's classification (1) is still used extensively, but it is not always quoted with complete accuracy. He mentioned Jacobsohn's severe form of arteriosclerosis, which consisted chiefly of vascular changes in the basal ganglia and brain stem and was primarily of neurologic interest. Among the cases of more importance to psychiatry, he distinguished the following types:

a) A mild form of cerebral arteriosclerosis, identical with Windscheid's type, the so-called nervous form, in which the mental symptoms were mild and did not show marked progression, and the histologic changes were relatively slight.

b) Severe progressive forms of arteriosclerotic atrophy of the brain, which occasionally began like the nervous form but were soon associated with more pronounced mental manifestations. Here the histologic features were marked vascular changes, with numerous foci of incomplete and complete softening scattered throughout the cerebrum. Within this large group, Alzheimer distinguished three subforms in accordance with differences in localization and in types of focal lesion, as follows: (i) Senile cortical devastation, *"Verödungen,"* due to changes in the small vessels supplying the cerebral cortex, which showed small acellular or devastated areas. The term "senile" was used by Alzheimer because he first discovered the lesions in patients of advanced age, and at that time the use of the term had not yet been limited to the parenchymal senile tissue process. (ii) Perivascular gliosis, in which there was a perivascular loss of cellular elements with an increase of glia fibrils. And (iii) Binswanger's chronic progressive subcortical encephalitis, characterized by involvement of the long medullary vessels supplying the white matter of the cerebral hemispheres, which showed widespread disappearance of myelin and axis cylinders without foci of complete softening. However, these three subforms do not represent clinical types of arteriosclerotic psychoses, and it will be brought out later that they do not constitute well-defined separate anatomic forms.

General somatic changes.—Striking disturbances are frequently noted in the cardiovascular system and the kidneys (49). Almost all cases show coronary and aortic sclerosis. Cardiac hypertrophy, often of marked degree, occurs in the great majority of instances. These alterations may be associated with infarcts of the myocardium. Chronic valvular disease of the heart and passive congestion of organs, with accumulations of fluid in body cavities or tissues, are encountered in a few cases. Approximately half the cases display chronic disease of the kidneys, chiefly arteriosclerotic infarcts and less frequently chronic progressive vascular nephritis. Terminal pulmonary infections are common.

Gross neuropathologic changes.—The arteries at the base of the brain show atheromatous lesions, usually of a severe nature, with the exception of rare instances in which the damage is confined to small vessels. In the great majority of cases the brain displays one or more areas of softening, which may be anemic or hemorrhagic. These lesions may be large or small, on the surface or deeper in the substance of the brain. They consist of softened, disintegrated tissue, which is sometimes completely liquefied. Small or large hemorrhages of old or recent origin are observed in about 25 per cent of the cases. On rare occasions grossly visible focal lesions are lacking. The changes may occur in any part of the brain, though the basal ganglia and temporo-occipital regions are affected with greatest frequency. The putamen is especially vulnerable, often exhibiting a number of small, cyst-like losses of substance, a status lacunaris. The cerebellum is involved in from 10 to 20 per cent of the cases and the brain stem much less frequently. In some instances the cerebrum is smaller than normal. In my material the weight of the brain ranged from 975 gm. to 1,510 gm., the average being 1,280 gm.

Microscopic changes of the blood vessels and meninges.—The small vessels regularly present involvement, which is usually severe and widespread. In the meningeal and choroidal vessels, the alterations are generally of the type described as arteriolosclerosis (Fig. 19). In the cortex the commonest type of lesion consists of adventitial thickening of the precapillaries, sometimes combined with endothelial swelling; hyaline changes are occasionally encountered. Hyaline degeneration and dilatation of the perivascular spaces occur frequently in the white matter and the basal ganglia, the latter usually showing greater vascular damage than any other region. In most instances the vessels of the globus pallidus contain calcareous deposits in their walls. While the lumens of blood vessels are often decreased, complete closure is not common.

Aneurysmal dilatations of intracerebral vessels are encountered in a few cases. The pia-arachnoid exhibits minor alterations, except for reactive disturbances near destructive cerebral lesions.

Microscopic changes in the cerebral cortex and white matter.— All cases present a variety of focal lesions, which may be described under the following headings:

1. *Foci of complete destruction, or areas of softening.* These lesions are infarcts, either anemic or hemorrhagic, usually the former. They occur in the majority of cases. They are characterized by complete destruction of the cerebral tissue over small or large circumscribed areas, with reactive phenomena on the part of the neuroglia and the capillaries (Fig. 20). The appearance of the lesions at different stages of the disintegrative process has been

described in detail by Spielmeyer (64), Neubürger (43), and others. Older foci, especially those of small size, may be organized to form mesodermal-glial scars.

2. *Foci of incomplete destruction.* Different lesions of this type are observed. The commonest forms are acellular or devastated areas (Alzheimer's senile cortical devastation, or *Verödungen*), which occur in most cases. They are characterized by more or less complete disappearance of nerve cells in circumscribed areas of the cerebral cortex, without dissolution of the nerve substance or noteworthy reactive phenomena on the part of the glia or blood vessels (Fig. 21). They vary greatly in size and shape but are seldom large enough to occupy a whole low-power field. Another type of lesion, Alzheimer's perivascular gliosis, is noted in practically all cases (Fig. 22) but not with sufficient frequency to be considered an important feature. Paled areas (*Erbleichungen*) are occasionally observed. In the white matter, foci of incomplete destruction consisting of areas of partial or complete demyelinization, corresponding to the type of lesion described by Binswanger (3) in chronic progressive subcortical encephalitis, are commonly encountered, though they are small and widely scattered, in contrast to the involvement of large areas or even whole lobes described by that writer.

3. *Small hemorrhages of old or recent origin.* These are observed in about one-third of the cases (Fig. 19); as a rule, they are not numerous.

The damage is usually most pronounced in the parieto- and temporo-occipital regions. Foci occasionally extend along one or more layers for short distances (Fig. 20), but widespread laminary involvement is rare. Sommer's sector of the cornu ammonis is frequently involved (Fig. 21). Apart from the focal disturbances, striking tissue changes do not occur in uncomplicated cases. There may be lipoid accumulations in many of the nerve cells. Marginal gliosis, perivascular neuroglial proliferation, and a diffuse increase of astroytes in the white matter are occasionally noted. Spielmeyer (64) believed that diffuse reduction of the cerebral parenchyma could occur on an arteriosclerotic basis. In my experience diffuse cerebral atrophy is not uncommon, but it is seldom pronounced. Corpora amylacea are often present. Complicating senile changes are encountered in about 50 per cent of the cases, though in most instances such alterations represent only a minor feature of the whole anatomic picture.

Microscopic changes in other parts of the brain.—As a rule, the basal ganglia show more pronounced changes than other parts of the brain. In occasional cases the damage to this region completely dominates the picture. Focal lesions, chiefly areas of softening or scars resulting therefrom, are very common. The perivascular spaces are often dilated and the surrounding tissue rarefied to an extent sufficient to produce the appearance of a status cribratus. Small cyst-like losses of tissue, constituting a status lacunaris, are by no means infrequent. The putamen generally shows the greatest involvement. Focal lesions are found frequently in the cerebellum and occasionally in the brain stem.

Classification and pathogenesis.—While the most important tissue changes are foci of softening and acellular areas, all brains show a variety of lesions. A scrutiny of the different lesions indicates that they are merely expressions of differences in the severity, tempo, and localization of the same pathologic process. They do not constitute separate anatomic forms of arteriosclerotic psychosis. This also applies to Binswanger's chronic progressive subcortical encephalitis, which has been traditionally regarded as a special type of arteriosclerotic disorder. Slight alterations of the type observed by Binswanger (3) are often noted, but they are merely one element in a broader anatomic process.

Although the damage may predominate to some extent in the cerebral cortex, the white matter, or the basal ganglia, none of these structures is completely spared. Therefore, a classification based on localization of the lesions, such as that of Kodama (29), fails to do justice to all the facts so far as the psychotic group is concerned. Rhein, Winkelman, and Patten (45) advocated a classification based on the size of the vessels involved. This is perhaps more justifiable, since the small vessels occasionally show severe changes without noteworthy alterations of the large arteries. But in most cases both large and small vessels are implicated, and it is not possible to delimit clear-cut clinical forms corresponding to such anatomic groupings. From an anatomic viewpoint, psychoses with cerebral arteriosclerosis present a multiform picture which does not lend itself to any rigid schematization.

Neubürger (43) classified arteriosclerotic psychoses into hypertensive and senile types; the former occurred chiefly in relatively young persons with cardiac hypertrophy and hypertension and the latter in older patients who presented a senile appearance, usually without hypertensive phenomena. However, these types are not restricted to any particular age; they represent rather groups with strong and weak compensatory somatic reactions. It has been shown (49) that such reactions are associated with a similar compensatory capacity in psychologic fields. Thus the concept of compensation is equally applicable at somatic and psychologic levels, and by its utilization the disorder is described in terms which refer to qualities of the living patient as factors in the disturbances. White (74) has stressed the value of such terms in lessening the use of the conflicting expressions "body" and "mind" and allowing the concept of the organism as a whole to function in a productive manner.

The pathogenesis of arteriosclerotic lesions has been discussed in detail by Cobb and Blain (12), Neubürger (43), and others. It is now generally believed that circumscribed damage to nerve tissue does not necessarily depend on complete or permanent closure of blood vessels. According to Spielmeyer (65), such damage can be produced by vasomotor disturbances. My observations suggest that impairment of cardiac function contributes to the development of focal lesions by causing general weakening of the blood flow. The importance of this factor has been mentioned by Wertham and Wertham (71) but has not been sufficiently emphasized elsewhere.

II. SPECIAL ETIOLOGIC CONSIDERATIONS

The etiology of arteriosclerosis is still a much-disputed problem, for a study of which one may refer to the volume edited by Cowdry (13). The questions why some persons develop arteriosclerosis much earlier and more severely than others and why the process may predominate in certain organs cannot be answered satisfactorily. It is commonly thought that hereditary influences are of importance, and even a cursory review of the material reveals a tendency to arteriosclerotic disease in the families of patients with arteriosclerotic psychoses. Some workers believe that there is a senile type of arteriosclerosis, that is, a form due to aging processes which affect the vascular system, and other types based on nonsenile factors. The relatively early age of onset in many cases tends to support such an idea.

As pointed out earlier, the nature of arteriosclerosis is such that one would not expect it to reflect general problems of aging as adequately as the diffuse senile processes associated with senile dementia. This does not necessarily mean that arteriosclerotic psychoses present no evidence of significant personal or social factors in the etiology, as suggested by Williams (75) and others. Undoubtedly, many cases of arteriosclerotic psychosis develop solely on the basis of damage to the brain, and it is probable that this occurs more frequently than in senile dementia. But in some cases the damage is not essentially different from that observed in certain persons who remain normal mentally, so that the presence or absence of a psychosis in such instances cannot be attributed to anatomic influences alone. It is true that traumatic situational factors seem to be much less common than in senile dementia. However, they occur occasionally, and they may then be of etiologic importance as in senile psychoses. Furthermore, it has been shown (47) that a considerable number of the arteriosclerotic patients possess inadequate and poorly balanced personalities, and as a result it is believed that they are highly vulnerable, breaking down mentally in the face of damage which could readily be overcome by persons of a more robust make-up. In this sense the personality may be a determining factor in the development of an arteriosclerotic psychosis, a point which will be elaborated in the succeeding section.

III. CLINICAL FEATURES OF PSYCHOSES WITH CEREBRAL ARTERIOSCLEROSIS

In 1945 psychoses with cerebral arteriosclerosis accounted for 15.1 per cent of first admissions to state hospitals for mental diseases in Massachusetts (38). The corresponding figures for 1938 and 1917 were 16.2 per cent and 7.1 per cent, respectively (37). Men are affected much more frequently than women, the ratio being approximately three to one in anatomically verified cases (50). In this material, the age of onset ranged from the middle forties to the eighties, with an average of 66 years for the whole group.

Prodromal symptoms.—Headache, dizziness, vague somatic complaints, and a more or less prolonged period of physical and

mental letdown are common as prodromal symptoms. Apoplectiform or syncopal attacks, symptoms of cardiac decompensation,
and, less frequently, convulsive seizures often precede the mental
disturbances, though they may occur at the onset or later in the
course of the illness.

Mental symptoms.—The onset may be sudden or gradual. An
acute onset is noted in more than half of the cases. This takes the
form of a sudden attack of confusion. It is often associated with
gross neurologic disturbances, conforming to the picture of postapoplectic or post-paralytic dementia of older writers. The patients
show marked clouding of consciousness, complete loss of contact
with their surroundings, incoherence, and pronounced restlessness.
Hallucinations may be added to produce a delirious picture. In
some cases there are few if any premonitory mental symptoms, but
as a rule the onset is preceded by a gradual reduction of physical
and mental capacities. The fact that this occurs in the younger as
well as the older patients suggests that it is really the first indication of an insufficiency of the cerebral circulation. Occasionally
the mental letdown may exceed the limits of normal, so that it
would be more accurate to speak of an insidious onset followed by
an acute outbreak of more outspoken psychotic disturbances. In
some cases this represents an admixture of a mild senile disorder,
as illustrated in the following brief example.

C. H., a man, aged 77, was admitted to the hospital on September 8, 1932. The patient had been showing gradual mental and
physical failure for several years, with a certain amount of forgetfulness and occasional indications of slight confusion. About nine
months prior to admission, he had what was said to be a "slight
shock," following which he displayed marked confusion and restlessness. He grew progressively worse, with some fluctuations in
the severity of the symptoms. Signs of cardiac failure and bronchopneumonia developed, and the patient died on October 16, 1932.
The brain exhibited widespread vascular and focal lesions and
mild senile parenchymal changes.

When the onset is gradual, the mental disturbances are similar
in many respects to those observed in senile dementia. There is
gradual intellectual failure, manifested by loss of efficiency, impairment of memory, and the like. The patient may display a
lowering of moral standards and irritable, aggressive, and quar-

relsome behavior. Subjective complaints, such as weakness, fatigue, uneasy feelings, and unpleasant somatic sensations, are frequently noted. Depressive feelings, emotional lability, and a fear of impending failure of physical and mental powers are often prominent features, and definite suicidal tendencies are by no means uncommon. Explosive outbreaks of weeping or laughter are occasionally encountered, usually in cases with gross neurologic alterations. Ideas of mistreatment or jealousy and transient persecutory ideas may be observed, but persistent well-developed paranoid pictures are infrequent. The impairment of memory tends to affect recent impressions but is apt to be spotty rather than diffuse. Fabrications are occasionally noted. Judgment is impaired, but there may be a certain degree of insight.

The following case, which was reported elsewhere (47), is presented as an illustration of an arteriosclerotic psychosis in which the onset was gradual and in which factors of personality were apparently of etiologic importance.

E. D., a married woman, aged 78, was admitted to the hospital on February 10, 1923. The patient had always been shiftless. She was a poor housekeeper, neglecting her home and her children and going out a great deal at night. About eight years ago, she began to steal articles from clotheslines and stores. She became untidy in her personal hygiene and finally showed a tendency to wander away from home. On admission, the patient displayed disorientation, rambling speech, and a very defective memory. She soon showed improvement, but during the course of her illness there were fluctuations in the severity of the symptoms. She had frequent spells of dizziness and at widely scattered intervals several major convulsions and two syncopal attacks. During the last years of her illness there was pronounced impairment of intellectual functions. Death occurred on March 22, 1931, with signs of cardiac failure. Examination of the brain disclosed a moderate number of arteriosclerotic focal lesions, chiefly in the white matter.

Comment.—In the foregoing case the illness was of exceptionally long duration. It resembled a senile psychosis by reason of its gradual onset and slow progression, at first differing from the latter only in the transient confused states; but in its further course the disease presented more characteristic features, such as attacks of dizziness and convulsive seizures. It should be noted that the neuropathologic changes were only moderately severe even at the end of a prolonged illness. Undoubtedly much of the damage occurred in the later stages of the psychosis, when the patient had a number of cerebral vascular attacks. One may therefore conclude that the alterations were mild at the onset and that the patient was highly vulnerable mentally because of an inadequate personality. In other instances, too, it has been shown (47, 49) that minimal cerebral damage may lead to a psychosis in persons with an ill-balanced make-up.

Apparently, the anatomical changes are just one of the etiologic factors in cases of this type. The whole life history of such persons reveals faulty adjustment with increasing difficulties pointing toward ultimate mental breakdown, so that the cerebral alterations appear to act merely as the "last straw." This does not occur in any specific type of personality. Instead, one finds a variety of special traits, of which the commoner ones are aggressiveness, violent temper, seclusiveness, odd and eccentric characteristics, restricted interests, and shiftlessness. The observations suggest that persons who are handicapped psychologically in any way are apt to show a high degree of vulnerability to arteriosclerotic psychoses.

Physical changes.—Neurologic changes are noted in the majority of cases at one time or another. They are often lacking or transitory early in the disease. Outspoken changes may be observed only in the terminal stages, and in a few instances they fail to occur at any time. While any type of focal lesion may be present, hemiplegia or hemiparesis is found with greatest frequency, occurring in about half of the cases. A variable increase of muscle tonus, tremors of an irregular type, and an unsteady gait are common. In occasional instances a well-defined parkinsonian syndrome is observed. The pupillary reactions are often sluggish, and there may be minor alterations of the tendon reflexes. Aphasic disturbances are encountered in from 10 to 15 per cent of the cases. Pseudobulbar involvement and brain-stem syndromes in general are of less frequent occurrence. Convulsive seizures are observed in approximately 15 per cent of the group. They may be only a minor component of the clinical picture, but in some cases the attacks are numerous enough to warrant use of the term arteriosclerotic epilepsy. They tend to affect patients who display certain complicating conditions, particularly advanced valvular disease of the heart, suggesting that such complications may be closely concerned in their origin.

Cardiovascular alterations are characteristic features of arteriosclerotic psychoses. Almost all patients exhibit sclerosis of the peripheral arteries, including retinal sclerosis. Cardiac hypertrophy, which may be pronounced in degree, is present in most cases, and coronary sclerosis is exceedingly common. Chronic valvular disease of the heart is occasionally noted. As a rule the blood pressure is high. In a group of 29 anatomically verified cases (50), the systolic pressure was below 150 in seven instances, between 150 and 200 in seventeen, and above 200 in five instances; the average for the group was 172 systolic and 95 diastolic. As a result of these cardiovascular changes, gross irregularity of the heart rate and signs of cardiac decompensation are often noted. Diabetes mellitus is occasionally observed. Somatic changes associated with old age, such as general wasting and arcus senilis, are by no means uncommon; but they are seldom severe except in cases complicated by senile cerebral involvement.

Minor urinary abnormalities are often encountered, and in occasional cases the kidneys may be damaged to an extent sufficient to produce a rise of the urea and nonprotein nitrogen content of the blood. In cases associated with diabetes an increase of sugar is noted in the blood and urine. With the standard methods of examination, the spinal fluid may show a slight increase of total protein, but it does not display other alterations except in a few cases in which it contains gross blood from rupture of a vessel in the subarachnoid space or from an intracranial hemorrhage breaking into the ventricular system or subarachnoid space. The Walter bromide test usually shows changes indicative of an increased permeability of the blood-cerebrospinal fluid barrier. Electroencephalographic disturbances similar to those described in senile dementia, with the addition of common focal abnormalities, are frequently observed in cases presenting severe intellectual impairment (32).

The course of the illness.—The course of arteriosclerotic disease shows great diversity from case to case and often great variations in the same case at different times. The disorder may consist solely of a state of confusion or clouding associated with cerebral vascular accidents, leading to a rapidly fatal outcome or constituting merely an evanescent disturbance. Such conditions, which are undoubtedly very common, are technically psychoses, even though they are of little practical importance from a purely psychiatric viewpoint. At the opposite extreme are chronic illnesses of many years' duration, the longest in my experience lasting for 16 years. The average duration for a group representing cases encountered in a hospital for mental diseases was 3.4 years.

The acute confused or delirious states which frequently initiate the psychosis may last for weeks or months. They are terminated by death in about half of the cases; in the other half they gradually subside, leaving the patient with a varying amount of intellectual impairment, which may occasionally be slight enough to constitute a good remission. The remissions may last for months or even years. Clow (10) studied 76 hospitalized cases and found that 7 patients were recovered, 8 were much improved, and 19 were improved; approximately 20 percent of his group were adjusting well at home. In other cases there are frequent fluctuations in the severity of the symptoms, periods of confusion and restlessness alternating with quiescent periods. In a considerable number of instances, the acute episodes are associated with attacks of cardiac decompensation.

The tendency to improvement after acute attacks of confusion represents a more or less successful compensatory attempt, which is a characteristic feature of many cases. Nevertheless, each new episode usually leaves the patient with an increased amount of permanent mental impairment, and even when acute exacerbations are lacking there is gradual progression in the signs of organic deficit. This does not differ essentially from that encountered in senile dementia, though as a rule the defects of memory and comprehension are not as massive as those observed in senile psychoses and a certain degree of grasp of the surroundings may be retained even at a late stage. Depressive features or other emotional disturbances, if present earlier, may persist for long periods. On the other hand, certain subjective complaints, such as headache, dizziness, and unpleasant somatic sensations, are apt to diminish and finally disappear. Arteriosclerotic patients do not as a rule show the profound physical and mental decay of the senile patient, and they are less likely to sustain fractures of bones; but they are often bedridden and helpless because of neurologic or cardiac involvement.

Death usually occurs from pneumonia, cerebral vascular accidents, or arteriosclerotic heart disease.

IV. DIFFERENTIAL DIAGNOSIS

Mistakes in differentiating arteriosclerotic psychoses from other mental disorders are of frequent occurrence. Most of these errors can be avoided by a careful analysis of the whole picture, longitudinally as well as in cross section. A detailed discussion of this subject is presented in a paper published in 1941 (50).

Differentiation of arteriosclerotic psychoses from senile psychoses.—Arteriosclerotic psychoses are confused with senile dementia more frequently than with any other condition. Anatomic study has shown (50) that more cases are incorrectly placed in the arteriosclerotic than in the senile group. Yet in a considerable number of cases, arteriosclerotic disorders are easily recognizable, with headache, dizziness, explosive emotional outbursts, and apoplectiform phenomena in the foreground. Less well known but equally characteristic features are syncopal attacks and cardiac disturbances, which are rarely associated with pure senile psychoses. Also, convulsive seizures point to arteriosclerotic disease; in my experience they do not occur in senile dementia. Severe renal or uremic symptoms suggest an arteriosclerotic rather than a senile condition, unless they are terminal manifestations. Mistakes in diagnosis are sometimes traceable to the wide-spread but incorrect belief that hypertension and sclerosis of the peripheral arteries point exclusively to an arteriosclerotic psychosis. In both disorders peripheral sclerosis is almost always present and the same wide range of blood pressures is noted. The fact is that high systolic pressures are only a little less frequent in senile patients than in patients with arteriosclerotic disorders. However, an increased diastolic pressure is more likely to occur in the latter. General tissue alterations of a senile nature suggest senile dementia, but they are by no means rare in arteriosclerotic disorders. Arteriosclerotic mental disease often affects relatively young persons, but there is so much overlapping of the ages in the two psychoses that this is of little diagnostic help in many cases.

The sudden attacks of confusion observed in arteriosclerotic psychoses are not necessarily accompanied by neurologic phenomena, so that they cannot be readily distinguished from the chronic confused states associated with senile dementia unless their manner of development is known or their tendency to subside reveals their arteriosclerotic basis. Since a fatal outcome is common during such attacks, it may be difficult if not impossible to make a correct diagnosis when an adequate history is not available. However, even in states of severe confusion due to arteriosclerotic disease, there may be fleeting periods of lucidity.

In a relatively small group of arteriosclerotic psychoses the onset is gradual and the course may be free of stormy episodes, thus resembling a senile disorder. In such instances early subjective complaints, anxiety concerning impending mental failure, and even outspoken suicidal tendencies are often prominent. Less pronounced symptoms of this type are occasionally observed in the paranoid form of senile dementia, but they are seldom noted in other senile cases. While the lack of severe intellectual impairment in the senile paranoid patient may be reminiscent of arteriosclerotic disease, the latter rarely presents florid and persistent paranoid syndromes. In general, more complex psychopathologic disturbances are less likely to occur in psychoses with cerebral arteriosclerosis than in senile dementia. The defect of memory is diffuse in the senile patient and somewhat uneven and less marked in the arteriosclerotic patient, with memory for remote events relatively well retained in both groups. Fabrications are encountered with equal frequency in the two conditions, though a well-defined presbyophrenic picture points to senile dementia. Early changes of personality expressed by a lowering of moral standards, including sex indiscretions or crimes, are sometimes regarded as typical of senile disorders, but in my experience they are actually more common in arteriosclerotic psychoses.

Mixtures of arteriosclerotic and senile psychoses.—Clinical pictures of a mixed nature are not as common as might be anticipated from the neuropathologic findings. As a rule, one or the other condition predominates, approximately equal clinical admixtures seldom being observed. In senile psychoses complicated by cerebral vascular disease, slight fluctuations in the severity of the intellectual disturbances provide a clue to the presence of the latter more frequently than neurologic changes, though hemiplegic or hemiparetic signs are occasionally encountered. In cases of arteriosclerotic psychosis, senile admixtures tend to occur in older patients in whom typical arteriosclerotic features are less distinctive than usual, and the senile component is revealed by profound mental deterioration and outspoken physical alterations of a senile nature.

Diagnostic problems involving disorders other than senile psychoses.—Arteriosclerotic psychoses may be difficult to distinguish from toxic or symptomatic psychoses. Both conditions may begin with a sudden attack of confusion or delirium. Since neurologic changes may not be present to reveal cerebral vascular disease, their differentiation in the earlier stages may depend on discovery of the physical factors underlying the toxic disorder. In arteriosclerotic patients the confused state may be prolonged and it is often preceded by prodromal symptoms, whereas many toxic psychoses begin without warning and are of brief duration. Of course, if the illness does not terminate fatally, its further progress will disclose its true nature. The difficulties may be especially pronounced in middle-aged or elderly persons with psychoses due to cardiac or renal disease. Disturbances of the heart are noted in the majority of arteriosclerotic cases, and renal disease may be added to the picture. Not infrequently the cardiac or cardio-renal component is a prominent feature, so that any estimate of the relative importance of each factor in the total picture would be largely arbitrary.

Diabetes may give rise to similar diagnostic problems. A variety of mental disturbances, such as depressive reactions and clouded or confused states, have been attributed to it. On the other hand, diabetes may be associated with arterial degeneration, as a result of which an arteriosclerotic psychosis may develop. A true diabetic psychosis should respond to appropriate therapy and not follow the course of an arteriosclerotic disorder.

When cerebral embolism occurs in the same age group, it may lead to a psychosis which is indistinguishable from arteriosclerotic mental disorders. This is understandable, since it produces essentially the same damage to the cerebral tissue. The differentiation here will depend on discovering the underlying etiology, usually endocarditic vegetations from which the emboli originate.

Severe depressive symptoms suggestive of involutional melancholia are occasionally observed in arteriosclerotic psychoses. In the latter, the presence of physical or mental changes typical of cerebral vascular disease should enable one to differentiate between the two disorders. In one recently published case (47) the only early features pointing to arteriosclerotic disease were occasional headaches, rare spells of dizziness, and a syncopal attack.

Vascular forms of neurosyphilis may closely resemble psychoses with cerebral arteriosclerosis, particularly when the latter affects the younger age groups, so that their differentiation will depend on serologic study of the blood and spinal fluid.

Alzheimer's disease often presents ill-defined focal neurologic signs, which may produce a superficial resemblance to an arteriosclerotic psychosis; but it can be distinguished from the latter by reason of its gradual onset, with diffuse intellectual impairment in the foreground, and its steadily progressive course leading to profound mental deterioration.

Pick's lobar atrophy, which may also give rise to difficulties in diagnosis, differs from arteriosclerotic psychoses in many ways. The onset is more insidious, acute mental episodes are lacking, and the subjective complaints and the somatic and gross neurologic accompaniments of arteriosclerotic disease do not occur.

Mistakes may occasionally be made in differentiating arteriosclerotic psychoses from chronic subdural hematoma and from tumor of the brain (18, 42). In these conditions careful neurologic study, including electroencephalographic and roentgenologic examinations, should establish the correct diagnosis.

V. TREATMENT

The principles and measures discussed in the treatment of senile dementia are equally applicable to psychoses with cerebral arteriosclerosis and therefore do not require further mention. In comparison with the senile patient, the arteriosclerotic patient is more likely to be a physically sick person in the sense that he is frequently burdened by serious cardiovascular, neurologic, or renal disturbances, which are rarely of importance in uncomplicated senile cases. Hence there is greater need for care of a purely medical nature. Activities which throw strain on the cardiovascular system should be interdicted. This should not lead to a life of idleness but rather to less strenuous activities which are useful and enjoyable. Complete rest in bed is indicated only during acute episodes, with appropriate therapy for cardiac disturbances if they are present. It should not be forgotten that even in cases requiring hospitalization there may be remissions of sufficient degree and duration to enable the patient to return home and perhaps resume many of his former activities. In many cases worthwhile results are obtained by psychotherapy of a supportive type. Electric shock therapy has been used successfully in patients with depressive and paranoid features; untoward results were not observed even though some patients showed cardiovascular or neurologic involvement (22). Occupational therapy is of great value not only for ambulatory patients but also for those needing prolonged rest in bed. Serpasil, thorazine, or mild sedatives such as phenobarbital or bromides may be useful in decreasing tension, worry, and the like. Beneficial results with the use of metrazol orally have been claimed, presumably because of its stimulating effect on the cerebral circulation. In patients with hemiplegia, return of function should be encouraged by massage and passive and active exercises.

REFERENCES

1. Alzheimer, A. "Die Seelenstörungen auf arteriosklerotischer Grundlage," *Allg. Ztschr. f. Psychiatrie*, 1902, 59: 695
2. Barrett, A. M. In W. A. White and S. E. Jelliffe, *The Modern Treatment of Nervous and Mental Diseases*. Philadelphia: Lea & Febiger, 1913
3. Binswanger, O. "Die Abgrenzung der allgemeinen progressiven Paralyse," *Klin. Wochschr.*, 1894, 31: 1137, 1180
4. Bleuler, E. *Textbook of Psychiatry.* New York: The Macmillan Co., 1930
5. Braunmühl, A. von. "Kolloidchemische Betrachtungsweise seniler und präseniler Gewebeveränderungen," *Ztschr. f. ges. Neurol. Psychiatrie*, 1932, 142: 1
6. ———. "Versuch um eine kolloidchemische Pathologie des Zentralnervensystems. Das synaeretische Syndrome als cerebrale Reaktionsform," *Klin. Wochschr.*, 1934. 13: 897
7. Cameron, D. E. "Studies in Senile Nocturnal Delirium," *Psychiat. Quart.*, 1941, 15: 47
8. Cameron, N. *The Psychology of Behavior Disorders.* Boston: Houghton Mifflin Co., 1947
9. ———. "A Study of Thinking in Senile Deterioration and Schizophrenic Disorganization," *Amer. Jour. Psychology*, 1938, 51: 650–64
10. Clow, H. E. "The Outlook for Patients Admitted to a Mental Hospital after the Age of 60," *N.Y. State Jour. Med.*, 1948, 48: 2357
11. Clow, H. E., and Allen, E. B. "A Study of Depressive States in the Aging," *Geriatrics*, 1949, 4: 11
12. Cobb, S., and Blain, D. "Arteriosclerosis of the Brain and Spinal Cord," in E. V. Cowdry (ed.), *Arteriosclerosis: a Survey of the Problem.* New York: The Macmillan Co., 1933

13. Cowdry, E. V. *Arteriosclerosis: a Survey of the Problem.* New York: The Macmillan Co., 1933
14. ———. *Problems of Ageing* (2d edition). Baltimore: Williams & Wilkins, 1942
15. Critchley, M. "The Neurology of Old Age," *Lancet,* 1931, 1: 1119
16. ———. "Ageing of the Nervous System," in E. V. Cowdry (ed.), *Problems of Ageing* (2d edition). Baltimore: Williams & Wilkins, 1942
17. Dayton, N. A. *New Facts on Mental Disorders.* Springfield, Ill.: Charles C. Thomas, 1940
18. Elsberg, C. A., and Globus, J. H. "Tumor of the Brain with Acute Onset and Rapidly Progressive Course: Acute Brain Tumor," *Arch. Neurol. Psychiatry,* 1929, 21: 1044
19. Fischer, O. "Die presbyophrene Demenz, deren anatomische Grundlage und klinische Abgrenzung," *Ztschr. f. ges. Neurol. Psychiatrie,* 1910, 3: 371
20. ———. "Ein weiterer Beitrag zur Klinik und Pathologie der presbyophrenen Demenz," *ibid.,* 1912, 12: 99
21. Fisher, M. "Senile Dementia—a New Explanation of Its Causation," *Canadian M. A. J.,* 1951, 65: 1
22. Gallinek, A. "The Nature of Affective and Paranoid Disorders During the Senium in the Light of Electric Convulsive Therapy," *Jour. Nerv. Ment. Dis.,* 1948, 108: 293
23. Garnett, R. W., and Klingman, W. O. "Cytochrome C: Effects of Intravenous Administration in Presenile, Senile, and Arteriosclerotic Cerebral States," *Amer. Jour. Psychiatry,* 1950, 106: 697
24. Gellerstedt, N. "Zur Kenntnis der Hirnveränderungen bei der normalen Altersinvolution," *Upsala Läkaref. Forh.,* 1932–33, 38: 193
25. Gitelson, M. "Emotional Problems of Elderly People," *Geriatrics,* 1948, 3: 135
26. Goldschmidt, H. "Social Aspects of Ageing and Senility," *Jour. Ment. Sci.,* 1946, 92: 182
27. Grünthal, E. "Klinisch-anatomisch vergleichende Untersuchungen über den Greisenblödsinn," *Ztschr. f. ges. Neurol. Psychiatrie,* 1927, 111: 763
28. Kallman, F. J., and Sander, G. "Twin Studies on Senescence," *Amer. Jour. Psychiatry,* 1949, 106: 29
29. Kodama, M. "Die regionäre Verteilung der arteriosklerotischen Veränderungen im Grosshirn," *Ztschr. f. ges. Neurol. Psychiatrie,* 1926, 102: 597
30. Kolb, L. "The Psychiatric Significance of Aging as a Public Health Problem," Supplement 168 to *U.S. Pub. Health Repts.* (Washington: Government Printing Office, 1942)
31. Kral, V. A. "Psychiatric Observations Under Severe Chronic Stress," *Amer. Jour. Psychiatry,* 1951, 108: 185
32. Luce, R. E., and Rothschild, D. "The Correlation of Electroencephalographic and Clinical Observations in Psychiatric Patients Over 65," *Jour. Geront.,* 1953, 8: 167
33. Malamud, W. "Current Trends and Needs in Research on Problems of the Aged," *Dis. Nerv. System,* 1941, 2: 37
34. ———. "Mental Disorders of the Aged: Arteriosclerotic and Senile Psychoses," Supplement 168 to *U.S. Pub. Health Repts.* (Washington: Government Printing Office, 1942)

35. Malamud, W., and Lowenberg, K. "Alzheimer's Disease: a Contribution to Its Etiology and Classification," *Arch. Neurol. Psychiatry*, 1929, 21: 805
36. Malamud, W., Sands, S. L., and Malamud, I. "The Involutional Psychoses: A Sociopsychiatric Study," *Psychosom. Med.*, 1941, 3: 4
37. Massachusetts State Department of Mental Health. *Annual Report for the Year Ending November 30, 1938*
38. ———. (Unpublished data)
39. Mayer-Gross, W. "Arteriosclerotic, Senile and Presenile Psychoses," in "Recent Progress in Psychiatry" (*Jour. Ment. Sci.*, 1944, 90: 316)
40. McGraw, R. B. "Recoverable or Temporary Mental Disturbances in the Elderly," *Jour. Geront.*, 1949, 4: 234
41. *Mental Health in Later Maturity*. Supplement 168 to *U.S. Pub. Health Repts.* (Washington: Government Printing Office, 1942)
42. Naumann, H. N. "Glioblastoma of Occipital Lobe Simulating Psychosis with Cerebral Arteriosclerosis in an Octogenarian," *Arch. Neurol. Psychiatry*, 1948, 60: 604
43. Neubürger, K. "Beiträge zur Histologie, Pathogenese und Einteilung der arteriosklerotischen Hirnerkrankung," in *Veröffentlichungen aus der Kriegs- und Konstitutionspathologie* (Gustav Fischer, 1930–31), Vol. 6
44. Noyes, A. P. *Modern Clinical Psychiatry* (3d edition). Philadelphia: W. B. Saunders Company, 1948
45. Rhein, J. H. W., Winkelman, N. W., and Patten, C. A. "Mental Conditions in the Aged," *Arch. Neurol. Psychiatry*, 1928, 20: 329
46. Roth, M. "Problems of Old Age and the Senile and Arteriosclerotic Psychoses," in "Recent Progress in Psychiatry" (*Jour. Ment. Sci.*, 1950, 2: 379)
47. Rothschild, D. "The Role of the Premorbid Personality in Arteriosclerotic Psychoses," *Amer. Jour. Psychiatry*, 1944, 100: 501
48. ———. "Pathologic Changes in Senile Psychoses and Their Psychobiologic Significance," *ibid.*, 1937, 93: 757
49. ———. "Neuropathologic Changes in Arteriosclerotic Psychoses and Their Psychiatric Significance," *Arch. Neurol. Psychiatry*, 1942, 48: 417
50. ———. "The Clinical Differentiation of Senile and Arteriosclerotic Psychoses," *Amer. Jour. Psychiatry*, 1941, 98: 324
51. ———. "Senile Chorea and Its Relation to Huntington's Chorea," *Jour. Mount Sinai Hospital*, 1938, 5: 517
52. ———. "Alzheimer's Disease: a Clinicopathologic Study of Five Cases," *Amer. Jour. Psychiatry*, 1934, 91: 485
53. ———. "The Practical Value of Research in the Psychoses of Later Life," *Dis. Nerv. System*, 1947, 8: 123
54. Rothschild, D., and Kasanin, J. "A Clinicopathologic Study of Alzheimer's Disease: Relationship to Senile Conditions," *Arch. Neurol. Psychiatry*, 1936, 36: 293
55. Rothschild, D., and Sharp, M. L., "The Origin of Senile Psychoses: Neuropathologic Factors and Factors of a More Personal Nature," *Dis. Nerv. System*, 1941, 2: 49
56. Rusk, H. A. "America's Number One Problem—Chronic Disease and an Aging Population," *Amer. Jour. Psychiatry*, 1949, 106: 270

57. Sachs, E., Jr. "Meningiomas with Dementia as the First and Presenting Feature," *Jour. Ment. Sci.*, 1950, 96: 998
58. Sands, S. L., and Rothschild, D. "Socio-Psychiatric Foundations for a Theory of the Reactions to Aging," *Jour. Nerv. Ment. Dis.*, 1952, 116: 233
59. Semrad, E. V., and McKeon, C. C. "Social Factors in Old Age Psychosis," *Dis. Nerv. System*, 1941, 2: 58
60. Silver, A. "Group Psychotherapy with Senile Psychotic Patients," *Geriatrics*, 1950, 5: 147
61. Simchowicz, T. "Histologische Studien über die senile Demenz," *Histol. u. histopath. Arb. u. d. Grosshirnrinde*, 1910, 4: 267
62. Simon, B., and Kaufman, S. H. "Psychiatric Problems of the Aged," *Dis. Nerv. System*, 1941, 2: 62
63. Spielmeyer, W. "Die Psychosen des Rückbildungs- und Greisenalters," in Aschaffenburg, *Handbuch der Psychiatrie* (Spec. Teil, Abt. 5). Wien und Leipzig: Franz Deuticke, 1912
64. ———. *Histopathologie des Nervensystems* (Allgemeiner Teil). Berlin: Julius Springer, 1922
65. ———. "Vasomotorisch-trophische Veränderungen bei zerebraler Arteriosklerose," *Monatsschr. f. Psychiat. Neurol.*, 1928, 68: 605
66. Stieglitz, E. J. *Psychiatric Hazards of Senescence* (Training Seminar held at Detroit, Michigan, under the auspices of the Committee on Medical Education of the American Psychiatric Association). Washington, D.C.: Office of the Medical Director, American Psychiatric Association, 1950
67. Strecker, E. A., and Ebaugh, F. G. *Practical Clinical Psychiatry* (5th edition). Philadelphia: The Blakiston Co., 1940
68. Symposium. "Problems of the Aged," *Dis. Nerv. System*, 1941, 2: 35–77
69. Tilney, F. "The Aging of the Human Brain," *Bull. N.Y. Acad. Med.* (2d series), 1928, 4: 1125
70. Warthin, A. S. *Old Age, the Major Involution*. New York: Paul B. Hoeber, Inc., 1929
71. Wertham, F., and Wertham, F. *The Brain as an Organ: Its Postmortem Study and Interpretation*. New York: The Macmillan Co., 1934
72. Wexberg, E. "Nutritional Deficiencies as Factors in Mental Disorders," Supplement 168 to *U.S. Pub. Health Repts.* (Washington, D.C.: Government Printing Office, 1942)
73. White, W. A. *Outlines of Psychiatry* (14th edition). Washington, D.C.: Nervous and Mental Disease Monographs, 1935
74. ———. "The Social Significance of Mental Disease," *Arch. Neurol. Psychiatry*, 1932, 22: 873
75. Williams, H. W., Quesnel, E., Fish, V. W., and Goodman, L., "Studies in Senile and Arteriosclerotic Psychoses," *Amer. Jour. Psychiatry*, 1942, 98: 712

Chapter XII

THE TOXIC DELIRIOUS REACTIONS OF OLD AGE

G. Wilse Robinson, Jr.

The problems of the abnormal mental reactions of old age were almost completely neglected by the medical profession up until twenty years ago. The infrequent discussions that arose were largely academic, and few practical, constructive advances were made. The last important step forward was made in the early days of pathological investigation. Arteriosclerosis and senile degeneration were found, studied, and named as "pathology" of senile diseases. There investigation stopped. The question seemed solved, the situation hopeless; and, until a method of preventing or curing arteriosclerosis was discovered, practical men were not interested in this important field.

For over fifteen years the staff of the Neurological Hospital has become increasingly interested in the problem of interpretation and treatment of the abnormal mental reactions of old age. Several reports have been published, outlining our observations and conclusions in these matters (26, 27, 28, 29, 30). One of the more common conditions in this age group, consisting of patients over 60 years of age, is the toxic, delirious reaction. Over 20 per cent of all patients over 60 admitted to the hospital had as their primary and sole abnormal mental reaction a toxic, delirious state.

In addition to this 20 per cent, approximately another 20 per cent had a toxic, delirious reaction superimposed upon some other type of abnormal mental reaction. This high incidence of approximately 40 per cent has not, in my opinion, been recognized in the past. These percentages have fallen markedly in recent years, especially in the primary cases. Most family physicians are aware of the situation and of the dangers of improper management of the older patients. The physician knows now that some things can be done for the older patient. He not only prevents "bronchial pneumonia" by proper management, but seeks psychiatric help for his mentally ill and elderly patients.

The term "toxic delirious reaction" as here used includes a

332

wide variety of cases which do not have a common etiological factor and probably do not have a common pathological or patho-logical-physiological picture. Likewise the symptomatology varies from a state of profound collapse, somewhat similar to that seen in macroscopic vascular accidents in the brain, to a delirious hallu-cinosis similar to delirium tremens. This group is heterogeneous and has only one common denominator: a distinct disturbance of the metabolic processes, not only of the brain but of the entire organism.

In all of the statistical evaluations and analyses made by our staff, the age of 60 has been used as the borderline between the involutional period and old age. This demarcation was selected because of Wartman's work (40). In 500 consecutive autopsies of patients who died from all possible causes he found that 90 per cent of the men and 85 per cent of the women over 60 years of age had marked cerebral arteriosclerosis. The remainder had some pathological condition in their brains at the time of death. These statistics confirm the concept that pathology is not the only factor. It is known that 90 per cent of the men and 85 per cent of the women over 60 years of age are not afflicted with mental symptoms. The age of 60, therefore, has been a convenient demarcation line, since this pathological study can be used as a standard for clinical interpretation. We know in advance that any group of mental patients over 60 years of age has a very high incidence of arterio-sclerosis.

However, in the evaluation of the individual case, from the standpoint of both the possible pathology and the clinical interpre-tation, arbitrary age limits have no practical value. It is well known that serious arteriosclerosis may occur in relatively young people, and that some live to advanced old age without any pro-nounced cerebral pathology. The older viewpoint was to attempt to correlate pathology and clinical symptoms in a simple cause and effect formula.

Pathological studies in the past have influenced thinking far out of proportion to their real importance. Efforts have been made to develop classifications of clinical syndromes based on pathologic studies alone, without taking into consideration any other factors. These have not been successful. One of the most exhaustive studies of this type was made by Rhein, Winkelman, and Patten (24).

However, over 30 per cent of their cases did not fit exactly into their classifications, based upon correlations between symptoms and post-mortem material. There has developed a trend of thought recently, confirmed by both pathological and clinical observations and studies, which has shown that older concepts are wrong and that all of the older attitudes and conclusions in regard to the mental diseases of old age should be revised.

Gellerstedt (11) and Rothschild (32) pointed out that there is no exact correlation between the intensity of mental symptoms and the severity of the pathologic findings. They found many brains with severe pathologic changes in cases in which there was no history of mental symptoms. Riggs (25) also has observed this. Rothschild (33) pointed out the difficulty of exact diagnosis and differentiation of senile dementia and arteriosclerotic psychosis, using pathologically proved cases for his material. He pointed out, also, the high incidence of other types of psychotic reactions which develop in the later years of life and which do not result from irreversible, pathologic changes. It would seem from these studies that pathology in the brain is not the major etiologic factor in the several psychotic processes seen in old age. Etiologic determinations in scientific medicine should be based on established laws. If a cause produces symptoms in one case, it will do it every time unless there are variable factors. It would seem from the foregoing that there must be variable factors which have not been taken into consideration in the past.

"Normal" people over 60 have severe pathological changes in their brains, and psychotic patients frequently have little or no pathological changes. I do not intend to deny the proper place of these changes in the total psychiatry of old age. Michael (19), in discussing the psychoses accompanying cardiac decompensations, expressed my concept. He said that arteriosclerosis may be one of the causes that modify the course of a mind disordered during cardiac decompensation to the extent that prompt recovery—the rule in patients who have recovered from heart failure signs—is delayed. This is true not only of cardiac "psychoses" but of all other types of abnormal mental reactions seen in the latter years. It is especially true of the toxic delirious reactions.

If this reasoning is correct and pathology can at last be placed in its proper place in the total thinking about this problem, medical science can proceed to search for the other and, perhaps, more important etiological factors. Many of them are already known, because the same principles of psychobiology and psychopathology which are applied to younger individuals can be used in approaching the older patient, once defeatism and rigid pathological interpretations have been eliminated.

Several clinical reports have been made which express optimism. I reported (26) a series of 16 older patients with acute confusional states who were treated actively with intravenous glucose infusions. Thirteen of these patients made a complete recovery. Larson (18) confirmed these observations on the acute delirious reactions.

One hundred patients with abnormal mental reactions which developed during the senile years were analyzed by Clow (6), and it was found that 49 recovered sufficiently to return home. Braceland, Palmer, and Hastings (20) reported upon the results in a series of arteriosclerotic psychoses and senile dementia patients. They found that 24.4 per cent of the total series, 23 arteriosclerotic and 7 senile dementia patients, recovered sufficiently to return home.

These clinical observations show that not all psychoses of old age are irreversible. Since they are not, the cause or causes should not be irreversible. In other words, the sole cause of all abnormal reactions of old age is not irreversible pathologic conditions in the brain, that is, cerebral arteriosclerosis, senile degeneration, or both.

The last formal report that was made from this hospital analyzed 128 patients over 60 years of age. Of this group 27 patients were thought to have as their major clinical condition a toxic, exhaustive, metabolic, delirious state. In addition to this group an equal number had a rather profound toxic, exhaustive, metabolic, delirious state superimposed upon some other psychotic condition. In recent years this high percentage of about 42 per cent incidence has been reduced.

Very few cases have a clearly cut, single etiology. The age of the patient may cause reduced resiliency and adjustability. The cardio-vascular system may be unable to meet emergencies. Etiological factors in this type of reaction are drugs, malnutrition, prolonged recumbency following major or minor illnesses, operations or trauma, hypertensive states, cardiac failure, and primary metabolic conditions such as diabetes mellitus. While all of these etiological factors are capable of producing toxic delirious reactions in younger people, an analysis of the older cases indicates that the older the person the more susceptible he is to this type of psychotic reaction.

Arteriosclerosis without occlusion or rupture does not seem to be an etiological factor of major importance. In spite of the arteriosclerosis which we know is present in the older patient, he can and does recover from the types of reactions seen in younger patients if he receives proper therapy. However, I feel that the physical and physiological degeneration seen in the older patient does play a part in the total etiology, in that it decreases resiliency and adjustability to physiological changes; and minor etiologies which would have no noticeable effect upon the younger patient may produce in an older patient a profound psychotic reaction which he is incapable of throwing off even when the activating etiology has been corrected or eliminated. If this is kept constantly in mind when the older patient presents himself for treatment, common therapeutic procedures which are innocuous in the younger patient but disastrous to the older patient will not be used.

The symptoms in these patients can be divided into three major types: psychotic, physical, and neurological. The outstanding psychotic symptoms are diurnal drowsiness, nocturnal restlessness, behavior disorders, hallucinations, clouding of consciousness, and deficient orientation and grasp, with occasional dream-like experiences. However, hallucinations and dream-like experiences are not as common in the older patient as they are in the younger delirious patient. The patients under consideration are apt to be noisy, confused, disoriented, overactive, frightened, and un-cooperative.

On the physical side there is a history of failure to eat properly and to take sufficient fluids. Bowel incontinence is rare, but lack of control of the urinary function is seen frequently. The malnutrition and dehydration are usually responsible for the physical findings other than those which are evidences of the etiology. There is usually a fever, which in the early stages is quite mild unless there is an acute infectious disease as the major contributing etiology, and a leucocytosis, which is mild, again unless there is an acute, major inflammatory process. There are loss of weight, exhaustion, and evidences of dehydration in the skin and mucous membranes. The red-blood-cell count and the hemoglobin may be high. In spite of the leucocytosis, the differential count may be normal. Other blood analyses indicate a tendency toward concentration, not only of cells and other solid matter but also of the various electrolytes. The N.P.N. is usually higher than is to be expected from this concentration factor. Urine is usually concentrated, of strong odor and acid reaction. Sugar and albumin are found in almost every case if repeated examinations are made.

If malnutrition has progressed very far there may be evidences of vitamin deficiency, but usually in the early stages and probably in the late stages the only evidence of malnutrition will be a diabetic-like glucose-tolerance curve. This phenomenon and its significance were reported by our hospital group (31).

The finding of the diabetic-like glucose-tolerance curve is, in our opinion, pathognomonic of this condition. However, failure to find this curve does not of necessity rule out a toxic delirious state. It may be that the patient is first seen too early in the process for a malnutrition curve to have developed, or if the process is late the curve is not specific. It may still be that of pseudo-diabetes from malnutrition, or may be a flat curve. The significance of these flat curves which occur in profound malnutrition has not yet been explained satisfactorily.

Neurological findings are tremor, in-coordination, reflex excitability, asthenia, ataxia, and perhaps some evidence of a major vascular disease or accident.

From the standpoint of prognosis it is necessary that this type of problem be differentiated from the true arteriosclerotic psychoses and cases of senile dementia. These syndromes, which in the past have been considered to be the most common of all the abnormal mental reactions of old age, have been found to have an incidence of 10.1 and 17.1 per cent, respectively. These are usually irreversible psychotic types, although some of the arteriosclerotic phenomena do improve with therapy. It must also be remembered that frequently, owing to improper medical and nursing care, there may be superimposed upon these two irreversible syndromes a toxic delirious state which has aggravated the symptoms and increased the nursing problem. However, we feel that clearly cut cases of the three types can be readily differentiated.

While the symptoms of a toxic delirious reaction frequently are similar to the symptoms of the other two types, the most important differential point is the speed and type of onset. Toxic delirious reactions usually come on with moderate speed. There is usually the history of some illness, operation, or trauma which required bed rest. During the bed rest the patient may or may not have been given drugs. Within a few days or a week or two after the precipitating episode, the patient becomes restless, perhaps irritable, and develops insomnia and anorexia. The usual therapeutic procedure instituted at this time by the majority of physicians is to give sedatives and vitamins. The sedatives aggravate the condition, and the vitamins have no apparent effect upon the clinical course. The patient rapidly progresses into a condition which makes it impossible for him to be kept at home or in a general hospital. When the psychiatrist is called in or the patient transferred to a psychiatric hospital, symptoms are usually fully developed as outlined above.

In a few cases, however, there is no history of this kind and apparently the condition developed without any clearly cut etiological background. The diagnosis of these cases must be made by ruling out the two types of irreversible phenomena. We have followed Muncie's criterion that a diagnosis of arteriosclerotic psychosis must not be made unless there is evidence of a prior vascular occlusion. We have usually found that it takes several vascular occlusions to precipitate a permanent psychosis. If there is no evidence of paralysis or anesthesia of a cerebral type, arteriosclerotic psychosis has been ruled out.

Senile dementia, on the other hand, is an insidious condition developing slowly over a long period of time, leading in many cases to a symptomatology similar to that seen in toxic delirious reactions but giving no history of an acute exacerbation or a sudden onset. It must be remembered that almost every person over 60 years of age will begin to develop senile mental and physical changes. These senile changes will progress slowly over a period of months or years. At some stage during this progression an acute illness, a turning to sedatives, or the development of a metabolic disturbance may precipitate a toxic delirious reaction. Correction of this reaction will leave the patient with a minimum of senile changes, well able to return home and sometimes to a gainful occupation if this is necessary. Therefore, the history of moderate senile changes before the acute episode does not of necessity contraindicate a therapeutic program directed at the correction of the superimposed toxic delirious reaction.

It is readily apparent what the major etiological factors are in these problems. The important thing to remember is that the older patient does not have the resiliency of the younger patient, does not have the physical and physiological adjustabilities, and, therefore, cannot tolerate the same type of therapeutic program that the younger patients can. The most common mistake made in this respect is the use of sedatives, the bromides and the barbiturates. There are many cases where a small dose of the barbiturates or a moderate, prolonged program of bromides has precipitated one of these illnesses. On the other hand, when the prodromal symptoms develop following illness, trauma, etc., such as restlessness and insomnia, the sedatives are usually resorted to and the small doses given are enough to unbalance the metabolic adjustment in such a way that a severe reaction is precipitated. It is my opinion that no sedatives should be given to the older patients. The opiates are harmful, also, in that they slow certain physiological processes, chiefly expectoration and other elimination processes from the lungs, and thus may lead to a pneumonic process.

We are now seeing a new element of etiology. We have had several patients admitted in recent years with a toxic, delirious reaction which seems to have developed directly from some of the newer wonder drugs. The agents we have noted are penicillin, artane, and cortisone. These have been infrequent, but we are convinced that in susceptible individuals they can produce a transitory, severe, abnormal mental reaction, which usually clears up when the drug is withdrawn.

LaPlace and Nicholson (17) pointed out an etiological factor in older people which may precipitate a toxic delirious reaction. This is prolonged recumbency. They felt very definitely that placing the older patient in bed flat on his back for any of several reasons will lead to changes in the dependent parts so that toxic material may develop and, of itself, solely initiate a toxic delirious reaction. This is commonly seen in surgical and traumatic cases, and the reaction is usually diagnosed bronchial pneumonia. LaPlace and Nicholson pointed out that the bronchial pneumonic process is always a terminal event made possible by the lack of resistance of the patient and resulting from the delirium with exhaustion. They do not feel that bronchial pneumonia precipitates these conditions but rather that the bronchial pneumonia results from the condition. The temperature curve seen in the early stages and the leucocytosis are reactions to the general metabolic breakdown, not reactions to infection. They pointed out that many of these cases die with no evidence of a pneumonic process in their lungs. They die a metabolic and exhaustive death.

The cerebral pathology, as well as the general pathology, is nonspecific. While there may be some evidence of vitamin deficiency in the changes in the brain, the usual findings at death are reversible changes with generalized intracellular edema and cloudy swelling of the ganglion cells. Rupture of the cell and nuclear membrane is seen frequently. Pyknotic changes may be found. In some of these cases the brains are hard, dry, much firmer than normal, without edema. In those cases the pyknotic change naturally predominates. Avitaminotic changes of the type described by Freeman (10) are not common findings in these patients. Avitaminosis is not a cause of this phenomenon. It is a more complete breakdown of all metabolic processes, and the vitamin deficiency is only incidental. Treatment with vitamins of any type, especially those of the B complex, or the use of nicotinic acid alone will not correct these conditions unless other therapeutic procedures are also used. When pathology in the nervous system results from deficiency of the B complex or any of its elements, rather specific types of neuropathies are produced. This type of pathology is not found in these cases, according to Riggs (25). Therefore vitamin therapy cannot be expected to correct the condition.

From the standpoint of therapy, 22 cases of primary toxic delirious reaction in patients over 60 years of age were given what I consider to be adequate treatment. Of this group, 18 made an apparently complete recovery and returned home apparently normal for their age. Three improved sufficiently to go home but did not return to their former occupations, and one died. Sixteen of the cases that made an apparently complete recovery had been out of the hospital six months or longer when the report was made; 15 cases are still completely well, indicating a recovery rate of 93.7 per cent in the complete-recovery group. These figures include only the primary cases. Many of the secondary cases had as their primary psychotic reaction a psychotic depressive state which was corrected with convulsive shock. Other cases had irreversible types and returned to a state where they could be kept at home or in a nursing home with a minimum of attention. I do not feel that I can statistically evaluate the secondary or complicated delirious cases, because of the several factors.

The major feature of therapy is daily infusions of 10 per cent glucose in plain water. During the first two or three days glucose in saline may be used, but it should not be continued. In the early stages, 1,000 to 2,000 c.c. may be given; but usually we find that 500 c.c. a day is sufficient throughout the entire time of hospital treatment. These infusions are given very slowly, never more than 50 drops a minute. It has been pointed out by Sparkman (34) that if glucose is given at this rate or at a slower rate, no embarrassment of respiratory or cardiac function is to be expected.

Two new drugs have come into wide use in recent years, chlorpromazine and rauwolfia. These drugs, especially chlorpromazine, have a place in the treatment program of these patients. They reduce overactivity, having a good sedative effect. I prefer chlorpromazine, although this drug has some toxic side effects. One of these is jaundice. This does not seem to arise from direct action on liver cells and does not aggravate the toxic delirious state. It is reversible and usually clears up when the drug is stopped.

There may be other side effects that can and will aggravate the mental state, but there have been few reports on these as yet. It is suggested that only small doses be used in these cases and that they be watched carefully for side effects and complications. Chlorpromazine should be used in preference to the barbiturates, which can cause serious toxic states.

Before glucose infusions were used in the treatment of these cases, a series of 16 patients showed 13 deaths, 2 partial recoveries, and 1 complete recovery. In all of the 22 treated patients noted above there is only one case that recovered completely immediately following the clearing up of the etiological factors. This was a case of straight barbital intoxication. There were several other cases of drug intoxication, however, where the general metabolic breakdown had progressed so far that recovery did not follow the stopping of the drugs but only followed the use of the infusion program. The rationale of this procedure is entirely empirical.

Throughout this presentation it has been apparent that the

group under discussion is heterogeneous in etiology, symptomatology, and, probably, pathology. The only uniformity is a response to a treatment procedure which in our hands and in the hands of others has been almost specific when a comparison is made between the treated and the untreated series. Any scientifically trained person recognizes the innumerable pitfalls confronting one who starts with a treatment and attempts to determine from results of treatment procedures etiology, pathological physiology, and pathology in a clinical condition. The variable factors are too great.

There are two known therapeutic actions of intravenous glucose: the hypertonic and the nutritive. In my first series of 16, a relatively small one, 50 per cent glucose was used without effect. This would seem to eliminate the hypertonic action from consideration, since large amounts of 10 per cent were effective and would be almost equally hypertonic. Fifty per cent glucose given in 50 to 100 c.c. quantities is quickly eliminated and has no practical nutritive effect. The failure of small amounts of concentrated solutions and the success of large amounts of weaker solutions would lead us to assume that the effect results from increased available nutrition with the restoration of a normal glucose metabolism.

It is my feeling that there is a similarity of pathological physiology in all of the toxic delirious states, regardless of the apparent etiology or the age of the patient. This is confirmed by the work of our group and others in delirium tremens. This condition results not from an excess of alcohol over a long period but rather from malnutrition. This concept has been proposed by others, as well as by our group; and, since many of the symptoms, physical findings, and laboratory determinations found in delirium tremens are also seen in the toxic delirious reactions of old age, it is probably worth while to review the literature of the former condition, as it has some bearing on the problem here under consideration.

Cline and Coleman (5) review the subject of delirium tremens extensively. They mention a theory in vogue at the turn of the century. According to this theory the delirium was caused by the action on the brain of a secondary or intermediate toxin. Bonhoeffer (2) suggested the gastrointestinal tract, Herz (14) the kidneys, and Döllken (8) the central nervous system as possible origins of these toxins. Cline and Coleman (5), however, come to the accepted conclusion that delirium tremens is a separate path-

not observed pathologically, or where observed are not advanced enough to be considered in their true light. The first type (acute fatty liver) is seen very frequently in city morgues in men picked up by the police, with severe acute intoxication with malnutrition. One naturally wonders about the livers of the countless excessive drinkers who do not die, and Connor points out that they go on into stage two. The progression is gradual over a period of years, resulting from repeated excesses which produce recurrent "fatty livers." These changes, both the acute and the chronic, certainly affect the function of the liver, and Puyuelo (23) has pointed out that the detoxication and metabolic functions of the liver are severely affected. He published several papers in 1935 covering the subject of liver function and the effect of alcoholism and decreased carbohydrate intake on liver structure and function, and indicated how this disturbance leads to delirium tremens. He also discusses many isolated reports of findings in alcoholics and delirium tremens cases which provide clinical and pathological proof of this conception. Space does not permit me to discuss this mass of material in detail, and only the barest summary will be presented. The student is referred to his several publications.

He points out that adequate glycogen content and proper glycogenesis are vital for proper liver integrity, both structurally and functionally. When the glycogen content falls below normal levels, fat is deposited. This fat deposit, at first in droplets and then in degeneration, progresses because of the low glycogen content and because of the disturbance of the functions of the liver from the loss of glycogen as a colloid protector. We have first the physical, chemical disintegration, and later the histological disintegration (the progression to the acute fatty liver and the fatty liver with definite fibrosis mentioned by Connor). The progression of this process gradually lowers the efficiency and resiliency of the liver by reducing the quantity of normal functionable liver tissue and liver tissue which can begin to re-function when glycogen is replaced. Throughout the years we would expect the liver to become less effective in its work and evidences of liver dysfunction under certain circumstances to be more apparent.

Delirium tremens, in our experience, has been primarily a condition of the middle years. The average age of our patients is 43.8 years. Only one case was under 30. We pointed out above that 11.5 per cent of all our alcoholics were under 30 and 33.2 per cent were between 30 and 40. Our series of delirium tremens showed 4.5 per cent under 30, 8.2 per cent between 30 and 35, and 25.1 per cent between 35 and 40. We consider this age incidence, while the series is small, to be very significant, as it rather closely parallels the age incidence when we might expect the liver of the average alcoholic to begin to break down. The less normal liver there is available the more susceptible the patient is, the less the "trauma" needs to be, and the more quickly the symptoms would develop in any condition affecting the liver, such as an alcoholic episode. As liver function decreases during the alcoholic experience, the concentration of intermediate metabolites in the blood stream gradually is increased, until finally this concentration reaches a toxic level. In this form of liver insufficiency, Puyuelo points out that we find elevation and prolongation of the glycemic curve, galactose in the urine after experimental administration, increase in amino acids and polypeptids with decrease of urea in the blood, acidosis, opsiuria, and increase of bilirubin in the blood. There is retention of pigments and toxins, increase of indican in the blood, and toxic change in the blood picture, with increase of sedimentation rate and bleeding time with fragile capillaries. He comments that much of this metabolic change may be attributed not to the liver cell itself but to the cells of the reticulo-endothelial system. These alterations of the biochemistry may not be enough of themselves to produce delirium, but it is pointed out that Hauptmann (13) and Stern and Lokinschina (37) have expressed the theory that in chronic alcoholism there is increased permeability of the membrane between blood and spinal fluid, thereby making it easier for the toxins to reach the cerebral tissue.

Two recent studies indicate this disturbance of liver function. Thomas, Semrad, and Schwab (39) reported that in 18 of 24 cases of delirium tremens the serum albumin was below the lower limit of the normal range, and that in 22 it was below this level on discharge, in spite of high-caloric and high-protein diets. They suggest that this is due to liver dysfunction. Brugsch (3) found that chronic alcoholics may excrete through the kidneys an abnormal amount of porphyrin. This is attributed to the damaging effects of alcohol on the reticulo-endothelial system, bone marrow, and liver.

Staub's (35) conception of the "pacemaking" effect of carbohydrate metabolism has an important bearing on this whole process. Carbohydrate metabolism must be started back upon its normal way in order that these other abnormalities may correct themselves or be corrected. Insulin is the hormone most vital to proper carbohydrate metabolism, and it is necessary for proper glycogenesis. Therefore, the injection of insulin with adequate carbohydrates is rational and, as clinical experience has shown, is effective. Two questions naturally arise. Why does not body insulin control this mechanism so that extra insulin is not needed? And why do most patients "spontaneously" recover in a few days as a rule? The two questions and their answers are intimately related. It has been shown that without glycogen reserves in the body, and especially in the liver, carbohydrate metabolism cannot function normally and pancreatic insulin is not secreted in normal amounts. The normal cycle is broken and the whole mechanism is on a dead center.

Chambers (4) reviewed the whole subject of undernutrition and carbohydrate metabolism. His material must be summarized, as the entire subject is too complex for the purposes of this chapter. It has been shown that with undernutrition there is disturbance of the carbohydrate metabolism-controlling mechanism. In the early stages of carbohydrate deprivation this dysfunction seems to depend on the amount or the lack of carbohydrate available to the cells. In the latter stages the endocrine control or dyscontrol is the most important factor. Insulin or the lack of it is the most important primary endocrine factor in carbohydrate metabolism, thus assuming a vitally important place in our concept. Two experiments need to be mentioned because of their importance. Ellis (9) notes that injected insulin quickly corrected the impaired tolerance produced by a ketogenic diet. Wierzuchowski (41) showed that dogs that had fasted ten days excreted 45 per cent of injected glucose during the first five hours, but that after the addition of insulin only 25 per cent of the glucose was excreted in the same length of time, showing a better utilization. Chambers comments that these and other observations seem to fit the theory that the endocrine function of the pancreas becomes suppressed by a lack of carbohydrates. Every clinician who has had any experience with alcoholics recognizes the fact that these individuals at times appear to be eating enough calories but that their diets are very high in proteins and fats (meats) and very low in carbohydrates (starches and sweets). There is evidence to show that high-protein, low-carbohydrate diets have a greater disturbing effect upon carbohydrate metabolism and, therefore, upon organism metabolism than complete fasting. The student is referred to Chambers' comprehensive review for the details of these mechanisms. This material would seem to show definitely that an outside agent, catalyst-like in its effect, should be used in order to re-correct the carbohydrate-metabolism cycle quickly. Insulin injected in the absence of body insulin provides this "catalyst" and re-establishes the cycle. Glycogen is formed and deposited in the tissues, especially in the liver, thus revitalizing the liver function with the re-establishment of normal general metabolism of all factors.

The "spontaneous" recoveries are simply a slower application of the same mechanism. Under treatment, carbohydrates are fed to the patient. Certain small amounts of body insulin are available, of course, and glycogen is slowly rebuilt so that after a period of days glycogen reserves have been replaced to the point of effectiveness, and carbohydrate metabolism has reached a point where the whole metabolism of the organism, and especially of the liver, reverses itself toward normal with a reduction of concentration of circulating toxic metabolites.

This detailed consideration of a condition which is related to the one under discussion has been inserted to bring out the general nature of the former and thus to point a way toward the determination of the general nature of the latter. Detailed studies of the toxic delirious reactions of old age, such as have been made in delirium tremens, are very desirable in order to prove the author's hypothesis that this reaction seen in old age is essentially a general disease with psychotic manifestations and closely related to delirium tremens and all other toxic, psychotic reactions to disease and chemicals.

This material shows the general character of a disease presenting many of the symptoms seen in the toxic delirious reactions of old age. In both conditions death may result from a terminal pneumonia. In both cases the processes are reversed by an attack upon a state of malnutrition with secondary reversible pathological changes, not only in the brain but in the body as a whole.

These general similarities do not prove that the two conditions are the same general type of process, and in the absence of complete pathological and clinical-pathological studies a definite statement cannot as yet be made. But it is not far-fetched to assume that these two delirious processes are at least similar in their pathophysiology and pathogenesis, and that other delirious processes may in time fit themselves into the same general pattern. We do feel that the toxic delirious reactions of old age are not a separate entity, but rather a type of process similar to the many toxic exhaustive, metabolic psychoses seen in patients of all ages, such as true post-operative psychoses, the deliriums accompanying acute inflammatory conditions, drug toxemias, and metabolic psychoses seen in uremia and diabetes mellitus.

At this time, my concept of all these conditions is that the common etiological background is a breakdown of carbohydrate metabolic functions with a failure of detoxication. This leads to a type of toxemia which we may call autogenous and which causes the symptoms by the action of the circulating toxins upon the brain cells and their functions. The cardinal principle of treatment is to restore the carbohydrate metabolic functions and to prevent any additional toxemia through the chosen therapeutic procedures.

If all patients in the older age group presenting a major mental reaction are studied with an open mind by all of the procedures available to the physician, most of these cases will be recognized early. Early therapy will reverse almost all of these processes before permanent damage is done; many lives will be saved and the permanent crippling of many minds will be prevented.

REFERENCES

1. Bielschowsky, —. "Histopathology of Nerve Cells," in Penfield (ed.), *Cytology and Cellular Pathology of the Nervous System* (New York: Paul B. Hoeber, Inc., 1932)
2. Bonhoeffer, K. *Die akuten Geisteskrankheiten der Gewohnheitstrinker.* Jena: Gustav Fischer, 1901
3. Brugsch, J. T. "Toxic Porphyrinuria Following Chronic Alcoholism," *Proc. Staff Meeting Mayo Clinic*, 1937, 12: 609
4. Chambers, W. H. "Undernutrition and Carbohydrate Metabolism," *Physiol. Rev.*, 1938, 18: 248
5. Cline, W. B., Jr., and Coleman, J. V. "The Treatment of Delirium Tremens," *Jour. Amer. Med. Assoc.*, 1936, 107: 404
6. Clow, H. E. "A Study of One Hundred Patients Suffering from Psychosis with Cerebral Arteriosclerosis," *Amer. Jour. Psychiatry*, 1940, 97: 16

7. Connor, C. L. "Alcohol Cirrhosis of Liver," *Jour. Amer. Med. Assoc.*, 1939, 112: 387

8. Dölken, —. *Die körperlichen Erscheinungen des Delirium tremens.* Leipzig, 1901

9. Ellis, R. W. B. "Some Effects of Ketogenic Diet," *Arch. Disease Childhood*, 1931, 6: 285

10. Freeman, W. *Neuropathology.* Philadelphia: W. B. Saunders Co., 1933

11. Gellerstedt, N. "Zur Kenntnis der Hirnveränderungen bei der normalen Altersinvolution," *Upsala läkaref. fören. förh.*, 1933, 38: 193–408

12. Goldsmith, H. "Spinal Drainage in Alcoholic Deliria and Other Acute Alcoholic Psychoses," *Amer. Jour. Psychiatry*, 1930, 86: 255

13. Hauptmann, A. "Zur Pathogenese alkoholischer Geistes- und Nervenkrankheiten (an der Hand von Untersuchungen über die Blut-Liquor-Schranke)," *Deut. Ztschr. f. Nervenh.*, 1927, 100: 91

14. Herz, —. Hosp-tid. 4 R. 6, 1899 (cited by Bonhoeffer, 2)

15. Holitscher, A. K. "Zur Frage von Abstinenzdelirien," *Psychiat.-neurol. Wochnschr.*, 1908–9, 10: 112–23

16. Hoppe, H. H. "The Treatment of Delirium Tremens by Spinal Puncture, Stimulation, and the Use of Alkali Agents," *Jour. Nerv. and Mental Disease*, 1918, 47: 93

17. LaPlace, L. B., and Nicholson, J. T. "Prolonged Recumbency as Contributory Cause of Death in Elderly Persons," *Jour. Amer. Med. Assoc.*, 1938, 110: 247

18. Larson, C. P. Personal communication to the author

19. Michael, J. C. "Psychosis with Cardiac Decompensation," *Amer. Jour. Psychiatry*, 1937, 93: 1353

20. Palmer, H. D., Braceland, F. J., and Hastings, D. W. "The Psychiatry of Old Age." Read before the meeting of the American Psychiatric Association, Cincinnati, May 20–24, 1940

21. Piker, P. "Clinical Evaluation of the Use of Fluids in Treatment of Delirium Tremens," *Arch. Neurol. Psychiatry*, 1938, 39: 62

22. Piker, P., and Cohn, J. V. "The Management of Delirium Tremens," *Jour. Amer. Med. Assoc.*, 1937, 108: 345

23. Puyuelo, S. E. "Las funciones hepáticas del alcoholismo crónico," *Siglo méd.*, 1935, 95: 508, 561, 590. "La biligenesis en el alcoholismo. Sugerencia para una terapéutica," *Med. Ibera*, 1935, 2: 385. "Contribución al estudio de la patogenia del delirium tremens," *Medicina Madrid*, 1935, 6: 190. "Fundamento de la terapéutica insulínica en el 'delirium tremens'," *Siglo méd.*, 1935, 96: 532

24. Rhein, J. H. W., Winkelman, N. W., and Patten, C. A. "Mental Conditions in the Aged," *Arch. Neurol. Psychiatry*, 1928, 20: 329

25. Riggs, H. E. Personal communication to the author

26. Robinson, G. W., Jr. "Acute Confusional States of Old Age," *Southern Med. Jour.*, 1939, 32: 479

27. ———. "Psychiatric Geriatrics," *Jour. Amer. Med. Assoc.*, 1941, 116: 2139

28. ———. "A Psychopathological Interpretation of the Psychiatry of Old Age." Read before the 97th annual meeting of the American Psychiatric Association, 1941

29. ———. "The Abnormal Mental Reactions of Old Age," *Jour. Missouri State Med. Assoc.*, February 1942, Vol. 36

30. ———. "The Toxic Delirious Reactions of Old Age," *Amer. Jour. Psychiatry*, 1942, 99: 1
31. Robinson, G. W., Jr., Shelton, P., and Smith, F. V., Jr. "Importance of the Dextrose Tolerance Test in the Diagnosis of Marginal Malnutrition," *Arch. Internal Med.*, 1941, 68: 945
32. Rothschild, D. "Pathologic Changes in Senile Psychoses and Their Psychobiologic Significance," *Amer. Jour. Psychiatry*, 1937, 93: 757
33. ———. "The Clinical Differentiation of Senile and Arteriosclerotic Psychoses." Read before the meeting of the American Psychiatric Association, Cincinnati, May 20–24, 1940
34. Sparkman, R. "Glycosuria Following Intravenous Administration of Glucose," *Kentucky Med. Jour.*, 1937, 35: 355
35. Staub, H. "Untersuchungen über den Zuckerstoffwechsel des Menschen," *Ztschr. f. klin. Med.*, 1922, 93: 89
36. Steinebach, R. "Ueber die Zerebrospinal-flüssigkeit und über die Wirkung der Lumbalpunktion beim Delirium potatorum," *Deutsche Med. Wochschr.*, 1915, 41: 369
37. Stern, L., and Lokinschina, E. S. "L'influence de l'empoisonnement chronique par l'alcool sur le functionnement de la barrière hématoencéphalique," *Compt. rend. Soc. Biol.*, 1929, 100: 307, 465
38. Strecker, E. A., and Ebaugh, F. G. *Practical Clinical Psychiatry* (4th edition). Philadelphia: P. Blakiston's Son & Co., 1935
39. Thomas, J. M., Semrad, E. V., and Schwab, R. M. "Studies of Blood Proteins in Delirium Tremens," *Amer. Jour. Med. Sci.*, 1938, 195: 820
40. Wartman, W. B. "Incidence and Severity of Arteriosclerosis in Organs from Five Hundred Autopsies," *Amer. Jour. Med. Sci.*, 1933, 186: 27
41. Wierzuchowski, M. "Intermediäre Kohlenhydratstoffwechsel über die erste Phase der Traubenzuckerassimilation," *Biochem. Ztschr.*, 1931, 237: 103

Chapter XIII

OLDER MENTAL PATIENTS AFTER LONG HOSPITALIZATION[1]

Eugenia Hanfmann

PURPOSE AND METHOD

THE LATE maturity and old age of many mentally ill persons are spent in mental hospitals. For the majority of these chronic cases the mental hospitals provide no specific treatment but only custodial care, protection, and a certain frame of life; in modern hospitals attempts are made to make the life of patients approximate normal life as closely as possible. In this article we shall not be concerned with the question to what extent prolonged hospitalization is unavoidable, and what favorable or unfavorable effects it may have upon the condition of the patients and the course of the disease (3, 7, 8, 14). Rather we shall attempt to describe the kind of lives that are actually lived in the institutions, as seen and evaluated by those who live them.

To obtain information on this subject a group of hospitalized mental patients were studied by the interview method.[2] The group consisted of 46 patients, 30 men and 16 women. The criterion of selection was the length of hospitalization. It was planned to study only patients who had spent more than five years in the hospital; but a few patients with shorter periods of hospitalization were included in the group, because their particular attitudes toward life in the hospital presented points of special interest. The selection was further determined by the patient's ability and willingness to communicate his ideas and attitudes to the interviewer. The group thus selected consisted largely of schizophrenics (two-thirds of the group), half of whom were classified as belonging to the paranoid subgroup. The rest of the patients belonged to various diagnostic categories. The group is fairly representative of the total population of the long-hospitalized patients in that it consists largely of

[1] From the Psychology Department of the Worcester State Hospital.

[2] The study was carried out during the years 1934 and 1935 in the Worcester State Hospital, Mass. Part of the work was done in co-operation with Dr. Tamara Dembo.

schizophrenic patients; it is a selected group, however, in that it shows better than average preservation of mental abilities. Below are given data on diagnosis, age at the time of the investigation, length of hospitalization, and age at the time of admission for the group studied.

Diagnosis	No. of Cases		Age on Admission	No. of Cases
Schizophrenia	30		15–20 years	2
Paranoid	15		20–30 years	11
Hebephrenic	2		30–40 years	16
Catatonic	1		40–50 years	11
Simple	2		50–60 years	4
Undiagnosed	10		60–70 years	2
General paralysis	3			—
Psychosis with cerebral syphilis	3		Total	46
Alcoholic psychosis	4			
Psychosis with mental defi-				No. of Cases
ciency	3		Present Age	
Manic-depressive psychosis ...	1		20–30 years	3
Involutional psychosis	1		30–40 years	7
Psychosis with epidemic			40–50 years	13
encephalitis	1		50–60 years	16
	—		60–70 years	4
Total	46		70–80 years	3
				—
			Total	46

Length of Hospitalization	No. of Cases
Less than 5 years	5
5–10 years	11
10–15 years	22
15–20 years	6
20–25 years	2
	—
Total	46

Before the interviewing was started, a list of questions was prepared pertaining to the patient's awareness and evaluation of the hospitalization as such, and to various aspects of the hospital life: the hospital hierarchy from physicians to patients; parole; living conditions on different wards; visits, friendships, work, and entertainment; and, finally, mental disease and treatment.

In preliminary interviews it was found that direct questioning of the patient was unfruitful, since it often resulted in stereotyped answers which in the course of his hospital career the patient has learned to be "good" or "correct." Such answers representing the viewpoint of the authorities are likely to be given by the patients in the situation of a formal examination. As an example, one patient on being asked in the interview for her opinion on hydrotherapy said dutifully that tubs and packs were helpful to the patients; in a later informal conversation, while relating her experience in the packroom, she said with great emotion that packs were terrible, "the meanest thing you could do to a patient," and expressed the belief common to the majority of the patients, that packs are a form of punishment.

To obviate this difficulty and to get at the patient's true attitudes a technique was evolved which might be described as a "disguised interview." The patients were called in ostensibly to take a mental test—a familiar experience for many of them—and were given some easy form boards. The observer appeared in the limited function of a mental tester and made it clear to the patient that she had no authority of any kind in the hospital. Further, the interview developed informally as a social conversation between and after the "tests." Considerable initiative was left to the patient. The questionnaire blank was not used, but the interviewer kept the questions in mind and tried to direct the conversation to the points she was interested in. In most cases she asked merely for information and not for the patients' opinions on different hospital topics. Notes were made only during the intervals of "testing" and after the patient had left. Thus the appearance of an informal conversation with no particular purpose behind it was preserved, in most cases making the patient relax and show his genuine feelings. Many patients obviously enjoyed the opportunity of talking freely to a sympathetic listener. Some apologized for having taken so much of her time, and one patient said with feeling that he had never before during his long stay in the hospital been allowed to talk at such length.

In spite of these favorable conditions not all statements of the patients can be taken at their face value. To check and supplement the material obtained in the interviews we used the data contained in the case-history records and in some cases made observations of the patient's behavior on the ward.

We are concerned in this study with the subjective side of the patient's adjustment, i.e., with their contentment or discontent. For the hospitalized mental patient there exist two main sources of contentment and discontent. The degree of satisfaction he derives from life depends first on the kind, intensity, and extent of his symptoms and on their place and function in his personality. Secondly, his contentment or discontent depends on his perception and evaluation of both the limitations and the assets of hospital life. On one side are to be booked loss of freedom and of status, exclusion from the outside world and from his previous work, separation from family and friends, subordination under the strict hospital routine, disturbance by other patients, and certain physical discomforts incidental to living in the hospital. On the other side, the patient is relieved of the necessity of providing for himself and others, or of worrying about the future; the necessities of life and medical care are provided for him; he is given opportunity for work and for companionship with patients and employees, and also some opportunities for entertainment and exercise.

The patient's subjective adjustment, however, cannot be considered merely a sum of the suffering or satisfactions coming from two separate sources, his disease and his hospitalization. The patient himself may connect the two; he may, for example, interpret his hospitalization in the light of experiences rooted in his disease, changing thereby its meaning and its emotional implications. The particular way in which the experience of disease and the experience of the hospital are integrated may determine the patient's conception of his life and the emotional tone of his existence.

SOURCES OF SATISFACTION AND DISSATISFACTION

These considerations suggest the outline for the presentation of the material of this study. It is our aim to describe a variety of life-situations of hospitalized patients as seen and evaluated by the patients themselves. The attitudes of the patients toward their life-situations fall into a number of rather well-defined patterns. These attitude-patterns can be described and analyzed from the point of view (a) of the satisfaction or dissatisfaction they entail and (b) of the respective contributions of the disease and of the objective situation to this satisfaction or dissatisfaction.

We shall start with the description of the attitudes of dissatisfaction, taking up, first, the dissatisfaction pattern produced by the patient's illness (Pattern I *a*) and, second, the pattern of dissatisfaction due largely to certain features of hospitalization (Pattern I *b*). After discussing an intermediate attitude-pattern characterized largely by indifference and resignation (Pattern I *c*), we shall describe attitudes of satisfaction: first the satisfaction pattern produced by the patient's psychotic experiences and misinterpretations of reality (Pattern II *a*), and then the pattern of satisfaction founded mainly upon the positive features of hospital life (Pattern II *b*). This scheme is used merely to facilitate an orderly presentation of the variety of the attitude-patterns observed and claims no general significance as a classificatory scheme.

ACUTE SUFFERING FROM THE DISEASE (PATTERN I *a*)

The first pattern of discontent (Pattern I *a*) is found in those patients in whom the disease process, in spite of many years' duration, is still active and produces emotional states that are strongly negative. The symptoms consist in feelings of inadequacy, unworthiness, and guilt, occasionally projected outward as vague nonfocused persecution ideas, or in feelings of physical weakness and disease, or in a state of disorientation and confusion. Whatever their content, these negative states are not clearly focalized but rather pervade the patient's whole life. In the interview it appears immediately that the patient is in a state of distress.

Following are some of the statements illustrating this: "I feel mean all over, all ugly inside; I feel terrible." "I am suffering right now." "I am damned, my soul is in hell." "I am sick, I cannot rest, can't sleep." "I am tired and sleepy all the time, my spine is weakened." "Eating makes me feel terrible, I should not eat so much." "Somebody is on my health, on my life." "I am stupid, can't do anything. Nobody will be friendly with me." "I want to pull myself together, be respectable." "I had a baby before I married (15 years ago). God will never pardon me. If only Miss L. had kept me I would never have gone wrong; it is too late now." "I am afraid; I imagine that there is no God and it makes me scared; it is a terrible thing to think." "Those things—voices and all that—they are still going on; once in a while they stop and then I have peace of mind, but it is awful when it goes on."

This negative feeling originating in the patient's own state affects his whole surroundings and makes the hospital life appear terrible too: "It all looks terrible here." "I should not have stayed so long in this awful place." "Take me away." "Oh, my life was a beautiful life before I came here. God will never pardon me for coming here." "One should dynamite this place." "You hate staying here too." "They are all sorry they ever came." "Staying here is so unnatural, life is terrible." "I am thinking how a person could be smart and rich and be at home." "The food is awful, I can't swallow it." "They don't give me what is right." "They [the other patients] walk away, don't care for me; they kill me. I want to know who is on my way in the hospital." "They told me, 'You go to the back wards for 5 years, and we won't speak to you.' There is no friendship for 5 years." "It is so hot on the farm, the work is hard: nothing I can do—pick and suffer."

In reading some of these complaints it may seem that the patient is depressed by some particular things or people in the hospital. Actually he seldom sees them as definite localized causes of his unhappiness or discomfort. One patient when we tried to pin her down as to why the hospital was so terrible was quite at a loss and said hesitantly: "It is too big . . . . I couldn't tell you . . . . Awfully noisy here . . . ." and quickly returned to complaints about her own wickedness. Another patient answered the question as to how he liked the hospital with an emphatic statement: "It is better for one to be dead than to be here." But, when asked why, he spoke about persecution by voices. The patients usually intermingled complaints about their own suffering and guilt and complaints about the hospital; but they seldom attempted to connect the two as cause and effect (e.g., the hospital as a cause of suffering or as a punishment for guilt). The experience of the disease and the experience of hospital life are for these patients not two separate entities which can be logically connected: they form an undifferentiated whole of general misery. The patients connect the two aspects, if at all, only vaguely, not exactly as cause and effect: "It is terrible, a place to lose one's thinking." "I suffer in the hospital."

Since the patients do not differentiate between their suffering from the disease and their discontent with the hospital life, one would expect that some of their attempts to escape from suffering might take the form of escaping from the hospital. Actually 4 out of 9 patients who show this attitude-pattern have records of repeated escapes, and only 3 patients have parole. Even during the interview some patients were preoccupied with the idea of leaving the hospital by one way or another, and strongly responded to mentions by the interviewer of all topics pertaining to it. How closely the desire to leave was connected with the patient's suffering from his symptoms was shown by the patient who thought it was better to be dead than to be in the hospital. Years ago this man voluntarily came to the hospital, because he could not stand any longer the abuse by voices that was going on outside; now he wants to leave the place for the same reason.

The 9 patients (6 men and 3 women) who show this attitude-pattern are all schizophrenics. It is interesting to note that even during the interview at least 6 of them showed signs of disturbance of thinking, of the kind that expresses itself in concretization of all mental processes (9, 10). Many seemed not to appreciate such "abstract" facts as the hierarchical organization of the hospital, the interviewer's place in this organization and their own status as patients who were held against their will. They naïvely confided to the interviewer their plans to "go over the hills" during a walk and to find their way to Springfield by looking through a City Directory. When actually attempting to escape, the patients of this group showed an equal lack of insight into the situation. Some of those who escaped repeatedly always went to the same place and were immediately returned each time. When asked about the reason why they came to the hospital in the first place, the patients merely described the concrete event: "I came in a car; my mother took me," etc. This concretization of thinking may account both for lack of elaboration and organization of symptoms and for the diffuse relationship between the symptoms and the hospital experience.

ACUTE DISSATISFACTION WITH HOSPITALIZATION (PATTERN I *b*)

The second pattern of discontent (Pattern I *b*) is shown by the patients who are just as strongly dissatisfied with their lives as the patients just described but whose discontent is definitely focused on factors inherent in the hospital situation as such. For these patients, limitations and negative aspects of hospital life predominate both over their disease experience and over the positive aspects of the hospital.

All patients who show this attitude-pattern realize that they are kept in the hospital against their will and resent loss of freedom, exclusion from normal life, or separation from the family. The hospital is virtually a prison or even worse. "I'd rather be in jail than with the d—— fools here." "It would be terrible to spend one's whole life here." Some are obsessed by the desire to be at home, where they belong, in their own country, with their wives or families. "I have real friends in the home country; here I am all alone. It is terrible not to be able to talk to anybody." One patient repeatedly made an appeal to the physician—as a father to another father—to let him go home to his daughters.

What is most resented in hospital life itself is the fact that the patients are not paid for their work. "I work from early till late, then go to bed—that's all." "I get nothing for my work—just a little tobacco—that's no good." "I've worked here long enough without pay." "Do they pay anybody here for their work?" "I want to work for myself, have my own trade." Lack of physical comfort, of decent clothes is another reason for complaint: "I am ashamed of these shabby clothes." "I am tired of wearing these rags." "My things got stolen." "They should fix my teeth." "The coffee here isn't coffee at all—in Germany even the poorest people wouldn't drink it." Occasionally there are complaints about disturbance and abuse by patients and attendants. "They fight and quarrel all the time—if I stay here long it might influence me." "One man started fighting me: he was older, so I got the worst of it." "After I escaped they put me on the worst ward for punishment; and that was not enough—they put me in packs! I struggled, so they choked the life out of me."

These patients try to improve their lot, either by escapes (5 out of 7 patients) or by attempting to obtain a discharge from the hospital. One schizophrenic patient (paranoid) keeps writing letters to both hospital and outside authorities explaining his case and suggesting arrangements that could be made for him outside of the hospital. Others attempt to make contact with relatives. One man wrote during the interview a letter to his wife, a mixture of Polish and English, with endless repetitions of the theme: "like go back home, stay home, work in mills." Those who have no parole (5 out of 7) are anxious to obtain it, as a first step toward release. All but one patient work, in spite of their objections to not being paid, and attempt in general to comply with rules and to give good "correct" answers to questions. All attempted to utilize the interview for their ultimate purpose: some asked pertinent questions about the way to obtain discharge, others asked for help in reaching relatives or friends. Some patients showed concern about their test performance, assuming that the outcome might influence the question of their discharge.

The disease aspect is conspicuously absent in the attitudes of this group of patients: their discontent and the reasons for it appear completely normal and realistic, and the interviews elicit hardly any mention of psychotic content. The group consists of 7 patients, 4 men and 3 women. It includes two cases of cerebral syphilis, two of psychosis with mental deficiency, one of alcoholism, one of involutional melancholia, and one of schizophrenia. The case histories show that in 5 of the 7 cases acute psychotic symptoms had either never been prominent or had subsided long before. The symptoms were largely defect symptoms, such as impairment of thinking and judgment, with only occasional episodes of depression or excitement. The only schizophrenic (paranoid) patient in this group presents a different picture. The case record shows that bizarre experiences and elaborate delusions of persecution were prominent during the first years of hospitalization, and according to many indications they are present still. The patient has learned, however, not to discuss the psychotic content, probably sensing that revelation of this material interferes with his desire to obtain release from the hospital. During the interview the patient said: "As to why I dress in this way [he wears rather juvenile clothes and uses rouge], I have my very private reasons, but it does not do any good talking about it." In speaking about the possible discharge from the hospital he said: "I want this matter settled *not* on the insane level," and actually he never permitted any delusional material to intrude into his discussions, which remained rational in spite of obvious paranoid affect. This achievement is made possible by a good structurization and segregation of his various experiences, reflected also in his excellent orientation in the hospital and in a discriminating evaluation of its various aspects. A similar though less successful attempt to cover up the symptoms during the interview was made by the woman suffering from involutional melancholia.

RESIGNATION (PATTERN I *c*)

The third pattern of dissatisfaction (Pattern I *c*) differs from the first two not by the patients' reasons for discontent, but by a lesser acuteness of this discontent, by a certain resignation of the patients to their fate. Their statements about their own condition and about the hospital, though mostly negative, are much milder than those in the first two subgroups. They state: "I am not in the condition now to enjoy anything; I don't feel well, either physically or mentally." "What I dislike about this place is that there is pretty much destroying going on." "The attendants treat me well, at least on the surface; of course I don't know what they may do in secret." "The food is all right—of course you know they get better food at home sometimes." "I feel quiet enough. The hospital is a pretty quiet place."

The 6 patients (5 men and one woman) who show this attitude are all schizophrenics. The case records of these patients show that the negatively toned symptoms such as vague persecution ideas and depressive states have either never been very strong, or have subsided in the course of the disease. Guilt feelings, which played such an important role in the first pattern of discontent, seem never to have been prominent in these patients. Some of them have always shown outward indifference and lack of affective expression; in the interviews it was difficult to elicit any expression of attitudes from them.

In addition to a lesser disturbance by symptoms and to a greater indifference, another factor seems to operate in producing a relative resignation of these patients to their state: this factor is the relative loss of hope of ever being able to leave the hospital. This loss of hope may have been caused by a long hospitalization. Three of these patients have spent 20 or almost 20 years in the hospital. Others have been repeatedly brought back from visits which they hoped would terminate in discharge. Another reason for loss of hope by some of these patients is the realization of their advanced age and of the difficulty of making a new start outside. Although the patients still feel that they should not be in the hospital, the institution has partly acquired for them the function of a refuge or the only remaining reality. Their attitude toward leaving the hospital reflects both their loss of hope and their own ambivalence and doubts. Typical comments are: "I went out once, but they brought me back again." "I haven't anything to say about that; I might have to come back again, so I might as well stay here." "Sometimes people have to wait if they do not want to get in trouble." "The doctors always say to the patients: there is a chance [to go home] . . . ., but I don't know." "I would like to go home, only my father and mother are both dead, so I do not know if I can go out." "I want to go home, but my boy is young yet, has no own home." "If released I will go; I don't know where I go to." "I might go and look for a job." "It might be better outside [with regard to being 'destroyed by spirits'] or it might not; it would be experimenting anyway." "I am so old now, I am willing to stay for the rest of my life; I am not strong enough to earn my living."

As a result of this attitude these patients do not attempt to escape, and four out of six have parole. Nor do they take any active steps to obtain discharge, though they talk occasionally about such steps. "I should try . . . . see about it some day . . . . Maybe some day I will ask one of the doctors or the lady doctor." Their prevalent philosophy is expressed in the statement: "I'll do as I am told."

SATISFACTION BASED ON TRANSFORMATION OF REALITY
(PATTERN II *a*)

We turn now to the attitudes of the patients in whose lives the positive aspects seem to outweigh the negative ones, and who are better satisfied with their existence. In the first pattern to be described (Pattern II *a*) the experiences of the patient that are rooted in the disease serve as the main source of satisfaction. These experiences are brought to bear upon the patient's conception of the hospital situation, and transform it from a negative into a positive, or at least an acceptable one. This transformation of reality, whatever its specific content, serves an adjustive function in that it gives the patient a satisfying, meaningful conception of his life. The possession of such a "philosophy of life" differentiates these patients from the bewildered and unhappy patients who suffer passively from their disease (Pattern I *a*). Even though they may not

be happy, and may protest against hospitalization, the patients whom we are now describing have a source of satisfaction in their inner lives; and by transforming reality in accordance with their needs they manage to rob their hospitalization of its worst thorns. Since this adjustment may take place in many different ways, it seems best to illustrate it by a few clear-cut individual cases.

One extreme way of dealing with the hospital reality is the dual orientation which is represented in our material by the case of Mrs. N. D. This patient, a paranoid schizophrenic who has spent eighteen years in the hospital, is an elderly woman of extremely dignified and reserved demeanor. In the interview she showed little spontaneity and answered questions politely, if unwillingly. When given a chance to ask questions in her turn, she refused because "that would be impertinent." She gave correct answers about her life in the hospital, emphasizing that she knows her place, appreciates the hospital rules, and has no complaints. "As for practical things, we do our beds, clean the ward, try to keep quiet, go outside each afternoon; they do not want us to touch things; keep quiet; it is for our own benefit; we know it!" Yet neither these "practical things" nor her own emphasized role of obedience and submission is really important for the patient. What is important is her inner life hidden from the eyes of others: "One sits and thinks his own thoughts, lives one's own living; each one is an individual, each one for herself." The content of this private life she was at first unwilling to disclose, but eventually part of it came to the surface and proved to have a greater reality for the patient than mere thoughts. In response to the observer's remark about the patient's English appearance she gave a quick startled glance and in a changed tone of voice asked her first spontaneous question: "Where do you think we are, in what world?" She then revealed after much urging that we were in the world called Cheshire; that the hospital was the Eagle Castle, a lovely big building with beautiful grounds belonging to a lord; that she was the lord's sister; and that the inmates were people who settled in the castle without being invited and who led an easy life there. It was not possible to discover the means by which the patient reconciled her role of the lord's sister with her subordinate position as one of the inmates who have "to mind the rules and obey the authorities." Ideas of being persecuted and held by enemies were not

revealed by Mrs. N. D.; her whole behavior was not that of a victim of persecution but rather of a monarch who travels incognito and voluntarily submits to limitations imposed on his subjects. When asked whether she wanted to leave the institution, the patient answered in a noncommittal way that she had not made her plans yet; she expressed astonishment at the persistent desire of other inmates to leave the place—"if they do not like it here and want to leave, why don't they?" She repudiated any knowledge of coercion in keeping them there. When in taking her back to the closed ward the observer asked her why the door was kept locked, she answered irritably that she did not know why and refused to discuss the matter. On the same trip to the ward she showed some proprietary interest in the hospital: she counted the chairs in the Chapel and stated that there was room for more and that she was going to put them there. This was the only instance observed in which, in talking about the everyday life of the hospital, she departed from her role of an obedient, law-abiding inmate.

Whether or not an underlying conception connecting her two roles as an inmate and as the lady of the Eagle Castle is present in the patient's mind, she has found a way to form and maintain two stable worlds—the Cheshire world hidden from the uninitiated, which is a source of gratification for her; and the real world of the hospital routine, which she accepts because it permits her to "think her own thoughts and live her own life." The coexistence of these two worlds is made easier by the definite segregation of their respective spheres of influence: the patient's outward compliant behavior is governed by the real world of the hospital, but is limited to the necessary minimum of participation; the Cheshire world governs her thoughts, which are usually guarded from others, and finds expression only in her mien and demeanor.

The two worlds—the inner and the outer—are much more closely integrated for Mr. B. H., a paranoid schizophrenic who has been hospitalized for ten years. At the time of the study he is staying on a "good" quiet ward, but refuses regular work and parole privileges. Intelligent and perfectly oriented in hospital life and politics, he does a little work on the ward as a favor for the attendants, with whom he is on very friendly terms. This work is of a supervisory or "intellectual" nature; he helps check patients, some of whom resent his functioning as an authority ("be-

cause I have no white jacket—just jealousy!"); and he makes out the weekly ward reports, in which he himself is classified as "idle." He refuses not only any "low" physical work ("I wouldn't go down on my knees to scrub the floor for a nurse!") but also any regular supervisory job, because to him an acceptance would mean giving assent to his illegal hospitalization: "I want no job in *this* place." His persecutory ideas are focused on the highest authority, the superintendent of the hospital, who keeps him there under the pretext of insanity. The truth is that the patient knows too much about the hospital: he has seen people murdered there ("They tell me it is just a delusion, but I know better!"), and would be a dangerous witness if discharged. He resents other employees in so far as they represent authority, but not indiscriminately. He tells with great satisfaction about verbal encounters with the superintendent and the "bossy" psychiatrists, encounters in which he always comes out on top: "He told me—'who is the boss here? *I* am running this hospital!' ... I said—'but you cannot run me!' etc." Yet he readily acknowledges that there have been many good doctors and tells about the reforms they have introduced in the hospital. Many of them before leaving come and tell him good-bye; of course they can do nothing for him—they know who keeps him there. He resents the authority of the nurses but speaks appreciatively of the work of the occupational therapists, who assume an attitude of comradeship with the patients. The attitude of superiority is resented even more strongly when it is coupled with incompetence and lack of professional experience. The students in training— medical interns, nurses, social workers, etc.—he especially objects to, and he well discerns incompetence in individual employees. Equal discernment is shown in his judgment of other patients. On the whole his attitude is that of a normal person toward mental patients, but he makes exceptions for some "sane people" to whom one can talk. B. H. particularly appreciates well-educated people and those who share his indignation about the authorities. He is often seen walking up and down the ward with some patient who listens sympathetically to his stories of triumphs over the psychiatrists. The greatest part of his time, however, is spent in writing messages "To whom it may concern" and circulating them among the employees. In these essays he denounces the "ignorant officials," "pseudo-scientists," and "fakirs of psychiatry," refutes the charge of insanity, and glories in his own "hypnotic and mystical powers" over others. For the rest his time is spent in reading papers, playing cards—"then people listen to me just like you are listening now—it breaks the monotony!" When asked whether he had any plans for attempting to obtain discharge he seemed startled by the question and declared that there was no way to achieve it; he would not escape, because he wanted to leave "in a honorary way" and he would not get a discharge until the superintendent himself was dismissed. This might happen some time, but all he can do is wait; this he said with a certain relief, and quickly dismissed the whole problem. One gained the impression that, in spite of his great desire for reinstatement in his rights as a sane and superior person, B. H. was not genuinely eager to leave the hospital.

Although B. H. clearly appreciates the reality of the hospital situation and resents his own inferior status within it, he succeeds in deriving a certain amount of satisfaction from his life. By bringing to bear his ideas of persecution and grandeur upon the hospital situation and using his intellectual resources as a weapon, he is able not only to maintain a subjective position of superiority but even to obtain a certain amount of real status. His attitude is that of a proud and unyielding victim of injustice whose poise in adversity rests on his feeling of being right and of being superior to his jailers. The satisfaction he derives from this role as well as from his minor victories over his enemies helps him to adjust to hospitalization.

Mrs. S. T., diagnosed as manic-depressive, is similar to B. H. in that she also keenly realizes her status in the hospital and gives a delusional explanation of it—she has been kidnaped and is being kept as a patient in the hospital, which was originally built by her relatives for herself, a physician. She is as sensitive as B. H. toward the humiliations to which she has to submit: "A woman who graduated from Vassar does not want to have that done to her." However, she attempts to hold her own not by verbal fights and direct self-assertion but by telling endless stories about her many degrees, professions, studies, estates, marriages, and children, her social position, and her practice of medicine. She delights especially in plans for a reform of the institution: all patients should appear before the court and plead their cause; the educated people, those who know how to behave in public, should be placed on open wards, and be treated with medicines and fresh air instead of packs and hypos; they should be taught interior decoration, so that they could apply it later in their homes. She describes in great detail all the accommodations the patients should have, and concludes with the emphatic statement: "Yes, if I were in charge here that would make a difference! I could have done so much." In spite of her ideas of grandeur she seems to realize that in the hospital she is merely a patient and that the reforms she depicts are merely daydreams.

In other cases the distortion of the hospital situation is even less marked. A few patients seem to acknowledge its reality implicitly in every point but one, namely, the question of discharge. They profess a firm belief that they are going to leave the hospital soon—today, next week, or next summer. This belief has no basis in reality, and the reasons for it given by the patients are either incorrect or insufficient; they came to the hospital to have dental treatment, which is now completed; they are no longer ill; it is not a place for them; they have stayed too long; it is a waste of time; staying is too expensive; etc. Frequently the patient does not even attempt to give a plausible reason, stating simply that he knows he is leaving soon, and refusing any further discussion. A similar disinclination is shown toward the discussion of hospital matters, the patients feeling that these do not concern them any longer. When this reluctance is overcome, the patients may complain and criticize the hospital but never appear actually indignant or distressed. In some cases one gets the impression that the patient, having transformed his wish for discharge into firm belief, is enabled to disregard as temporary the disturbances inherent in hospital life and in the meantime to get along comfortably enough. One patient even plays with the idea of staying in the hospital as an employee of the institution after the expected discharge has taken place.

The pattern of delusional transformation of reality is shown by 9 patients: 3 men and 6 women. There are 5 schizophrenics in this group, 2 chronic alcoholics, 1 manic-depressive patient, and 1 patient suffering from psychosis with mental deficiency. The more elaborate delusional transformations of reality originate with the schizophrenic patients, whereas the two alcoholics and the mentally deficient patient are among those who merely expect a speedy discharge.

SATISFACTION BASED ON ACCEPTANCE OF REALITY (PATTERN II *b*)

The last attitude-pattern to be described (Pattern II *b*) is shown by the patients whose main sources of satisfaction lie within the reality situation, i.e., actually within the situation of the hospital. This pattern is not limited to patients who are free from acute psychotic experiences. A few patients have hallucinations of either a disturbing or an enjoyable nature, or delusional ideas which color their interpretation of some aspects of hospital life. However, these experiences are somehow assimilated by the patients and are not any longer in the center of their attention. The interviews focused on hospital adjustment elicited little psychotic material; instead the patients gave detailed reports of their past and present lives in the hospital, supplementing them in many cases by more impersonal discussions of the hospital life as such.

The factors within the hospital life which served as main sources of gratification were different for different patients. Of this group all but two patients worked regularly, and half made their work the center of their lives. Some patients have held the same job for many years. When telling about their past these patients often mentioned a change of job as an important landmark in their hospital careers. A psychiatrist who had left long ago would be remembered as the one who "first put me on this job." Even if the job he held was of a routine nature, the patient often displayed great satisfaction in his work. He spoke of the work with animation and told with pride of the number of dishes he had washed or of beds he had made. "They can send any attendant to this ward because I can do part of the work."

About one-third of the group held more complex jobs involving a certain amount of independence. These patients seemed to obtain the greatest satisfaction from their work; they emphasized the importance of the job and the responsibility they felt for it. One patient asked to have the interview postponed because the time happened to be a busy one in the kitchen where he worked. Another insisted on showing the observer the apartment she took care of, calling it "my apartment." A third one, in telling of tending furnaces in some cottages where there were children, said emphatically that he knew that a great deal of hot water was needed for the babies, "and this furnace never went out." When changing from one job to another this patient behaved in an equally responsible fashion; he told his "boss" of his plans a long time ahead and did not leave until someone was found to take his place.

These patients take the same responsible attitude toward their work in the hospital that they would have taken toward a real job outside, and apply the same criteria of evaluation. The type of satisfaction they obtain from their work seems to be the same in both cases. One patient tells that if discharged he would like to find a job of the same kind as the one he had in the hospital, "but of course for pay." This last point makes a difference of which all patients are well aware. However, for them (in contrast to the dissatisfied patients in Group I *b*) the pay is not as essential as the satisfaction they get from the work itself; the difference does not create a chasm between work in the hospital and outside. For these patients work is work and is valuable as such: "There are two ways: working and loafing; I have always worked." "I never went on the bum; one has to earn one's living somewhere." "All people here would have been better off working, girls too. I have always worked and always felt fine."

For many patients the satisfaction obtained from work is closely connected with the satisfaction obtained from their association with the hospital employees. In talking about their work these patients stress that they are trusted and praised by those for whom they work, and dwell with pleasure on little signs of appreciation and friendship shown them. "Mrs. A gave me dinner in her kitchen: I did not even have to go to the cafeteria." "Once when I was very lonely they spent an afternoon with me, just talking." "I told Mrs. S I wanted to go home for Thanksgiving to roast my own turkey, and she told me she never yet did her own. . . . . She is very nice." "Mr. L [the supervisor] lets me go home as often as I want to." "Miss C is my boss now. She always gives me cigarettes and matches; I never ask for them—I am not a person who asks for things—she offers them herself." "Mr. D, the boss, came up and said [to another patient]: 'if I catch you talking like that to Mr. Peter [the patient] I'll put you on a bad ward'."

With a few exceptions the personal contacts the patients have with employees are limited to those with or for whom they work, or to attendants and nurses on their wards. The psychiatrists as such are distant strangers whom the patients see once a year and whom they are rather reluctant to approach: "I do not like to bother them." This attitude is typical not only for this group but for the majority of the long-hospitalized patients who are not any longer subjects of active therapeutic concern (16).

Most of the patients who enter actively into contact with employees also maintain social relationships with the other patients. They enjoy conversations and social games: "I asked to be transferred back to this hospital because the patients in the other one were worse, more insane; you didn't find a sensible person with whom you could talk; this hospital here has more sensible people in it than any." "I was on the hospital baseball team, and we traveled around." "I make friends with everyone, never get mad, never step on anybody." "Some want to play checkers—I play checkers. Some ask me—want to play pool—sure, I play. Pass the time. The more people the better. I like everybody."

Some of the patients, however, who appreciate social contacts with the employees have no active contact with the other patients. Although in talking to the interviewer they seldom admit the insanity of their fellow inmates and tend to explain and justify their "crazy" behavior, in actuality they often seem to avoid them. Some of the patients admit with a certain reluctance or concern that they find it difficult for some reason to make friends in the hospital. Possibly the unpleasant experiences most of them have had with some patients make them wary and insecure in their relations with all patients (15).

The more withdrawn patients take no active part in social pastimes but enjoy picture puzzles, reading, movies, and other entertainments provided by the hospital. One patient spends most of his time in the library reading books and newspapers, and follows with great interest the football games: "There were quite a few surprises last week!" Another one is well informed by the attendants concerning the movie programs in the city and goes to some of them. A third never misses a hospital movie, maintaining that the programs are excellent—better than in Boston; he never saw a poor picture in the hospital. Many patients go regularly for long walks on the hospital grounds. Some have special hobbies— studying plants, building little rock gardens, fixing radios. These occupations and diversions play some part in the lives of all patients of this group, but for a few they seem to have a much greater personal significance and to provide one of their major interests in life.

Some patients, especially those who have real or imaginary physical complaints, appreciate the medical help and care provided by the hospital. They tell with satisfaction about their improved state of health: "They fixed me wonderfully; Dr. S, he is a fine man, he told me he did not think I would live six days." "I am pretty good now—I was pretty bad two years ago—I was slim, all broken." "The tubs calmed me and I was able to go to sleep: I have to give them credit for that." "My mind was disordered but kept improving; Dr. P said I responded to treatment unusually well." Most of these statements came from the patients who suffered from organic psychoses and who have actually benefited from treatment.

Although the living conditions on the wards and the quality of food were prominent topics of discussion among most of the patients, only two or three patients seemed to derive their main satisfaction from being provided for and sheltered in the hospital. One of them expressed the opinion that hardly any patient would want to leave the hospital: "I think they are better off here; outside business is slack; here they get better food, do not have much work." He himself refused work, saying that the insurance company might stop payments to his wife if he worked and that he came for treatment, not for work. Although he occasionally asserted that he himself wanted to leave and earn his living, his excellent adjustment to the routine and his obvious enjoyment of all the comforts and entertainments offered by the hospital suggest that the attitude he ascribes to other patients is actually his own. Another patient who has spent only two years in the hospital expressed this attitude openly and clearly, both in his actions and in his words: "I have no place to go, no home, no money. I would starve or have to commit suicide. I will do any kind of work if they only let me stay here." Since this patient suffered from cerebral syphilis and had at the time a good insight into his condition, his attitude happened to be well founded in reality. At the same time it was an expression of his depressed mood. It seems that a high evaluation of the hospital as a shelter and refuge reflects feelings of inadequacy and fears of the outside world and does not insure the best possible adjustment even within the hospital situation.

At one point in the interview the patients were asked for their opinion about the hospital in general. The explicit evaluation of the hospital thus obtained did not always reflect the actual degree of the patient's satisfaction as judged by his behavior and his own report of his activities. For example, the patient who refused to work, and who seemed to accept and enjoy the hospital for the shelter and comforts it provided, spoke of it very sarcastically, denouncing it as an institution based on meanness and graft: "I would not like to be in Dr. B's [the superintendent's] place when he dies and has to give an answer for all that is going on here." The other extreme of evaluation was represented by a patient who endorsed and praised the hospital enthusiastically as a place where everything was being done for the patients in the best possible way. Prevalent in this group, however, was the moderately positive evaluation which actually reflected the relative satisfaction of the patient with the state of affairs: "The place is all right, I have nothing against it." "Had it been bad, why, after 25 years here I would not want to live; but I am getting along all right." "In this place if you behave well they treat you all right."

One might expect that since these patients are relatively satisfied with the hospital they would not be averse to the idea of continued stay. For the majority, however, this is not the case. Precisely the patients who showed the greatest appreciation of the hospital and who enjoyed their work there, when asked if they would like to stay, answered most decisively in the negative: "Oh, no! Not me . . . . Give me my discharge, and I'll walk fifty miles to get out . . . . Do not try to tell me . . . ." "A woman who works as hard as I do should not be here." "I am not a baby, can look after myself." Most of the answers were less vehement, but not less definite. "Yes, I liked it here pretty well; but at the same time I have a husband and child. I want to go home." "The place is all right, but—you know—it is better at home." Even some of the very old patients are not reconciled to the idea of staying but rather consider the short time of life left to them as another reason for returning home soon: "I am 65 now, and not as strong as I used to be; even if I live to be 71, there is not much time left."

"They tell me I am too old, but if I am strong enough to take care of Dr. S's apartment, I can take care of my own. I want to get home before I get too weak and infirm." A few patients actually make attempts to obtain a discharge. One patient found a job for himself in the city, and although he was refused discharge because of his old age he plans to try once more. Other patients repeatedly approach the psychiatrists with the request to arrange for their release; they utilized the interviews for asking the observers to put in a good word for them with the authorities.

The few patients in the group who express willingness to stay seem to feel that there is no place for them outside. "I am willing to stay as long as I have a job I like . . . . Well, not really; if I had a chance to stay with my people I would do it; but I would not want to stay with strangers." "I could not do much with my wooden leg. I am not smart; I used just to pick and shovel." "I do not know—I guess I just as well stay. . . . I lost my fingers here—cannot work in a factory any more." All such responses were usually given in a hesitant fashion which indicated a certain conflict. Occasionally this conflict showed itself more clearly in a quick change from resignation to hope. One rather childish patient who was telling quite contentedly about the details of his life in the hospital, when asked whether he wanted to stay or to leave, at first said uncertainly: "I do not know what they . . . ." and then, with a sudden hope, "Do you think they will let me go if I ask them nicely?" Only one patient who considered the hospital a place of refuge seemed to be completely whole-hearted in his desire to stay in the hospital.

If one examines the case records of the patients of this group one finds that, with a very few exceptions, the resigned attitude they show has developed in the course of long years. Many patients who are now resigned to hospitalization, during their first years in the hospital protested against it violently or attempted to escape, and partly because of this behavior were for a long time deprived of parole. Many patients in telling their stories mention this fact with a certain bitterness: "I was locked up for 10 years." "It took them 6 years to give me parole." Other patients are aware that their attitudes toward the hospital have changed in the course of years. "When I first came here I kept asking everyone who came to back wards to let me go home." "When I first came I wanted to get out, like everybody else; but then I got more and more institutionalized." "One gets accustomed, you know; one gets accustomed."

This resignation, however, does not lead to complete indifference; for all patients of this group their "hospitalized life" is still an emotional problem. This is indicated by their very uniform reaction to one question of the interview, the question about the length of time spent in the hospital. Not even the most indifferent patients answered this question in a matter-of-fact, unemotional way, and the majority stated immediately not only the number of years but also that of months, weeks, and sometimes even days. "I have been here 15 years .... Just think of it—15 years! I came on May 2d, 1919. I thought I came for 6 months .... " "If I live to see the 13th of December it will be 9 years—9 years!" "It will be 15 years next April—that is a long time." "It was in September—it will be 13 years soon. I was a young fellow when I came here—I was 29." "I have been here for 25 years! It will be exactly 25 in November. I thought I came for two to three months, and they stretched to 25 years!" "Yes, it was on October 22 of 1926, at 10 o'clock in the morning—9 years and 9 days!" Many of the patients brought the point up spontaneously and kept returning to it throughout the interview. They showed an equally strong emotional reaction in relating the episodes of temporary releases or escapes from the hospital. Some of the more indifferent patients became animated only while speaking about the periods of time they spend away from the hospital.

The pattern of positive acceptance of the hospital reality is shown by 15 patients, 12 men and 3 women. The group includes 9 schizophrenics, 3 general-paralysis cases, one patient with cerebral syphilis, one alcoholic, and one postencephalitic patient.

From the survey of the attitudes of this group of patients we may conclude that the best adjustment in the hospital is still not a perfect one, and that life in the institution is felt by the patients to be inferior to normal life outside. Moreover, it would seem that dissatisfaction with hospitalization as such and an active desire to leave are an integral part of the optimal hospital adjustment. The patients for whom their work and social relationships were of the greatest importance seemed to lead the most normal and satisfying lives. The same patients, however, showed the strongest and most genuine desire to leave the institution, whereas the less active, less happy, and more discouraged patients (including the dissatisfied or indifferent patients in Group I *c*) were willing to stay. Thus the best possible hospital adjustment seems to imply a conflict which may be eventually reduced by the patient's resigning himself to the unavoidable stay in the hospital, but the conflict seems never completely resolved.

REVIEW OF CLINICAL DATA

We shall now briefly review the groups described with regard to the incidence of parole and work, present age and age on admission, length of hospitalization, and diagnosis. The comparisons are based on very small numbers, and can only suggest certain trends.

Almost four-fifths (78 per cent) of all the patients studied do some work, and almost half of them (48 per cent) have parole. Within the different groups the incidence of work varies from 55 per cent to 100 per cent, the incidence of parole from 11 per cent to 80 per cent. The "disturbed" Group I *a* is lower than the average both in work and parole. The "protesting" Group I *b* is higher than average in work but lower in parole; this is understandable since the patients try to reach their goal of leaving the institution both by means of work and by escapes. The "resigned" Group I *c* and the "adjusted" Group II *b* are high both in work and in parole, whereas the "unrealistic" Group II *a* is the lowest of all in both. If one considers work and parole as constituting a positive objective hospital adjustment, Group I *a* appears poorly adjusted both subjectively and objectively, and Group II *b* equally well adjusted in both respects. Group I *b* and Group I *c* are relatively well adjusted objectively but subjectively dissatisfied; in Group II *a* this relationship is reversed.

With regard to present age the "disturbed" Group I *a* is the only group that deviates slightly from the pattern of distribution typical for the studied group as a whole (compare data on p. 302) in that it contains more patients under 40 (one-third of the group) and none older than 54. The average age of patients in this group is 44, as compared with 48 for the total group.

This difference is due not to a longer than average hospitalization of the patients of this group but to the fact that they have been hospitalized at an earlier age; the average age on admission was 31 for this group, as compared with 37 for the whole group. On the other hand, in the best-adjusted Group II *b* more patients have been hospitalized at a relatively late age, their average age on admission having been 40. The differences suggest that the late onset of the disease is favorable for the hospital adjustment. This may partly be explained by the assumption that older persons who have formed stable patterns of behavior and formulated for themselves a certain philosophy of life are more likely to preserve them than are those who enter the hospital at an earlier age. This is partly borne out by the observation that the four patients in Group II *b* who were admitted in their fifties and sixties did not seem to consider hospitalization a complete undoing of their lives, great parts of which had already been lived, and were among the best-adjusted patients in this group.

The comparison of the groups with regard to length of hospitalization shows that the "protesting" Group I *b* has spent a shorter than average time in the hospital, and that the "resigned" patients of Group I *c* have been hospitalized for a longer than average time (averages of 8 and 15 years, respectively, as compared with the average of 11 for the total group). It seems plausible that the length of time spent in the hospital is one of the factors in determining to what extent the patient still actively attempts to regain his freedom or resigns himself to the stay in the hospital. The other groups show no differentiation with regard to length of hospitalization.

Two-thirds of the 46 patients studied are schizophrenics. Since all other diagnostic groups are very small, we shall limit our discussion to this group. Groups II *a* and II *b* show approximately the same proportion of schizophrenic patients as the total group; Groups I *a* and I *c* consist exclusively of schizophrenics; whereas in Group I *b* only one of the 7 patients is a schizophrenic, the rest being divided about equally among the other diagnoses. This would seem to indicate that among the long-hospitalized patients the schizophrenics are the ones whose attitude toward hospitalization is likely to be colored by their continued suffering from the disease or by their general indifference; on the other hand, they are less likely than the non-schizophrenic patients to display a continued strong drive to leave the institution, based on realistic objections against hospitalization and on a desire to be at home.

With regard to the schizophrenic group itself our material indicates that a certain proportion of them do reach a satisfactory adjustment in the hospital. Out of 30 schizophrenic patients 10 are found in the acutely dissatisfied groups (I *a* and I *b*); 6 seem to be more or less indifferent or resigned (Group I *c*); 5 lead subjectively satisfying existences in the unreal world they have created for themselves (Group II *a*); and 9 lead relatively normal lives, obtaining their main satisfaction within the reality situation itself (Group II *b*). Taking into consideration both the subjective and the objective aspects of adjustment—the latter judged by incidence of parole and work—one might say that about one-third of the schizophrenic patients are adjusted very poorly (I *a*, I *b*), one-third approximate the optimum adjustment possible in the hospital (II *b*), and one-third are lacking in either the subjective or the objective aspect of positive adjustment (I *c*, II *a*). These conclusions, however, cannot be generalized, both because of the limited size of our sample and because of the selection excluding the extremely deteriorated and the completely inaccessible patients.

The small size of the schizophrenic groups precludes us also from determining, for this group, the role of clinical factors in bringing about different patterns of adjustment. Neither diagnostic subgroups which were available for 21 patients, nor the patients' age, nor length of hospitalization show any significant relationships to the patterns of adjustment. The only positive findings are the slightly earlier age of onset in the acutely disturbed Group I *a*. This group also has fewer paranoid patients than any other group, while Group I *c* has more than the others; but the differences are very small.

Since the interviews were not planned as detailed psychiatric examinations, the mental status of the patients showing different adjustment patterns can be only roughly estimated on the basis of general impressions and the yearly psychiatric notes. According to such general impressions the "disturbed" Group I *a* is characterized not only by the prevalence of guilt feelings and depressive states but also by an extreme concretization of thinking which may account for the peculiar disorientation of these patients and for the lack of structurization of their experiences. There seem to be no systematized delusions in this group, and hallucinations are rare. On the other hand, the patients of the "unrealistic" Group II *a* and of the "adjusted" Group II *b* give on the whole the impression of a better preservation of their mental abilities; their psychotic experiences are either better elaborated and systematized (in Group II *a*) or better segregated from the rest of their lives, leaving them relatively free to seek satisfaction in normal activities (Group II *b*). Thus the comparison of our worst- and best-adjusted groups bears out to a certain extent the conclusion of Kant (12) who found that "extreme degrees of behavior disturbance are always accompanied by extreme inner disorganization." As far as our material goes, the subjective adjustment of a chronic schizophrenic would seem to depend both on the emotional coloring of his symptoms and on the patient's ability, which may be reduced by the disorganization of thinking, to overcome the disturbing emotional states either by localizing them in hallucinations, systematized delusions, etc., or by segregating them from the rest of his life. Since the forms of schizophrenia that are characterized by a late onset usually show less deterioration, the late onset may be considered favorable for a good institutional adjustment of the schizophrenic patients.

SUMMARY AND DISCUSSION

The purpose of this study was to give a description of lives that are led in mental hospitals by the older patients who have been hospitalized for a long time and who have little chance of returning into the community. The study was carried out by interviewing systematically but informally a group of forty-six long-hospitalized patients, two-thirds of whom were schizophrenics. It resulted in a series of life-pictures drawn by the patients themselves. These life-pictures fall into the following five patterns: I *a*, acute suffering from the disease; I *b*, acute dissatisfaction with hospitalization; I *c*, resignation; II *a*, satisfaction based on transformation of reality; II *b*, satisfaction based on acceptance of reality.

The patients showing the first pattern (I *a*, 9 patients) are acutely disturbed by the content of their psychosis; the hospital to them is a terrible place, not because of any of its particular features but simply as a place where they suffer. The patients show-

14. Lehrman, S. R. "The Psychotherapy of Hospitalization," *Psychiatric Quart.*, 1939, 13: 309–21

15. Rowland, H. "Interaction Processes in the State Mental Hospital," *Psychiatry*, 1938, 1: 323–37

16. ———. "Friendship Patterns in the State Mental Hospital," *ibid.*, 1939, 2: 363–73

17. Slotkin, J. S. "The Nature and Effects of Social Interaction in Schizophrenia," *Jour. Abnorm. Soc. Psychol.*, 1942, 37: 345–68

18. Sprague, G. S. "The Role of the Psychiatric Hospital," *Mental Hyg.*, 1937, 2: 569–78

19. Storchheim, F. "Of Utilizing Institutionalized Mental Patients to Influence Other Patients Psychotherapeutically," *Amer. Jour. Psychiatry*, 1935, 92: 69–73

20. Vié, J., and Quéron, P. "La vieillesse de quelques déments précoces," *Ann. med. psychol.*, 1935, 93: 190–207

21. Wells, F. L. "The State School as a Social System," *Jour. Psychol.*, 1938, 5: 119–24

22. Wildermuth, H. "Schizophrene Endzustände," *Ztschr. f. ges. Neur. Psychiatrie*, 1938, 163: 643–55

ing the second pattern (I *b*, 7 patients) are relatively free from disturbing symptoms of the disease but are acutely aware of the limitations of their lives in the hospital, and feel unhappy because of that. Their thoughts revolve around the possibility of leaving the institution. The patients showing the third pattern (I *c*, 6 patients) are resigned both to the negative features of their mental state and to the limitations of institutional life; while these patients do not seem to suffer acutely, they do not derive much satisfaction from their existence. The fourth pattern (II *a*, 9 patients) consists in a delusional transformation of the hospital reality in accordance with the patient's own needs and desires. Life in this unreal world may make the patient relatively content. The patients who show the fifth pattern (II *b*, 15 patients), while aware of the limitations of the hospital environment, still find within this environment sources of satisfaction that enable them to lead a relatively happy and normal existence. Work, especially of a qualified and responsible nature, and personal relationships with the other patients and with employees are the most important sources of satisfaction for these patients.

The development of these attitudes seems to depend on the character and acuteness of the patient's symptoms, on his ability to elaborate these symptoms or to segregate them from the rest of his existence, and to some extent on the length of time he has spent in the hospital and on his age at the time of admission.

Considering the total group of our subjects from the point of view of the amount of satisfaction they obtain from life, we find that 35 per cent of the patients studied are acutely unhappy (I *a*, I *b*); 13 per cent are not happy but are resigned to their fate (I *c*); and 52 per cent of the patients obtain a certain amount of satisfaction from their life, which makes it worth living (II *a*, II *b*).

Analyzing the different patterns from the point of view of the sources of the patient's satisfaction and dissatisfaction, we find (omitting the resigned patients) that in 39 per cent of the cases (I *a*, II *a*) experiences and attitudes rooted in the patient's disease are foremost in determining his happiness or discontent. In 48 per cent of the cases (I *b*, II *b*) the patient's satisfaction or dissatisfaction depends primarily on situational factors, i.e., on the assets and limitations of institutional life. The attitudes of these patients are not basically different from those of normal aging persons who, because of their financial or family situation, must end their lives in an institution.

What are the practical applications of these findings? They emphasize once more the dual function of mental hospitals. Primarily the hospital is a place for treatment and cure, and as such a transitional place for the patient whose desire to leave the hospital is valuable as an incentive in treatment (5). If treatment fails, however, the hospital unavoidably acquires the function of a domicile for the chronic patient. As time goes on the hospitalized person becomes decreasingly a patient and increasingly an inmate, who, unless he becomes acutely disturbed, is little known to the psychiatrist and whose life is regulated by the routine of the institution and supervised by the nonmedical personnel.

The modern mental hospital has a tendency to center its main efforts on the treatment of the recently admitted patients. This is justifiable, since these patients admittedly represent the most hopeful cases for treatment (8). It is likely, however, that neglect of the older patients actually results in therapeutic losses. Among the old patients who lead a relatively normal life in the hospital there are many who can claim with good reason that they could get along outside if there only were a place for them there. A more prolonged and persistent therapeutic effort in the case of these patients might have led to a discharge before they became too old or lost all contact with the outside world.

With the present state of the therapy of psychoses and the therapeutic facilities of the state hospitals we cannot hope to increase the number of discharges to such an extent that the problem of chronic patients would become nonexistent. As long as the mental hospitals actually have the secondary function of providing a permanent place of life for the chronic patients, they should not neglect this function. The present study shows that for the adjustment of a large group of long-hospitalized patients (almost half of the group studied) situational factors are of primary importance. For these patients it is worth while to consider the possibility of changes and improvements in the hospital routine. It is true that the basic sources of dissatisfaction with hospitalization cannot be removed; most patients, the best-adjusted ones more than any others, resent the limitations of their freedom and independence imposed by the institution or the stigma attached to being an inmate of a mental hospital. There are, however, other important sources of dissatisfaction which might be removed. One might consider, for example, the feasibility of giving the patients a small compensation for their work; this measure would give the patient the feeling of being a valued member of the hospital community and would remove one of the most frequent causes of dissatisfaction with hospital life.

Beyond such general measures there is room for psychiatric supervision and guidance in adjusting the chronic patient to the hospital. If the psychiatrist could give the necessary time to get some insight into the attitudes and problems of the individual patient, much could be achieved. The patient's needs could be taken into consideration in making plans for him with regard to such basic sources of satisfaction as work, privileges, and social contacts. For many patients, satisfying work, an appreciative employer, and congenial company may make the difference between an extremely unhappy and a relatively satisfying existence.

REFERENCES

1. Anon. "The Asylum Environment, by an Ex-patient," *British Jour. Med. Psychol.*, 1931, 10: 344–64
2. Black, N. D. "Patients' Observations on Care and Treatment Made on Leaving the State Hospital," *Psychiatric Quart.*, 1937, 11: 507–16
3. Bogen, E. F. "Effects of Long Hospitalization on Psychotic Patients," *Mental Hyg.*, 1936, 20: 566–78
4. Bumke, O. (ed.). *Handbuch der Geisteskrankheiten.* Berlin: Springer, 1932. Vol. IX, spez. Teil V; *Die Schizophrenie*
5. Dembo, T., and Hanfmann, E. "The Patient's Psychological Situation upon Admission to a Mental Hospital," *Amer. Jour. Psychol.*, 1935, 47: 381–408
6. Fleck, U. "Ueber Beobachtungen bei alten Fällen von Schizophrenie," *Arch. f. Psychiatrie Nervenkr.*, 1928, 85: 705–60
7. Fuller, R. G. "Expectation of Hospital Life and Outcome for Mental Patients on First Admission," *Psychiatric Quart.*, 1930, 4: 295–323
8. Fuller, R. G., and Johnson, M. "The Duration of Hospital Life for Mental Patients," *ibid.*, 1931, 5: 341–52
9. Hanfmann, E. "Analysis of the Thinking Disorder in a Case of Schizophrenia," *Arch. Neurol. Psychiatry*, 1939, 41: 568–79
10. Hanfmann, E., and Kasanin, J. *Conceptual Thinking in Schizophrenia.* Nervous and Mental Disease Monographs, No. 67, 1942
11. Jenkins, R. L., and Curran, F. J. "Evolution and Persistence of Groups in a Psychiatric Observation Ward," *Jour. Soc. Psychol.*, 1940, 12: 279–89
12. Kant, O. "Clinical Analysis of Schizophrenic Deterioration," *Psychiatric Quart.*, 1943, 17: 426–45
13. Lawton, G. "Happiness in Old Age," *Mental Hyg.*, 1943, 27: 231–37

Chapter XIV

THE AGED SUBNORMAL

Oscar J. Kaplan

Wₕₑₙ...

While a large number of older persons are resident in our institutions for the mentally defective, an even larger number of middle-aged and senile subnormals are to be found among the noninstitutional population. These individuals are deserving of careful study because they afford us the opportunity of observing the psychological effects of the aging process upon an intellectually retarded group and because they command attention in their own right. Some conception of the size of the subnormal group can be gathered from Woodworth's (23) estimate that approximately 27 per cent of our population have IQ's of less than 90 and that 3 per cent score below 70. Whether these estimates are accepted or not, it is generally agreed that the subnormal group is very large and that many of its members survive to the later decades.

I. LIFE DURATION

Since intelligence is distributed roughly in the form of a bell-shaped curve, one would expect to find more seniles in the upper brackets of mental deficiency than in the lower ones, owing to differences in initial population. Moreover, the death rate progressively decreases as the normal range of IQ scores is approached. It is well known that idiots and imbeciles, on the average, submit to early death, and Dayton (5) has reported a death rate for morons only slightly higher than that of the general population. It is reasonable to suppose that those in the IQ group between 70 and 90 have a life duration comparable with that of the mentally normal. Thus seniles who in youth scored in the borderline or dull-normal categories constitute the overwhelming majority of the aged subnormal.

Notwithstanding the higher death rates to which, on the average, idiots and imbeciles are subject, many persons of these grades survive beyond middle life and into the senescent period. Figure 23 summarizes a study made by the writer (9) on the life dura-

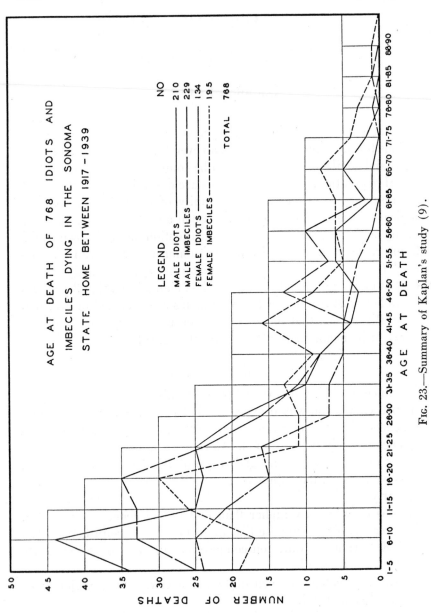

Fig. 23.—Summary of Kaplan's study (9).

tion of low-grade mental defectives at the Sonoma State Home, Eldridge, California. The study was based on the death ages of 768 idiots and imbeciles who died during the years from 1917 to 1939. The average life span of the 424 imbeciles was 26.60 years, and that of the 344 idiots was 19.04 years. However, it is worthy of note that 15.80 per cent of the imbeciles and 7.00 per cent of the idiots survived beyond 50 years of age and that in 1939 there were living at the Sonoma State Home 209 low-grade aments above 50, a majority of whom were imbeciles. Confirmatory evidence for the view that low intelligence does not necessarily lead to early death is to be found in the case of a microcephalic woman with a brain weight (at autopsy) of 530 grams, who died at the Sonoma State Home at the age of 89.

Since the idiot and imbecile groups do not represent homogeneous categories from the etiological standpoint, and since there are variations in the severity of symptoms even within etiological groupings, it is not surprising to find the wide differences in life duration referred to above. Although clinical type is a factor in life expectancy, even in types with very low averages, there are some who live remarkably long in a protected environment. For example, a man diagnosed as belonging to the Mongoloid-deficiency group died recently in California at the age of 69; the average person in this group is dead before the age of 20. It has frequently been demonstrated that there is a high correlation between physical stigmata and life duration, those deviating most from the normal having the briefest life expectancy.

Respiratory and circulatory diseases are the leading causes of death in low-grade mental defectives. Tuberculosis and pneumonia, in particular, are important as primary causes of death. Relatively few mortalities are directly due to nervous lesions or disease, and such deaths as are attributable to these causes usually occur in the early years of life. Modern methods of treatment are effecting significant reductions in mortality rates for pneumonia and tuberculosis and will eventually be reflected in the lengthened life duration of mental defectives. Penrose (15) has reported a marked decrease in the tuberculosis rate of mental defectives in England, and some progress in the control of this disease has been made in American institutions. In a healthful environment and with good medical care, subnormals of all grades may be expected to continue to share in the steadily rising life expectancy of the general population. It is reasonable to look forward to an important increase in the number of older persons who have been deficient in intelligence from birth or an early age. During the past decade new medical procedures, in particular the use of antibiotic drugs, have markedly lengthened the lives of institutionalized defectives.

II. MENTAL ABILITY

The practical difficulties which stand in the way of the accurate measurement of the intelligence of normal and psychotic seniles (see chapter v) are equally operative in the case of the aged subnormal. Examination of these persons must necessarily be individual and is particularly tedious because they present behavior which reflects both advanced age and low mentality. Not only are there the variabilities which are to be found in all human groups, but a further element of heterogeneity is added by the existence of different clinical types. Even in persons of identical IQ, the prognosis with age may be different. In view of the decline in intelligence which accompanies the aging process in normals, it is to be expected that a similar or even greater loss would occur among the aged subnormal. This expectation is borne out by a number of investigations.

Almost insurmountable obstacles preclude the accurate measurement of intelligence in aged idiots and low-grade imbeciles, owing to communication and other difficulties. It seems clear, however, that idiots and imbeciles, taken generally, are unusually prone to mental deterioration. Support for this generalization comes from the work of Moore (13), who has found that mental decline in idiots begins at an early chronological age.

Deterioration may be more rapid in certain clinical types than in others. For instance, it has been established by Benda (1) that deterioration is present at all age levels in Mongoloid deficiency, including atrophy of the cortex and hemorrhages affecting the brain and cord. Further evidence on the course of decline in Mongoloid deficiency has been submitted by Tennies (20), who has shown that there is an inverse relationship between life duration and the seriousness of the physical symptoms. In this connection, it may be mentioned that the premature appearance of senile features in persons with Mongoloid deficiency is not uncommon: loss of mental ability usually accompanies physical decline. It is probable that there are many persons in the Mongoloid-deficiency group who do not submit to the early decline characteristic of the category as a whole; for individual differences are to be found in this group as in all others. Little is known regarding the fate of intelligence in older cretins, birth-injury cases, microcephalics, and other clinical types; but the writer is convinced by his own observations that wide individual differences prevail, making generalizations hazardous. One of the tasks still before us is the follow-up of large numbers of feeble-minded persons of various clinical types with the purpose of ascertaining whether or not there is a differential decline in intelligence with age in the recognized groups.

A longitudinal study of mental decline in older morons was undertaken by Kaplan (10), based on an undifferentiated population of '23 male and 43 female patients of the Sonoma State Home. Patients suffering from psychoses or exhibiting serious physical handicaps were excluded from consideration. The 1916 Stanford-Binet was used in making the original test and was also employed when the group were retested. Average age at first test was 41.17 years, average interval between tests was 14.95 years, and the average IQ at first test was 57.01. During the interval between tests the group experienced an average decline of 6.65 mental-age months. Individual differences were very marked, 9 patients showing increases in mental age. The average gain of the 5 males was 4.4 mental-age months and that of the 4 females was 3.8 mental-age months. There were no marked differences in decline when the cases were segregated according to sex, age at first test, interval between tests, and IQ at first test.

An item analysis comparison of responses on the two tests revealed some interesting facts. Vocabulary, for example, remained remarkably constant during the period of the study, consistent with the findings in normals of similar age. Using List 1 of the 1916 Stanford-Binet as the basis for determining vocabulary level, the average vocabulary change was +0.12 words. The males showed an average gain in vocabulary of 1.91 words and the females an average loss of 0.83 words. However, examination of individual records indicated that there was a considerable turn-

over of words during the interval between tests, some words passed
on the first test being failed on the retest and vice versa.

Not all mental abilities held up equally well during the interval
between tests, as shown in Table 31. This table indicates that Item
IX, 2 (lifted weights), was the item in which the greatest change
took place, 38 who passed it on the first test failing it on the second.
This may be attributed to sensory changes, memory loss, and loss
in ability to comprehend and follow directions; failure may occur
as a result of any one of these factors. Other items in which
marked loss took place were VIII, 1 (ball and field), VIII, 3
(comprehension), IX, 5 (using 3 words in a sentence), and X, 4
(reading memory). Items depending primarily on speed or memory were failed more frequently at the second test than items based
essentially on information or experience, paralleling the trend in
normals.

Since the testing was done in an institutional situation, a high
measure of co-operation was obtained from the patients. Persons
in homes for the mentally defective recognize that the results of
mental-ability tests are given consideration in the placement of
patients and usually their best efforts are forthcoming. Furthermore, the Stanford-Binet, being individual in administration and
largely oral, provides unusual opportunities for the establishment
of examiner-subject rapport.

TABLE 31.—ITEM ANALYSIS OF BINET SCORES

	Passed on 1st Test, Failed on 2d		Failed on 1st Test, Passed on 2d		Passed on Both Tests		Failed on Both Tests	
	Male	Female	Male	Female	Male	Female	Male	Female
Year V								
1........	..	..	..	..	..	2	..	..
2........	..	..	..	..	..	2	..	..
3........	..	..	..	..	..	2	..	..
4........	..	..	..	..	..	2	..	..
5........	..	..	..	..	..	1	..	1
6........	..	..	..	..	..	2	..	..
Year VI								
1........	..	..	..	..	6	18	..	..
2........	1	..	..	1	5	17	..	..
3........	..	1	..	..	6	17	..	..
4........	2	1	..	..	4	17	..	..
5........	..	..	..	..	6	18	..	..
6........	3	1	..	..	3	17	..	..

TABLE 31.—ITEM ANALYSIS OF BINET SCORES—*Concluded*

	Passed on 1st Test, Failed on 2d		Failed on 1st Test, Passed on 2d		Passed on Both Tests		Failed on Both Tests	
	Male	Female	Male	Female	Male	Female	Male	Female
Year VII								
1.........	..	1	..	..	16	32	..	..
2.........	4	2	..	1	12	32	..	..
3.........	3	5	1	2	11	20	1	6
4.........	..	1	..	..	15	32	1	..
5.........	4	4	..	1	12	24	..	4
6.........	2	4	1	1	10	20	3	8
Year VIII								
1.........	8	13	1	6	12	22	2	2
2.........	7	6	..	1	16	26	..	10
3.........	7	9	2	3	13	29	1	2
4.........	7	5	2	3	10	28	4	7
5.........	2	7	4	7	14	26	3	3
6.........	1	1	..	1	21	41	1	..
Year IX								
1.........	3	..	..	6	19	35	1	2
2.........	13	25	..	2	2	2	8	14
3.........	6	5	2	3	9	12	6	23
4.........	3	4	..	2	5	10	15	27
5.........	8	11	..	3	10	22	5	7
6.........	4	8	1	3	5	7	13	25
Year X								
1.........	..	5	5	6	10	22	8	10
2.........	2	2	3	1	1	10	17	30
3.........	3	8	..	1	2	5	18	29
4.........	3	14	1	4	6	7	13	18
5.........	3	4	2	4	..	10	18	25
6.........	4	4	2	..	1	4	16	35
Year XII								
1.........	1	8	2	1	4	7	13	21
2.........	3	6	2	1	3	17	12	13
3.........	4	1	1	8	2	6	13	22
4.........	2	6	1	2	1	4	16	25
5.........	..	2	1	1	..	1	19	33
6.........	..	5	..	..	1	..	19	32
7.........	..	8	1	1	2	4	17	24
8.........	1	3	..	1	2	2	17	31
Year XIV								
1.........	..	2	2	..	..	..	9	23
2.........	..	..	..	..	..	..	11	25
3.........	1	1	..	..	..	..	10	24
4.........	1	4	..	..	..	2	10	19
5.........	..	..	1	..	..	..	10	25
6.........	1	..	..	..	..	..	10	25

Qualitatively, the older morons exhibited less emotional lability and were more deliberate in their responses than younger patients of equal mental rank. It is significant that the 1916 Stanford-Binet places little emphasis on speed; for this reason the test results fail to reveal fully the slowness of response which was so painfully apparent to the examiner. In a number of cases more than two hours were required to complete the examination.

The results described above must be understood in terms of the group examined and are specific to the test instrument employed. It should be noted that selective factors are operative in institutions and that patients in homes for the mentally defective are not wholly representative of subnormals residing outside of institutions. Since most of the subjects of this inquiry were considerably below 70 years of age at the time of retesting, it can safely be assumed that the rate of mental decline would have been much more pronounced if the average age of the group had been higher.

Although it has been used extensively with adult defectives, the Stanford-Binet was designed primarily for children; we therefore must view the results obtained in the Sonoma State Home study with certain reservations. The small amount of loss which occurred in the average subject can be partially attributed to the fact that the test which is a good indirect measure of capacity in children and adolescents is not equally valid with older adults; the latter capitalize on their greater experience without being penalized for increased chronological age. Evidence indicating that experience gained during the adult period is reflected in performance on certain Stanford-Binet items is to be found in the work of Rautman (16) and Wladkowsky (22). Using the revised Stanford-Binet, Rautman (16) reports that older defectives have less difficulty than younger ones of comparable mental ability on test items dealing with picture identification, definitions, vocabulary, and comprehension. Adult experiences increase the probability of success on these items.

Wladkowsky (22) has retested an institutionalized defective group, using the 1916 Stanford-Binet on both occasions. The oldest subjects in this study ranged in age from 17 to 58 at the time of re-examination, with a mean age of 28; the average interval between tests was approximately 6 years. The mean mental age on the second test was 6 years, 8 months, an average gain of 2 mental-age months; 56.7 per cent of Wladkowsky's subjects improved their mental-age scores. Numerous investigations of mental growth in normals have shown that there is no appreciable increase in intelligence beyond the age of 20 or 22; there is, on the other hand, a good deal of evidence indicating that mental growth ceases earlier in defectives than in normals. The resumption of growth reported by Wladkowsky presumably is due to the use of a test instrument which places a premium upon experience. In the light of these data, it appears that the older morons studied by Kaplan would have exhibited a sharper decline if they had been examined with a test stressing speed, immediate memory, and items of an abstract nature.

Wright (24) has investigated the decline of performance abilities in 137 morons ranging in age from 16 to 69, employing items known to be failed by a considerable percentage of normal aged persons. The study was confined to patients showing no symptoms of mental disturbance, of secondary causation, of epilepsy, or of belonging to any of the recognized clinical types. Commenting on the results obtained with eleven different performance tests, Wright concludes that performance-test abilities "showing a decline for normals show an earlier decline for the feebleminded with a regularity which must arise from a real difference in the trend with age for the two groups." In the same study, Wright collected information on the vocabularies of her moron subjects, using the Wechsler-Bellevue vocabulary list as her measuring device. She found no appreciable loss in the understanding of words, confirming the results reported by Kaplan.

III. SOCIAL AND ECONOMIC ADJUSTMENT

Age is both a favorable and an unfavorable factor in the economic and social adjustment of older defectives. With a lifetime of experience behind them, many have come to terms with their environment and have found for themselves some small niche where their meager talents suffice. On the other hand, age adds to a mental handicap which is already severe, making adjustment even more difficult, particularly for those who are living outside of institutions. Since most noninstitutionalized subnormals are economically in the marginal group, and since they are engaged principally in unskilled manual labor, it becomes harder for them to obtain employment as their physical vigor diminishes. It therefore is not surprising that large numbers of these people find their way to county poor farms or to the public relief rolls; undoubtedly they contribute more than their share to the nation's dependency load.

Charles (4) reports a follow-up of the ability status and general progress of 151 of 206 persons studied by Baller in 1935. At the time of the follow-up, the mean age of the subjects was 42. Charles found wide individual differences in achievement; many of the subjects were making an excellent adjustment.

Older defectives who enjoy the protection of an institution in their declining years frequently are more fortunate than normals of the same age group; many of them recognize their situation to be a desirable one and do not wish to exchange their security for the greater freedom of an extra-institutional existence.

As is true in the case of the normal aged, the presenile personality of the defective has an important bearing upon its senile successor. This continuity is borne out by the fact that those subnormals who have adjusted well all their lives are likely to adjust satisfactorily during the senile period, barring physical or mental disease, and especially if they are not subjected to radical changes in environment.

The stabilizing influence of family living which helps to cushion the changes that attend the aging process in normals is less evident in the senile feebleminded. Subnormals are less likely to marry than normals, and marriages contracted by them are more likely to terminate in divorce or separation (11). The influence of conjugal life upon the psychology of later maturity has been thoughtfully considered by Dunham in chapter vi.

Viewing social competence as a function of physical and mental integrity, Doll (6) has attempted to measure social maturity in older feeble-minded males. Using the Vineland Social Maturity Scale and basing his conclusions on twelve subjects all over the age of 50 and all institutionalized for at least thirty years, he found no appreciable changes in social behavior in the period between 25 and 70 years of age. Premonitory symptoms of decline were noted between 50 and 70, but the symptoms reflected a decreased amount of activity rather than a marked drop in level. On the average, increase in score on the Vineland scale ceased among the feebleminded after the age of 25. Binet scores were available for the group studied by Doll, and it is significant that no appreciable changes in mental age took place during the period covered by the investigation. Since the subjects of this inquiry were institutionalized, it is not permissible to generalize from the findings stated above to subnormals outside of homes for the defective. In this connection it is pertinent to call attention to the follow-up study of Muench (14), who has presented data showing that community living provides good opportunities for the social and mental development of defectives. He suggests that opportunities for social and intellectual growth are more limited in institutions than outside of them. The problem of determining which type of environment is most favorable to the preservation of mental abilities and of social competence is one which must be settled by future investigations.

IV. PSYCHOTIC STATES

Although most hypophrenics never manifest psychotic symptoms, some succumb to the dementias of old age. Following the reasoning stated earlier in this chapter, one would expect most subnormal senile psychotics to come from the IQ group with a range of 70 to 90; this coincides with the known facts. The number of morons who develop mental disease in later life is also appreciable. Idiots and imbeciles rarely survive to the ages at which senile dementia and arteriosclerotic psychosis are most prevalent; however, they may present these conditions earlier than normals or brighter defectives.

Defectives who develop psychoses prior to the senile period exhibit higher mortality rates than nonpsychotics of the same intelligence level. This is shown by the work of Malzberg (12), who studied the life durations of New York State mental-hospital patients diagnosed as suffering from psychoses associated with mental deficiency. After making allowance for age differences between patient population and general population, he found that patient mortality was 2.6 that of the general population. Moreover, he found that these patients had an excessive mortality in comparison with nondemented subnormals. It may therefore be assumed that few of them survive into the senile period.

As is true of normal seniles, older defectives may develop all of the forms of mental illness which afflict younger persons of the same intelligence level. In addition, they may present syndromes peculiar to the later years. Senile dementia is known to occur in feeble-minded individuals, and mental defect confers no immunity against the presenile or arteriosclerotic psychoses. The classification of psychoses in subnormal individuals is far from satisfactory and is complicated by the widespread tendency to place all such patients under the heading of "Psychosis with Mental Deficiency." This designation does not refer to a well-defined clinical entity, including a wide variety of disorders. Hunsicker (8) has expressed doubt that a primary psychosis develops among the subnormal. Herskovitz and Plesset (7) have indicated that functional psychoses are unusual among persons below the moron level and some authorities have completely denied their occurrence among idiots and imbeciles. Even in those defectives who are capable of developing schizophrenia or manic-depressive psychosis, symptoms may not be evident until the latter half of life.

From the diagnostic standpoint, it is important to recognize that even a person of normal or superior intelligence may test in the feeble-minded group when acutely disturbed or when suffering from a deteriorating mental or nervous disease. It is also worthy of note that many defectives are subject to transient periods of mental upset which are not easily classified in terms of the traditional categories. A dementia in a low-grade ament bears little resemblance to any of the psychoses seen in persons who have once been normal in intelligence.

Butler (3) reports a case of senile psychosis developing in an older defective who had spent the greater part of her life at the Sonoma State Home. He failed to find a single case of involutional melancholia in the 287 cases comprising his psychotic group; this is surprising because of the large number of middle-aged men and women in the California institution. Rohan (18) reminds us that although the mental defective has an emotional life more tempestuous than that of the average person, the defective's upsets usually are more transient and lacking in continuity. It is unfortunate that subnormals succumbing to the psychoses of later maturity have received so little attention in the literature; the Butler study is one of the few investigations which even mentions these conditions.

It is extremely easy to differentiate between senile psychotics, regardless of type or history, and older defectives without psychosis. The latter are intact personalities, oriented with respect to their environments. Although they may manifest decline in certain mental abilities, rarely is the loss great enough to interfere seri-

ously with routine activities. They are definitely not dements, although it is conceivable that some of them will become psychotic
if they live sufficiently long.

The demented senile subnormal can be distinguished by means
of past history from the aged psychotic who has once enjoyed normal intelligence. A record of institutionalization in a home for the
defective would, of course, constitute positive proof of type. Other
items of personal data helpful in making a discrimination are records dealing with education and occupation, although such records
are conclusive only when the patient is found to have had an extensive educational background or to have functioned successfully in
an occupation requiring at least normal intelligence. For instance,
if a person is a college graduate or has profitably directed a large
business, it can safely be assumed that the person was once mentally normal. On the other hand, data showing a limited education
or low occupational status must be balanced against other information before a conclusion is drawn, since lack of achievement is not
always indicative of low intelligence.

Boehm and Sarason (2) found that Wechsler's deterioration
index is unreliable in distinguishing mental deficiency from mental
loss if there is a familial tendency to perform poorly in some of the
Don't Hold tests. Sloan (19) also has questioned the validity of the
Wechsler deterioration quotient in mental defectives. After examining high-grade defectives aged 16–30, he concluded that the quotient was invalid for his group. It also is of interest that in the 56
cases where previous IQ was known, the IQ difference on retest,
after an average interval of approximately 10 years, was less than
one point.

Although all of the recognized later dementias seem to occur in
older defectives of the higher grades, psychological symptoms almost invariably are influenced by the original mental defect. When
delusions are present, they tend to be impoverished with regard to
content. The generalization can be made that the higher the intelligence of the demented hypophrenic, the greater will be the resemblance of his symptoms to those exhibited by psychotics of the same
type but with a history of normal intelligence. Also of value in
diagnosis is the finding that senile psychotics with a history of
normal intelligence often retain some of their earlier abilities in a
patchy sort of way; indeed, this is the basis for several well-known
tests of deterioration.

Robertson and Wibberley (17) found that the original ability of dull, demented, middle-aged housewives was best represented by tests dealing with visuo-spatial material. Robertson and Wibberley suggest that information tests might be developed which would indicate the early adult levels of older defectives with psychosis.

It is clear that senile psychosis is not the inevitable fate of the older defective, certainly not at sixty or seventy. Here we have further proof that low intelligence is not an essential prerequisite to the development of dementia in later life, nor does mental defect per se predispose to such psychosis.

V. FURTHER RESEARCH

As we become increasingly concerned with aging and the aged we must not forget the fourth of our population which is subnormal in intelligence. This group, on a per capita basis, will present us with more social problems than any other section of our people. It is to be regretted that our knowledge of the senile period in this group is so incomplete; information on the psychological status of defectives beyond the age of seventy is almost nonexistent.

At the present time we can only speculate regarding the fate of sensory and psychomotor functions, since these appear never to have been charted in the aged subnormal. Similarly, we can only conjecture regarding the effect of age upon criminality, sexuality, suicide, and other important forms of behavior which presumably occur in older hypophrenics. Although our information on these topics is very incomplete, even for the normal aged, no data at all seem to exist for senile defectives.

There is need for a carefully controlled, comparative, longitudinal study of physical and mental decline in institutionalized and noninstitutionalized subnormals. It is possible that the process of reduction in the two groups does not conform to the same pattern. Such a survey, therefore, would yield information on the effect of a protected versus an unprotected existence upon the preservation of mental, physical, and social abilities.

REFERENCES

1. Benda, C. E. "Central Nervous System in Mongolism," *Amer. Jour. Ment. Deficiency*, 1940, 45: 42–47
2. Boehm, A. E., and Sarason, S. B. "Does Wechsler's Formula Distinguish Intellectual Deterioration from Mental Deficiency?" *Jour. Abnorm. Soc. Psychol.*, 1947, 42: 356–58

from the competitive field. Conversely, old age has more difficult problems in a competitive group, particularly if the individual is not in a position to withdraw from competition.

It is obvious however that individual emotional determinants play a very important role as regards the psychology of aging in the same cultural and social economic circumstances. Thus the individual who ought to retire because of aging may have the emotional need to continue in his position and occupation because retirement means an unbearable blow to his self-esteem.

Considering the problem from the point of view of the large average in our culture, the critical period for aging frequently begins at about 40. It is the period characterized in the female by the approach of the menopause and in general by the increased incidents of circulatory diseases such as hypertension and coronary disease, the latter more frequently in the male. Depressive reactions likewise become numerous at this age. As age advances, the incidence of these disorders increases and they merge with the effects of senescence.

On the basis of this discussion we can differentiate two types of psychosomatic disturbance in the older patient: (*a*) psychosomatic disturbances which are essentially identical with those observed in individuals at any age; (*b*) psychosomatic disturbances which represent aggravations of and reactions to functional and structural disturbances connected with aging.

I. PSYCHOSOMATIC DISTURBANCES IN INDIVIDUALS AT ANY AGE

It is not uncommon to encounter psychosomatic disturbances in older people which are not connected with the aging process as such. It is very important to recognize this fact; otherwise the diagnostic and therapeutic approach to the patient miscarries.

CASE I   A 66-year-old man complained of attacks of palpitation, sinking sensation in the stomach, and loss of appetite. These attacks were accompanied by fear of death or of heart or stomach ailment. Still more frequently, however, the fear consisted of anxious expectation without special content.

Physical examination did not reveal any gross structural damage. His heart was essentially normal, as revealed by X-ray and electrocardiograph examination; his blood pressure was within normal bounds 150/80.

3. Butler, F. O. "Psychosis in the Mentally Defective," *California & Western Med.*, 1937, 46: 84–89

4. Charles, D. C. "Ability and Accomplishments of Persons Earlier Judged Mentally Deficient," *Genet. Psychol. Monogr.*, 1953, 47: 3–71

5. Dayton, N. A. "Mortality in Mental Deficiency over a Fourteen-Year Period," *Proc. Amer. Assoc. Stud. Feebleminded*, 1931, 55: 127–212

6. Doll, E. A. "Measurement of Social Maturity Applied to Older People," in *Mental Health in Later Maturity*, Supplement No. 168, *U.S. Pub. Health Repts.* (Washington: Government Printing Office, 1943), pp. 138–43

7. Herskovitz, H. H., and Plesset, M. R. "Psychosis in Adult Mental Defectives," *Psychiatric Quart.*, 1941, 15: 574–88

8. Hunsicker, H. H. "Symptomatology of Psychosis with Mental Deficiency," *Proc. Amer. Assoc. Ment. Deficiency*, 1938, 43: 51–56

9. Kaplan, O. J. "Life Expectancy of Low-Grade Mental Defectives," *Psychol. Record*, 1940, 3: 295–306

10. ———. "Mental Decline in Older Morons," *Amer. Jour. Ment. Deficiency*, 1943, 47: 277–85

11. ———. "Marriage of Mental Defectives," *ibid.*, 1944, 48: 379–84

12. Malzberg, B. "Mortality among Patients with Psychoses with Mental Deficiency," *Training School Bull.*, 1936, 33: 125–32

13. Moore, L. "Mental Growth of Low-Grade Feebleminded," *ibid.*, 1929, 26: 88–95

14. Muench, G. A. "A Follow-up of Mental Defectives after Eighteen Years," *Jour. Abnorm. Soc. Psychol.*, 1944, 39: 407–18

15. Penrose, L. S. *Mental Defect.* New York: Farrar & Rinehart, 1934

16. Rautman, A. L. "Relative Difficulty of Test Items of the Revised Stanford-Binet: an Analysis of Records from a Low Intelligence Group," *Jour. Exper. Educ.*, 1942, 10: 183–94

17. Robertson, J. P. S., and Wibberley, H. "Dementia Versus Mental Defect in Middle-Aged Housewives," *Jour. Consult. Psychol.*, 1952, 16: 313–15

18. Rohan, J. C. "Mental Disorder in the Adult Defective," *Jour. Ment. Sci.*, 1946, 92: 551–63

19. Sloan, W. "Validity of Wechsler's Deterioration Quotient in High Grade Mental Defectives," *Jour. Clin. Psychol.*, 1947, 3: 287–88

20. Tennies, L. G. "Some Comments on the Mongoloid," *Amer. Jour. Ment. Deficiency*, 1943, 48: 46–54

21. Thompson, C. W. "Decline in Limit of Performance Among Adult Morons," *Amer. Jour. Psychol.*, 1951, 64: 203–15

22. Wladkowsky, E. "A Preliminary Study of Mental Growth after the Age of Fourteen Years in an Institution for Mental Defectives," *Proc. Amer. Assoc. Ment. Deficiency*, 1938, 43: 181–87

23. Woodworth, R. S. *Psychology* (4th edition). New York: Henry Holt & Co. 1940

24. Wright, C. "The Nature of the Decline of Performance Abilities in Adult Morons as Compared with That of Normal Adults." Unpublished doctoral dissertation, Stanford University, 1943

Chapter XV

PSYCHOSOMATIC MEDICINE AND THE OLDER PATIENT

BELA MITTELMANN

To CLASSIFY and discuss psychosomatic disturbances of aging is the aim of this chapter. The term "psychosomatic" implies that either in the symptomatology or in the dynamics of healthy or pathological functioning a correlation can be established between psychological phenomena such as fear or outbursts of anger, on the one hand, and either functional or irreversible structural alterations in the organism, on the other.

A. SOMATIC PSYCHOLOGICAL AND CULTURAL ASPECTS

The concept of aging implies a decline in the structural and functional efficiency of the organism. Used in this broadest sense, aging begins at approximately the age of 21. This may be a surprising statement, but there is both experimental and experiential evidence for it. It is not an accident that a champion nearly always is beaten by a younger athlete. Prizefighters or tennis players become champions about the age of 25. There is no doubt that the experience of the champion increases with further practice and so does his judgment; but in so extreme a need for superior performance the aging process is the winner over experience. Likewise it was found that at the age of 28 a flyer may be at a definite disadvantage for extreme conditions of high-speed flying, and that the period of blackout after a dive lengthens from the previous five to eleven seconds.

The aging process that sets in at 21, however, is of no practical importance for most of the average activities. In some high-pressure industrial work the age of 40 is a critical period. His speed may decrease so much that, after 40, a man may find it difficult to hold certain jobs. Obviously the occupation of the individual is of considerable importance as regards the significance of the aging process. Where experience and judgment play a dominant role, as in the work of a scientist, the age of 40 to 60 may

be more valuable than the age of 30, and is unquestionably much more valuable than the age of 20. The three leaders of the United Nations in World War II, Churchill, Roosevelt, and Stalin, were all past 60.

The deterioration quotient,[1] as measured on the Wechsler Bellevue Scale, has been found to decline in the average population from 97.9 at the age of 22.5 to 74.8 at the age of 57.5. Of the various subtests, Information, Comprehension, Object Assembly, and Vocabulary hold up with age, whereas Digit Span, Arithmetical Reasoning, Digit Symbol, Block Design, and Similarities show conspicuous age decline. Further, there is a lengthening of the reaction time, which is the largest factor in the decline of the scores mentioned, along with a decrease in the individual's power and endurance, at least in sustained vigorous activity (18).

"Aging" is a universal process. The diminution of the elasticity of the skin, of the lens in the eye, and of the blood vessels is observable in all individuals (4). Yet there are individual differences in degree in such gross organic alterations. Psychologically the individual differences are even greater and in the emotional life of the individual aging may be absent. It is very important to realize this point in the approach to certain psychiatric and psychosomatic manifestations in people of 60 and 70 years of age. Individuals of that age may be more elastic than many individuals at any age in their lives. They may branch out successfully into a new creative field of endeavor.

In the American male population studied by Kinsey *et al.* (8), the mean frequency of orgasm gradually declines from a peak of 3.0 per week in the age group 26–30 to 2.2 per week in the age group 56–60. The percentage of the population studied which was impotent rises from 0.1 per cent at age 20 to 27.0 per cent at age 70. The authors cite the case of a Negro of 88 who was having regular intercourse with his wife of 90.

One of the significant determinants of the psychology of aging is the cultural environment. Aging is easier in a civilization in which older people are revered by the very fact of their age and in which their status is strengthened by aging. Aging is furthermore easier to bear for a man if he has accumulated money to provide him with security and to enable him to retire if he wishes

[1]This score is obtained by dividing the sum of those subtest scores which show definite decline with age by the sum of those which show little or no decline with age.

His life history was quite remarkable in that there was a steady progression of activities and interests up to the present. The present complaints were the first serious emotional disturbances in his life. He had been married for 30 years. His wife was sterile and they had no children, but this did not cause any serious marital unhappiness. They had many interests in common and, outside of trivial disagreements, no serious clash ever occurred between them. He had counseling jobs in various youth organizations. He had always been successful at them and had always been liked by the children and young men, who in fact took him as their model and came to him with their problems for advice and help.

About six months before he consulted a physician concerning his complaints he was made head of the central office of one of these organizations. It was the best-paid and most responsible job he had held in his life. Another remarkable feature was that he had taken up painting two years before (at the age of 64), pursuing it in his leisure time, and had succeeded so well that he had exhibited his paintings a few months before at the age of 66. It is quite obvious that this man had remarkable elasticity and possessed remarkable powers of development and creative tendencies even at this advanced age.

Precipitating situation.—In his capacity as head of the central office of an organization this man had to meet and have conferences with board members as well as other individuals in higher positions. In the course of the psychiatric interviews it became clear that his attacks of anxiety occurred usually at meal time, particularly at lunch time. Soon the information was elicited that he always met the board members for lunch. It thus became clear that his symptoms represented reactions to meeting these individuals.

Childhood and adolescent history. — The patient was the youngest of three siblings. He had affectionate and devoted parents. He was weakly as a child and the siblings were inclined to dominate him, but the parents protected him. His relationships with his classmates had been similar. His weakliness angered him and made him uncomfortable, but he appreciated his parents' help. When he became a counselor in youth organizations he put into practice the kind of handling he himself always wanted and had received from his parents. An undercurrent anxiety concerning people who were his equals or his superiors remained, but he had never been seriously put to the test until at the age of 66 he received his present appointment. Then he reacted with anxiety symptoms.

Comment.—This case illustrates in a particularly striking manner that at an advanced age psychological "old age" may be completely absent. The situation to which the individual reacts may be the first challenge of the kind that precipitates illness. Treatment conducted in the same manner as with younger individuals may then give excellent results.

The case mentioned did not have a severe type of psychomatic disturbance. The diagnosis was anxiety hysteria, that is, a psychoneurosis. Illness of this type has the advantage that the determining factors can be traced from the patient himself through the information gathered from him. More difficult, to be sure, but in a sense even more dramatic are cases in which a psychotic disturbance of the functional type first occurs at an advanced age. In such instances the inclination to attribute disturbances in old age to the pathology connected with the aging process is even more tempting and misleading. A brief example will be given:

CASE II   A 75-year-old man was admitted to a psychiatric hospital because he was downhearted, spoke very little, had no appetite, lost weight, and took no interest in his environment. A careful examination made it evident that he presented no impairment of his intellectual functions. His memory for recent and remote events was good, his ability to calculate was adequate, his responses were slow in harmony with his depression, but there were no signs of organic structural damage. The patient's first attack of depression was essentially of the simple type which may occur at any age, not of the involutional, agitated type. The patient recovered from his depression after a year's stay in the hospital.

II. PSYCHOSOMATIC DISTURBANCES CONNECTED WITH AGING

The general pattern of disturbance in this group can be characterized as follows: Some organ system in the patient has undergone a pathological structural and functional alteration commonly encountered as a result of aging. Conflicts, with their concomitant physiological changes, either (*a*) intensify this process, or (*b*) produce additional symptoms in the psychological sphere or in the somatic sphere. In the latter case a complex picture results which combines the effects of the structural alteration and the functional correlates of emotional disturbance.

The disturbances as they are encountered in the individual are to be looked upon not simply as direct results of the physiological and structural alterations (11). In all somatopsychic disturbances the individual's reactions to the structural somatic change are of paramount importance in the final dynamics and symptomatology.

The proper evaluation of the psychological and psychosomatic disturbances of this type takes the following factors into account: (*a*) The individual is aware of a radical alteration in some phenomena requiring new emotional adjustment. Such phenomena are: slight decrease in memory function, alterations of sexual function, decrease in speed, joint pains, or more severe disturbances such as arterial hypertension or coronary disease of the heart. Such alterations may mean the loss of a very important function which is indispensable to the individual's image of himself and to his self-evaluation (narcissistic blow, castration trauma). The reaction may further be a feeling of the impossibility of correcting life situations which the individual had hoped to correct through action for years. Thus a woman may have had serious conflicts with her husband and have planned for ten years to leave him, but repeatedly postponed doing so, for various reasons such as small children. When the menopause sets in she feels that she can never carry out this plan. (*b*) The distress from such symptoms as hot flushes accompanied by cold perspiration, or dizziness and light-headedness may be reacted to, in addition to the above implications, as a serious threat to physical welfare which the individual cannot master. (*c*) This may merge with anxiety from different sources, such as fear of retribution for hostility. Because of the feeling of helplessness, inadequacy, worthlessness, deficiency, and threat from all the sources mentioned, the individual's dependency on the environment and his demand for help, assurance, and affection increase and are doomed to disappointment. This leads to renewal of the various anxieties and hostilities with a renewal of fear of retribution, injury, and abandonment. The physiological changes are then evaluated by the sufferer as a realization of these processes.

Varieties of psychosomatic disturbances connected with the problems of aging.—It is convenient to group psychosomatic disturbances connected with the problems of aging into the following categories:

1. General reactions to the aging process
2. Disturbances of the glands of internal secretion
3. Disturbances of the circulatory system
4. Disturbances of the auditory system
5. Disturbances of the eyes
6. Disturbances of the respiratory apparatus
7. Disturbances of the digestive system

Of these, the last three will be first discussed briefly.

The two most common eye diseases of aging are glaucoma and cataract. Cataract consists of a cloudiness of the crystalline lens of the eye, which is entirely a primary histogenic (somatic) disorder, but the difficulty in vision may become fused with anxieties from various sources in the form of fear of blindness. Glaucoma is an increase in the intraocular pressure. In this disorder, reactions to life situations play an important role, and it may occur at a younger age (early thirties) also. Irritability may be a marked symptom in both disorders. Both glaucoma and cataract, as a rule, require operative treatment. Both may require psychotherapy to help the patient adjust to his changed function and, in glaucoma, to prevent aggravation of the process (2).

The respiratory apparatus may show chronic bronchitis and emphysema in old age. The difficulty in breathing and the cough resulting from these sources fuse with similar symptoms arising out of anxiety or frustrated hostility.

The digestive system is very frequently involved in the psychosomatic reactions but only occasionally becomes a dominant seat of the psychosomatic pathology of aging. When it does, it is apt to be connected with the fear of cancer; and then it colors anxiety reactions in this special way. In fact the whole anxiety reaction may be precipitated by the news that someone else in the family or among the patient's friends has developed or died of cancer. The many gastrointestinal symptoms will be presented in connection with subsequent case histories.

B. GENERAL REACTIONS TO THE AGING PROCESS

The most characteristic reaction is depression, particularly of the involutional type. This psychosis, encountered beginning with the age of 40 to 50, is characterized mainly by agitation and nihilistic delusions (7) referring often to the gastrointestinal system. The various psychodynamic factors that appear here have been previously discussed. This reaction is not a response to and manifestation of purely endocrine disturbances and the substitutive therapy is therefore ineffective. In more recent years it has been found that shock therapy—particularly electric shock or metrazole (17)—accompanied with psychotherapy was effective in a large percentage of cases. The case to be described under the next heading illustrates many of the factors involved in this reaction also.

C. DISTURBANCES OF GLANDS OF INTERNAL SECRETION

The main disturbances in this group are represented by the menopause. The endocrinology of the menopause is highly complex (16). It is certain that there is a decrease or disappearance of the ovarian hormones, particularly of the follicular hormone. Most likely the main pathology is the resultant increase in one of the hormones of the anterior pituitary gland, mainly the follicle-stimulating hormone. The physiological disturbances such as the hot flushes probably result from this excess of pituitary hormone. The physiological disturbance is correctible through the administration of the follicular hormone in a large percentage of cases. There are practical laboratory methods available to determine the degree of follicular-hormone deficiency and the amount needed for the correction, through the examination of the vaginal cells or assay of the hormone in the blood (5, 13).

The most common menopausal disturbances on the psychological level are moodiness, depression, irritability, anxiety, and insomnia; those on the physiological level are hot flushes, with excessive perspiration, dizziness and light-headedness, gastrointestinal complaints, palpitation, and headaches. Since the development of the follicular hormone the treatment of menopausal disturbance proper is rather successful. Hormone therapy should be accompanied by psychotherapy.

The following case will illustrate most of the points made in the discussion. The case to be described had successful phases in the treatment, although the ultimate outcome was an unfortunate one. The case is not representative of the average menopausal disturbance but is a dramatic illustration of all the salient problems encountered in menopause.

CASE III A 44-year-old librarian applied for psychoanalytic treatment because of a depression. She often felt disinclined to attend to her work or felt tired and made errors. She was sensitive to any remarks which she considered critical or corrective. She was mostly disinclined to seek other people's company. She felt that if she didn't obtain help she would quit or lose her job. The patient had had periods of depression repeatedly at various times in her life. The present depression was the severest one, although neither the current nor the past ones had the quality or intensity of psychotic depression. She had stopped menstruating a year and a half before she applied for treatment.

Past history.—The patient was the third of seven siblings. She spoke about her parents and her siblings in contradictory terms, starting affectionately but always ending up with the complaint that they discriminated against her and dominated her. These complaints went back as far as the age of 4 and 5. Her father drank, and when inebriated was threatening and domineering toward the whole family. Whatever sexual activity the patient ever engaged in she spoke about with considerable shame, feeling of worthlessness, and guilt. She had engaged in some sexual play as a child. There had been very occasional masturbation and two episodes of embracing and petting at about the age of thirty. She had never married, and was virgin at the time she entered treatment.

Course of treatment.—The patient improved quickly after the treatments started and continued to improve steadily for about six months. She became more efficient at her work, got along better with people, and resumed contacts with her friends. Then, however, she took a turn for the worse and her depression reappeared. She dreamed at this time that she was lying naked on a bed in the court of the house where the analyst's office was and that the bed then suddenly moved into the analyst's office. It became obvious at this point in the treatment that the patient was hoping the analyst would fulfill hopes and desires never realized in her life. In the contacts with him she could feel that she was not rejected, that she was forgiven for hostility, and that she could accept in some measure her sexual desires. As previously mentioned, she was still a virgin; she wanted the fulfillment of her desire from the only man toward whom she could feel a measure of closeness with any degree of safety. In the dream, this desire is fulfilled in a disguised manner. The feeling of exposure and the attendant feeling of deficiency and of worthlessness are in the background. Inasmuch as any fulfillment of such desires was automatically frustrated in the analytic situation, the patient reacted with a renewed feeling of rejection, deficiency, and worthlessness. Interpretations as to this effect were of no help because the patient took them only as expressions of rejection and contempt on the part of the analyst. She lacked the strength to look for a fulfillment of her lifelong longings elsewhere.

The continuation of the regular analytic procedure being too dangerous, the patient was asked to sit up and face the analyst. He reassured her that she could make friends, that she had a worthwhile personality. The next day the patient returned with a mild flight of ideas and with a slight feeling of elation and a feeling of not having mastery over herself, as if she were two persons. It was obvious that she took the analyst's reassuring remark as a guaranty of her worth-whileness, overriding her feeling of worthlessness. To terminate the hypomanic reaction, the analyst pointed out to her that she was overreacting to his reassuring remark. Next day the patient returned, as depressed as on the previous occasion. Twice following this, the patient had reactions of elation to reassuring remarks and recurrence of depression to the analyst's attempt to tone down the effect of the remark.

Obviously the patient was in a mild psychotic state. In casting about for possible other therapeutic measures, the therapist considered the possibility of the physiological background of the menopause, in spite of the fact that the patient had never voluntarily offered any complaints characteristic of menopause. On direct questioning, however, she stated that she had been suffering and was still suffering from hot flushes accompanied by profuse perspiration. She also felt dizzy occasionally. The follicular hormone was administered in sufficient amount to correct the deficiency indicated by the vaginal smear. The patient's alarming psychiatric symptoms disappeared in about two weeks.

Resumption of any deep analysis of the patient's problems now seemed too risky; psychotherapy, therefore, was continued on current problems in weekly interviews parallel with the administration of follicular hormone. The patient was now in better shape and said that she was better than she had ever been in her life. Her performance on her job was good; she passed an examination for promotion, and her social life was more satisfactory than at any time. When she was under special stress she complained of slight dizziness or slight flushes, and of some difficulty in hearing. These symptoms now were obviously of a psychogenic nature.

The patient continued on this regime and struck up friendship with a 50-year-old man friend of one of her female acquaintances. He was a gifted and charming man, but he was a dipsomaniac, addicted to very severe drinking bouts about once in three months, each lasting about two weeks. The patient had an affair with him with considerable feelings of guilt and finally married him in spite of the therapist's caution that difficulties might arise during the marriage. The husband promised never to drink again. The patient would not consider, under any circumstances, refraining from the marriage, as she considered this her first and last chance of fulfillment of lifelong desires.

The marriage got along well for about six months, with occasional guidance from the therapist. Then, following a disagreement and disappointment, the husband had his first dipsomanic bout. The therapist helped the couple over such bouts four times in the course of one year. The patient's reaction to these bouts became more and more intense, and when it became obvious that the husband would not undergo treatment she became hostile and depressed. She refused to consider the possibility of separation and gradually merged into a psychotic state characterized by paranoid ideas and delusions, such as people talking about her or calling her obscene names. She finally had to be hospitalized. She had not recovered from her condition in two years of observation.

Comment.—The case illustrates particularly strikingly the following points: (*a*) The menopausal reaction had a lifelong background of intense disturbances in self-evaluation and of conflict. (*b*) The physiological disturbance played a very important part in the patient's psychopathological reaction. It intensified her feeling of lost hope and her feeling that she was losing the possibility of fulfilling lifelong desires. It further resulted in a frenzied attempt to gain those goals and a feeling of hostility, deficiency, rejection, and worthlessness over the lack of fulfillment. (*c*) In spite of previously successful psychotherapy and replacement therapy the patient had a psychotic breakdown when a new life situation shattered her fulfillment and threw her into intense conflicts of hostility and sexual guilt.

The desire for sexual activity and the ability to reach an orgasm persists as a rule in the woman after the onset of menopause. In the man the onset of sexual changes is much less definite as to time, but when it sets in there is a definite decline in potency. This too may require adjustment in the psychological sphere, just as menopause requires adjustment by the woman. At present there is an active hormone—testosterone (3)—available to correct a deficiency if that is desired and advisable. About twenty years ago an operation which consisted of ligation of the vasa deferentia (Steinach) had a brief popularity. This operation leads to a hypertrophy of the internal secretory cells in the testes and to a brief recurrence of potency, lasting about three months. The operation was discontinued because of its merely temporary effect. The following brief case report illustrates the emotional problems that may be connected with the decline in potency.

Case IV   An 80-year-old man who was of exceptional intelligence and breadth of knowledge became moody and felt inadequate because of decline in his potency. He had never had a serious psychoneurotic or character disturbance, at least overtly. He had always had a need, however, to be right and to appear perfect. The decline in potency was therefore a serious blow to him. He had the operation performed, and there was a three months' restitution of his potency. During these three months he felt happy; then the decline set in again. His depressive reaction now was quite severe. He lost his appetite and was disinclined to see people. It persisted until his death six months later.

D. DISTURBANCES OF THE CIRCULATORY SYSTEM

Disturbances here are best grouped under two main headings: (i) Arterial Hypertension; (ii) General Arteriosclerosis with Special Local Accentuation, resulting in (a) coronary disease of the heart or (b) sclerosis of the cerebral blood vessels. Disturbances under these headings will be discussed in detail. Two other disturbances less frequently encountered will be mentioned first.

Intermittent claudication (limping) is due to sclerosis and narrowing of the blood vessels of the leg muscles. As Mittelmann and

Wolff (12) have shown clinically and experimentally, anxiety and emotional conflict are accompanied by spasms of the blood vessels of the extremities. Spasm from this source aggravates the limping.

Aneurism of the aorta due to arteriosclerosis is a condition which also may be accompanied by psychosomatic disturbances, mainly because of the patient's refusal to accept limitations his condition places on his efficiency.

CASE V   A 59-year-old man suffered from general arteriosclerosis. Many of the peripheral vessels were hard and tortuous. The most important finding on X-ray examination was the widening of the arch of the aorta. He complained of vague pains and discomfort in the chest and in the abdomen. He was an excitable individual, very proud, readily taking offense. He had been that way most of his life. He felt very resentful of the fact that because of his advancing age and physical limitations he was not able to get or hold jobs as well as in his youth. He was a machinist, and his opportunities for employment were narrowing with age. He had enough money saved to live on, but he did not want to retire, nor did he want to accept any limitations on his work. Whenever he was thus upset his symptoms were worse. He purchased on his own a so-called "magnetic belt." This was a mechanical appliance that he could buy in a drugstore. It was a wired belt which became magnetic if plugged into the lighting system. He was much impressed by the fact that hairpins and other metallic objects stuck to its wall and insisted that it had curative effects on him. The physician's reasoning in this respect had no effect on him. He did not respond openly to psychotherapy. He could not accept the idea that he was reacting emotionally to physical difficulties and insisted that his complaints were all physical. Nevertheless, in spite of all his opposition, his emotional stress and physical complaints were reduced by about one-half.

I. ARTERIAL HYPERTENSION

Hypertension is commonly integrally connected with constellations of aggression (1, 6). This aggression may come from a variety of sources, such as frustrated dependency needs, hurt self-esteem, threat to a dominating position, and sexual injury. The personality type with functional hypertension, however, is apt to be one of two types:

a) A very active, lively, aggressive individual who organizes half a dozen different things, snipes at everybody, and fights for everything. In this type the aggression is most commonly connected with hurt self-esteem and threat to position and achievement. The aggression may be overt and excessive.

b) A well-behaved, outwardly calm, submissive individual. Persons of this latter type do not necessarily lack initiative and push, but in their behavior with human beings and situations they submit themselves to rules.

CASE VI A 48-year-old woman had been suffering from arterial hypertension (blood pressure 200/110, with fluctuations) for three years. At one period she had a congestive heart failure of moderate degree. She improved under medical treatment. She received bed rest, digitalis, and mercupurin. She used to talk spontaneously about all kinds of trivial problems to her internist, asking his opinions about her reactions. The internist referred her for psychotherapy. She expected from the analyst unqualified approval and always to be considered right in any disagreement with anybody. She objected to every interpretation that implied in any way that she had emotional problems. She discontinued treatment after six weeks, mainly because she could not tolerate the inferior position that the therapeutic relationship gave her in her emotional opinion. Nevertheless there was some improvement in her blood pressure (185/100).

She was a very active person—was a member of five organizations, took a leading role in three of them, argued actively for her opinion, and was sharp with people who contradicted her. In the treatment she argued her point with the analyst and criticized him whenever he disagreed with her. Although she justified her position all the time and would have objected to her reactions being called hostile or angry, there was very little doubt about her excessive drive, her need to maintain self-esteem, and her thinly disguised hostility when she was crossed.

CASE VII A 36-year-old patient applied for psychoanalytic treatment because of severe attacks of anxiety, accompanied by trembling, sweating, and feelings of faintness and dizziness. He was a salesman by occupation and rather efficient at his job. He was always well-behaved and polite, and although he had clear convictions he complied with the requests of his employer and of his girl friend, although they were both unreasonably critical, domineering, and abusive. His blood pressure was usually 170/110 at the first taking. Five or ten minutes later it often dropped down to 150/95, even on days when he was disturbed, and to 140/80 on days when he was not disturbed. The patient behaved in a well-mannered way in the treatment also; but it was not difficult to detect the angry tone in his voice when he was talking about his employer or his girl friend whenever he felt unfairly treated and humiliated. Nevertheless it took six months for him to recognize that he had been in a perpetual state of anger. During this whole period he had anxiety dreams; and following this period he had continual dreams in which he argued violently with people or actually attacked them. The patient's analysis lasted four years. He became a particularly able salesman with a higher earning capacity than he had ever had; his anxiety attacks disappeared; and as a rule his blood pressure did not rise above 130/80.

Comment.—It is to be remembered that the problems of neither of these patients were limited to that of hostility. Dependency needs, fear of closeness, fear of domination, fear of sexual injury were present in both. The dominant constellation in relation to the hypertension, however, seemed to be the hostile reaction.

The personality types described are not the exclusive ones that one finds in hypertension. At times even the schizoid personality with a dominant anxiety reaction can present hypertension.

II. GENERAL ARTERIOSCLEROSIS WITH SPECIAL LOCAL ACCENTUATION

a) Coronary disease of the heart.—The personality of individuals with coronary disease is also apt to be perfectionistic, driving, or at any rate ambitious, with a steady devotion to goals and purposes. Dunbar (6) has found that it is characteristic of patients with coronary disease that they finish school, get good marks, and hold on to jobs. Impulsive changes in life situations are infrequent. The conflict constellation connected with coronary disease itself is apt to be either resentment over failure, and thus over not living up to ideals, and over humiliation; or it is apt to be that of resentment over rejection with fear of abandonment and guilt over hostility and sexual strivings.

CASE VIII   A 61-year-old man was referred by his physician for psychiatric treatment. The patient had a variety of vascular symptoms. He had arterial hypertension, with blood pressure fluctuating between 170/90 and 210/110. Four years before applying for psychiatric treatment he had had an occlusion of one of the branches of the coronary artery. After that he had suffered from an attack of precordial pain. At times he had mild congestive failure of the heart. He had to take digitalis continually and carried nitroglycerine with him all the time after he started to work again. He worked on half-time with very little endurance, and discontinued all spontaneous activity such as writing articles, giving speeches, or conducting meetings. He was an educator of note.

Since his first attack of coronary thrombosis he had been afraid of dying, was very anxious, and continually asked his physician for reassurance but never felt secure for more than half an hour after he got it.

The analysis of this man was truly remarkable. Intellectually, as it turned out, he showed no gross aging, regained his active mind to everybody's surprise, and engaged in active writing again. Very briefly the psychological story was this: In the beginning of the analysis he had dreams in which he was in the synagogue on the day of atonement; he had to leave the synagogue, and saw his friend dead on the street; he was in search of a place, wandered aimlessly, and could not find it; nobody would recognize him or pay attention to him. The guilt and the feeling of abandonment, of "excommunication," was quite obvious in these dreams. Later he had dreams in which he attacked people who hurt him violently, and murdered them by choking them to death.

When he was a child, the oldest of six siblings, his father had been quite strict and was very abusive to his mother. The patient was deeply hurt by this and when he was about ten years old he got up on the chair, shook his fist in his father's face, and said, "You can't talk to my mother like that." After he got married at the age of 23 he was profoundly hurt by his wife's frigidity. She never refused him sexually, but, he said: "She didn't respond. She lay there like a piece of wood. I used to feel terribly hurt and desperate. She told me, 'What do you want of me? It doesn't mean anything.' But I felt deeply wounded. Sometimes at night I would look at her and get so angry that I wanted to choke her." The patient later hoped that by finding another woman he would have consolation. When another woman fell in love with him he felt

that she was a "redeeming angel." However, when he had opportunity to have sex relations with the woman he postponed it, and
never saw her again. Similar developments occurred with three
other women. Between the successive appearances of these women
the patient felt lonely. He would stand on the street corner at times
and invite a prostitute to sit with him in a restaurant and talk with
him, and then would pay the woman for the time. The patient's
ability to work and his interest in his work declined, particularly
after his wife became suspicious about the last of the women for
whom he had felt a sentimental attachment.

Comment.—The patient's resentment toward his wife in the
course of the marriage at first was conscious. Even at the time, the
problem about it was its terrific intensity and its murderous quality.
His wife's "coldness" represented to him rejection, a threat to his
manliness, a statement of his worthlessness. His self-evaluation
was disturbed, beginning with his clashes with his father in his
childhood. The betrayal by the woman (his mother) whom he had
risen to defend against his father was deadly. His wife's frigidity
represented to him such a betrayal. His guilt over his hostility and
over his attempt to get the recognition and love from other women
was intense. This continuous conflict unquestionably intensified
the results of the aging process and aggravated his vascular disease.
Even after the coronary accident occurred, he was restored to almost
full bloom of life at the advanced age of 61, through psychoanalysis. He even resumed sex relations with his wife after abstaining
from such activity for a year and a half.

b) Sclerosis of the cerebral blood vessels.—This group of disorders is of special interest because the alterations in the blood
flow and, in general, in the aging of the cells of the brain if it
reaches pathological extent have a direct influence on psychological
functioning. This direct influence naturally may be slight or it
may be marked. The symptoms can be grouped into three categories: (i) decline in intellectual functions, such as memory and
the ability to calculate, and decline in judgment; (ii) emotional
irritability or sentimentality; (iii) deterioration of social and
moral judgment and restrictions.

What is of further particular interest is that the individual then
reacts to these alterations in general emotional terms. The reactions in general may be of three types: (*a*) The individual is aware

THERAPY

The method of treatment and the therapeutic results have been indicated in connection with the various syndromes and the cases presented. A brief résumé will be given here and some general rules established.

1. Psychosomatic disturbances at an advanced age, which are of the same nature as disturbances at any age, have to be treated in the same way as at any age, namely, through interview therapy and, if advisable and necessary, through psychoanalysis (11). If the general mental capacity and the general emotional outlook show no gross aging, the results of psychotherapy are good and at times excellent. Not only may symptoms be relieved, but even character changes can be accomplished. The prejudice that old individuals give poor psychotherapeutic prognoses is unjustified. It is possible that, statistically, older people react less well to psychotherapy than young individuals; but in the writer's experience those people of advanced age who come for consultation and agree to treatment give good results.

2. Whenever there is a clear-cut organic ailment, it should receive the treatment required. Thus in menopausal psychiatric reactions, as well as in reactions to decline in male potency, substitution therapy is indicated. In coronary disease and hypertension, adequate rest, diet, and drug therapy are in place. Psychotherapy should be instituted as soon as convalescence sets in, if the patient has had a severe attack, and then should proceed parallel with the organic treatment. The general method of treatment is the same as psychotherapy in any situation, with, however, one warning: caution is of paramount importance concerning any topic likely to cause an emotional crisis. A topic such as hostility should be approached with great care, and it is very useful to warn the patient in advance when a risky topic is approached that it may disturb him and that physical symptoms may appear. This, together with making the interpretations rather noncommittal—the therapist gives tentative constructions, he emphasizes that there is ample time to come to a decision and that he is willing to drop and change his constructions—serves to prevent the crisis and to minimize the disturbance. If these rules are followed, the therapeutic results are good and at times excellent in such conditions as hypertension and coronary disease, with the complication even of mod-

erate or mild congestive failure of the heart. The organic pathology of course does not disappear, but the resultant functional disturbance is considerably reduced and for practical purposes may disappear for long periods of time.

3. Whenever there is organic brain damage the therapeutic possibilities are limited. The most that can be accomplished is to reduce the irritability and the moodiness through the patient-physician relationship (transference) and to give the patient at least some understanding of the nature of his reactions and thus diminish the blow to his self-esteem and the threat to his body image. Altering the patient's living arrangements so that he will not be exposed to the stress situations—and he often has to be persuaded to agree to this—further helps in this matter. If the organic damage to the brain is severe and if the psychotic symptoms are pronounced, psychotherapy accomplishes nothing permanent. Then institutional treatment is necessary or, if the patient is treated at home, the simple custodial care together with measures to diminish excitement and to insure sleep by hydro- and drug-therapy are the only possibilities.

SUMMARY

1. The process of aging and the individual's reaction to it have to be viewed in the cultural-social and economic setting of the individual. Aging means greater or lesser stress depending on whether the general cultural attitude toward older individuals is that of reverence and obedience or that of rebellion and competition. It is equally important, whether the individual is engaged in an occupation where continuous high speed and perfect physical prowess are required or he is economically secure, to retire from competition and stress when his powers begin to wane.

2. The aging process shows very great individual variations. It further shows variations as far as various organ systems are concerned even in the same individual. Some persons show very little aging outside of the diminution of the elasticity of certain tissues of the body. In other individuals the aging process may appear very early in certain organ systems. Of particular importance is the fact that psychologically or, better, emotionally the individual may show practically no aging even in advanced years. He may even branch out into entirely new activities.

3. The aging process requires emotional adjustment on the part of the individual. If sources of conflict, anxiety, and insecurity exist, then the results of the physiological or pathological aging lead to crisis. The threat that the aging process represents has the following components: (*a*) threat to the body image; (*b*) threat to self-evaluation, particularly self-esteem; (*c*) feelings of worthlessness and of being rejected; (*d*) punishment for hostile and sexual strivings.

4. The following organ systems are particularly significant from the point of view of psychosomatic disturbances: (*a*) general decline in the speed and endurance of the individual; (*b*) menopause and to a less extent decline in male potency; (*c*) disturbances of the vascular system and of circulation in general as it affects the blood pressure and the condition of the blood vessels, particularly the coronary arteries and the cerebral circulation; (*d*) disturbances of the auditory apparatus. The disturbances that result from these changes combine with emotional reactions to them, of the type already indicated in the previous section, to form a resultant syndrome.

5. The psychotherapeutic procedures in old age are the same as at any age in adulthood, with the addition that great caution is required whenever stormy subjects are approached. If there is definite or serious organic pathology, the physical treatment should be combined with psychotherapy. If there is no serious organic brain damage, the results of therapy are good and at times excellent.

REFERENCES

1. Alexander, F., and Saul, L. J. "Essential Hypertension," *Psychosom. Med.*, 1939, 1: 139
2. Cobb, S. *Borderlands of Psychiatry.* Cambridge, Mass.: Harvard University Press, 1948
3. Corner, G. W. *The Hormones and Human Reproduction.* Princeton: Princeton University Press, 1942
4. Cowdry, E. V. (ed.). *Problems of Ageing* (2d edition). Baltimore: Williams & Wilkins, 1942
5. DeAllende, I., Hartman, C., and Shorr, E. *A Comparative Study of the Vaginal Smears Cycle of the Rhesus Monkey and Human.* Washington, D.C.: Carnegie Institution of Washington, 1943
6. Dunbar, F. *Psychosomatic Diagnosis.* New York: Paul B. Hoeber, Inc., 1943

7. Henderson, D. K., and Gillespie, R. D. *A Textbook of Psychiatry* (6th edition). London: Oxford University Press, 1944

8. Kinsey, A. C., Pomeroy, W. B., and Martin, C. E. *Sexual Behavior in the Human Male.* Philadelphia: W. B. Saunders Co., 1948

9. Lawton, G. *New Goals for Old Age.* New York: Columbia University Press, 1943

10. ———. *Aging Successfully.* New York: Columbia University Press, 1946

11. Maslow, A. H., and Mittelmann, B. *Principles of Abnormal Psychology* (rev. edition). New York: Harper & Bros., 1951

12. Mittelmann, B., and Wolff, H. "Emotions and Skin Temperature: Observations on Patients During Psychotherapeutic (Psychoanalytic) Interviews," *Psychosom. Med.,* 1943, 5: 211

13. Papanicolaou, G. N., and Shorr, E. "The Action of Ovarian Follicular Hormone in the Menopause as Indicated by Vaginal Smears," *Amer. Jour. Obstet. Gynecol.,* 1936, 31: 806

14. Phillips, W. C. *Diseases of the Ear, Nose, and Throat.* Philadelphia: Davis Co., 1927

15. Ripley, H. S., and Wolff, H. G. "Life Situations, Emotions, and Glaucoma," *Psychosom. Med.,* 1950, 12: 215

16. Shorr, E. "Menopause," *Bull. N.Y. Acad. Med.,* 1940, 16: 453

17. Smith, H. "Electroshock Treatment in the Psychoses," *Amer. Jour. Psychiatry,* 1942, 98: 558

18. Wechsler, D. *The Measurement of Adult Intelligence* (3d edition). Baltimore: Williams & Wilkins, 1944

Chapter XVI

PSYCHOTHERAPY IN THE OLDER INDIVIDUAL

Fred V. Rockwell

This chapter deals with the treatment of all disorders of personality as they occur in the older individual and includes the organic-reaction types as well as major and minor functional disorders.

The first requisite for sound psychotherapy of the aging person is a knowledge of what is normal from the standpoint of somatic processes, personality changes, and special life situations which are common to the period of transition from maturity to old age. The process of aging in an individual is best measured objectively by the decline in his various functions at all levels of integration.

We normally reach the peak of our abilities in the third decade of life, following which there is a steady decline until death. Viewed in this light, aging actually begins between the ages of twenty and thirty. However, in most cases, aging factors do not play a dynamic role in the production of personality disorders until the fifth decade. This is so because it is the subjective factor of becoming aware of one or more of the concomitants of the aging situation that seems to be of primary importance dynamically, and it is in the fifth decade that many persons suddenly become aware of growing older. They may be disturbed by physical changes, chief among which are baldness or graying of hair, skin changes, decay and loss of teeth, menopause, and decrease of general energy and endurance. Social changes brought about by the deaths of friends and relatives within one's own age group, the awareness of aging in acquaintances one has not seen in years, and difficulty in obtaining new positions are other factors frequently encountered. Parents who have been overly attached to children are usually upset when sons and daughters leave home to marry; during the present war the entrance of a son into the Armed Forces has been frequently observed to precipitate personality difficulties in this type of parent. Gradual changes due to aging in an individual may be obvious to others in the environment but not to the individual. Such an individual may then be confronted with attitudes and actions on the part of others which may become disquieting and bewildering. Many personality disorders are precipitated by changes in work (including promotion and demotion) or in living conditions (e.g., moving to a new home or community after years of stability).

The somatodynamic and sociodynamic factors which are characteristic of the aging situation must be evaluated in terms of the special personality changes common to individuals passing through this period of life. Wechsler (12) and Miles (10) have shown that general intelligence decreases steadily after the third decade, and that certain mental abilities decline much more rapidly than others. General information, comprehension, and vocabulary hold up quite well, while attention, concentration,[1] and abstract reasoning decline with fair rapidity. In the field of emotions, anxiety is more easily aroused, owing to lessened security. Confidence is more easily shaken in one's physical and personality fitness and in one's ability to deal successfully with changing social and economic situations. A need for greater security leads to protective attitudes, to a tendency to hold on to what one has obtained, and to increased caution and indecision. Decreasing physical security leads to a greater interest in bodily functions, with attention to minor discomforts which would previously have been ignored. The most striking change seen in the personality organization is a loss of plasticity, with resulting unbending and rigid attitudes. Such attitudes may then lead to conflicts which a more pliable person could avoid by accepting the inevitable or by modifying strivings or goals.

During the aging period there may occur an intensification of interest in religion, which sometimes results in attraction to a particular cult. Sexual desires which have been consciously controlled or repressed during maturity seem to become stirred up and to threaten the security of many people during their fifth decade. A transient period of homosexual stirrings is not uncommon in this decade, even in well-adjusted individuals who never develop any

---

[1] These words are used according to the definitions given in Warren's *Dictionary of Psychology* (11), viz.:

Attention—"The process of focusing certain portions of an experience so that they become relatively more vivid." "Two kinds of attention are usually distinguished: (a) primary—passive, involuntary, spontaneous, automatic, instinctive, or reflexive; and (b) secondary—active, or voluntary."

Concentration—"The centering of attention on certain parts of an experience."

outspoken personality disorder. Promiscuity impulses and desire for sexual adventure arise with relative frequency and are often a source of varying degrees of uneasiness, anxiety, or guilt (3). In other persons previously repressed anal-sadistic strivings may become prominent. These may express themselves in a displacement of sexual interest to the anal region, and in mildly sadistic love play, or may lead to that personality reaction which one connects with repressed anal-sadistic strivings (1).

Menopause to some women is a relief; but to others it is a threat, representing the end of sexual attractiveness or reproductive usefulness. An attitude of expectancy of involutional difficulties may play a role in its actual occurrence. The role of purely endocrinologic factors in the psychobiology and psychopathology of the menopausal period is unknown. It is more than likely that biological changes of the menopause function as psychodynamic factors rather than as intrinsic somatodynamic factors in the production of personality difficulties at this time. On growing older the average person has an increased need for self-dependence. Persons who during maturity never developed a satisfactory self-dependence may in the aging period become almost entirely dependent upon others, particularly their mates or their children. In this general setting of socio-economic insecurity one sees mild suspiciousness based on guilt feelings or feelings of inadequacy.

The foregoing personality changes are the most important normal prototypes for the major as well as the minor psychopathological reactions of the aging period. These considerations and much of the ensuing discussion of psychopathological syndromes are based upon the previous work of Diethelm and Rockwell (7).

It is convenient to divide the patients encountered during the aging period into six categories:

1. Previously well-integrated people, free from hereditary taint and from organic cortical damage.

2. People who avoid any outspoken personality disorder up to the aging period by developing a system of neurotic defenses, which remain adequate during maturity but break down during the difficult fifth and sixth decades. Such defenses often take the form of rigidity of personality or of various other personality reactions of a less obvious nature.

3. Persons who also had no previous circumscribed personality disorders but have over many years exhibited quantitative or qualitative deviations in various personality functions that might be regarded as the forerunners of more clear-cut and circumscribed reaction types. In this group we find the sexually maladjusted, persons with compulsive personality traits, persons who experience anxiety with unusually little provocation, the superficially outgoing, shallow and egocentric type of person, persons characterized by an exaggerated need for self-assertion coupled with an over-concern about the opinions of others, and unusually seclusive, day-dreaming individuals. When one of this group develops his first circumscribed personality disorder in the aging period, the reaction is generally a sweeping one of a major character, and takes a form determined by the previous personality deviation.

4. Recurrent affective disorders, and schizophrenic, psychoneurotic, and psychopathic reactions are correspondingly modified as the individual passes into the aging period; and our understanding of the psychobiology of aging may well be applied in the treatment of these patients.

5. A special group of manic-depressive psychoses occurring for the first time in the later life period, studied by Doty (8). In many of these patients the personality organization seemed to be consistent with the general type of personality make-up that has been described as frequently observed in manic-depressive cases. Doty's patients showed a high incidence of personality disorders in the family background, suggesting an important hereditary tendency of a somewhat specific type in that it becomes manifest in affective illness occurring in later life.

6. Organically determined psychopathological reactions.

I. TREATMENT IN GENERAL

The word psychotherapy in this article is used in its broadest sense, and includes: direct influences brought to bear on psychodynamic factors; the management of the patient-physician and nurse-patient relationship; the adjustment of the work of the patient, including occupational therapy; planned recreation; and dealing with problems of group adjustment. To these may be added the judicious use of chemical and physical sedation as an integrated part of the total therapy. These measures will be discussed briefly from a general standpoint and subsequently more specifically in connection with special psychopathological syndromes.

The direct influences on dynamic factors are brought to bear during the interview with the patient, starting from an analysis of the complaint and of situational factors, and utilizing suggestion, advice, and explanation. In the age group with which we deal, free association techniques are less valuable than in younger persons. Where analysis of dynamic factors is indicated, it is preferable to make use of the technique of distributive analysis and synthesis proposed and outlined by Adolf Meyer and discussed in some detail by Diethelm (5). This consists of an analysis of all the factors involved, starting from the complaint, and taking into consideration the psychodynamic and somatic features, the situational conditions, and the constitutional make-up. Each interview is terminated with a constructive formulation synthesizing the material covered. The analysis is distributed along the lines suggested by a careful anamnesis and by the subjective needs of the patient as they become apparent during treatment. The physician assumes full obligation for the twenty-four-hour day of the patient and utilizes data collected currently by nurses or other observers. The reader is referred to the original article for details regarding the method.

For the patient who continues to work during treatment it is necessary to evaluate the nature of the work carefully and consider whether it should be modified or curtailed. This must be decided on the basis of the psychopathological findings and their variations in the course of the working day. The patient unable to carry on his normal work should be provided with some substitute in the form of occupational therapy. This should serve three main functions—to distract the patient from painful preoccupations, to provide satisfaction from carrying out various steps in the work itself, and to provide further satisfaction from the completion of the project successfully.

To plan recreation successfully as part of treatment the physician must know what facilities are available in the community, what recreational interests are current in the social group to which the patient belongs, and what suits the individual's needs, interests, and skills. In planning a program of recreation with a patient, one considers his intellectual tastes and needs, his aesthetic interests, and the possibilities for entertainment at theaters or sporting events. Participation in athletics is encouraged to the extent that the physical condition of the patient and his normal mode of living indicate.

Occupation and recreation also serve in a measure to satisfy the group needs of the patient in so far as he works or plays with others. An optimum amount of contact with others is important in the program of treatment of the older individual. It works best to provide the patient with opportunities to fit into a group of mixed ages. Otherwise he may witness the gradual decimation of his associates, with resultant narrowing of interests and social outlets. It is a fact that many elderly men survive happily for relatively long periods because they are able to keep alive their interest through maintaining contact with business associates. It suffices for such men to take a relatively small part in the business in which they were formerly active. One such patient known to the writer finds a good deal of pleasure and satisfaction from visiting for one hour each day the business he formerly built up and managed. He discusses the business with his son, who now runs it, but takes no active part, and actually enjoys most the personal contacts with his loyal former employees. In the sicker patient who must be attended by a nurse, housekeeper, or relative, it is highly important for the physician to be sensitive to the relation between the patient and the attendant, as well as to the patient-physician relationship. The attendant who has been on the case too long tends to develop a possessive and domineering attitude toward the patient which can lead to unfortunate reactions on the part of the patient, tending to prolong invalidism and to promote rut formation.

Adequate psychotherapy must take into account all the foregoing considerations, and the physician must see to it that the twenty-four-hour day of the patient fits into a general plan of treatment.

In this presentation it seems most appropriate to emphasize the psychotherapeutic approach to those psychopathological syndromes which are most characteristic of individuals in the aging period. Treatment is based primarily upon the psychopathology presented by the patient. The principles to be discussed apply equally well whether the patient is treated at home, in a psychiatric hospital, in a general hospital, in a c   scent home, or in some similar type of institution. The maj   opathological reactions will be considered first, since thei   nding leads easily to a grasp of the minor reactions ar   nically determined reactions.

II. PSYC   GICAL CONSIDERATIONS

The outstanding   ological reactions observed in the aging group are a   epressive and paranoic reactions. Anxiety is express   s forms, among which the most common are somatic   nild insecurity feelings, agitation, anxiety depressions   d panic phases, and depressions with markedly limit   d often little display of emotion ("frozen affect"). D   ntent often consists of feelings of hopelessness, futility   tion. Paranoic attempts at self-assertion, with their   amic factors, may lead only to transient suspicions, or may result in systematized delusions of persecutory, erotomanic, hypochondriacal, and jealousy types. Other important psychopathological reactions which may appear either as leading features or as complications are: apathy due to hopelessness, narrowed interests, or defeat; aversion to accepting illness or treatment due to humiliated pride, suspicion, and unbending personality make-up; and rut formation due to aversion, resentment, paranoid self-defense, hopelessness, and narrowed interests.

Many patients develop a marked thinking disorder which leads to confusion, bewilderment, and perplexity. A combination of depressive thinking disorder, of anxiety, and of psychobiological aging factors produces defects in attention and concentration, and may result in subjective and objective retention difficulties. An exact knowledge of the extent and type of thinking disorder is applied to psychotherapy in two ways. In the first place, as has been mentioned, in all patients it is necessary for the physician to plan an optimum routine of daily activities. The patient is encouraged to assume as much responsibility as possible for ordinary self-care. He is encouraged to take part in group recreational activities and in occupational therapy. It is the duty of the physician to outline to nurses how much prompting and reminding are indicated on the basis of the thinking disorder. Likewise it is up to the physician to plan for recreational activities and occupational-therapy work which will be difficult enough to absorb the patient's attention but which will not make an impossible demand upon his ability to pay attention, concentrate, retain, and recall. In addition to planning these aspects of treatment on the basis of the thinking disorder, the physician must modify his own formulations to the patient in such a way that they can easily be grasped. Obviously, if a retention disorder is present, it is of little or no use to attempt to treat symptoms by any extensive analysis of involved dynamic factors. Factual statements of reassurance may have to be repeated many times. In this connection, one must be sure to distinguish between an inability to retain and an insatiable neurotic need on the part of the patient. Excessive dependence on reassurance is merely increased by giving in to the patient's demands.

The leading emotional feature most often encountered is marked anxiety, which, in rigid and self-assertive personalities, especially when aversion is present, may express itself in fretfulness and peevishness. By aversion is meant the emotional reaction of being unwilling or unable to accept a situation or certain persons. It involves such complex emotions as dislike, antipathy, disgust, and varying degrees of resentment. Aversion may be directed to the patient's life situation, his illness, or the hospital, including one or more of the professional staff attending him. Resentment and aversion color many depressive reactions, and lead readily to suspiciousness. Without judicious management, these reactions of aversion and resentment result too often in rut formation and chronicity. To prevent such developments in the rigid and self-assertive person, special attention must be given to an individualized modification of the hospital routine, taking into account special sensitivities, and making it clear to the patient that consideration is given to him as an individual. The first psychotherapeutic task is to establish a workable rapport with physicians and nurses. Nurses who work too long on one floor with a similar group of patients may become somewhat arbitrary and dictatorial. It is helpful for the physician to spend a little time with the nurse discussing the special individual needs and sensitivities of the patient, and it is a good hospital policy to shift nurses to a different type of floor periodically. With the patient, it is helpful to discuss neutral topics and to avoid contradictions and arguments. Early respectful attention to the patient's physical condition and somatic complaints can lay the foundation for a sound rapport. If visits by relatives stir up demands to leave the hospital, it may be necessary to exclude visitors. In the case of an affective illness with morning-evening mood variations, interviews should be planned for the late afternoon when the patient is at his best, aversion is minimal, and rapport is most easily established. When, in spite of attempts at prevention, aversion and resentment occur, the physician must watch himself closely, lest he react with counter hostility. Aversion is especially prone to occur in the setting of marked disorders of thinking such as frequently occur in the later life depressions. When perplexity, suspiciousness, or thinking difficulties are present, every move should be explained carefully in a manner which is intelligible and acceptable to the patient. Even in the case of a stuporous reaction, it pays to explain such necessary procedures as tube feedings before they are given.

In many patients, resentment is primarily directed toward the first hospital into which their illness pushed them. It not infrequently happens that what appears to be a discouragingly chronic illness, with marked rut formation due to aversion and resentment, clears up dramatically upon transfer to another hospital or after relatives remove the patient against the physician's advice. Any attempt to study the dynamic factors involved in the attitude of aversion should be delayed until the psychosis in which it occurs has disappeared. The chief aim is to help the patient through his suffering with a minimum of pressure, urging, and nagging. Where paranoid delusions exist, one can do no better than follow the advice of Meyer (9), who stated that it is well for physician and nurse occasionally to express their own sane standpoint but, as a rule, to leave it to implication; they must make it clear that they and the patient must agree to disagree; and they must demonstrate to the patient by their actions that such a relationship is possible. For a more complete discussion of aversion the reader is referred to the original paper of Diethelm (6).

General states of fear, or expressions of fear in connection with delusions (especially fear of insanity and delusions of doom), are frequent, and are best understood in terms of the special life situation of the patient. The development of a state of maximal fear—a full-fledged panic reaction—is a not infrequent occurrence in the later-life affective disorders. Such a state is one of maximal suffering for the patient, and presents a very difficult treatment problem. Hence it is most important to anticipate and prevent the development of panic reactions.

Diethelm (4) states: "Panic is not merely a high degree of fear, but a fear based on prolonged tension, with a sudden climax which is characterized by fear, extreme insecurity, suspiciousness, and a tendency to projection and disorganization. The projections are delusions of persecution and auditory hallucinations; the disorganization may lead to a schizophrenic picture." The same author found homosexual, heterosexual, and autoerotic tendencies in various panic reactions. In general, it may be said that the most frequent dynamic factors behind panic reactions are stirred-up sexual desires which are unacceptable to the patient and represent a threat to him. Owing to the psychobiology of the aging period, we find homosexual strivings relatively easily aroused. Particularly in men, rectal manipulations such as digital examinations, rectal temperature taking, and giving enemas have frequently been observed to precipitate full-fledged panic reactions. In most of our patients who have no special physical complications we have found that routine axillary temperatures are adequate. A carefully planned diet, supplemented by the regular use of mild laxatives, will generally make the repeated use of enemas unnecessary. Where there is definite medical indication for a rectal examination, it has been found best to have this done by a physician other than the one treating the patient. In general, it is a safe rule to avoid when possible any physical manipulations which may stir up unacceptable sexual urges, whether these be homosexual or otherwise.

In addition to the consideration which must be given to physical manipulations if we are to avoid panics, careful judgment must be exercised in regard to the discussion of sexual topics. The patient may have a need to confess what he considers improper sexual acts or impulses to the physician. In many cases, such a confession does not relieve guilt and anxiety but may be followed by suspiciousness and the development of frank paranoid projections. Such patients may also wish to confess to a spouse, and this must be actively discouraged for obvious reasons. Many women in this age group show rather marked erotic tendencies, which may be overlooked unless the physician is on the alert for this type of behavior. A premature sexual discussion by a male physician with such a patient may result in the development of a full-fledged sexual excitement, with marked disorganization of behavior. Such an excitement often responds remarkably well to barbital, given in doses of approximately 0.15 gram three to four times daily.

When it is evident that a patient suffers from anxiety in connection with sexual preoccupations, and when a direct discussion seems dangerous, the physician should relieve the anxiety by other means. One may utilize sedative hydrotherapy, repeated doses of barbital of approximately 0.15 gram three to four times daily, and distraction by means of occupational and recreational therapy.

It is often possible to reassure a patient who has sexual concerns, without forcing him into a confession, by the expedient of talking with him in a general way about the common sexual problems of people in his own age group, emphasizing the universality of the occurrence of such problems and the possibilities of successful solution. The analysis of sexual dynamic factors in the more sweeping types of personality disorders, if indicated at all, is carried out cautiously during the period of convalescence.

It is to be expected that hypochondriacal concerns and delusions occur frequently in this period of general body insecurity. Body overconcern and marked anxiety are expressed in complaints of head sensations, fatigue, serious disorders of the eyes, teeth, or skin, and inability to eat or defecate. The complaints of the hypochondriacal patient are treated with respect, and he is assured that he will be studied carefully from the standpoint of possible organic disease. He is given a thorough physical examination, followed as soon as possible by any special laboratory tests which the physician needs in order to be certain in his own mind that an organic basis for the complaints does not exist. The results of the tests and examinations are then carefully conveyed to the patient. When the patient is informed that no organic disease exists, it is helpful to explain further that this does not mean the physician feels that his discomforts are imaginary but, on the contrary, that he appreciates and understands the patient's distressing sensations. He goes on to explain the various sensations as due to a combination of the effects of emotion on various aspects of bodily functions combined with an increased tendency on the part of the patient to pay attention to bodily sensations that would be ignored in the setting of a normal state of emotions. It is further formulated that treatment will be directed at the underlying emotional disturbance, ignoring the secondary symptoms of bodily discomforts. The patient is then given the responsibility of combating his tendency to pay too much attention to body sensations. This re-educational procedure succeeds when the patient begins to become aware of a train of preoccupations early enough to throw them off before he is too much involved in their grip.

Having satisfied himself as to the physical condition of the patient by suitable studies, the physician must then be prepared to stand his ground. If he makes the mistake of giving in and repeating laboratory examinations merely to satisfy the patient, he at once implants the strong suggestion that he himself is in doubt and thereby markedly impairs the therapeutic adequacy that his suggestions might have carried. In some patients the hypochondriacal concerns will persist with delusional or near-delusional strength in spite of one's most careful efforts. When this situation arises, one must then apply the same principles that have been previously formulated for dealing with paranoid delusions. In individuals with strong neurotic features, somatic complaints are repeatedly flung at the physician in the form of a challenge. This phenomenon is related to aversion, and occurs in proud sensitive persons who are unable to accept the fact that they are suffering from a personality disorder and who defend themselves by attacking bitterly the physician as one incompetent to discover and cure the real, i.e., the organic illness from which they need to believe they suffer. Such a situation is a heavy tax on the patient-physician relationship, and the physician must frequently review his own emotional responses to such patients. The hypochondriacal patient, like any other, may develop in the course of treatment various new physical diseases. The physician must therefore be doubly alert for unaccountable changes in the physical condition of the patient. Should these arise, and should on this account additional tests, studies, and treatments be necessary, these procedures must be carefully explained to the patient so that he may understand clearly on a factual basis the need for a seeming change in policy of treatment.

A reaction of apathy is frequently observed in the older individual. In these patients it is not related to autistic withdrawal, as in schizophrenics, but is explainable by narrowing of interests, persistence of dominant interests, or feelings of futility. Apathy is a serious symptom, since it may readily lead to more or less lasting deterioration of behavior, and it is treated only with difficulty. A careful review of the life history is necessary, searching for previous interests. Occupational therapy is planned in a manner calculated to revive such previous interests. Such interests often provide a good neutral topic for discussion, and the talking in itself may be of some value as a stimulant to their revival. If initial attempts fail, owing, e.g., to depth of depression, the question may profitably be revived at a later stage in the illness—and should not be discarded, but rather put aside. Feelings of futility and inadequacy are best treated by a careful analysis with the patient of various past successes in life, making use of his own statements to point out to him the features of his personality that are assets or potentially so. It is necessary to be able to assist the patient to form concrete plans for a constructive and satisfactory existence during the remainder of his life span, and this can be done only by utilizing a sound knowledge of his capabilities and assets, based on past performance and an understanding of his personality as it now stands. Deliberately irritating an apathetic person can hardly be justified, but, at times, irritations unintentionally brought about result in a dramatic interruption of apathy. If the physician weathers the storm of the patient's outburst, he may then achieve a rapport previously unattainable.

In reactions of elation in an older person there is practically never a pure mood of elation. Underlying anxiety, fear, depressive trends, and hypochondriasis are frequently encountered. Irritability and anger often are based on underlying anxiety and fear, and attention to the complicating emotions does much to relieve difficult nursing problems caused by the combativeness, assaultiveness, and other distressing forms of behavior to which the fearful manic is subject. When anxiety or fear are present in any considerable degree, it has been found useful to use repeated doses of barbital. This is in direct contrast to the treatment of younger manics, in whom sedatives produce undesirable emotional reactions. The difference seems to lie in the factor of anxiety, which is seen in almost all aging manics but is not prominent in younger elated patients. Erotic features are often marked in the aging manic. The tendency to play up to the opposite sex in an erotic fashion should never be mistaken for evidence of a desirable positive transference phenomenon.

It is not to be expected that hysterical reactions, phobic disorders, and obsessive-compulsive neuroses will make their initial appearance in a well-integrated person as late as the fifth decade except when the personality becomes disturbed through cortical damage (usually due to cerebral arteriosclerosis, syphilitic changes, or brain tumor). For the same reasons a dissociative schizophrenic illness is not expected to start so late in life, except in connection with toxic or neurogenic factors or as an exacerbation of an old schizophrenic illness. When we have encountered, for example, a compulsion neurosis becoming manifest for the first time in the aging period, the patient, upon careful study, was always found to have cortical damage or else to belong to the group previously described, the members of which have exhibited for years compulsive personality traits. The same considerations apply to other psychoneurotic pictures observed in the aging group.

When the aging person presents a syndrome of psychoneurotic symptoms, he is generally affected in more sweeping and disabling fashion than the younger psychoneurotic. For this reason and because of other factors related to age, an orthodox psychoanalytic approach is usually not considered desirable. There are exceptions to this rule, and competent modern psychoanalysts have found it possible to treat a limited number of aging psychoneurotics, using more or less modified psychoanalytic techniques. It is more often possible to undertake a distributive analysis and synthesis with emphasis upon current attitudes and reactions to situational factors. In these cases, one must be on the alert for evidence of an underlying depression, and for the presence of thinking difficulties. The foregoing considerations may be considered the most essential factors in determining the modifications necessary in the treatment of psychoneurotic reactions in the older person.

Before going on to discuss minor psychopathological reactions, it seems advisable to summarize briefly what has been discussed so far. The dynamic factors of the aging situation and the psychobiology of the aging individual have been discussed briefly, with an effort to incorporate well-established advances in our knowledge. Any attempt to formulate principles of therapy based on so-called disease entities has been discarded, and attention has been focused on psychopathological entities. Principles of treatment have been formulated on the basis of our present understanding of both dynamic factors and the phenomenology of the clinical pictures encountered.

In most textbooks of psychiatry, personality disorders are divided into psychoses, which are considered to be the major reaction types, and the psychoneuroses, which are said to be the minor reaction types. This does not express a scientifically valid distinction, and has only a limited use as a practical distinction. It is the viewpoint of the writer that an illness is major when it is so sweeping in character as to interfere seriously with the normal way of living of the patient, and it is minor when it permits the individual to function with efficiency such that he can carry on at least a modified routine of normal living. It is incorrect to say that a personality disorder is minor if it involves only a part of the personality. Otherwise, the individual with paranoia must be considered to have a minor illness, since most parts of his personality function quite well. The patients who develop minor personality disorders in the aging period are generally found to have been previously fairly well integrated and to have little if any direct heredity of psychopathology. The group of minor reactions studied by the author and Diethelm (7) dealt chiefly with mild anxiety or depressive reactions in a previously well-adjusted personality; also somatic symptoms related to anxiety and resentment were frequently encountered. These patients did not utilize repression, dissociation, and substitutive mechanisms; the somatic symptoms were usually more direct physiological responses to emotions of which the patients were more or less conscious.

III. CASE DISCUSSION

The following case illustrates well several of the principles involved in the therapy of the minor psychopathological reactions of the aging period.

The patient, a 56-year-old married farmer of Polish origin, was admitted to the Medical Pavilion of the New York Hospital on September 2, 1943. He appeared first in the Surgical Out-Patient Department, August 10, 1943, complaining of nausea,

vomiting, epigastric pain, occasional dizzy spells, pain and paraes-
thesiae in the right arm and hand, and anorexia with loss of 40
pounds over a two-year period. A diagnostic work-up was initiated.
X-ray examination of the stomach and duodenum revealed gas-
troptosis. He was placed on a six-feeding, gastric-soft diet and given
belladonna and supplementary vitamins. On the day of admission,
in the course of a gastric analysis he developed a severe reaction
to histamine with right frontal headache, profuse sweating, weakness, fibrillations in the muscles of the right chest, arm, and leg,
and transient sensory changes over the right side of the body from
the lower chest down. He was at once admitted to the Medical
Pavilion. On September 3 a spinal tap was normal except for the
presence of a few RBC (89 per cu. mm.). During the next three
days, the poorly defined sensory changes disappeared entirely. He
was continued on the gastric diet, which relieved his abdominal
pain and vomiting entirely. However, he presented a marked problem of aversion and resentment. He was irritable; he complained
that he was weaker than before admission, that he was not receiving
enough to eat, that he had been even more weak and dizzy since
a vena puncture done at the time of admission, and that he had
suffered from headaches since his lumbar puncture; and he was
on the verge of leaving the hospital against advice in a very dis-
gruntled mood.

On September 9, he was seen in psychiatric consultation. At
this time, it had been discovered that he had advanced localized
osteoarthritis of the region of the fifth and sixth cervical vertebrae,
presumably explaining to some extent the pains in the arm and
hand of which he complained.

When interviewed, he was quite tense and was preoccupied with
the many somatic complaints noted above. He was moderately
averse to the hospital situation, and tended to project the blame
for his symptoms upon various diagnostic procedures and his diet.
He was allowed to express his views freely, without interruption
or argument. This resulted in a noticeable relief of his tension;
he became more friendly, and with a minimum of encouragement
began to talk about his life in general. The following facts
emerged:

He was born and raised on a farm in Poland, and later learned
the trade of baking. He came to the United States at 19, being un-

able then to read or write. He educated himself to the extent that he can read a newspaper, write simply, and speak English adequately. Up to the age of 24, he worked as a baker, then as a migratory farm hand, traveling widely. At 30 he came to New York and married a Scotch domestic, a plain sensible woman, who was a loyal and devoted wife. They both worked, and at 35 he bought a farm in New Jersey. He worked an average of sixteen to seventeen hours daily, never missed a day's work, prospered, and about two years ago invested $2,500 of his savings in War Bonds. This resulted in his prosperity becoming widely known in his small community. For three years it had been increasingly difficult for him to get any help on his farm and he had spent more and more time at work, often not stopping to eat adequately. Two years ago, he and his wife were saddled for six months with the care of a psychotic child of some distant relative. In the setting of increased strain of work due to lack of farm help and a tense home situation due to the presence of the psychotic child, he began to develop epigastric distress. About six months before admission, a widow, to whom he delivered milk, began to make sexual advances to him. According to him she was quite repulsive physically, and he was disgusted at her advances but at the same time found himself stirred up sexually with an unwanted desire to submit to her enticements. She told him that he would never recover from his stomach trouble until he went to her; she followed him around town and finally went to his wife and asked the wife to divorce him. With this he became more nervous, lost his appetite completely, began to vomit frequently, and was disturbed by peculiar sensations in the lower abdomen and on top of his head. He became depressed and anxious, could not concentrate, and had such marked difficulty with memory that he had to write down everything. The situation and his symptoms became so intolerable that he had finally sold his farm and come to New York to seek treatment.

In discussing his personality he said that when younger he had been a very happy person who loved to be gay, laugh, and joke. He had possessed remarkable strength and vitality, of which he was very proud. He was shy and bashful with women until he had his first heterosexual experience at 27. He then found himself possessed of a strong sexual drive. When not working he could enjoy intercourse up to three times daily. On his farm he worked so hard he had little energy left, and had intercourse with his wife about once a week or every two weeks. He found her a satisfactory partner, although her desires occurred less frequently than his. They never used contraceptive measures; the failure of his wife to conceive had not troubled either of them consciously.

In the course of the interview the patient's complaints concerning his memory were utilized as a basis for carrying out formal testing of intellectual functions. He was found to be correctly oriented and was able to give an accurate chronological account of recent and remote past experiences. When he became aware of the more formal test situation involved in repeating words, digits, and a test story, he showed what we have observed in many anxious patients of the aging group, namely, a moderate defect of retention, without any tendency to confabulate. He was able to do simple calculations adequately, e.g., to calculate mentally, with fair speed, the cost of seven bottles of milk at fifteen cents per bottle.

As he became more at ease and developed a friendly relationship with the consultant, the latter pointed out to him that it was more than likely that his gastro-intestinal symptoms were related to the dynamic factors which he had discussed. He appreciated, in a common-sense way, that emotions can readily disturb digestive functions, and very little had to be said to crystallize his latent spontaneous insight. He was obviously markedly concerned over his promiscuity impulses. This anxiety was markedly alleviated by explaining to him that such stirrings at his age were within the field of normal personality problems. He was himself convinced that his best course was to avoid the disturbing female and to remain faithful to his wife. The writer assured him that he would be most comfortable if he lived up to his own moral and ethical standards but also assured him that he was in no way to blame himself for the fact that such wishes were aroused. He went on to discuss constructive plans for the future, which centered around the purchase of a small farm in Pennsylvania, and planning his work along less ambitious and driving lines. The interview was concluded with a review of his minor complaints against the hospital situation. By this time these had narrowed down to the fact that he wasn't getting enough to eat on his gastric diet. This was at once changed to a high-caloric general diet, which he tolerated perfectly well. His complaint of pain in his shoulder and arm was now seen by him in its proper perspective, as a minor inconvenience. He was quite willing to accept the formulation that these pains were due to arthritis for which our treatments are far from perfect, and he was able to accept palliative treatment in the form of physiotherapy and occasional doses of salicylates. Subsequent to the psychiatric consultation, which lasted about one hour, the patient lost completely his aversion and resentment, and he remained cheerful and co-operative until his discharge on September 16.

This case illustrates many of the psychopathological features commonly encountered in the aging individual as seen in general practice and on the general wards of any hospital. The leading features were: the somatic symptoms due to anxiety; the state of tension with mild depression and with thinking difficulties due to anxiety and depression in the setting of early cerebral arteriosclerosis; and the aversion reaction in the hospital due to anxiety and to initial failure to recognize and deal with the underlying psychodynamic factors. The minor character of the reaction and the fact that he had been in the past a relatively well-adjusted individual made it possible to deal directly with his sexual concerns, with resulting prompt relief from anxiety. This is in direct contrast to the major reaction types discussed, in whom sexual discussions at an early date often produce distressing results. The ability of the physician to convey reassurance is to a large extent dependent upon his own sound knowledge and understanding of the psychopathology of the condition with which he deals. The physician's own self-confidence or lack of self-confidence is conveyed unmistakably to the patient.

IV. CEREBRAL ARTERIOSCLEROTIC IMPLICATIONS

The remainder of this chapter will be devoted to a brief discussion of the application of psychotherapeutic principles to the organically determined reactions of the aging period. The most common of these, cerebral arteriosclerosis, will be used as a prototype for the general therapeutic considerations. The cases fall roughly into two groups:

1. The first group consists of patients who gradually develop simple arteriosclerotic deterioration, with varying degrees of impairment of intellectual functions, emotional lability, and a caricaturing of the previous personality. These patients are best cared

for at home. They lack any reserve strength in their homeostatic mechanisms, and delirious reactions are easily precipitated by minor physical ailments. They have a need to remain in familiar surroundings. They should have their activities planned, utilizing a flexible routine covering twenty-four hours of the day. Daytime activities should include exercise according to the patient's general health, also rest periods and, above all, some form of occupation, planned on the basis of previous interests.

It is highly important to understand the psychodynamic factors involved in the production of delirious reactions. The best experimental work on this topic has been done by Cameron (2). He writes, "The delirium [of senile patients] usually appears after retiring to sleep and clears soon after getting up the next day." He was able to produce delirium in senile patients by putting them in a darkened room for an hour during the daytime. These patients suffered from marked impairment of recent memory, which resulted in considerable impairment of the capacity to orient themselves. They could not retain the identity of members of the staff unless they saw them continually. They could not locate themselves in time. Their ability to keep themselves oriented in space depended upon the frequent refreshing of their spatial images by repeated direct visualization. When blindfolded, or placed in a darkened room, they rapidly lost their ability to orient themselves in space. This resulted in insecurity, emotional disturbances reflected in a rise in blood pressure, and the development of a full-fledged delirium.

These considerations explain why many senile patients get along well at home, where the familiarity of surroundings makes it easy to remain oriented in space, while they readily develop delirious reactions when removed from their home environment to a hospital. Hence follows the important therapeutic consideration that these patients should be kept in familiar surroundings whenever possible. If they must be hospitalized, their room should be simply arranged, they should be transferred from one bed to another as little as possible, and they should have frequent contact with the same personnel. At night, a light should be left burning in the room, at least while the patient is not sleeping soundly. Should the patient show signs of developing a delirium during the night, he should be seen by a familiar person.

In more advanced stages of senile and arteriosclerotic delirium we encounter restlessness and motility disturbances in the form of perseveration and stereotyped movements. If one studies the movements carefully, some form of occupational therapy can be devised which will involve similar monotonous, repeated movements, and this is possible in very advanced stages of deterioration. For example, it is very clear that it is more constructive to allow a patient to tear up rags into strips, to be used for making rugs, than to keep him in restraint because he would otherwise occupy himself tearing up hospital sheets. By a little exercise of imagination countless possibilities of utilizing motility disturbances in some simple form of occupational therapy can be developed.

2. The second group of the organic reaction types consists of the patients who, in the setting of varying degrees of cortical damage, develop in addition one of the functional reaction types of disorder. In some of these the organic changes seem to play an essential role in the psychopathology. Such patients generally show a depressive reaction, with bizarre somatic delusions of a nihilistic character, expansive depressive delusions (délire d'énormité), and often disturbances of perception (micromania). In others, the functional disorder, usually an affective reaction, is the leading feature, with the organic changes acting as complicating factors. The general principles of dealing with the psychopathologic syndromes encountered are the same as those outlined in the consideration of the purely functional disorders. In addition, one must bear in mind that distressing emotional states, in the presence of cortical damage, cause a marked increase in the thinking difficulties. One result of this has been discussed in considering the psychodynamics of deliria. In addition, difficulties in orientation, grasp, and retention easily lead to paranoid misinterpretations in situations the patient finds it difficult to understand, particularly in the setting of varying degrees of anxiety. Earlier in this chapter were set down the special considerations involved in the treatment of patients in the functional group who showed thinking disorders on the basis of depression, anxiety, and psychobiological aging factors. If one utilizes these principles along with special considerations for the prevention of delirious reactions, it is not too difficult to get the arteriosclerotic patient through an affective illness, and to return him to his home environment in a relatively comfort-

able condition in which he can enjoy a quiet and pleasant routine of living without becoming an undue burden upon his family.

V. SUMMARY

To summarize briefly, it may be said that the successful psychotherapy of the older individual depends upon planning all therapeutic procedures on the basis of a concrete and specific knowledge of the psychopathological syndromes with which one deals. With this end in view, it has been necessary to discuss in some detail our present knowledge of psychopathology from the standpoint of phenomenology and dynamic factors. The problems discussed are encountered frequently both in general practice and in the general hospital, as well as in a psychiatric hospital. The more complex situations outside the hospital should be treated by the specialist in psychiatry, but many of the simpler reactions may be handled by the general practitioner, generally to better advantage with the assistance of a little advice from the specialist. The specialist can be of particular assistance to the general practitioner by helping to plan a twenty-four-hour routine for the patient, based on the psychopathology, and by pointing out the relation of emotional factors to somatic complaints. In dealing with the older patient in the general hospital, the psychiatrist can be of particular help during the period of convalescence from various physical illnesses. It is during this period that the early arteriosclerotic may develop rut formation, with anxiety and hypochondriasis, a resentment reaction over his inability to return to work, or a reaction of apathy. It is the task of the psychiatric consultant to formulate plans to lead the patient through convalescence back to his normal way of living, avoiding if possible the complications just mentioned, and helping to deal with them if they arise. In the modern psychiatric hospital, with competent psychiatric nursing care and observation, and provision for occupational and recreational therapy, for group social activities, and for adequate physical care, the principles outlined in this chapter can be applied to their fullest extent.

REFERENCES

1. Abraham, K. "A Short Study of the Development of the Libido, Viewed in the Light of Mental Disorders," in his *Selected Papers on Psychoanalysis* (London: Hogarth Press, 1927)

2. Cameron, D. E. "Studies in Senile Nocturnal Delirium," *Psychiatric Quart.*, 1941, 15: 47–53
3. Deutsch, H. *Psychoanalyse der weiblichen sexual Funktionen. Neue Arbeiten zur ärztlichen Psychoanalyse*, Vol. 5. Leipzig: Internationaler psychoanalytischer Verlag, 1925
4. Diethelm, O. "Panic," *Arch. Neurol. Psychiatry*, 1932, 28: 1153–68
5. ———. "Investigations with Distributive Analysis and Synthesis," *ibid.*, 1936, 35: 467–86
6. ———. "Aversion and Negativism," *ibid.*, 1937, 37: 805–16
7. Diethelm, O., and Rockwell, F. V. "Psychopathology of Aging," *Amer. Jour. Psychiatry*, 1943, 99: 553–56
8. Doty, E. J. "A Study of Manic-Depressive Psychoses Occurring during the Later Life Period," *ibid.*, 1942, 98: 645–49
9. Meyer, A. "The Treatment of Paranoic and Paranoid States," in W. A. White and S. E. Jelliffe, *Modern Treatment of Nervous and Mental Diseases*. Philadelphia: Lea & Febiger, 1913, Vol. I, chap. 14, pp. 659–60
10. Miles, W. R. "Psychological Aspects of Ageing," in E. V. Cowdry (ed.), *Problems of Ageing* (Baltimore: Williams & Wilkins Co., 1939), pp. 535–71
11. Warren, H. C. (ed.). *Dictionary of Psychology*. Cambridge: Houghton Mifflin Co., 1934
12. Wechsler, D. *The Measurement of Adult Intelligence* (2d edition). Baltimore: Williams & Wilkins Co., 1941

Chapter XVII

THE USE OF ELECTRIC SHOCK THERAPY IN OLDER PATIENTS

CURTIS T. PROUT, EDWARD B. ALLEN,
AND DONALD M. HAMILTON

ELECTRIC shock therapy was first used in 1938 for the treatment of mental illness and soon proved to be a valuable addition to the treatment of all functional mental disorders and particularly the depressive states. For some years, however, there was a great reluctance to employ this treatment in patients over 60 years of age because of the presumed added hazards in this elderly group. This hesitancy gradually yielded to experience which proved that marked benefit could be derived for patients of advanced years from the use of electroshock therapy. Complications resulting from this form of therapy have been minimal when adequate psychiatric and medical evaluation of the patient's condition has preceded its use. In a report on pathological studies, Rothschild in 1941 stated that there were no contraindications to the treatment of mental conditions appearing in patients above the age of 60, on the basis of any universally present pathology dependent upon age alone. While this paper did not specifically apply, at the time, to electroshock therapy, it lent support to further attempts to use it in the treatment of older patients. In 1939 and in the early 1940's, however, frequent reports of injuries, and even in some instances fatalities, contributed to a period of caution. Ebaugh et al. (2) tabulated in detail the data in 9 cases of fatalities following electric convulsive therapy which had been reported in the literature up to July 1942. One of these was 75 years of age at the time of therapy and showed histologic changes associated with arteriosclerosis. (The cause of death was not given.)

In 1943 Evans (3) was one of the first to report more specifically on the convulsive shock therapy of elderly patients. Although Impastato and Almansi (8) had originally established an age limit of 40, Evans chose 50 years as his minimal age and treated 50 patients over that age. Seventeen of these were over 60 and 5 were over 70. The only reported complications were 2 fractures of the

446

humerus and 1 fatality from pneumonia two days
ond treatment. Thirty-seven of these patients re
8, electroshock therapy; and 5, both electro
metrazol. His results are shown below.

TABLE 32.—RESULTS OF E

Diagnosis	No.	
Involutional Psychosis ...	21	21 ı
Manic-depressive psychosis	19	19 we
Dementia praecox	6	10 wei ved
Psychoneurosis	4	81+% were sent home

In 1945 Alexander (1) reported on the therapeutic efficacy of
electroconvulsive therapy in 100 consecutive cases, including 12
whose age ranged from 60 to 71 years. The standard by which he
evaluated the success of treatment was the patient's ability to leave
the hospital and return to community life within thirty days following the last treatment. Of the 12 cases, 5 were considered as successfully treated by the above standard and in 5 more their condition was improved by the treatment. No complications or untoward
results were indicated in his report. He felt that his experience lent
support to the theory that it is only in those cases of mental illness
wherein recovery with other forms of therapy is possible that electroconvulsive therapy serves to hasten the process.

In 1945 Mayer-Gross (15) reported a series of 500 patients
treated with electroconvulsive therapy. Of these, 76 were over 60,
with the following age distribution:

Age	No.
60 to 64 years..............	38
65 to 69 years..............	24
70 to 74 years..............	12
75 years and over..........	2

Sixty-two of these 76 were women and 14, men. His diagnostic
grouping was interesting in view of the results obtained.

TABLE 33.—RESULTS OF MAYER-GROSS' SERIES

Diagnosis	No.	Recovered or improved
Melancholia	29	23 ⎫ (79.6%)
Melancholia and senility........	20	16 ⎭
Schizophrenia and paraphrenia..	13	12
Manic-depressive illness	8	7
Senile-arteriosclerotic dementia and confusion	6	3

Although the physical condition of this group was considered to be good in only 25, fair in 21, frail in 10, and poor in 20, it was found that after the course of convulsions many of those described as frail or in poor condition had shown marked improvement in color, weight, and general physical health. He considered blood-pressure findings before treatment as only of relative importance as a danger signal and he considered a systolic pressure over 200 mm. Hg. as no absolute contraindication to electroconvulsive therapy, provided the function of the heart and circulation proved satisfactory on clinical examination. One of his patients with a pretreatment blood pressure of 200/110 died with signs of coronary thrombosis which first appeared two days after the convulsive therapy.

The number of convulsions given to each patient varied from 2 to 13, but in 27 patients only single convulsions or "small series" were used as a "maintenance treatment."

The frequency and kind of complications were only slightly different from those which appeared in younger patients. He encountered one spinal compression fracture, one dislocated shoulder, and one sprained ankle. One had an unsuspected fragility of bones with consequent fractures. In 3 cases, a prolonged postshock confusion lasting "a few days" was observed. He concluded that electrically induced convulsions can, without undue risk, be employed in the treatment of the elderly.

In 1946 Kalinowsky and Hoch (10) stated that it was their belief that age alone should not exclude patients from the benefit of shock therapy. In the same year several other reports indicated that its value was being recognized in the treatment of patients over 60 years of age, and experience was accumulating in the management of such complications as might occur. Hayman (7), in reporting on the prophylaxis of cardiac complications in electroshock therapy, declared that auricular and ventricular fibrillation, as well as various other types of cardiac arythmia occurring during electric shock applications, might be regarded in part as pathophysiological results of stimulation of the sympathetic and parasympathetic nervous systems. Other complications might be due to vascular changes. He reported 3 cases between 64 and 69 with cardiac complications which were successfully treated by using quinidine prophylactically. One of these, a woman aged 69, had been depressed for three years. She had a presystolic murmur over the whole precordium, transmitted to the axilla and vessels of the neck, and was known to have had heart disease for thirty years. Although there was slight tortuosity of the retinal arteries, the blood pressure was 115/80, the electrocardiogram was normal, and there were no signs of decompensation. After the 9th electroshock treatment, she developed periodic arythmias without a consistent pattern. She was given 0.8 gm. (12 gr.) of quinidine daily through her 13th treatment. Her electrocardiogram remained normal and the blood pressure rose to 140/80. The other two patients were given quinidine before treatments were instituted. Doses of 6–12 gr. daily for from five to nine days were reported.

In 1946 Kino and Thorpe (12) gave an interesting comparative survey of results (Table 34) from electroshock therapy as administered to 300 selected cases of melancholia in women. While the subdivisions were small, this was the most comprehensive study by age groups.

TABLE 34.—RESULTS OF KINO AND THORPE'S STUDY

Age Group	No.	Recovered		Improved		Unimproved	
		No.	Per Cent	No.	Per Cent	No.	Per Cent
25 years and under	26	21	81	5	19	..	..
26 to 40 years...........	114	95	83	15	13	4	4
41 to 50 years...........	67	55	82	9	13	3	5
51 to 60 years...........	57	37	65	15	26	5	9
61 years and over	36	31	86	2	5	3	9

It is interesting to note 86 per cent recoveries in the age group of 61 and over (91 per cent "recovery plus improvement"), as compared with the 79.6 per cent reported by Mayer-Gross in his 49 cases with melancholia.

The authors report that these cases were treated without curare derivative, nor was any presedation mentioned. Transient memory disturbances were noted but no persistent confusion. Skeletal complications occurred in 11 instances out of a total group of 1,000 patients, but the age group in which they occurred is not indicated.

An excellent report of the use of electroshock therapy in elderly patients was made by Feldman *et al.* (4) in 1946. Their study included a more detailed review of the physical findings and laboratory studies prior to the treatment of their total of 53 patients over the age of 65. Thirty-three of these 53 patients revealed signs of cardiovascular disease, as indicated by electrocardiographic tracings or high blood pressure. (Blood pressure below 160/100 was accepted as normal.) Many of the electrocardiographic tracings were reported as showing diffuse myocardial damage and possibly coronary disease, and one had definitely had a coronary thrombosis. (Other physical complications included ventral hernia, kyphosis, bilateral inguinal hernia, syphilis, and asthma.) They reported that the proportion of persons with cardiovascular impairment over the age of 65 was so high that each patient was a problem in which the cardiovascular threat to life when treatment is given must be weighed against the severity of the mental illness. Of the 53 patients reported by Feldman *et al.*, 43 had a record of 1 admission, while 10 had multiple admissions to a total of 24.

TABLE 35.—RESULTS OF STUDY BY FELDMAN *et al.*

Diagnosis	No.	Recovered	Much Improved	Improved	Unimproved
Involutional melancholia..	30 ⎫	11	15	4	6
Manic-depressive psychosis	6 ⎭				
Manic-depressive manic ..	4	..	2	..	2
Psychoneurosis with depression	7	1	1	5	..
Paranoid psychoses	6	..	2	1	3

Complications were one congestive heart failure and a questionable fracture of a rib in one other patient.

Of the 43 patients with 1 admission, 10 recovered, 16 were much improved, 9 improved, and 8 were unimproved.

Of the 10 patients with multiple admissions, 4 recovered, 9 were much improved, 10 improved, and 1 was unimproved, thus giving a total of 39 much improved or recovered while only 9 were considered to be without benefit. In other words, 86 per cent were at least improved.

Of further value was their report that a review of the literature revealed that of 17 deaths recorded up to that time, 9 were due to heart failure; 7, due to questionable origin but conceivably cardiac; and 1, from other cause. Of these, only 3 were over 65 and 4 over the age of 60. It was the opinion of these authors that the only contraindications to electroshock therapy in mental disorders, "other than senile dementia," in patients over 65 years of age, should be "Extreme defects in the physical state, particularly in the cardiovascular systems."

In 1947, reports indicated that the practice of treating patients over 60 years of age with electric shock therapy was increasing, and that the results obtained adequately compensated the therapist for the risks entailed. Wilbur and Fortes (18) reported a series of 30 patients, all over 70 years of age and suffering from affective disorders, who were treated with a maximum of 14 convulsions with an average of 6.5 per patient. Twenty-eight of these patients were between 70 and 78, 1 was 80, and 1 was 83 years old. Each patient had at least one organic disease, predominantly cardiovascular but with a good representation of muscular and skeletal diseases with a "sprinkling of surgical lesions, respiratory, gastrointestinal, and neurological diseases." Also, miscellaneous conditions were noted relative to eyes, skin, infections, blood dyscrasias, and drug addictions. Of the 30, only 3 had been ill over one year and 27 for less time. Improvement occurred in response to electroshock therapy in 28, 1 remained unimproved, and 1 died. A follow-up after 3 months to $6\frac{1}{2}$ years showed that half had sustained this remission of symptoms. These authors report no serious complications and state that they employed curare in a ratio of more than 1 mg. per kg. of body weight. It was their conclusion that their experience indicated that convulsive shock therapy was well tolerated by the aged and that curare modification made it safer for these patients.

Gallinek (5) also reported in 1947 on the treatment of 18 patients over the age of 60, who had electroshock therapy on an ambulatory basis. He had given a series of from 1 to 10 treatments, beginning with a frequency of 3 times per week, then 2, and—with the appearance of memory defects—then 1. He observed that the average convulsive threshold in elderly women is high and that the blood pressure lowered with the lessening of agitation, often after a temporary increase. His patients were able to leave the office within $1\frac{1}{2}$ hours and confusion did not seem to last materially longer than in the younger patients. He felt that curare should never be used routinely except with a special indication. Only 3 of his patients were considered unimproved. As complications, 1 patient suffered a compression fracture of the fifth dorsal vertebra, 1 committed suicide, and 1 sustained a spur broken from an osteoarthritic patella.

Lingley and Robbins (13), in a discussion of fractures following electroshock therapy, reported that of 230 patients (age not given) where no mechanical restraint or preliminary paralyzant was used, 23 per cent sustained fracture of 1 or more bones. They observed that fractures occurred more frequently in the young and in the old—which they attributed to the vigorous musculature of the young and the tendency to decalcification in the old. They added, however, that, among the older age group, though extensive spur formations and other degenerative changes throughout the thoracic and lumbar spine were commonly present before treatment, this finding was not correlated with the frequency of subsequent fracture, nor was there any change in already existing abnormalities present. There were certain bony conditions which they felt did appear to contraindicate therapy, such as osteoporosis, malignant lesions, Otto's pelvis, possibly Paget's disease, and syphilitic lesions. The occurrence of fracture per se is not considered grounds for discontinuing therapy.

Moore (16), in the light of results obtained in the treatment of 1,596 intramural patients with electroshock, discussed, in 1947, a revision of former contraindications to this form of therapy. Thirty-nine of his patients were over 60, 15 over 65, and 2 over 70. Eighteen of his patients had generalized arteriosclerosis and 190 had varying degrees of hypertension, yet in these cases there were no complications following treatment. He felt that in the light of experience and judgment greater freedom should be permitted in the use of electroshock therapy in the treatment of the mentally ill, and that this applied particularly with respect to complicating cardiovascular diseases with or without hypertension and the complications of advancing age.

Lovell (14), in reporting the results of electroshock therapy in the aging, found that in his series of depressed patients about 50 per cent of those under the age of 64 were considered to have derived good results while only 34 per cent over that age had benefited. This is not consistent with other reports nor with our own findings. He reported that, in this series, patients with old rheumatic heart disease with valvular lesions but without cardiac failure withstood treatment well. He also felt that well-compensated patients who had recovered from coronary occlusions for six months might be treated with relative safety if they had had a satisfactory electrocardiograph for six months.

Kaldeck et al. (9) added strength to the growing conviction that with proper management many former contraindications to electric shock could be eliminated. In a discussion of the physical risks of electroshock therapy on a basis of 8,082 treatments administered to 628 patients, the authors report that 36 were over 60 years of age; 50 had signs of cardiovascular disease such as arteriosclerosis, enlargement of the heart, abnormal electrocardiographic findings, rheumatic heart disease, and hypertension; 1 had definite signs of coronary artery disease; and 1 had a severe congenital abnormality of the heart. In spite of these findings, they had successfully completed therapy. These authors considered that the dangers in the use of curare outweighed the advantages of this drug.

In 1948 Gallinek (5) reported his studies of three groups of disorders among elderly patients, which responded successfully to electroshock therapy. He described first those almost purely affective and depressive reactions occurring for the first time during the senium and marked by agitation as well as grotesque somatic delusions and a hypochrondriacal trend. These were usually accompanied by signs of retinal, cerebral, and generalized arteriosclerosis. Second, he described cases characterized by paranoid trends, with an affective admixture in which the trend was of loose structure and with illusions and delusions more common than true hallucinations. Third, he described those cases characterized by occurrence of manic-depressive episodes during the senium in patients who have had identical episodes prior to this period.

In all three groups the results of electric shock therapy were surprisingly good, although less satisfactory in the paranoid group than in the other two. It was the author's opinion that almost all these cases would be diagnosed as psychosis with cerebral arteriosclerosis or senile psychosis. He concluded that electroshock therapy can be applied with little risk even in cases with serious organic disease of the cardiovascular system. In his experience a course of 10 treatments or less was sufficient.

In 1948 Page and Russell (17) investigated the effect of increased voltage and duration of stimulus during electroshock therapy. The voltage was gradually increased from a minimum necessary to produce a major convulsion (about 100 volts) to a fixed standard of 150 volts, and the duration of stimulus was increased from 0.3 to 1.0 seconds. Treatments were administered daily. The authors reported that they had treated 98 cases ranging in age from 16 to 74 years and that 30 of these were over 60. In this latter group they found the convulsions much less severe, and attributed this to a weaker musculature. In their opinion, this treatment procedure halved the number of treatments per patient and also halved the average number of days under treatment by each patient. They further stated that the relapse rate also seemed to be halved. Further substantiation—at least in so far as the older group is concerned—has not been observed.

In 1949 Kaplan and Freund (11) described their results in the use of electroshock therapy in more than 2,000 patients, 280 of whom had organic disease of such severity as to contraindicate such therapy on the basis of pre-existing standards. They employed the "Fractional Summation Method," which they state has resulted in no deaths or fractures of extremities in approximately 20,000 treatments. In this method an attempt was made to initiate the slow, gradually progressive seizure of the epileptic. Similar results in the treatment of similar organic disease complications have already been reported in this chapter, using standard procedure.

A review of 104 patients between the ages of 60 and 82 who had electroshock treatment was made by Prout, Allen, and Hamilton. A variety of organic conditions were encountered, with a minimum of treatment complications. A derivative of curare was used routinely, with a carefully planned, supervised, and executed procedure of treatment being carried out intramurally in each case. No complications due to the use of curare were encountered.

In this series there were 52 men and 52 women, with the following age distribution:

Age Group	No.
60 to 65 years	67
66 to 70 years	28
71 to 75 years	6
76 to 80 years	2
82 years	1

Results of treatment are shown in the following table.

TABLE 36.—RESULTS OF STUDY BY PROUT, ALLEN, AND HAMILTON

Diagnosis	No.	Recovered	Much Improved	Improved	Unimproved
Manic-depressive group.	59	27	19	3	10
Involutional psychoses..	32	13	12	4	3
Psychoneuroses	10	3	7	..	..
Paranoid condition	2	..	2	..	..
Psychosis with cerebral arteriosclerosis	1	..	..	1	..
Total	104	43	40	8	13

These figures indicate that over 87 per cent of these patients were benefited by the treatments. The complications of treatment are considered worthy of more detailed evaluation. Cardiovascular difficulties appeared in 6 patients, with 1 of these describing precordial pain and presenting a short period of cardiovascular collapse after the 8th treatment. Only 4 suffered marked or severe confusion, and 1 of these had a history of carbon monoxide poisoning. These confusion states all cleared satisfactorily within a maximum of four weeks. As others have reported, the incidence of unusual confusion was not greater than that found among younger patients. One patient developed phlebitis, necessitating a temporary cessation of treatments, and 4 sustained skeletal injury: 1 fracture of the left humerus, 1 impacted fracture of the head of the left femur, 1 compression fracture of the first lumbar vertebra, and in another patient a slight wedging of the third dorsal vertebra. In the light of the organic conditions present before treatment and the obvious benefits obtained in the mental symptoms, these complications seem relatively unimportant.

Cardiovascular changes were the most frequent and commonly present complication prior to treatment. A history of angina was obtained in 2, coronary thrombosis in 5, evidence of coronary insufficiency (by electrocardiograph) in 13, evidence of other abnormal electrographic findings (including 2 instances of heart block) in 41, hypertension (blood pressure over 160/90) in 20, evidence of retinal arteriosclerosis of varying degree (including 1 with retinal hemorrhage) in 54, and sclerosis of the peripheral vessels in 18 patients. These represent some of the more significant cardiovascular symptoms selected from a large group.

A second frequent and consistent organic finding was arthritis of the spine. In this study the degree of arthritic change was classified as one plus—showing minor productive changes; two plus— moderate productive changes with lipping of vertebrae; and three plus—marked productive changes, including spur formation and bridging between vertebrae. In this series of 104 patients, 28 revealed arthritic changes graded as one plus; 21, as two plus; and 5, as three plus. Four revealed marked decalcification of bone; 1 patient had very severe arthritis with marked limitation of motion of the extremities; and another, severe arthritis leading to ankylosis of her knees at a 90° angle.

The list of organic conditions other than the two already discussed covers a wide field and can be roughly grouped as follows: marked emaciation, 16; healed tuberculosis, 7; other lung conditions, 6; blood changes, 9; skeletal changes (old or recent fractures), 18; eye conditions, 4; surgical (recent or indicated), including 5 hernias, 26; and other chronic medical conditions such as pleural blebs, diabetes, Parkinsonism, secondary anemia, and so forth. These findings are quite consistent with those reported in the literature and cannot be regarded as serious barriers to the careful application of electroshock therapy, when indicated by the severity of the mental disorders.

A review of the literature makes it readily apparent that with refinements in the technique of administering electroshock treatments, and with increased experience on the part of the therapists, it has become in each succeeding year since its advent in 1938 a more safe and effective form of therapy for disordered emotional states in patients who have lived to the age of 60 or beyond. The discriminative use of preshock sedation and of curare derivative, with proper precautions and technique, have lessened the dangers and made electric shock a relatively safe procedure in skilled hands for the treatment of emotional disorders in the elderly patient. The question of treatment in each case will be dependent upon a careful review of the life history of the patient. It will necessitate a knowledge of his previous physical illnesses and his resistance to them.

From the foregoing review, some important considerations to be made *before* using electroshock in the treatment of patients over 60—become apparent:

1. The patient should be suffering from a mental illness which is fundamentally functional in nature.

Some degree of impairment of the intellect and sensorium is normally associated with advanced age: decrease in attention and concentration span; lessened efficiency in learning and integrating new concepts; and milder memory defects, particularly for recent events. Functional mental illnesses in the elderly may be complicated by exhaustion as well as by toxicity due to prolonged and heavy sedation, and by inadequate fluid and caloric intake, as well as inadequate elimination. Such factors may add symptoms of confusion and delirium to what is fundamentally a functional psychosis. Medical attention to the toxic and exhaustion factors ordinarily results in prompt relief from the mental symptoms caused by them.

Emotional depression is known to retard organ function in a sweeping manner and can result in an interference with compensatory mechanisms which are already heavily taxed in individuals with arteriosclerosis. With this added burden elderly patients may display organic mental symptoms such as confusion, disorientation, and gross memory defects, which are alleviated or may even disappear with recovery from the depression. Some patients with psychoses due to arteriosclerosis, in whom evidence of cerebral damage is not marked and who are deeply depressed, therefore do benefit from electroshock therapy which relieves the depression.

2. The elderly patient should have had the opportunity to respond adequately to the usual, more conservative forms of psychiatric therapy. Recovery among elderly patients from mental illness was well known before the advent of the electroshock therapy.

3. A careful evaluation of the adequacy of the cardiovascular system is essential.

Hypertension, abnormal electrocardiograms, history of angina pectoris or coronary thrombosis, and inactive rheumatic heart disease with valvular lesions are not in themselves contraindications to electroshock therapy. In our experience the strain of this treatment upon the cardiovascular system has been exaggerated. An individual who has sufficient cardiac reserve to walk a hundred yards without unusual distress is able to withstand the cardiovascular strain of electric shock treatment, particularly when the muscular response is modified by curare. Agitation and excitement in themselves may put more strain upon the heart than the convulsion. Five patients in the authors' series had suffered a coronary thrombosis from 2 months to 6 years before electric shock treatment. Three of these patients had their attack 6 months or less before treatment. One suffered a myocardial infarction associated with his second electric shock treatment in a hospital other than where he was treated in the series reported by the authors. The second series of treatments took place under preliminary curarization 2 months after the coronary thrombosis. Serial electrocardiograms were taken on all the patients in the authors' series who had a history of coronary disease. Reports of electrocardiographic findings indicating "evidence of healing" followed by "stabilization of the EKG" were accepted as evidence that sufficient healing of the infarction had taken place, whereupon electroshock treatment was given. In none of these 5 patients was there any evidence of cardiovascular complication during the course of treatment. Three of these patients, however (all of whom recovered from their psychiatric disorders and went home), have since died of coronary thrombosis from 6 months to 3½ years after their last treatment.

Of the 13 patients with electrocardiograph evidence of coronary insufficiency, 2 died (both at home, recovered) from coronary thrombosis, 4 months and 1 year, respectively, after their last electric shock treatment. In addition to this careful evaluation of the cardiovascular system, each elderly patient should have a thorough physical examination, laboratory studies (including an electrocardiogram), chest and spinal X-rays preliminary to treatment, and X-rays of the spine following the conclusion of the course of treatment.

4. It is our experience that the use of curare preliminary to electric shock treatment, when carefully administered by trained and experienced physicians, is a safe procedure with elderly patients and distinctly lessens the strain on the cardiovascular system. Curare can be safely given if necessary in such doses that there is no convulsive reaction, i.e., no tonic or clonic muscular response but only isolated fibrillary twitchings which are not capable of moving the extremities. Such heavy curarization preceded the treatment of a patient 64, who two months before had fractured the head of the femur under electric shock treatment, as well as that of a 77-year-old woman with osteoporosis and an arthritic ankylosis of the knees at a 90° angle. As indication of the brittleness of her bones, this latter patient suffered a complete fracture of the middle third of the femur some weeks later after gently falling from her bed, a distance of sixteen inches. A younger patient of 34, who suffered a comminuted fracture of the clavicle the night before his first electric shock treatment, was also given a series of treatments without complications, under similar heavy curarization. We emphasize, however, that such curarization should never be employed except by properly trained physicians, who have adequate resuscitative equipment available.

REFERENCES

1. Alexander, G. H. "Therapeutic Efficacy of Electroconvulsive Therapy. A Comparative Classification of Treatment Results Determined With and Without the Use of a Time Factor in Their Evaluation," *J. Nerv. Ment. Dis.*, 1945, 102: 221–30
2. Ebaugh, F., Barnacle, C., and Neuberger, K. "Fatalities Following Electric Convulsive Therapy," *Arch. Neurol. Psychiatry*, 1943, 49: 107–17
3. Evans, V. L. "Convulsive Shock Therapy in Elderly Patients. Risks and Results," *Am. J. Psychiatry*, 1943, 99: 531–33
4. Feldman, F., Susselman, S., Lipetz, B., and Berrera, E. "Electric Shock Therapy of Elderly Patients," *Arch. Neurol. Psychiatry*, 1946, 56: 158–70
5. Gallinek, A. "Electric Convulsive Therapy in Geriatrics," *N.Y. State J. Med.*, 1947, 47: 11, 1233–41
6. ———. "The Nature of Affective and Paranoid Disorders During the Senium in the Light of Electric Convulsive Therapy," *J. Nerv. Ment. Dis.*, 1948, 108: 293–303
7. Hayman, M. "The Prophylaxis of Cardiac Complications in Electro-Shock Therapy," *Am. J. Psychiatry*, 1945–46, 102: 316–17
8. Impastato, D. J., and Almansi, R. "The Electrofit in the Treatment of Mental Disease," *J. Nerv. Ment. Dis.*, 1942, 95: 395
9. Kaldeck, R., McLaughlin, W. F., Gurri, J., and Wassersug, J. I. "Physical Risks of Electroconvulsive Therapy," *N. E. J. Med.*, 1948, 239: 773–78
10. Kalinowsky, L. B., and Hoch, P. H. *Shock Treatments and Other Somatic Procedures in Psychiatry.* New York: Grune and Stratton, 1946
11. Kaplan, L. A., and Freund, J. D. "Electro-Shock Therapy in Patients with Severe Organic Disease," *Ill. Med. J.*, 1949, 95: 96–101
12. Kino, F. F., and Thorpe, L., "Electrical Convulsive Therapy in 500 Selected Psychotics," *J. Med. Sci.*, 1946, Vol. XCII, No. 386 (New Series 350), pp. 138–45
13. Lingley, J. R., and Robbins, L. L. "Fractures Following Electro-Shock Therapy," *Radiology*, 1947, 48: 124–28
14. Lovell, H. W. "Electric Shock Therapy in the Aging," *Geriatrics*, 1948, 13: 285–93
15. Mayer-Gross, W. "Electric Convulsion Treatment in Patients over 60," *J. Med. Sci.*, 1945, 91: 101–03
16. Moore, M. T. "Electro-Cerebral Shock Therapy. A Reconsideration of Former Considerations," *Arch. Neurol. Psychiatry*, 1947, 57: 693–711
17. Page, G. M., and Russell, R. J. "Intensified Electrical Convulsive Therapy in the Treatment of Mental Disorders," *Lancet*, 1948, 254: 597–98
18. Wilbur, C. B., and Fortes, A. "Convulsive Shock Therapy in Patients over Seventy Years of Age with Affective Disorders," *Am. J. Psychiatry*, 1947, 104: 48–51

Chapter XVIII

MENTAL HYGIENE IN LATER MATURITY

Nolan D. C. Lewis

AGING is a normal biological process or a series of processes, but it is usually hastened, exaggerated, or modified in some fashion by abnormal or disease trends incident to life in a quantitative or qualitative relationship, trends which are sometimes not readily distinguished from normal senile developments. However, senility is the favorable time of life for the development of several serious disorders, such as cardiovascular disturbances, kidney diseases, diabetes mellitus, and cancer, which complicate the general problem in specific ways involving any mental hygiene program that may be under consideration.

As compared with most other animals, human beings have a long span of life. Man is one of the few members of the animal kingdom to live beyond fifty years of age. Not only is the span of life of practically all vertebrates, such as mammals, birds, reptiles, and fishes under fifty years, but the lives of the invertebrates are not long enough to furnish any comparison. It is also to be noted that very few primitive people either in the past or in the present live on the average beyond the fifty-year mark, and until the present century even a civilized man could not be expected statistically to live beyond it.

At the time when Cicero wrote his *De Senectute* the average life expectancy at birth for a Roman was but 23 years. According to the information available, the average life expectancy increased very slowly during the next nineteen hundred years. By 1850 it was about 40 years in our New England states, and by 1900 it had increased to 48 years for the United States. Owing to the advances in medical and other sciences, the rise in life expectancy at birth has been rapid and today it exceeds 63 years. It is estimated that there are in the region of 13,000,000 persons of 65 years or over in this country at the present day; and our experts in the field of census statistics predict that if the increase continues at its present rate this age group of our population will more than double in the next 40 years. The implications are rather obvious. This increase in longevity will either become a social evil, destructive to national economy, or it will be made a valuable asset through more wisely laid plans to utilize the potentialities of the elderly.

Chronological age as measured in years is not identical with biological age. It is conceded that at times these two processes coincide, but biological age characteristically varies with each individual. Many persons are either physiologically older or younger than their years of existence. Moreover, no individual is uniform in the physiological age of the different structures of the body. Society has never taken this fact into consideration in any logical way and continues to base its estimations of individuals upon chronological age alone. For example, in many of its special activities society continues to require the retirement of a worker at a certain chronological age regardless of his good health or of its need for abilities which he may have retained intact and which could be used in his special work to great advantage. On the other hand, in certain situations many persons in their dotage are kept in active charge of departments of education, research, and industry when they should have been retired years before. We are greatly in need of technics for the measurement of health and of physiological age, as in some respects it constitutes one of the major problems of present-day society. Its solution if ever attained will depend upon the co-operative researches of the physiologist, the biochemist, the biologist, and the psychiatrist.

Each individual is born with certain endowments or capacities and with the ability to mature. These capacities are unequal in strength and function, and it should be recognized that a number of them progressively decline after the individual has passed the prime of life. These irregularities in capacity account for many if not most of the individual differences in attitude and behavior. In old age, whether chronological or physiological, some important endowments and functions have attenuated, have become distorted through conversion, or have disappeared entirely. Thus we are dealing with a different individual after age has required the readjustment of the whole psychobiological reaction setting.

As compared with the interest taken in children's problems by general physicians, psychiatrists, psychologists, social workers, and public-welfare organizations, the interest and care accorded the aged is insignificant, amounting to nothing less than neglect. Here and there one finds a small organization interested in old people, chiefly from the standpoint of housing and feeding. One may admit some excuse for this attitude on the basis that the aged are generally, although by no means always, economically worthless, and become more so with added years, while the child has an increasing economic value and, in addition, a prospective maturity which may be favorably influenced by helpful interference at the proper maturation phases.

Along with the diminution in physical strength and activity there appears a depressive mental attitude, probably due to the recognition or the anticipation of the approach of old age, with its unfulfilled hopes and plans, and the increasing difficulty in dealing with the ordinary problems of life—a failure of compensation at the psychological level where conflicts, formerly resolved successfully, now break through and overwhelm such constructive forces as are available. The failure of the psychological protective processes may be enhanced by, or associated with, the vascular changes of senility, as well as with other complicating physical and toxic factors.

Among the features of senility are the impairment of retentive ability and general failure of memory, depression, fears, and self-depreciation, with loss of confidence in ability, all of which may be increased or brought into prominence by overwork or fatigue in complicated situations which were once handled with ease but which now, owing to increased fatigability, become almost impossible burdens. Many are able to work steadily and comfortably without difficulty at a lower mental level than the original one attained with ease during the earlier years; and, as the old person is struggling to keep his place in the world, the hygienist should weigh all factors carefully before interfering with any work program. The "puttering" activities of the aged, so frequently called "imaginary duties" by their relatives and associates, who are annoyed by what appears to be unimportant work or obstructions to the work of others, may be of the utmost value to the individual, saving mechanisms by which he holds on to his ego importance in the community. Old people are often regarded as a heavy burden upon the finances and emotions of the family group, with the result that they become the objects either of open antagonism or of suppressed and subtle ill will. Old-age pensions are relieving many such family situations; but these are not the solution. Many persons find little if any difficulty in making the adjustments incident and necessary to old age. Others are reluctant to relinquish the activities formerly pursued, wish to continue their work and their pleasures as formerly, and in spite of an obviously failing capacity become charged with the belief that they are as good as ever. When pressure is brought to bear upon one of these situations a great deal of tact is necessary inasmuch as a pathological response may be easily effected. The realization of what is interpreted by them as a great loss may precipitate an episode of some severity and still further complicate the powers of adjustment.

Although there are numerous exceptions, old people are not as a rule pleasant patients for physicians; moreover, the conditions and types of disease from which they suffer are apt to be therapeutically hopeless or at best to lend themselves only to symptomatic relief. It may also be said that the aged are unpleasant, even repulsive, from the aesthetic standpoint, the degree being determined both by the condition of the patient and the aesthetic state and capacities of the observer.

Woltman (14) has emphasized that in addition to hypertension, malignant tumors, arthritis, cardiac and peripheral vascular diseases, obesity, various organic neurological disorders, prostatic conditions, diabetes, and established psychoses, neuroses are of high frequency in the aged. Gastrointestinal neuroses, depressions, chronic fatigue states, and anxiety neuroses were all represented in the group of patients studied.

The aging person adapts himself less and less readily to changes of habit in eating, sleeping, and working, and, when for purposes of health and hygiene a major change becomes necessary, it should be accomplished with a great deal of tact and consideration for the whole situation. The dread of going to a hospital for treatment, which is rather universal (with some exceptions), is greatly increased in old people who, in addition to the general dislike of changes in their daily living arrangements, are afraid that they may die away from home. On the other hand, the senile patient should be prevented if possible from getting the idea that nothing can be done to relieve him because he is old. Hernia, various abdominal conditions, prolapsed uterus, and hemorrhoids, among other disorders, may be safely treated surgically in those cases not too involved in complications.

Old persons sleep lightly and seem to require less sleep than young ones, and with them sedatives should be used carefully. The use of coffee, tea, and tobacco should not be denied unless there are pretty definite objective reasons for doing so. Strenuous exercise after 50 should be discouraged, as there is no evidence that it is useful and it may do harm. Light exercises, with emphasis on the "light," may be beneficial—physically as well as for their mental effect.

Older patients should not be confined entirely to bed for a day longer than is necessary and safe following an illness or an operation. Getting them up may avoid hypostatic pulmonary congestion, prevent loss of general interest in daily affairs, and stimulate the appetite and create or increase the important impression that improvement is present, and recovery is expected and is on the way. However, there are situations that indicate physiologic rest in order to relieve the worn and often tired organs which are perhaps nearing the limit of their functional capacity. For example, those aged persons who have hypertension or some edema, those who are overweight, or who suffer from a failing heart should have frequent short rests in bed. One day in bed each week or ten days has a beneficial effect on these and other disorders.

There are several physical and mental characteristics of old persons which account for their unpleasantness or repulsiveness to others. Of the former, there are the various evidences of physical decay and distortion, which carry with them implications threatening the future: disagreeable odors and, frequently, neglect of clothing and other duties of cleanliness and personal hygiene. The mental reasons are probably by far the more important, and the behavior of the senile is frequently annoying, displaying peevishness, irritability, wilfulness, childishness, ill-tempered and offensive behavior, expressions of depressive affect, foolish obsessions and suspicions, and tendency to prolixity and to prolonged conversations in which past experiences are related without discrimination as to what is important and what irrelevant. Many of their reactions are interpreted as selfishness and many suffer from ill health over which they become worried and depressed, some to the extent that suicide is selected as a way out. Some combination of these expressions is present in practically every aged individual and, if it is not neutralized by an understanding attitude on the part of companions, it will act destructively and counteract sympathy and active interest in the welfare of the old. There are logical reasons for the unpleasant mental attitude of the aged person. The energy, capacity, and enthusiasm of youth are gone, and with them the ability to adjust to the complex and ever-changing circumstances of life. As a result, in the midst of this decline in life, their attitude can be none too optimistic; and it is not strange that any unusual occurrence in the family routine, any increased pressure of extraneous circumstances, stressful situations, or unexpected disappointments, may partially or even totally overwhelm them. Perhaps the well-known conservatism of old people regarding the acceptance of new ideas constitutes something of a virtue. It may serve as a balancing factor in our culture.

The retained constitutional capacity for adaptation may in large part determine whether the reaction released will be merely an exaggeration of the usual senile tendency to ruminate over losses, a domination by self-centered ideas or regretful thoughts and doubts of the present, or feelings of inadequacy, weariness, and resignation toward the future. When the original make-up is more rigid, rendering adaptability still more difficult, there will be more serious responses, with depression in pure form, or with agitation and self-depreciation, accompanied by pronounced sleep and digestive disorders. Fluctuating mental confusion, apathetic states, and episodes of elation resembling manic reactions, with exaggerated ideas of self-importance, are occasionally released in similar circumstances.

In some seniles there is a phase of behavior which is known as "sexual recrudescence." This may express itself in the form of infatuations for younger persons of the opposite sex, revealing itself in talk and silly actions noticeable only to the immediate family or to the interested neighbors, or its expression may become a source of active annoyance to the household of the object of these attentions or to acquaintances living at distances who may be selected as love objects and communicated with through correspondence. This activity may be diffuse or may be sharply localized in one love object. It may lead to medico-legal action; and, in the case of old men with latent or revived character twists or with psychoses, it may result in the seduction or rape of young children or of mature women. This same trend or drive may lead to marriages displeasing to relatives because of inheritance or other rights. These marriages or threatened marriages may become the foci of many family quarrels, while the immediate participants may be discontented or satisfied with their intimate personal relationship.

In women, in addition to the possibility of an erotic flair in senility, the maternal instinct—or whatever it is that is usually known as the "maternal instinct"—may be markedly in evidence. This is true even of aged virgins, and the tendency may survive even after the higher intellectual faculties have disappeared, as is amply demonstrated daily on the wards of large institutions for the mentally ill. A great need for affection is also revealed in the normal ones at home, where their need for love and their craving for attention create family difficulties, particularly in the grandchildren situation. The possible grandparent-child-parent relationships, hates, loves, jealousies, conflicts, and complications are too well known to elaborate here.

Why some seniles show merely a quantitative decrease in abilities, capacities, and adaptations, while others exhibit pathological deviations and finally develop active mental disorder, is an unsolved problem which emphasizes the need of studying the physiologic and psychologic aspects of old age with more precision. Thus far, not only have investigations of the physical factors failed to reveal important differences but similarities have been found in the histopathologic picture in the brains of cases of senile dementia and normal seniles. As a matter of fact, the diagnosis of senile dementia as such cannot be made histologically, as the line of demarcation is too thin between it and the normal changes characteristic of simple senility. Moreover, there is a lack of correlation between the severity of the pathological changes and the degree of intellectual impairment, and equally severe alterations have been found in the brains of old persons of normal mentality.

As indicated above, in accordance with the life pattern of every living thing the human organism undergoes an aging process as a part of its cycle of existence from birth to death. The rate of decay, like the rate of growth, differs among organisms and is also different for the various component parts of the same organism. It is important for the individual to learn, early in life if possible, what will delay this decay, which is inevitable sooner or later, and what measures can be taken to make the mind last as long as the body.

Special attention to vitamin deficiency, adequate diet, warm clothing in winter, comfortable living quarters, and prompt correction of bodily disorders are not sufficient to secure and maintain mental health into the old-age period. In order to postpone the psychological manifestations of senility every person should learn what they are, and should realize that they tend to begin insidiously and to increase as the life span extends. One should know, by being instructed earlier in life, that there will be the tendency to an increase in mental fatigability, to a weakness of initiative, to a lessening of the capacity for work, especially for mental work, with an impairment of the ability to concentrate and to think rapidly and accurately, and to a progressive memory disturbance. One should know also that there is the tendency toward an attenuation of interest in new things and situations, that some of the finer sentiments may be lost, that emotional instability may obtain, that childishness, stubbornness, and obstinacy may appear, that dictatorial and meddlesome trends may develop, and that neglect of personal appearance is an outstanding characteristic. All of these phenomena tend to become exaggerated and should be combated early with insight gained by means of the mental tools which we now have at hand.

Many aging persons relinquish, too early, their jobs and other active interests in life. In some instances there are still twenty years of efficient work which they would be able to accomplish. There is something about work that tends to keep the person young in mind and body, if it is not too strenuous and too humdrum. The old person who has led a very busy life and who has been retired in the midst of this often becomes a pest because his active mind meddles with everyone's business. This is one of the attempts to escape from boredom which is not understood, appreciated, or tolerated by those whom they annoy. Many of the aged avoid mental exercise and fail to undertake new abstract learning, which, by the way, is as appropriate to adults as schools and colleges are to the young. They should avoid the mechanisms of escape from life and reality and do something to prevent the tendency to retrospection and rigidity which strives to carry the individual backward to primitive intellectual patterns. There is a growing tendency for families to vacate large estates and roomy quarters and to live in smaller homes and apartments. This brings the old and the young into closer contact, often creating anxieties and misunderstandings.

The aged individual should avoid living with his children if possible. It is better to live in simple style than to exist luxuriously in a subordinate position with all the possibilities of unhappiness which abound there. Naturally there are exceptions to such situations and the problem has to be worked out on the basis of the facts; but no one can deny that dependence on one's children has unpleasant features for oldsters who have been independent and dominant in their activities. If the old person is financially independent, perhaps to the point of having some excess, he should keep most of this surplus in his own hands. Many old people make the mistake of turning their funds and fortunes over to their children or other relatives with the condition that the latter take care of them for the rest of their lives. Devoted children will not demand this action, and the greedy ones are more to be dreaded than any other type of grafter.

From another angle of the same question, the old person should avoid attempting to run the personal affairs of his children. Should it appear that the grown children are making a "mess" out of their existence, perhaps it is just as well to allow them to do so in their own way rather than complicate everything by introducing ideas that may be outworn and inapplicable to the case in question. The older a person becomes the more rapidly his friends die off and he is likely to become lonely and unable to make new friends in the present generation to which he is not entirely attuned.

It is well for the aged to maintain an attractive personal appearance. Too many oldsters think that their age and years of service entitle them to neglect their clothing and other features of their personal hygiene.

Many old people think that they are wise just because they have attained advanced age. Because one has reached the age of 70, one is not automatically wise. One can live all of these years without learning very much, as Knut Hamsun stated in his novel, *The Wanderers*: "Age may bring nothing but age." Moreover, great age does not allow one the privilege of making himself disagreeable. Peevishness, fretfulness, ill-tempered reactions, and bad manners are very common indulgences exhibited by old people, whose families may develop impatience for the time when they can be relieved of these annoyances.

Many old people are considered to be bores because of their relentless tendency to relate over and over again the events of their past lives, forgetting that most of their acquaintances can repeat them verbatim. It would seem to be a good plan for an old person never to relate anything that happened earlier than the year just past.

Bad health conditions should be avoided. Nutritional and glandular deficiencies or disorders should be corrected as soon as they are discovered. Infections should be investigated at once. It is well known that such conditions may retard children mentally and physically, but it is not so often emphasized that such conditions may bring elderly adults to a complete cessation of their personal as well as their economic resources and adjustments.

Old age, despite its physical and mental and certain social handicaps, has assets which vary among individuals and which can be stimulated to the extent of the emotional limitations and according to the strength of the compensatory striving elements in the personality. The feeling of inferiority constitutes a definite emotional handicap in the aged when they attempt to learn new things. Often, when they try at all, they take more time than is necessary because of the inhibiting conviction that the learning process is retarded to a greater extent than is actually the case.

In past years there has been very little recognition of any special necessity of preparing for old age. Apparently educators have assumed that the individual will grow old gracefully and usefully without particular guidance and information about the characteristics of this time of life. Adult education is being grossly neglected on the basis of the misconception that aging people are unable to learn, although it is a fact that they very often decline to try to learn. When once the inertia is overcome, the ability to learn is not strikingly reduced in advanced age. We hear a great deal about the necessity of preparing the child for his adult existence, and it might be well to do something toward preparing the adult for old age or, rather, to aid him in preparing himself for this period of life. The incentive and the urge to learn are lacking in the average old person. The aged seem to find no reason for acquiring new skills or for learning new subject matter. A few old persons, who have formed the habit earlier in life, are able not only to utilize their intellectual resources but also to acquire new information and put it to use.

Some effort should be made to stimulate older people mentally and to encourage any spontaneous desire they may have to utilize their minds on new material. Guidance services should be provided and special courses of study should be designed to accommodate the abilities, capacities, and special trends of the individual. There could be a lot of aid for the senile on the basis of adequate social planning.

People differ from one another at all ages—in their rate of developmental and devolutional changes, in their abilities to adjust to new situations, and in their capacities for learning at the intellectual level. Some are gifted and highly intelligent in the first place, while others are dull and subnormal from birth. Therefore the general over-all problem of evaluation is no different from that of any other age group. What the old person is in attitude and adjustments depends upon his early training and experience and upon the habits of thought and action instilled when young; but at any time the old person may gain enough insight to modify the senile mind trend.

Psychologic and psychiatric guidance can be given where it is needed. After maturity persons may be helped somewhat, but not fundamentally, as far as any basic change in personality is concerned. The patterns of thought are "cemented" in old people. We have difficulty enough in trying to change youngsters, particularly if they have neurotic traits. The oldster with neurotic traits is not susceptible to any outstanding therapeutic modification. The way to insure a comfortable old age is by proper education during the earlier years of life.

There are no reliable tests as yet to determine the degree of an oldster's deterioration; although tests already in existence may help a little, they should not be taken too seriously—they measure certain deviations of temporary significance, that are not deteriorations at all as understood by the psychiatrist. At present each person investigated is a special research problem. We try to do the best we can with inadequate tools.

We are in great need of special techniques to evaluate the individual's equipment for adjustment to life, i.e., the skills, pe. interests, emotional pattern, and interpersonal relations. The now in existence are not good enough. This situation with its gent need should stimulate research workers to greater effort, t one may suppose every reaction is measurable by the proper tech nique. We are also in need of some modification of our social situations and resources to allow for the inclusion of activities of aged participants. *In short we should have here, as in all other problems requiring solution, a thorough application of the scientific method.* This sums it up in one condensed statement. More and more the status of the aged will depend upon a combination of previous education and the art and science of medicine. Making the aged comfortable and happy is the task and the obligation of medicine and society at large.

Everywhere the usual personal problems will arise and must be met by the individual. If there is an incapacity to adjust to the more serious personal problems, problem situations may precipitate a senile psychosis. If there is sufficient unimpaired compensatory ability in the integration, the adjustment may occur without the development of a psychosis. There is a wide range of difference between individuals in their capacities to compensate for untoward environmental factors as well as for the numerous lesions in the body. A lesion in the brain, a toxic focus in the body, or a thwarting family situation may release a psychosis in one individual, while one of these may, in another, bring into play compensatory capacities and adjustments, thus avoiding a more serious breakdown.

There are a number of aspects to the situation in the actual practice of mental hygiene as applied to the senile. Hard-and-fast rules for avoiding or relieving troubles cannot be formulated; each case is a problem for special study and recommendations. However, certain general considerations may be kept in mind by those who have responsibility for the aged.

Utilization of the senile individual economically, or at least in a fashion to assure him that he is still a part of the world of affairs, is important and necessary to the business of whatever forms the background of the situation. Moreover, many facts indicate that a reasonable variety in mental occupation is a factor in retarding mental senility.

Confidence in one's ability should be maintained. The fear

of aging and the anticipation of the loss of functions in those not previously prepared for the future practically always exert an unfavorable influence on the life adjustment. The attitude of industry toward an early retirement for many still useful or even in their prime is illogical. It is exceedingly difficult for most persons to retire, as doing so seems to signify the end of their importance in the organization and to the community. Many are not prepared for leisure, fear the incompleteness of the future years, and usually say very little about it. Fears may appear in the disguise of irritability and antagonistic attitudes—childishness and unusual behavior. Whatever is done about it should be started years ahead of the retirement time, that is, the development of an interest in gardening, horticulture, or other hobbies, or, what is better, some useful labor and the acquisition of a new skill. There are some unavoidable handicaps to consider in many cases, namely, reduction in muscular co-ordination, reduction in physical endurance, reluctance to change ways, and inability to transform from older to newer conditions. The old person haunted by the threat of exclusion may see discrimination where it is not particularly obvious, hesitates to start new projects because of his age ("will not live to see them through"), and feels unwanted; he may dread insecurity, while actually in need of a change of scene and work. Early retirement even on a pension is not the answer; the old employee should be fitted into the industrial structure in connection with new work. Adjustments vary with the individual, and jobs should change with the changing capacities. When the time arrives for retirement, the proceeding should be such as to avoid inducing the feeling of insecurity, to maintain intact the dignity of the aged person, and wherever possible to capitalize his experience as a worker, a thinker, or an adviser.

Upon the elderly person's retirement from his life work or occupation he should have other important duties to perform—not just "anything to keep him busy" but tasks that are worth doing, that have to be done by someone, and which thus contribute to the daily welfare of himself and others. Some special attention to this factor may prevent or postpone the development of the egocentric tendency so characteristic of aged unemployed. Many older people fear idleness and uselessness more than death.

What is often considered to be mental fatigue may be something far less transitory than fatigue in the usual physical sense of the term. Seniles fatigue easily, both physically and mentally; therefore changes of work and frequent rest periods should be arranged.

The senile individual should be relieved to some extent from worry, mental strain, anxieties, and feelings of financial insecurity, and should be periodically withdrawn from the whirl of effortful existence. Some enjoy spending longer periods of time under simple, pleasant conditions in retirement, away from annoyances, out of the influence of the perpetual sense of hurry and the sequence of incidents which exhaust the attention and which are nowadays a part of practically every environment. However, the senile should not be overprotected to the extent of retiring him to the background, thus damaging his individuality.

With the gradually devitalizing processes in mind, especial care should be taken to avoid physical discomforts, vitiated air, infections, and overeating. Many elderly people eat too much and are unwise in their selection of foods. The relief from sluggishness, obstipation, and irritability that can be obtained by making certain sensible modifications in their diets and giving attention to their elimination processes is often astounding.

The senile should be protected from injuries, as they readily develop the post-traumatic constitution, with its characteristic changes in disposition. A physical trauma may definitely change the personality either temporarily or permanently, or it may merely increase the general irritability which often becomes prominent in old people, particularly at night and early in the morning. Physical injuries may produce or increase a tendency to hypochondriasis and self-scrutiny, as well as increase the feeling of uncertainty that is already present.

It is important to avoid any heavy burden on the sense organs through which exhaustion of the central nervous system may occur. The exaggerations of natural weakness or partial loss of the functions of sight and hearing often seriously impair social efficiency in the contacts made by senile individuals and help to explain some of the personality changes. Tolerance of the situation and some aid from others may do much toward preventing a narrowing of the sphere of interests and a tendency to focus attention on the self. Physicians are prone to pay close attention to the changes in the individual himself and to neglect taking into consideration the effect of various social forces and attitudes.

The younger and more able associates of the senile should recognize and make allowances for the, at times, obvious loss of acuity, in dealing with situations that require fine discrimination and tact, in individuals who in their earlier days were able to handle such situations perfectly. A little diplomacy and encouragement may do much to relieve their tension. In many disagreeable seniles the picture is merely an exaggeration of an originally somewhat difficult personality of the projective type, in which self-control is now lost or weakened, allowing the character traits free play.

Tolerance and understanding should be exercised in connection with those aged people who by virtue of a temperament that may become exaggerated or distorted by complicating factors show a marked egoism, along with uneasiness, restlessness, and a tendency to harp on their difficulties. Some show a pronounced vulnerability of the psyche to small or relatively insignificant misunderstandings, which they may interpret as insults that provoke aggressive responses; while others react with a feeling of panic and complete helplessness whenever complicated situations present themselves. Thus the practical handling of these problems may be complicated in various ways and require some special study, but in general it can be said that anything should be done that will reduce the conflicts within the individual or between him and the social groups.

One cannot emphasize too strongly that chronological age is not an index of physiological age, and that physiological age is no index of psychological age or deterioration. Therefore each individual senile reaction must be considered in relation to the particular situation to be evaluated. But most cases should be approached with a realization that the physiological and mental mechanisms are less elastic than formerly, so that adjustments and compensations may not be readily accomplished. However, lack of plasticity is a personality phenomenon which age does not create but usually aggravates. The application of sound common sense, mixed with an understanding of the problems faced by the aged and reinforced by human sympathy, will do much to smooth out the difficulties inherent in the nature of human relationships. Social and cultural patterns must be changed, as simple advice to individuals will in many cases be ineffective. A new philosophy of life is needed, involving less striving for false goals, less worry, and less tension.

The attitude of the public toward the aged is a most important issue, and with proper education it can be changed, as it has already been regarding other important health matters.

REFERENCES

1. Bortz, E. L. "Geriatrics: New Light on Old Folks," *Clinics*, 1942, 1: 336
2. Carlson, A. J. "The Older Worker," *Sci. Monthly*, 1943, 57: 5
3. Davis, N. S. "Factors Which May Influence Senescence," *Ann. Internal Med.*, 1943, 18: 81
4. Diethelm, O. "Psychopathology of Aging," *Amer. Jour. Psychiatry*, 1943, 99: 553
5. Frankel, E. "Mental Hygiene Problems of the Aged," *Jour. Med. Soc. N.J.*, 1946, 43: 79–83
6. Frohlich, M. M. "Mental Hygiene in Old Age," in C. Tibbitts (ed.), *Living Through the Older Years*. Ann Arbor: University of Michigan Press, 1949, pp. 85–97
7. Gilbert, J. G. *Mental Efficiency in Senescence*. New York: Archives of Psychology, 1935
8. Kaplan, O. J. "The Mental Health of Older Workers," in M. Derber (ed.), *The Aged and Society*. Champaign, Ill.: Industrial Relations Assn., 1950, pp. 204–18
9. Korenchevsky, V. "The War and the Problem of Aging," *Jour. Amer. Med. Assoc.*, 1942, 119: 624
10. Lawton, G. (ed.). *New Goals for Old Age*. New York: Columbia University Press, 1943
11. Lemkau, P. V. "The Mental Hygiene of Aging," *Pub. Health Repts.*, 1952, 67: 237–41
12. Lewis, N. D. C. "Mental Hygiene of the Senium," *Ment. Hyg.*, 1940, 24: 434
13. Thewlis, M. W. "Care of the Aged," *Jour. Amer. Med. Assoc.*, 1942, 120: 749
14. Woltman, H. W. "Neuropsychiatric Geriatrics," *Arch. Ophthalmol.*, 1942, 28: 791
15. Zeman, F. D. "Constructive Programs for the Mental Health of the Elderly," *Ment. Hyg.*, 1951, 35: 221–34

Chapter XIX

ORIENTATION OF THE PROBLEMS

Edward J. Stieglitz

The problem of mental disease in later life is, in truth, many problems. Mental illness cannot be segregated from physical disease; disease cannot be sharply differentiated from health; and aging is a relative and asymmetric phenomenon. It cannot be overemphasized that the difference between "normal" and "abnormal" is nebulous and variable.

We do not know just where mental and physical health end and mental and physical disease begin. The disorders discussed in the previous chapters are in most instances obvious abnormalities. But they are not obvious in their beginnings, and it is at their beginnings that we may hope to find their causation and to apply corrective measures with reasonable anticipation of effectiveness.

These problems are so vast, so interrelated and overlapping that, without an attempt at orientation and organization, fundamental research and clinical application become disconnected and concerned with artificially isolated fractions of the whole. There are many ways in which we may attempt orientation; the present approach is certainly not the only one. Nor is it necessarily the most logical or pragmatic. Basically the problem as a whole resolves itself into two broad subdivisions: (a) the factors affecting mental health or illness arising from changes due to *aging of the individual,* and (b) the generic characteristics of the somatic and psychotic *disorders* most frequent and characteristic in this age group.

Any and all problems must be viewed from three perspectives to be fully comprehended. First, we need to study the problem with the naked eye; second, we must apply magnification to its component parts and activities; and last, we must step far enough back so that the problem may be inspected through a telescope and thus related to its external environment. Man lives in two environments: the external physical and social world, and the internal milieu of tissue juices, enzymatic activity, anabolism, and catabolism. Both environments are in a constant state of flux and kinetic adjustment. Both are significant to the unitary organism, man.

Translated into other terms, full comprehension of the potentialities of medicine involves three approaches: (*a*) the indivisible individual, psyche and soma as one, is the unit of study of clinical medicine; (*b*) magnification of the component parts—the biochemical reactions, electrical potentials, and cellular units which make up the individual—are the concern of the biological sciences, upon which clinical medicine depends for understanding the entity, man; and (*c*) man as a member of society, a unit of the external environment, is the concern of social medicine. He is affected by other people, climate, housing, food, threats of disaster, and at the same time his behavior affects his environment (32).

The concept of this triad of perspectives is an intellectual tool which has many applications. In the area of mental disease in later life, it provides a pattern for correlating primarily clinical individual problems (where man is the unit of thought) with the structural, biochemical, and physiologic phenomena of senescence (where the cell is the unit of attention), and the immensely complicated problems introduced by the recent unprecedented shifts in population structure toward a dramatic increase in the proportionate number of aging and aged (sociologic gerontology).

It may be useful to express the significance of the three perspectives in a slightly different manner. In the center we have man, the core of all our objectives in clinical medicine and all our endeavors in research and in study. Each man is composed of several billion cells. Thus, when we apply magnification and the cell becomes the unit of study rather than the individual as a whole, we see that we are dealing with several billion individual units which in complex combination make up the organism man. When these cells function harmoniously, man is healthy. On the other hand, society over the world at large is composed of over two billion human beings. Thus, society can be considered as a composite individual, having as its component parts individual men and women. Social illness or disorder arises when the individuals creating society fail to function properly and co-operatively, often because of their own impairment of health (8).

The problems of mental disease in later life are a subdivision of the greater whole—gerontology. Gerontology is the science of aging in all its aspects. Pursuit of knowledge over this wide continent of thought involves practically every scientific discipline thus far evolved. Gerontology is logically divided into three major categories, exemplifying the three perspectives discussed above:

1. Geriatric Medicine: The Clinical Problem of Aging Individuals

    1.1 "Normal" senescence

        1.11 Somatic aspects

            1) Relativity of health (27)

            2) Asymmetry of aging change (36)

            3) Optimum vs. average or "normal"

            4) Evaluation of a) biologic age

                                  b) degree of health

            5) Role of nutrition

        1.12 Psychic aspects

            1) Intellectual maturation

                a) Changes in values; perspective (29)

                b) Ability to learn (18, 30)

                c) Memory (11)

                d) Originality; imagination

                e) Role of intellectual habits (43)

                f) Judgment

            2) Emotional maturation

                a) Motivations

                b) Development of insight

                c) Development of self-discipline

                d) Genesis of asymmetric maturation (43)

                e) Role of education of fostering (or
                    retarding) maturation

                f) Role of familial and social milieu in
                    maturation (including religion)

                g) Role of psychologic traumata or stresses in
                    development of strength or weakness
                    (33)

    1.2 Disorders of the senescent period

        1.21 Modifications of diseases by age change in patient

        1.22 Characteristics of disorders typical of senescent
            period

1) Classification (major groups)
   a) Circulatory:

$$\text{arteriosclerosis}\begin{cases}\text{cerebral}\\\text{coronary}\\\text{aortic}\\\text{extremities}\\\text{pancreas}\\\text{kidney}\end{cases}\quad\begin{cases}\text{apoplexy}\\\text{dementias}\\\text{amentias}\end{cases}$$

        hypertensive disease

   b) Metabolic:
        diabetes mellitus
        gout
        anemia
        thyroid dysfunction
        climacterics
   c) Neoplasmata
   d) Arthropathies

2) Generic characteristics (26, 37)
   a) Multiple, obscure, endogenous, cumulative etiology
   b) Asymptomatic onsets
   c) Progressive course (prolonged disability)
   d) Overlapping: superimposition of several disorders simultaneously; enhancement of vulnerability (28)

2. The Biology of Senescence: Phenomena of Evolution and Involution
  2.11 Anatomic (structural)
  2.12 Physiologic (functional)
  2.13 Homeostatic
  2.14 Biochemical

$$2.15\ \text{Psychological}\begin{cases}\text{memory}\\\text{motivation}\\\text{learning capacity}\begin{cases}\text{rate}\\\text{accuracy}\end{cases}\\\text{judgment}\end{cases}$$

  2.16 Nutritional

3. Sociologic Gerontology (38, 39)

    3.1 Economic

        3.11 Employment

            a) Costs of premature retirement

            b) Costs of delayed retirement

            c) Placement

        3.12 Chronic illness and invalidism; institutional facilities (4, 5)

        3.13 Pensions; retirement

        3.14 Cost of dependent aged on $\begin{cases} \text{families} \\ \text{communities} \end{cases}$

        3.15 Housing and care facilities for aged $\begin{cases} \text{``normal''} \\ \text{physically infirm} \\ \text{amented} \\ \text{psychotic} \end{cases}$

    3.2 Cultural

        3.21 Education for senescence of $\begin{cases} \text{youths} \\ \text{adults} \\ \text{senescents} \end{cases}$

        3.22 Marriage (widowhood)

        3.24 Social attitudes toward aging

        3.25 Family attitudes toward aging (43)

        3.26 Cultural maturation $\begin{cases} \text{local} \\ \text{national} \\ \text{international (43)} \end{cases}$

This delineation of the problems of aging is, of necessity, highly condensed and indicates merely the major skeletal divisions. Each part or section includes subdivisions too numerous to record here. The outline is intended to be suggestive rather than fully comprehensive. These all present many unanswered questions in urgent need of elucidation. Theoretically, growth, development, differentiation, and maturation are just as much consequences of aging as are the involutional atrophies and metabolic changes of senescence, for the two groups of phenomena overlap and occur simultaneously throughout life from conception until death. The changes consequent upon aging progress at a diminishing rate over the life span.

The triad of primary categories which constitute the fundamental basis for gerontology are intimately and inseparably related, both pragmatically and theoretically. Though widely differing disciplines and techniques of scientific research must be applied in studies into the problems of aging, the observations and conclusions derived therefrom will still fit into the pattern and thus amplify the whole. Advances in any subdivision depend greatly upon parallel or preceding progress in other categories. It cannot be overemphasized that the more that is known about the fundamental biologic mechanisms of the aging process, the more effectively can clinical medicine treat the aging and aged. Likewise, the more comprehensive our clinical knowledge concerning the altering capacities and limitations of normal elderly persons and the prevention, control, or retardation of the chronic and progressive mental and physical disorders of later years, the more intelligently can the many serious social problems be attacked.

More specifically, geriatric psychiatry must include within its field both the so-called "normal" changes consequent to senescence and the mental disorders characteristic of later maturity. These disorders arise and progress in individuals who are altered by reason of their age. Thus the pattern of change is affected by (*a*) the characteristics of aging individuals; (*b*) the characteristics of the significant disorders, which involves analysis of their etiology, pathogenesis, and prognosis; and (*c*) the social environment in which the disorders arise and are perpetuated, thus creating sociologic problems of great urgency (24, 27, 38).

Prevention of disease has been the ideal of medicine for many generations. As an ideal this objective needs revision, for it is based upon an outmoded definition of health. Definition of health as that state of being existing in the absence of disease is, or should be, obsolete. We know now that health is a relative state, with quantitative attributes involving reserve capacities. Mere absence of demonstrable disease does not mean we are in full vigorous health, mentally and physically. Normal, which implies average or mean, is not enough. Optimum or ideal health is probably never attained, although we may approach it.

If we view the problems of health and disease in the light of these ideas it becomes possible to add to the conventional objectives of therapy (prevention, cure, palliation) the objective of actively

constructing a greater degree of health. The treatment of the sick
and disabled is an attempt at the reconstruction of health, but we
can and should go one step farther, by treating the *apparently*
healthy and making them healthier (23). This approach we have
termed constructive medicine (25, 27).

A constructive approach to mental health is just as feasible as
efforts to build greater physical health. In fact, the two are inseparable. In psychiatric circles the growing emphasis upon mental
hygiene implies increasing awareness of the potentialities of this
viewpoint.

The greatest obstacles to preventive medicine have been the general feeling that preventive measures are negative and restrictive,
and the fact that the results of preventive activities are demonstrable
only statistically. Statistics have little emotional appeal; they rarely
induce intense enthusiasm or maintained, conscientious co-operation. We have no means of proving that prophylactic measures save
any specific individual from disaster. The inertia against active
efforts toward prophylaxis should be definitely diminished by a
change in attitude from attempts at mere prevention of disaster to
efforts to improve the individual's personal status. With such an
approach the patient is directly aware of his improvement in vigor,
endurance, and enthusiasm.

Constructive medicine, in contrast to preventive medicine, must
be much more individualistic. The wholesale or public-health
measures of sanitation, mass immunization, and control of hazards
in the environment are utterly inapplicable to the disorders common to senescence. Public health works from without; private
health must come from within. Smallpox, diphtheria, typhoid fever,
and the like are invariably exogenous; environmental control can
and does prevent them. But arteriosclerosis, diabetes mellitus,
hypertension, melancholia, and neurosis are endogenous. Neither
quarantine nor sanitation will prevent these "degenerative" diseases. To prevent or retard these disorders we must work with individuals. The only wholesale measure which remains appropriate
to constructive medicine among mature adults is education. That
there are gross deficiencies in our programs of adult education must
be apparent to all (27, 29).

But spoon-fed education—whether for adults or for children—
and even highly individualized guidance will not be enough. The

basic prerequisite to any worth-while accomplishment along these lines is a reawakened recognition and acceptance of individual responsibility. Life does not owe us health any more than life owes us wealth, freedom, or a place in the sun. As health is a privilege, it entails the responsibility for its maintenance and improvement, just as owning an automobile is a privilege involving a not dissimilar responsibility. This sense of individual responsibility has been permitted to atrophy; pampering paternalism and social measures to increase dependence of the individual on the state have actively fostered this greatest of all the many intrinsic weaknesses which contribute to impairment of mature mental health.

Paralleling the concept of constructive medicine is the idea of *anticipatory* medicine. Knowledge of the changes inherent in senescence and in the slowly progressive, chronic disorders of later maturity has now reached a point where it is possible often to predict the future course with a reasonable degree of accuracy. For example, an acceleration of arteriosclerotic change can be predicted if hypercholesterolemia, obesity, and the late type of diabetes mellitus coexist. Control of the diabetes and a low-fat, weight-reducing program can do much to retard the development of cerebral arteriosclerosis and its associated mental deterioration. Similarly, the cardiac consequences of hypertensive disease can be anticipated and cerebral circulatory failure greatly delayed by appropriate anticipatory therapy (34, 36).

An attitude of anticipation, and therefore of prevention of avoidable injury, is particularly feasible in the field of emotional problems. Geriatric psychiatry must develop a strong sense of anticipation if it is to fully utilize its great potentialities. There are many *predictable emotional hazards* in senescence; forewarning and preparation can and do prevent and avoid much damage. Among the many predictable traumata are such experiences as loss of children, loss of parents, excessive survival of parents, loss of beauty and vigor, the emotional trauma of mutilating surgery (mutilating to the patient, though perhaps not appearing to be mutilating to the surgeon), inadequate promotion, excessive promotion, retirement, and many others. We do not know *just when* these traumata will occur, but certainly they are part of the calculated risk of senescence. By anticipation and preparation through education, motivation, and the development of multiple channels of interest, much of the injury inherent in these vicissitudes of existence can be averted.

However, before constructive or anticipatory medicine can be applied to mature adults, an analysis of the individual's health is necessary (31, 36). It does not suffice merely to search for evidences of disease. Health has quantitative attributes. If, for the sake of the present discussion, we define *health as that state of being existing when all the functional capacities of the organism are maximal for the species,* we see that perfection is truly unattainable, though approachable, even in the absence of disease. For example, at an age when the capacity to run the 100-yard dash is at its maximum, the capacity for judgment is by no means fully developed; by the time judgment attains its greatest vigor, the ability to run rapidly has grossly depreciated. Thus the mensuration of health is something quite different from diagnosis directed solely to the discovery of disease (1, 12, 36).

Health is kinetic and cannot be measured under static conditions. The only way in which reserve capacities can be determined is by observing the promptness and effectiveness of response to stress. Every function, be it mental or physical, has its ceiling; every one of us will break if the stresses are made severe enough. There are limits to what the normal heart can stand in physical effort, and there are limits to what the normal psyche can tolerate in the way of fear and repression of rage. These limits vary from individual to individual, from function to function, and from hour to hour. Fundamentally, the difference between many of the chronic sick and the well is that the former have thresholds or ceilings so low that they fail in their adjustments under the usual stresses of living.

Perhaps our greatest need is for methods of measuring functional reserve capacities of all sorts; if we were able to do this effectively it would be possible to discover depreciations in health long before the appearance of frank, florid disease. The earlier such discovery can be made, the more we can learn regarding the causation of health depreciation and the pathogenesis of various progressive diseases, and the more effective can be control or retardative therapy (11, 15, 36).

The measurement of mental or physical health is extremely difficult. In addition to the inevitable individualistic variation, which is characteristic of all living organisms, we have to keep in mind the effects of aging per se upon the efficiency of various bodily and mental activities. Training, habits, education, prolonged use or disuse, hereditary constitution, and many other factors introduce other variables in apparently normal individuals. Aging intensifies variability. The complex phenomena of senescence are definitely asymmetric. Aging does not progress at the same rate in different individuals, nor in different parts of the same individual. Aging proceeds at different rates at different periods of the life span. Biologic time, or the rate of living, does not parallel chronologic or solar time except in a very crude and approximate manner. To use chronologic age as the basis for comparison of different functional capacities leads to confusion in the interpretation of results. Several students of this complex problem have attempted to set up weighted criteria for the evaluation of health or biologic age (1, 12), but because of the infinite variation they result in approximations only a little less crude than those arrived at by that intangible but precious sense called "clinical judgment."

The sum total of the functional capacities of the aging organism declines. But some capacities depreciate more rapidly than others, and a very few may actually increase during senescence and even early senility. Certainly judgment improves with senescence, for judgment is based upon experience and experience is a factor of time or age. Obviously aging does not *create* critical judgment; it fosters its growth when intelligence exists in youth and the faculty is continually exercised. The young fool will become the old fool if he lives long enough. But the bright boy *should* become a seer.

The significance in the differential depreciation of various faculties lies in the fact that we may hope to retard loss of vigor in those capacities which usually depreciate the slowest. Training during maturity and early senescence has potentialities which have never been fully appreciated. Though it is always possible to teach an old dog new tricks if the teacher knows more than the dog, the truly senile have relatively little motivation for the requisite expenditure of energy. Exercise, which always encourages growth, whether it be of the muscle fibers of the biceps or of creative imagination, must be *started early* and *continued* until the end. It is highly probable that depreciation in learning ability (11, 18, 43), in muscular strength, in judgment, and in emotional adaptability are effected more by disuse than by aging alone.

We have tried to point out above the great complexity and difficulty in measuring somatic health. The question of assessing mental health is even more difficult. Intellectual and emotional capacities are more often than not extremely asymmetric. A considerable battery of tests, not yet devised, will be required to obtain an approximation of psychic health. Most of the psychological tests have been prepared for children, adolescents, or young adults (18). New methods are requisite for the more mature, with new criteria and new standards of so-called "normal" performance (7). Furthermore, methods of measuring emotional maturity must await the time when psychiatric science can more adequately define what emotional maturity is. It is essential to keep in mind, however, that the fundamental criterion for the mensuration of any functional capacity is the ability to respond to stress. Therefore, all test procedures which are set up to evaluate reserves must experimentally create specific functional stress.

To age is to change. The aging or aged individual is a different person than he was in his youth. There is a parallelism between the concepts of pediatrics and those of geriatrics. Pediatric medicine made little advance until it was realized that the child is something different than merely "a little man." When it was finally appreciated that infantile and juvenile nutrition, anatomy, physiology, immunity, intelligence, and emotional equilibrium are peculiar to the age, pediatrics made impressive and rapid strides. Precisely similar attitudes should apply when we are dealing with the other end of the life span. The aged should not be considered as identical or even closely similar to individuals in middle life, merely chronologically older.

The changes which come with age are not due *solely* to the passage of time. In addition we accumulate the consequences of innumerable insults. The greater the age, the greater the accumulation and the more significant the consequent scars become. In every life there occur repeated infections, intoxications, fatigues—psychic and physical traumata—which in summation constitute the unavoidable vicissitudes of existence. It is significant that no two people experience identical sources of injury; variation in content, severity, and sequences are inevitable. This is a major factor in the increasing divergence and variation between individuals. Constant awareness of the necessity for individualization in the study and care of the aging and the aged is fundamental to good geriatric medicine (36).

Detrimental experiences are part of living, for existence in a sterile and completely sheltered environment can hardly be called life. Such would be mere existence. Though the price paid for experience is an accumulative scarring, the profit in richness, accomplishment, satisfaction is worth the cost. Life is a kinetic phenomenon, and stresses and conflicts serve as stimuli encouraging growth and vigor in all structures and functions. For example, it is doubtful whether an infant fed from birth on nothing but purified amino acids, fats, and glucose, with suitable vitamins and minerals, would ever develop sufficiently vigorous digestive secretions to be able to enjoy and digest a steak in later years.

Fear has been called a psychologically injurious experience. There are those who insist that the child be sheltered from *all* fear, that a sense of complete security is the desideratum of healthy, happy living. That this is absurd becomes apparent when one admits, first, that security is a myth, nonexistent and but a product of delusive, wishful thinking; and second, that fear is absolutely essential for the development of courage. The absence of fear is not courage. It is stupidity, an unawareness of hazard. Courage cannot grow or be exercised without the concomitant stimulation of fear.

Thus we reiterate for emphasis: the physical and psychic traumata of living are simultaneously potentially detrimental or destructive and potentially useful or constructive. The factor which determines which consequences will predominate is not the nature of the experience, but the character of the individual's reaction to the experience.

This is not the place, nor is there sufficient space, to discuss all the many changes in structure, function, nutrition, and the like which take place with aging (29, 36). We must let it suffice to state that functional capacities change, and that not all the alterations are necessarily in the direction of decline. There is great individual variation, and some changes are definitely amenable to improvement. The changes are very slow, insidious, and may become truly extensive before the functional capacity falls to levels of minimal functional demand.

Section 1.2 of the schema on page 478 enumerates most of the particularly significant disorders characteristic of later life and indicates the more pertinent of their generic characteristics. Particularly important are the common denominators in etiology, onset and course, progression, and overlapping. These disorders all arise from multiple and variable etiologic factors. They are endogenous. The causative influences are cumulative and obscure. In no two instances is the causation necessarily identical. A combination of insults lasting over a long period of time, individually differing in character, sequence, and intensity, cause the degenerative lesions. Each case is a wholly individual problem. No one will ever find "the cause" of hypertensive disease or diabetes. Causation is always multiple. As both curative and preventive therapy must be based upon correction of etiology to be truly effective, the obscurity of the causation of these disorders constitutes our greatest handicap to successful treatment. Unremitting search and research for contributing factors is prerequisite to therapeutic success.

These disorders begin asymptomatically. They are "fifth-column" diseases, silent saboteurs. Thus, to be discovered early they must be searched for. Furthermore, what symptoms do arise are secondary and indirect. For example, there is no kinesthetic sense by which the patient is made aware of the fact that his arterial tension is high: impairment of the circulation to the brain produces neurologic symptoms and signs; and impairment of the pancreatic circulation may cause diabetes mellitus with an entirely different set of clinical phenomena; yet all are due to fundamentally identical circulatory inadequacy. Symptoms are expressions of functional changes of the parenchymatous structures, although the primary disorder exists in the matrix tissues. Damage is done by impairing the nutrition of various parenchymal tissues. One or more of the following mechanisms are involved:

1. Inadequate nutritional supply
2. Ineffective nutritional transport
3. Inefficient nutritional utilization
4. Insufficient removal of metabolic debris

These factors often overlap. For example, histanoxia, or cellular oxygen inadequacy, may be induced by a combination of lowered cardiac efficiency, hypertensive arteriolar constriction with capillary stasis, and anemia. If glucose combustion is likewise impaired because of hypo-insulinism, the impairment of tissue metabolism is further aggravated. Recovery from congestive cardiac failure is often much accelerated by liberal oral glucose administration and/or large doses of the vitamin B complex in addition to the conventional therapy of digitalization and bed rest. The nutrition of an exhausted or injured structure is vitally significant.

Progression, slow but diabolically persistent, is characteristic of all these degenerative disorders. None is self-limited. Three therapeutic implications of this universal attribute are worthy of mention:

1. To be successful, therapy must be instituted early in the course of these diseases before permanent, irrevocable, and irreparable organic changes become manifest. To discover arteriosclerosis, diabetes mellitus, and the like early, we must search for them in the relatively well adult.

2. Frequently, maintenance of the patient in the status quo is a true therapeutic accomplishment. Late in the course of these disorders all we can hope to attain is an arrest or retardation of the progression. It is often wisest to explain this to the patient, who then may cease searching for impossible miracles.

3. Prolonged disability prior to final death is to be expected. From the viewpoint of geriatrics as a social problem, this is perhaps the most important facet of the whole question (4). These disorders are not curable in the usually accepted sense, but they are controllable and can be retarded in their progression. There is often greater hazard in limiting the activities of the chronically ill senile than in encouraging them to be more active. Our primary objective in treating the aged is to increase the spread between disease, disability, and death.

These disorders rarely occur alone. Usually several are superimposed. None of them confer immunity; rather do they make the patient more vulnerable to other so-called degenerative depreciations (28). Mixed forms are common and one must be on his guard against too precise definitions of entities. For example, arteriosclerosis with preponderant cardiac (coronary) symptoms probably does not occur without less obvious but significant cerebral and renal arteriosclerosis. In hypertensive arterial disease (40) one must assume simultaneous cardiac injury. Hypothyroidism impairs the efficiency of all tissues. In the aged, one frequently finds hypertrophic arthritis and gout superimposed. Anemia is more often than not of mixed pathogenesis, due both to nutritional deficiency and primary hematopoietic failure.

An attempt at classification of the more specifically psychiatric disorders common in the geriatric age range may assist to orientation. The following is but one of several possible classifications:

1. Mental Disease Secondary to Progressive Somatic Changes
   1.1 Impairment of cerebral circulation (nutrition)
       1.11 Artériosclerotic dementia (6)
       1.12 Senile amentia (3)
       1.13 Encephalopathy of hypertensive disease
           a) Chronic, progressive
           b) Acute psychosis of $\begin{cases} \text{vascular crises} \\ \text{relative hypotension (21)} \end{cases}$
           c) Cerebral apoplexy (2)
       1.14 Alzheimer's disease (2)
       1.15 Pick's disease
       1.16 Intracranial aneurysms
       1.17 Parkinson's disease
   1.2 Precipitated by endocrine impairment (presumed)
       1.21 Involutional melancholia (basically a personality problem) (14, 16)
   1.3 Toxic psychosis (aggravated by impaired elimination)
       1.31 Bromidism
       1.32 Barbiturate intoxication
       1.33 Delirium of infections
       1.34 Alcoholic encephalopathy

2. Pre-existing Psychosis Persisting into the Senium (*any* chronic mental illness)
   2.1 General paresis
   2.2 Schizophrenia
   2.3 Manic-depressive psychosis
   2.4 Etc., etc.

3. Psychoneuroses (*most important*)
   3.1 Prolonged anxiety (rage, fear, etc.) leading to somatic consequences and etiologically significant in the genesis of hypertensive disease (17, 19, 20, 21, 22)
       peptic ulcer
       colitis

constipation
obesity (29, 35, 41)
diabetes mellitus
etc., etc.

There are three reasons for emphasizing the importance of the psychoneuroses in geriatric psychiatry: (*a*) the immense numerical frequency of prolonged anxiety states; (*b*) the serious somatic consequences which develop insidiously and lead to long and increasing disablement (20) (the factor of duration of anxiety states is at least as significant and probably more important than the factor of intensity in the genesis of psychosomatic disorders); and (*c*) the fact that, if discovered early, these disorders are amenable to both somatic treatment and psychotherapy (10, 19, 42).

We must not ignore the profoundly significant implications inherent in the all too common sequence of events: Prolonged anxiety (neurosis) → somatic vascular disease (hypertensive) → cerebral malcirculation and malnutrition → organic psychosis. Though this development of irreparable damage to the brain is very slow, the progression is persistent and the duration of somatic and psychic disablement is very long. The percentage of mental patients requiring institutional care because of cerebral vascular disease has increased alarmingly. Its future increase may be expected to be even greater. This fact alone, even ignoring many other important facets of the problem, justifies constant reiteration of the necessity of developing the potentialities of anticipatory medicine, both in research and clinical practice.

The tremendous and increasing economic load of mental incapacity among the aging and the aged of our population should be a matter of grave concern to everyone (9, 29). Solution of this problem will require much labor and the co-operative efforts of the best minds in many disciplines. There is no easy road. The dramatic increase in the elderly in the population, due largely to the saving of lives in youth, would be a glorious triumph of medical and social progress were it not for the fact that increased longevity is too rarely associated with continued health, happiness, and usefulness. It might be wise to pause and question whether the beautiful, chivalrous, and sublimely generous attitude of doing everything within our power to assist the survival of the relatively unfit is also wise. The time may not be far off when the enhanced survival of the unfit makes survival of the fit increasingly precarious.

In the twenty-five years from 1910 to 1935 annual admissions to mental hospitals per 100,000 of the population of persons aged 60 and over increased from 184 to 418, or 227 per cent greater. The rate of admissions because of arteriosclerotic disease of the brain increased 536 per cent within these two and a half decades (9). In New York State, 21.3 per cent of all patients in the state mental hospitals were 60 years or over in 1915; in 1930 this age group constituted 24.9 per cent of the patient load; and in 1947, 33.2 per cent. Where and how to care for these patients is a problem deserving much more energetic effort than it has heretofore received (5).

The question of housing and care of the elderly is logically divisible into the following categories:

1. The Elderly
2. The Elderly and Infirm
3. The Elderly Sick
   3.1 The acutely sick
   3.2 The chronically sick, potentially remedial
   3.3 The chronically sick, probably irremedial
4. The Psychiatrically Sick
   4.1 Amented; confused
   4.2 Neurotic
   4.3 Psychotic

It should be obvious that these different groups require differing facilities for proper, decent care and maintenance. However, they are not sharply demarcated groups; there is much overlapping and a given individual may shift from one category to another quite abruptly. Equally important to the existence of the proper facilities is creating means for rapid, easy transfer from one type of facility to another. If reams of red tape must be unwound before an elderly patient recently over the acute phase of an illness can be transferred to a place dedicated to convalescent care and/or back again, the whole system will break down. At present, neither the proper facilities nor transfer arrangement exists.

One basic and urgent reason for the need of decent and much more comprehensive facilities for the care of the infirm aged (including under infirmity both psychic and somatic disease) is the very serious problem created by the continued residence of elderly individuals in the homes of their children. Two adult generations do not survive well together under the same roof. Both suffer. There comes a time when parents should leave home. This is no isolated or occasional problem; it is numerically immense. The Bureau of the Census has estimated that 20 per cent of men between 70 and 74 years of age live with their children, and that 35 per cent of similarly aged women live with their descendants.

The aged are uncomfortable in the households of their children. They are aware of their uselessness, recognize that they are intruding, feel guilty over being an economic burden, and bitterly resent their loss of independence and the privilege of making their own decisions. The members of the younger generation naturally resent the obstacle to their freedom of activity and their social life, as well as the additional economic burden, but, having been brought up to feel grateful and obligated to their parents, are beset by guilt. This guilt often leads to absurd overcompensation in the form of extreme solicitude. Adults, as a rule, love their aged parents but do not like them. Not until people become aware of the terrible psychologic price being paid by both generations will the nation create the needed facilities. At present, facilities are grossly inadequate. Usually they are either barely decent or prohibitivly expensive. Here is one area in which psychiatry and the social sciences working co-operatively can do a great deal. For example, there are to my knowledge no reported analyses of the desires and tastes of the aged. As a result, no one has the slightest notion just what sort of "Home for the Aged" is most appropriate. Young men and women have planned the present homes; we might assure much greater happiness for the senile if we tried to fit the shoe to the foot rather than to force the foot into the shoe. The need is urgent.

In conclusion, we reiterate that we have hoped only to orient mental disease in later years in the immensely broad field of gerontology. Mental diseases constitute, however, one of the most urgent and fundamentally important segments, for upon the mental integrity of the seniors of our population depends the future of mankind.

Advance into the largely unexplored realm of the involutional period of life must be multidisciplined. The various sectors are mutually interdependent. New knowledge in any one area affects the strategy of research in all other areas. Because of this interdependence, there is need for orchestration of individual efforts. Such orchestration is brought about by symposial volumes such as this, and by conferences at which the different specialties of clinical and experimental medicine are represented.

Aging is a process which affects all of us, and the consequences of this process are varied. The changes are both mental and physical and cannot be separated. A man must be considered as a unit. The whole of a man is greater than the sum of his component parts. Tremendously increased longevity is here. It will certainly increase further. Lengthening of the life span may become either a curse or a blessing, depending upon whether longevity is associated with disabling illness or with health. The present rate at which hospitals for mental disease are admitting older patients is cause for real alarm. Chronic disablement from progressive physical disorders of later years is already a heavy social burden. But the future is not all dark. Science has explored far into the physical world about us. Application of our new knowledge has exploited many wondrous potentialities for our benefit. It is the future task of science to explore the potentialities of man himself. The full capacities of man will not be revealed until senescence is more fully understood. If medical and psychiatric guidance can make the later years of life ones of *continuing maturation*, the future of man should be bright indeed. The time has come at last when men are living long enough to have time to think.

REFERENCES

1. Benjamin, H. "Biologic Versus Chronologic Age," *Jour. Gerontol.*, 1947, 2: 217
2. Camp, C., "Organic Diseases of the Brain, the Spinal Cord and the Peripheral Nerves," Chapter 19 in E. J. Steiglitz (ed.), *Geriatric Medicine* (3d edition). Philadelphia: J. B. Lippincott, 1954.
3. Cobb, S. *Borderlands of Psychiatry*. Cambridge: Harvard University Press, 1943
4. Commission on Chronic Illness. *Proceedings, Conference on Chronic Illness: Preventive Aspects*. Chicago, 1951
5. Committee on Hospitals, Group Advancement of Psychiatry. "The Aged Patient in the Public Psychiatric Hospital," *Geriatrics*, 1951, 6: 57
6. Dörken, H., and Kral, V. A. "Psychological Investigation of Senile Dementia," *ibid.*, 1951, 6: 151
7. Granick, S. "The Psychology of Senility: A Review," *Jour. Gerontol.*, 1950,

5: 44; "Studies in Psychopathology in Later Maturity," *ibid.*, 1950, 5: 361
8. Halliday, J. L. *Psychosocial Medicine.* New York: W. W. Norton and Co., 1948
9. Landis, C., and Page, J. D. *Modern Society and Mental Disease.* New York: Farrar and Rinehart, 1938
10. Levine, M. *Psychotherapy in Medical Practice.* New York: The Macmillan Co., 1945
11. Miles, W., and Miles, C. Chapter 5 in E. J. Stieglitz (ed.), *Geriatric Medicine* (2d edition) (Philadelphia: W. B. Saunders, 1949)
12. Murray, I. M. "Assessment of Physiologic Age," *Jour. Gerontol.*, 1951, 6: 120
13. National Institute of Mental Health. "Patients in State Mental Hospitals: 1948," Mental Health Statistics, U.S. Public Health Service. Washington, D.C.: Government Printing Office, June 1950
14. Palmer, H. D. "Mental Disorders of Old Age," *Geriatrics*, 1946, 1: 60
15. *Proceedings of the Conference on Mental Health in Later Maturity, May 23-24, 1941.* Supplement 168 to *U.S. Pub. Health Reports.* Washington, D.C.: Government Printing Office, 1942
16. Stevens, H. "Psychiatric Disorders of the Senium," *Clinics*, 1946, 4: 1301
17. Stevenson, I., Duncan, C. H., and Ripley, H. S. "Variations in the Electrocardiogram Changes in Emotional State," *Geriatrics*, 1951, 6: 164
18. Thorndike, E. L., Bregman, E. O., Tilton, J. W., and Woodward, E. *Adult Learning.* New York: The Macmillan Co., 1936
19. Weiss, E. *Emotional Factors in Cardiovascular Disease.* American Lecture Series, Monograph 97. Springfield, Ill.: Charles C Thomas, 1951
20. Weiss, E., and English, O. S. *Psychosomatic Medicine* (2d edition). Philadelphia: W. B. Saunders, 1949
21. Stieglitz, E. J. *Arterial Hypertension.* New York: P. B. Hoeber, 1930
22. ———. "Emotional Hypertension," *Am. J. Med. Sci.*, 1930, 179: 775
23. ———. "The Potentialities of Preventive Geriatrics," *New England Jour. Med.*, 1941, 225: 247
24. ———. Chapter 33 in E. V. Cowdry (ed.), *Problems of Ageing* (2d edition) (Baltimore: Williams & Wilkins, 1942)
25. ———. "Senescence and Industrial Efficiency," *Proceedings Industrial Hygiene Foundation of America.* November 10-11, 1943
26. ———. "Pertinent Problems of Geriatric Medicine," *Annals Int. Med.*, 1943, 18: 89
27. ———. *A Future for Preventive Medicine.* New York: Commonwealth Fund, 1945
28. ———. "Difficulties in the Clinical Recognition of Degenerative Diseases," in *Biological Symposia*, Vol. XI, *Aging and Degenerative Diseases* (edited by Robert Moore). Lancaster, Pa.: J. Cattell Press, 1945
29. ———. *The Second Forty Years.* Philadelphia: Lippincott, 1946
30. ———. "Geriatrics," *Jour. Gerontol.*, 1946, 1: 153
31. ———. "The Periodic Health Inventory," *Clinics*, 1946, 4:1322
32. ———. "The Importance of Perspective," *Medical Annals of the District of Columbia*, 1947, 16: 506
33. ———. "Factors Contributing to Mental Disease in the Aged," *Jour. Gerontol.*, 1947, 2: 280

34. ———. "Preventive Geriatric Medicine," *Journal-Lancet*, February 1945, 65: 60; "Preventive Medicine in Later Maturity," *Health Ed. Jour.* (London), October 1947, 5: 151

35. ———. "Therapy of the Aged," *Medical Annals of the District of Columbia*, 1948, 17: 197

36. ———. (ed.). *Geriatric Medicine: The Care of the Aging and Aged* (3d edition). Philadelphia: J. B. Lippincott, 1954

37. ———. "Medicine in an Aging Population," *Med. Clin. No. Am.*, March 1949

38. ———. "Integration of Clinical and Social Medicine," in I. Galdston (ed.), *Social Medicine: Its Derivations and Objectives.* (New York: Commonwealth Fund, 1949)

39. ———. "Orientation in Gerontology," in *Biological Foundations of Health Education* (New York: Columbia University Press, 1950)

40. ———. "Arterial Hypertension," Chapter 34 in W. D. Stroud (ed.), *The Diagnosis and Treatment of Cardiovascular Disease* (3d edition) (Philadelphia: F. A. Davis, 1950)

41. ———. "Nutrition Problems of Geriatric Medicine," *Jour. A. M. A.*, 1950, 142: 1070

42. ———. "Psychiatric Hazards of Senescence," *Proceedings, Training Seminar*, April 30, 1950, American Psychological Association, 1950

43. ———. Unpublished data

INDEX

Abraham, K., 425
Ackelsberg, S. B., 117
Ackermann, P. G., 60, 182
Adams, C. W., 106
Addis, T., 68, 69
Adlersberg, D., 37
Adolph, E. F., 57
age, physiological, 461
aging, physiology of, 47–49
Akelaitis, A. J., 275, 281
Albright, F., 182, 184, 246, 247
alcoholics, 28
Alex, M., 59
Alexander, F., 410
Alexander, F. A. D., 70
Alexander, G. H., 447
Allen, E., 71, 305
Allen, W. M., 71
Allen, W. R., 107
Allibone, E. C., 53
Almansi, R., 257, 259, 446
Altmann, E., 272
Alvarez, W. C., 68
Alving, A. S., 68
Alzheimer, A., 263, 267, 291, 312
Alzheimer's disease (*see* presenile dementias)
Ames, L. B., 135, 136
amyotrophic lateral sclerosis, 35
Andrew, W., 47, 48, 63, 64
anoxia and mental functioning, 75
Anschuetz, R., 69
anticipatory medicine, 483
Arataki, M., 63, 68
Arey, L. B., 69, 74
Army Alpha intelligence test, 104, 105, 108
Arnott, W. M., 56
arteriosclerosis, 3, 60; and Chinese, 4; and heredity, 37
arteriosclerosis, cerebral, with psychosis, 37–38, 39, 312–27, 490; anatomic changes in, 312–17; course of, 322–24; diagnosis of, 98–99, 324–27; ecology of, 158–63; etiology of, 317–18; mental symptoms, 319–21; physical changes in, 321–22; prodromal symptoms of, 318; treatment of, 327–28
Atkin, S., 223, 225
attitudes of society toward aged, 168–70
attractiveness, maintenance of, 205–6, 468
Aub, J. C., 69

Ault, C. C., 71
awareness of aging, 136–37, 423
Ayman, D., 37

Babcock, H., 116
Babcock test of mental efficiency, 116
Baldwin, E., 67
Barker, L., 203, 219, 228, 239
Barnacle, C., 446
Barnes, A. R., 70
Barnum, D. R., 56
Barrett, A. M., 291
Barry, E., 53
Bauer, J., 37, 71
Baumann, E. J., 63
Baumgartner, L., 70
Bayley, N., 61
Bebin, J., 35, 36
Becker, P. E., 36
Beeton, M., 29
Belknap, I., 173
Bell, A. G., 29
Bell, J. P., 51
Benda, C. E., 386
Benedict, F. G., 62
Benjamin, B., 65
Benjamin, H., 484, 485
Bennett, A. E., 259
Berens, C., 72
Berg, E. A., 113
Berg, M., 179
Berger, E. Y., 59
Berger, H., 276
Berkson, J., 62, 68
Berlin, L., 280
Bernard, C., 49
Bertrand, I., 272, 281
Best, C. R., 280
Bick, M. W., 72
Bielschowsky, 343
Bigelow, G. H., 69
Bigelow, N., 257, 259
Binet, L., 62
Bini, L., 263, 264, 272
Binswanger, O., 291, 315, 316
Birren, J. E., 64, 72, 73, 102, 103, 107, 115
Blain, D., 312, 316
Blanchard, J., 69
Bland, E. F., 60
Bleuler, E., 308
Bleuler, M., 36

497

Bliss, S. W., 52
blood: acid-base balance of, 55–56; regulation of electrolytes, 57–59; regulation of sugar, 51–55; regulation of water, 57–59
Bloomfield, A. L., 68
blow, swiftness of, 114
Boas, E. P., 37, 67
Boehm, A. E., 395
Boek, J., 178, 182, 185
Bogaert, L. Van, 264, 281
Bogdonoff, M. D., 60
Bogen, E. F., 352
Boice, M. L., 72
Bondy, E., 33
Bonfiglio, F., 271, 272, 273
Bonhoeffer, K., 342
Boothby, W. M., 29
Bortz, E. L., 54
Botwinick, J., 73, 102, 115
Bourcier, A., 204, 228
Bourlière, F., 62, 69
Bowie, M. A., 63
Bowman, K. M., 76, 77, 233
Boyd, D. A., 268, 272
Braceland, F. J., 77, 335
Bradley, J., 76, 77
Bramwell, J. C., 66
Brandfonbrener, M., 53, 67
Braunmühl, A. von, 35, 36, 271, 272, 274, 296, 297
Breed, E. S., 67
Breen, W. J., 74
Bregman, E. O., 118, 120, 495
Brenner, L. O., 70
Brew, M. F., 218, 256
Brewer, W. D., 178, 182, 185
Brikates, P., 257, 259
Britton, S. W., 52
Brodie, B. B., 59
Brody, E. B., 74
Brody, M. B., 117
Brody, S., 47
Brouha, L., 77
Brown, C. F. G., 70
Brown, C. W., 107
Brown, E. C., 178, 182, 185
Brown, M. M., 117
Brucer, M., 66
Bruck, M., 66
Brugsch, J. T., 346
Buccianti, L., 48, 63
Bucher, N. L. R., 69
Buhler, C., 135
Bunch, C. C., 73
Burch, G. E., 62, 67

Bürger, M., 47, 53, 60, 61
Burgess, E. W., 135
Burlingame, C. C., 71, 246
Burn, J. H., 52
Burns, E. L., 69
Butler, F. O., 394
Buvat, J. F., 272

Cady, L. H., 56
calcium, metabolism of, 59–60
Caldwell, B. M., 71, 102, 128
Cameron, D. E., 124, 127, 128, 135, 147, 300, 442
Cameron, N., 122, 125, 208, 305, 307
Camp, C. D., 110, 490
Cannon, W. B., 49, 52
capacity, vital, 114–15
Cardona, F., 274
Carlson, A. J., 59
Carrel, A., 60, 69
Carter, H. D., 114
Casperson, R. C., 73
Cavan, R. S., 135
CAVD test, 107, 108
Cederquist, D. C., 178, 182, 185
cells, aging of, 3
Census (see U.S. Bureau of the Census)
cerebellar ataxia, 35
Chamberlain, K., 182, 189
Chambers, W. H., 347
Chapman, W. P., 48, 73
Charles, D. C., 392
Chase, W. P., 107
Chaves, A. D., 29
Chen, K. K., 70
Chesrow, E. J., 67
Chieffi, M., 183
Child, C. M., 47, 48
Chittick, R. A., 78
chlorpromazine, 341
Ciocco, A., 73
Cleveland, S. E., 115
climacteric: female, 71, 245, 425; male, 71, 245
Cline, W. B., Jr., 342, 343
Clow, H. E., 305, 323, 335
Cobb, S., 312, 316, 404, 490
Cogswell, H. D., 71
Cohn, A. E., 62, 67
Cohn, J. V., 343
Coleman, J. V., 342, 343
collagen, 75
Colledge, L., 73
Comroe, J. H., Jr., 56
Conner, C. L., 344
Conrad, H., 121

Conrad, H. S., 104, 105, 113, 114
conservatism of aged, 213
Cooper, E. R. A., 64
Corbin, K. B., 73
Cornaro, L., 178
Corner, G. W., 409
Corsini, R. J., 105
Corwin, W., 53
Cournand, A., 67
Covell, W. P., 73
Cowdry, E. V., 37, 48, 58, 59, 60, 64, 67, 71, 72, 73, 74, 107, 131, 144, 182, 202, 206, 212, 218, 219, 220, 224, 228, 239, 291, 297, 316, 399
Cox, A. J., Jr., 68
Cresseri, A., 38
Creutzfeldt, H. G., 36, 277
criminality, 141–44; incidence of, 141–42
Critchley, MacD., 276, 291, 298, 308
culture and senile psychoses, 146–49
Cupcea, S., 127
Curtius, F., 36

Dahmann, H., 53
Dalton, A. R., 69
Danziger, L., 71
Darley, J. G., 107
Darling, R. C., 77
Davidoff, E., 218, 253, 256, 257, 259
Davies, D. F., 56, 68
Davies, D. T., 68
Davis, A., 187
Davis, H. J., 66
Davis, J. O., 67
Davis, S. C., 71
Davison, C., 277, 278
Dawson, P. M., 51, 66
Dayton, N. A., 289, 383
De Allende, I., 405
De Gispert, C. J., 35, 36
De Smedt, E., 35, 264
De Wan, J. G., 51
De Wulf, A., 272
Dearing, W. H., 70
death rates, 8–11
Dedichen, L., 68
Delay, J., 272, 276
Dell'Amore, D., 143
delusions, 138–39
Delys, L., 110
DeMonchy, S. J. R., 37
Dennis, W., 106
Desclaux, P., 272, 276
Deutsch, H., 425
Dhar, N. R., 47
Di Palma, J. R., 62, 67

Diethelm, O., 172, 233, 425, 427, 431, 432, 437
digestion, 67–68
Dock, W., 68
Dölken, 342
Dogliotti, G. C., 64
Dolkart, M. B., 117, 122, 123, 124
Dolkart, R. E., 70
Doll, E. A., 392
Donaldson, H. H., 58
Donner, S. E., 37
Dorken, H., 135, 490
Dorn, H. F., 157
Doty, E. J., 426
Douglas, R. J., 246
Dragstedt, L. R., 60
drugs and toxic substances, susceptibility to, 70
Du Bois, E. F., 61
Du Nouy, P., 69
Dublin, D. I., 54
Dublin, L. I., 30, 54, 66, 67, 69
Dunbar, F., 410, 412
Duncan, C. H., 490
Dunham, H. W., 162
Dunn, H. L., 62, 68
Dunning, M. F., 59
Duran-Reynals, F., 70
Dysinger, D. W., 115

Ebaugh, F. G., 300, 301, 343, 446
Ebeling, A. H., 69
educational background of older psychotics, 129–31
Egaña, E., 77
Eiden, H. F., 268
Elderton, E. M., 114
electric shock therapy, 446–59; and aged, 451, 453, 454–55; contraindications for, 457–58; curare in, 451, 453, 457, 458; deaths in, 450; effect of increased voltage and stimulus duration in, 453; Fractional Summation Method in, 454; and fractures, 450, 451–52; history of, 446; indications for use of, 456–57; in involutional psychoses, 258–59
electrolytes, regulation of, 56–59
Eliaser, M., 67
Ellis, R. W. B., 347
Elsberg, C. A., 327
Elvehjem, C. A., 76
Engle, E. T., 71
English, H. W., 264
English, O. S., 67, 478, 490, 491
enzyme systems, 76–78
epilepsy, 35

Essen-Moller, E., 35, 264
Essex, H. E., 70
Eusterman, G. B., 68
Evans, V. L., 446
excretion, 68–69
exercise, 65–67
Eysenck, M. D., 113

Falk, K. G., 62, 63
family life: changes in, 163–68, 174, 175;
    Chinese and American, 165–68
Faris, R. E. L., 162
Fassett, K. K., 105
Fazekas, J. F., 70
Federal Bureau of Investigation, 141
Fei, H. T., 166
Feifel, H., 116
Feingold, L., 30, 33, 34
Feldman, E., 67
Feldman, F., 449
Ferguson, M. H., 68
Ferraro, A., 264, 273
Ferree, C. E., 72
fibrin, 75
Finestone, I., 53
Fischer, O., 291
Fish, V. W., 147, 293, 318
Fisher, F. P., 72
Fisher, M., 297
Fisher, M. B., 64
Fliegelman, T., 37
Flind, I., 35
Flynd, J., 264
Folsom, J. K., 165, 221
Forbes, W. H., 77
Fortes, A., 451
Foster, F. I., 62, 67
Foulds, G. A., 118
Fowler, W. S., 56
Fox, C., 72, 115, 117
Fox, T. T., 67
Francis, R. L., 67
Frank, L. K., 173, 217
Frank, R. T., 250
Freeman, W., 340, 343
Freeman, Z., 67
Freund, J. D., 454
Fried, E. G., 135, 136
Friedenwald, J. S., 72
Friedfeld, L., 62
Friedrich, G., 36, 272
Friedsam, H. J., 173
Frostig, J. P., 52
Fry, E. G., 52
Fuller, R. G., 352
Fuller, S. C., 263

Fünfgeld, E., 269, 280

Gallinek, A., 305, 308, 311, 328, 451, 453
Gallup, G. H., 105
Gans, A., 271, 272
Gardner, E., 63
Gardner, E. D., 73
Garn, S. M., 60
Garnett, R. W., 311
Gaunt, R., 58
Geill, G., 194
Geist, L., 67
Gellerstedt, N., 63, 291, 292, 297, 334
genetics, 26–46; and adjustment, 29; in-
    fluence of, upon later life disorders, 27;
    and longevity, 27, 30, 32–33; and pre-
    senile conditions, 27; and psychometric
    performance, 33–34; and senile psycho-
    ses, 27; and twin family method, 31
geriatrics, 478
gerontology: definition of, 477–78; outline
    of, 478–80
Gerritzen, P., 60
Gertler, M. M., 60
Ghiselli, E. E., 107
Giese, F., 136
Gilbert, G. M., 119
Gilbert, J. G., 130
Gildea, E. F., 53
Gillespie, R. B., 249
Gillespie, R. D., 281, 405
Gillespie, simple presenile dementia of
    (*see* presenile dementias)
Girden, E., 106
Gitelson, M., 293
Glezina, O. M., 63
Glinos, A. D., 69
Globus, J. H., 327
Gofman, J. W., 60
Goldberger, M. A., 250
Golden, J. S., 68
Goldfarb, W., 64, 74
Goldhamer, H., 135
Goldman, R., 117, 118, 122, 123, 124, 130
Goldschmidt, H., 293, 298, 310
Goldsmith, H., 343
Goldstein, K., 115, 275
Goodell, H., 73
Goodman, L., 147, 293, 318
Goodstone, G. L., 253, 256
Gorer, P. A., 30
Gourevitch, M., 69
Granick, S., 486
Gray, J. S., 56
Graybiel, A., 77
Greenfield, J. G., 281

Greifenstein, F. E., 56
Greisheimer, E. M., 59
grip, strength of, 114
Grosch, H., 35
Gross, K., 72
Gruhle, H. W., 28
Gruneberg, H., 30
Grunthal, E., 35, 36, 264, 267, 272, 280, 291
Gruvitz, M. S., 113
Guild, S. R., 73
Guillain, G., 272
Gurri, J., 452
Gutmann, M. J., 37

Hackovec, V., 272
Halliday, J. L., 477
Hallock, P., 66
Halstead, H. J., 113
Hamilton, G. V., 131, 144, 206, 208, 213, 217, 223, 225, 236
Hand, E. A., 37
Hanfmann, E., 28, 358
happiness, 137–38
Hardy, J. D., 73
Hare, C. C., 51, 67
Harris, H. F., 180
Harrison, R., 182, 189
Hartman, C., 405
Häskovec, V., 35, 36
Hassin, G. B., 274
Hastings, A. B., 56, 58, 335
Hastings, D. W., 77
Hatai, S., 58
Hauptmann, A., 346
Havighurst, R. J., 135
Hawkinson, L. F., 244, 246, 249, 250
Hayes, E. R., 60
Hayman, M., 448
hearing, 73; and neurosis, 208–9; and pitch, 114
Heinrich, A., 67
Hellebrandt, F. A., 84
Henderson, D. K., 248, 249, 281, 405
Henninger, J. M., 145
Henry, C. W., 254
Hentig, H. V., 143
Herrington, L. P., 66
Herrlich, H. C., 70
Herskovitz, H. H., 394
Hertel, H., 70
Herz, E., 269
Hilferty, M. M., 62
Hill, A. V., 66
Hillman, C. C., 66
Himsworth, H. P., 55
Himwich, H. E., 51, 70, 76, 77

Hines, E. A., Jr., 37
Hirsch, E., 116
Hirschmann, J., 34
Hoch, P. H., 448
Hochrein, M., 66
Hoctor, E. F., 71
Hodges, C. V., 69
Hofstatter, L., 53, 60, 62, 182
Holitscher, A. K., 342, 343
Holmes, S., 182, 189
homeostasis: changes in, 49–51; definition of, 49; heredity and, 35
Hopkins, B., 115
Hoppe, H. H., 343
Horn, A., 121
Horn, L., 273, 276
Horonick, A., 63
Horvath, S. M., 53
Howell, T. H., 61, 66, 67
Hsiao, H. H., 114
Huggins, C., 69
Hunsicker, H. H., 394
Hunt, J. McV., 78
Huntington's chorea, 35, 307
Hurdum, H. M., 278
hypoglycemia and mental functioning, 75

immune reactions, 70
Impasto, D. J., 257, 259, 446
individual differences, 470, 484–85
Ingle, D. J., 52
institutional changes and the aged, 162–65
intelligence, 99–128; decline in different functions of, 113; and education, 103; individual differences in, 110–15; and motivation, 100; of normals, 103; and physical factors, 101; of psychotics, 115–16; and speed, 102, 106–10; of subnormals (see subnormal aged); of twins, 33–34; and vitamins, 102
interests, changes in, 134–35
involutional psychoses, 35, 39, 40, 41, 246–59; classification of, 253–56; definition of, 246–47; educational background in, 130; electric shock in, 258–59; estrogens in, 250, 256–57; and heredity, 39; intelligence in, 116; in men, 250–51; personality, role in, 247–49; prognosis in, 256; sex ratios in, 250; symptoms of, 251–53; therapy in, 250, 256–59
involutional syndrome without psychosis, 244–46
Ionasiu, L., 127
Ivy, A. C., 67

Jackson, L., 178, 182, 185

Jacob, H., 36
Jakob, A., 277, 278
Jakob's disease, 35–36
James, T. G. I., 68
Jansen, J., 267, 279
Jelgersma, H. C., 126
Jelliffe, S. E., 248, 291
Jervis, G. A., 264, 273, 278
Jetter, W. W., 102
Johannessen, E., 53
Johnson, M., 352
Johnson, O. H., 59
Johnson, R. E., 77
Jolliffe, N., 76, 77
Jones, C. M., 48, 73
Jones, H. B., 60
Jones, H. E., 104, 105, 108, 113, 114, 121
Jones, L. W., 136
Joslyn, E. P., 54

Kahle, P. J., 69
Kahn, E., 209, 220
Kaldeck, R., 459
Kalinowski, L., 257, 259, 448
Kallmann, F., 28, 29, 30, 33, 38, 39, 298
Kaltreider, N. L., 56
Kaplan, L. A., 454
Kaplan, O. J., 28, 117, 129, 132, 383, 384,
    387, 392
Kardiner, A., 171, 215
Kasanin, J., 263, 297, 358
Katz, S. E., 275
Katzin, B., 52
Kaufman, M., 215, 224, 225
Kaufman, S. H., 310
Kay, H., 101, 121
Kehrer, F., 282
Kerr, R. B., 55
Kessler, M., 62, 67
Kessler, W. R., 70
Kettel, K., 70
Keys, A., 60, 77, 198
King, A. L., 66
King, J. T., 51
King, R. M., 56
Kino, F. F., 449
Kinsey, A. C., 399
Kirk, E., 59
Kirk, J. E., 48, 60, 183
Kirschbaum, W., 279
Klaesi, J., 138
Klineberg, O., 147
Klingman, W. O., 311
Klondy, M. H., 70
Knott, J. R., 76, 77
Kodama, M., 316

Kohl, H., 53
Kohler, L. H., 71
Kolb, L., 289
Kondo, B. O., 67
Korbsch, H., 35
Korenchevsky, V., 65, 77, 78
Korsakoff's psychosis, 309, 490
Kotsovsky, D., 65, 69
Kountz, W. B., 53, 60, 62, 182
Kraepelin, E., 247, 249, 262, 263, 264, 279,
    280, 282
Kraepelin's disease (*see* presenile demen-
    tias)
Krafft-Ebing, R. V., 146
Krafka, J., Jr., 66
Krag, C. L., 62
Kral, V. A., 135, 293, 298, 490
Kretschmer, H. L., 50
Kreuzmann, H., 67
Kubo, Y., 119
Kuhlen, R. G., 136, 137
Kuhlman, D., 52

La Barre, J., 52
La Place, L. B., 67, 339
Laird, D. A., 74
Landau, H. G., 107
Landis, C., 134, 148, 491
Landis, J. T., 137
Landowne, M., 67
Lange, J., 132
Langley, G. J., 53
Lansing, A. I., 47, 48, 58, 59, 67, 71, 72, 73
Larson, C. P., 335
Latch, S. S., 56
Laursen, T. J. S., 48
Lawton, G., 134, 138, 217, 218, 219, 220,
    221, 224, 233, 239
Lazovskaya, L. N., 62
Le Compte, P. M., 60
Learned, J., 135, 136
learning, 118–28; in normals, 119–22; in
    psychotics, 122–28
Leary, T., 60, 61
Lebo, D., 138
Lechner, H., 268
Lehman, H., 106
Lehrman, S. R., 352
Leites, V., 29
Lemmer, R., 69
Leonhard, K., 35, 36, 272, 274
Levine, M., 491
Levine, R., 52
Levitin, D., 274
Levitt, G., 67
Levy, B., 56

Levy, R. L., 66
Lewis, E. F., 72
Lewis, N., 233, 236
Lewis, N. D. C., 475
Lewis, R. A., 52
Lewis, W. H., Jr., 59, 60, 62, 66, 67, 68
Lewy, F. H., 47, 48, 76
Lhermitte, J., 273, 276
Lichstein, J., 78
Liebers, M., 280
life duration and heredity, 30, 31, 32–33
life expectancy, increase in, 460
Life Extension Institute, 69
Lindgren, A. G. H., 36
Lindgren, F. T., 60
Lingley, J. R., 451
Lipetz, B., 449
lipids, metabolism of, 60–61
living arrangements, 468, 492–93
Lloyd, R. I., 72
Lockinschina, E. S., 346
Löfving, B., 127
Löhr, H., 67
Long, C. N. H., 52
long-hospitalized mental patients, 352–82;
review of clinical data, 375–78; schizo-
phrenics, 376–77; sources of satisfaction
and dissatisfaction, 355–75; types of,
352–53
Lorge, I., 107, 130, 212
Lotka, A. J., 30, 54, 67, 69
Lovell, H. W., 452
Lowenberg, K., 35, 264, 265, 272, 297
Lowry, O. H., 58
Luce, R. E., 307
Lüers, T., 35
Luria, S., 63
Lyon, T. P., 60

McCay, C. M., 185, 187, 196
McCullagh, E. P., 71
McCurdy, J. T., 248, 249
McFarland, R. A., 75, 76
McGraw, R. B., 311
McIver, M. A., 52
McKay, E. M., 68, 69
Mackay, J., 102
McKay, L. L., 68, 69
McKeon, C. C., 171, 293
McKim, G. F., 50
MacLachlan, S. H., 281
McLaughlin, W. F., 452
McMenemey, W. H., 35, 263, 264
McNamara, R. J., 67
McNeel, B., 51
MacNider, W. D. B., 47, 48, 56, 57, 70

McSwiney, B. A., 66
Maere, M., 35, 264
Malamud, I., 306
Malamud, M., 132, 137
Malamud, N., 36, 99, 272
Malamud, W., 214, 264, 292, 297, 306
Mallison, R., 36
Malzberg, B., 17, 23, 39, 393
manic-depressive psychosis, 39
Marcus, H., 137
Marinesco, G., 47
Marks, H. H., 54, 66
Marks, H. P., 52
Marshall, F. W., 53
Martin, C. E., 399
Martsinkovski, B. I., 61
Maslow, A. H., 403, 419
Mason, H. L., 77
Massachusetts State Department of Men-
tal Health, 298, 318
Master, A. M., 66, 67
Masters, W. H., 71
Matheson, H. W., 56
Mayer-Gross, W., 291, 447
Mazer, M., 67
mechanisms in geriatric disorders, 488–89
Mecheles, H., 179
Meggendorfer, F., 36, 38, 278
memory, 119–28; in normals, 119–22; in
psychotics, 122–28
Menninger, W., 270
mental hospital statistics, 6–25; admis-
sion rates, 11–24, 492; age distribution,
13; characteristics of patients aged 60
or over, 17–19; economic status of patients, 22–23; education of patients, 21–
22; environment of patients, 19–20;
marital status of patients, 20–21; psychoses with cerebral arteriosclerosis, incidence of, 16; race and nativity of patients, 23–24; sex distribution of patients, 14–16
mental hygiene, 460–75
metabolism, basal, 3, 62–65
Metchnikoff, E., 47, 194
Metraux, R. W., 135, 136
Meyer, A., 36, 272, 279, 426
Meyer, G., 30
Meyer, J., 68
Michael, J. C., 334
Michelsen, O., 60
Miles, C. C., 64, 74, 104, 110, 133, 478, 484, 485
Miles, W. R., 64, 74, 104, 107, 110, 133, 136, 202, 206, 212, 219, 224, 424, 478, 484, 485

milk, 194–95
Miller, E. v. O., 60
Miller, I., 56, 66
Miller, W. C., 270
Minkowski, E., 127
Minot, C. S., 47
Mittelmann, B., 403, 410, 419
Mollaret, P., 272
Mongoloid defficiency, mental decline in, 35
Monrad-Krohn, G. H., 267, 279
Montgomery, H. C., 73
Monzingo, F. L., 74
Moog, F., 47
Moore, L., 386
Moore, M. T., 78, 452
Moore, R. A., 63, 68, 69
Morgan, M., 138
Mosenthal, H. O., 53
Moul, M., 114
Moyano, B. A., 271
Mueller-Deham, A., 54, 62, 69, 70, 73
Muench, G. A., 393
Murray, I. M., 484, 485
Myers, J. A., 56, 67

National Office of Vital Statistics, 141
Naumann, H. N., 327
Nechaeva, P. V., 53
Necheles, H., 68
Nelbach, J. H., 66
Neubürger, K., 291, 312, 315, 316, 446
Neumann, C., 62, 67
Neumann, M. A., 271
neuroses, 201–43, 490; anxiety states, 231–32; and attractiveness, 205–6; biological factors in, 202–14; and brain changes, 209–10; compulsive disorders, 232–33; and conflict and aggression, 225–26; and cultural factors, 214–22; depressions in, 234–35; dynamics of, 202–27; and economic and social dependence, 215; and emotion, 210–11; and general capacities, 211; and hearing, 208–9; hypochondriasis, 229; hysteria, 233–34; neurasthenia, 230–31; personal factors in, 222–27; and reactions to bodily change, 223; and reactions to social change, 223–25; and retirement, 218–20; sex deviates, 235–37; and sex life, 206–8; and significance, loss of, 216–18; and social restrictions, 220–22; and strength and endurance, 204–5; therapy of, 237–42; and visceral dysfunction, 209; and vision, 208–9; and withdrawal and fantasy, 226–27

Neuwelt, F., 68
Newman, B., 60, 63
Newton, R. D., 35
Nichols, I. C., 276
Nichols, M. P., 60
Nicholson, J. T., 339
Nizzi Nutti, G., 64
Nöllenburg, W., 30
Norbury, F. P., 136
Norris, A. H., 53, 65, 66
Norris, J. L., 69
Northup, D. W., 68
Noyes, H. M., 62, 63, 308, 315
nutrition, 3, 178–200; and community action, 190–94; and food habits in the United States, 181; and mental disease, 180; in mental hospitals, 185–90; and needs of older persons, 182–85; rules for, 178–79; special foods for older people, 194–99 (*see also* vitamins)
Nyssen, R., 110

Ohlson, M. A., 178, 182, 185
Oksala, O., 279, 280
Olbrich, O., 68
Oliver, J., 47, 48, 60, 63, 68
Olsen, E., 194
Onari, K., 271
O'Neill, F. J., 278
Orla-Jensen, S., 194
Otis mental ability test, 107, 108
Overholser, W., 133, 176, 229
Owens, W. A., Jr., 111

Page, E. M., 114
Page, G. M., 453
Page, I. H., 60
Page, J. D., 491
pain, 73
Paine, R. M., 66
Palmer, H. D., 77, 132, 247, 248, 249, 255, 335, 490
Papanicolaou, G. N., 246, 254, 405
Parades, V., 35, 36, 43
paralysis agitans, 35
Parets, A. D., 37
Paris, S. K., 65
Parsons, J., 60
Paterson, D. G., 72
Patten, C. A., 316, 333
Patterson, D. F., 107
Patterson, M. B., 71, 246
Pearl, R., 30, 47, 48, 207, 283
Pearl, R. D., 30
Pearson, G. H. J., 73
Pearson, K., 29

pellagra, 180
Penrose, S. L., 385
Penton, C., 77, 78
perception, speed of, 106
Perrin, J., 272
personality: changes in, 131–36; and involutional psychoses, 132; in older psychotics, 132, 133; sex differences in, 133, 134; and social factors, 170–72
Peters, J. P., 58
Picado, T. C., 53
Pick, A., 271
Pickering, G. W., 62
Pick's disease (*see* presenile dementias)
Piersol, G., 215, 219, 220
Phillips, W. C., 416
Piker, P., 343
Pirkosch, W., 278
Platt, R., 37
Plesset, M. R., 394
Poeschel, R., 68
Pollack, B., 115, 118
Pollack, O., 143, 172
Pomeroy, W. B., 399
population trends, 6–8
Porter, E., 53
Pottenger, F. M., 28
Povolny, C., 69
Prados, M., 135, 136
presbyophrenia (*see* senile dementia)
presenile dementias, 262–88; Alzheimer's disease, 35–36, 263–71, 282, 296, 309–10, 327, 490; with cerebellar atrophy, 281; classification of, 262–63; with degeneration of the thalami, 281; of Gillespie, 281; Jakob's disease, 277–80, 282; Kraepelin's disease, 280, 282–83; Pick's disease, 35–36, 271–77, 282–84, 309–10, 327, 490; primary, 262; secondary, 262; Stern's type, 282
Price, B., 72, 114
Proctor, L. D., 51
progesterone, 245
protein, metabolism of, 60–61
Prout, C., 204, 228
psychosomatic disturbances, 398–421; with aging, 402–4; and auditory apparatus, 416–18; and circulatory system, 409–16; and endocrine glands, 405–9; in individuals of all ages, 400–402; and sex activity, 399; treatment of, 419–20
psychotherapy, 423–45; abnormal personality types, 425–26; implications of cerebral arteriosclerosis for, 441–44; psychopathological considerations, 429–41; and treatment in general, 426–29

Puyuelo, S. E., 345
Pyke, M., 182, 189
Pyrkosch, W., 36

Quesnel, E., 147, 293, 318

Rabin, A. I., 115
Rabiner, A. M., 277, 278
Rabson, S. M., 54, 62, 69, 70, 73
Rackow, J. R., 189
Raffaele, A., 256, 257, 259
Rafsky, H. A., 60, 63
Raiford, T. S., 73
Rand, G., 72
Rath, M. M., 66
Rautman, A. L., 390
Rauwolfia, 341
reaction time, 74
recumbency, 464
Reich, F., 271
Reifenstein, E. C., Jr., 182, 184, 246, 256
Reiner, J. M., 63
Reisinger, J. A., 67
Reisner, D., 29
research, planning of, 493–94
resistance to injury and disease, 69–70
retirement, effect of, 4, 472–73
Rhein, J. H. W., 316, 333
Ribot's law of regression, 126, 127
Rich, A. R., 29
Richards, D. W., 67
Richner, H., 30
Richter, M., 272
Riemer, M. D., 28
Riggs, H. E., 334, 340
Riley, R. L., 67
Ripley, H. S., 254, 490
Rizzoli, H. V., 51
Robbins, E. B., 70
Robbins, I., 212
Robbins, L. I., 451
Robertson, G. W., 72
Robertson, J. D., 59
Robertson, J. P. S., 396
Robinson, F. H., 246
Robinson, G., 228
Robinson, G. W., Jr., 332, 335, 337
Robinson, S., 56, 62, 65, 66
Robinson, S. C., 66
Robson, J. S., 68
Rockwell, F. V., 172, 233
Roessle, R., 63, 68
Rohan, J. C., 394
Romano, J., 270
Romcke, O., 53
Rones, B., 72

Root, H. F., 62
Rosenbaum, M., 76, 77
Rosenthal, O., 63
Rosenthal, T. B., 59
Ross, E. A., 167
Roth, M., 115, 291
Rothschild, D., 37, 209, 263, 265, 289, 291, 292, 293, 294, 295, 297, 298, 301, 305, 306, 309, 310, 312, 316, 318, 320, 321, 324, 334
Roulet, F., 63, 68
Rowland, H., 370
Ruch, F. L., 118, 120, 121, 213
Ruger, H. A., 114
Rush, T. W., 50
Rusk, H. A., 310, 311, 312
Russek, H. I., 66
Russell, J. A., 52, 453
Ryan, M., 59

Sachs, E., Jr., 309
Salaman, R. N., 197
Salmon, U. J., 250
Salon, D. D., 272
Sander, G., 30, 298
Sanders, J., 36, 272
Sands, S. L., 291, 306
Sarason, S. B., 395
satyriasis mitis, 146
Saul, L. J., 410
Saxton, J. A., Jr., 66
Schäfer, W., 70
Scheele, H., 38
Scheerer, M., 115
Schenk, V. W. D., 36, 272
Schenken, J. R., 69
Schilder, P., 144
schizophrenics, 28, 35, 39–40
Schlesinger, E., 51
Schlesinger, H., 61
Schlomka, G., 60, 67
Schmitz, H., 272
Schmitz, H. A., 36
Schneeberg, N. G., 53
Schneider, C., 271, 274, 275
Schottky, J., 264
Schulz, B., 37, 38, 39
Schwab, R. M., 346
Scott, W. W., 69
Sebrell, W. H., 77
Selle, W. A., 70
Selye, H., 51
Semrad, E. V., 171, 293, 346
senile dementia, 38–43; anatomic changes in, 294–97; course of, 307; definition of, 289; diagnosis of, 98–99; differential diagnosis of, 307–10; ecology of, 158–63; etiology of, 292–93, 297–98; heredity, 38–39, 41–43; historical considerations, 290; incidence of, 289; intelligence in, 115–16; learning and memory in, 122–28; mental symptoms in, 299; paranoid type, 301, 303–4, 305; physical changes in, 306–7; presbyophrenic type, 300–301, 309; treatment of, 310–12; types of, 300, 305; vocabulary changes in, 116–18
Sevringhaus, E. L., 71, 246, 249, 250
sexuality, 144–46, 206–8, 235–37, 399, 424–25, 432, 433, 465–66
Shakow, D., 117, 118, 122, 123, 124, 130
Sharp, M. L., 292, 295, 298, 309
Shattuck, G. C., 62
Shelton, P., 337
Sherman, S. H., 248
Shipley-Hartford Retreat Scale, 115
Shock, N. W., 49, 53, 55, 56, 57, 60, 62, 63, 64, 65, 66, 67, 68, 69, 72, 73, 75, 78, 84, 106, 121
shock therapy (see electric shock therapy)
Shorr, E., 246, 254, 405
Silver, A., 311
Silverstone, F. A., 53
Simchowicz, T., 291, 297
Simmons, L., 220
Simms, H. S., 30, 58
Simon, A., 99
Simon, B., 310
Simonson, E., 64, 65, 74
Sinclair, J., 178
Sjögren, H., 36, 263
Sjögren, T., 36
Sloan, W., 395
smell, 74
Smith, B.F., 77
Smith, C. G., 63, 74
Smith, F. V., Jr., 337
Smith, H., 405
Smith, H. C., 72
Smith, H. W., 68
Smith, L. E., 53, 55
Smith, P. G., 50
Snoddy, G. S., 120
Søbye, P., 37
Social Security program, 176
Solnzew, W. I., 60
Soltz, S. E., 264
Sonnenberg, A., 53, 60, 62
Sorenson, H., 111
Sorokin, P. A., 168, 173
Sorter, H., 68, 179
Soskin, S., 52

Sparkman, R., 341
Spatz, H., 271, 273
Speir, E., 68
Sperry, W. M., 60
Spiegelman, M., 54, 67
Spielmeyer, W., 291, 312, 315, 316
Spies, S. N., 56
Spies, T. D., 76, 77
Sprague, H. B., 67
Standi, R., 66
Stanford-Binet test results: with older morons, 387–90; with senile sex offenders, 145
Staub, H., 341
Steele, J. M., 59
Steinebach, R., 343
Steiner, N., 68
Steinhaus, A. H., 51
Stender, A., 277, 279
Stengel, E., 269, 270, 273, 276
Stephenson, W., 77, 78
Stern, F., 37
Stern, K., 288
Stern, L., 346
Stern, presenile dementia of (*see* presenile dementias)
Stertz, G., 271, 275
Steven, D. M., 72
Stevens, H., 490
Stevens, R. E., 69
Stevenson, I., 490
Stewart, C. P., 68
Stieglitz, E. J., 47, 54, 60, 63, 64, 67, 68, 70, 74, 308, 477, 478, 479, 480, 481, 482, 483, 484, 485, 487, 489, 490, 491
Stiffle, A. M., 102
Stoll, M. R., 72
Stolman, A., 58
Stotz, E., 78
Stoessiger, B., 114
Strecker, E. A., 247, 249, 300, 301, 343
Strisower, B., 60
Strong, E. K., Jr., 134, 135, 214
Stroud, W. D., 66
Strube, H., 36, 278
Su, S. G., 167, 168
subnormal aged, 382–97; causes of death in, 385–86; length of life of, 382–85; mental ability of, 386–91; Mongoloid deficiency, 386–87; psychotic states in, 393–96; research needs in regard to, 396; social and economic adjustment of, 391–93; and Vineland Social Maturity Scale, 392; and vocabulary, 387–88
suicide, 139–41
Susselman, S., 449

Sward, K., 111
Swickard, M. T., 195

taste, 74
Teichmann, E., 279
temperature, regulation of body, 61–62
Tennies, L. G., 386
Thewlis, M. W., 145, 146
Thomas, J. M., 346
Thomas, R. M., 60
Thompson, W. R., 59, 60
Thomsen, O., 70
Thorndike, E. L., 118, 120, 485, 486
Thorndike, R. L., 105
Thorner, M. W., 47, 48, 76
Thorpe, L., 12
thyroid, functioning of, 64
Tiffen, J., 72
Tillmanns, H., 67
Tilney, F., 47, 63, 298
Tilton, J., 118, 120, 485, 486
Tinker, M. A., 72
Titley, W., 247
Todd, R. L., 60
Tornblom, N., 69
toxic delirious reactions, 332–51; and avitaminosis, 340; and bronchial pneumonia, 340; and carbohydrate metabolism, 347–49; and cerebral pathology, 340; definition of, 332–33; and delirium tremens, 342–46; differential diagnosis of, 333–34, 335; etiology of, 336, 339–40; incidence of, 332; and recumbency, 340; symptoms of, 336–38; therapy of, 335, 340–42
Trelles, J. O., 273, 276
Tremaine, M. J., 74
Trowbridge, E., 102
Trowbridge, L., 102
Trueblood, C. K., 127
Truex, R. C., 63
tuberculosis, 29
Tunbridge, R. E., 53
twin family method, 30–31

U.S. Bureau of the Census, 11, 20, 22, 24, 25, 129, 141

Van Bogaert, L., 35
Van Liere, E. J., 68
Van Slyke, D. D., 60
Van Zile Hyde, H., 56
Vanzant, F. R., 68
Veen, P., van, 36, 272
Verhaart, W. J. C., 272
Verzar-McDougall, E. J., 128
vibratory sensitivity, 73

Vineland Social Maturity Scale (*see* subnormal aged)
Vinther-Paulsen, N., 182, 185
vision, 72, 114; and neurosis, 208–9
vital capacity, 114
vitamins, 76–78, 102, 199, 467
vocabulary: changes in, 116–18; in cerebral arteriosclerosis with psychosis, 117–18; in involutional psychoses, 118; in morons, 117; in senile dementia, 117
Voelker, C. H., 73
Vogt, A., 30
Vogt, M., 272
Voronoff operation, 1

Waggoner, R. W., 35, 36, 264, 272
Wagner, H., 30
Wagoner, G., 63
Waife, S. O., 70
Walker, R. N., 135, 136
Warren, H. C., 424
Warthin, A. S., 47, 297
Wartman, W. B., 333
Wassersug, J. I., 452
water, regulation of body, 56–59
Waterhouse, J. A. H., 56
Watson, R. I., 63, 71, 102, 128, 136
Watters, T., 229
Weaver, J. C., 67
Webb, M., 60
Wechsler, D., 104, 109, 113, 399, 424
Wechsler-Bellevue Performance Scale, 2, 104, 105, 109, 115, 391, 399
Weinberg's sampling method, 31
Wegner, O., 264, 267
Wegner, W. C., 276
Weinberger, H. L., 37
Weiss, E., 67, 478, 490, 491
Weitz, W., 37
Welford, A. T., 106, 107
Wenger, O., 35
Werner, A. A., 71, 244, 245, 246, 250
Wertham, F., 316
Weston, H. C., 72
Wexberg, E., 300, 311
Wexberg, L. E., 147, 148

Wezler, K., 66
White, P. D., 66
White, W. A., 248, 291, 300, 316
Whitfield, A. G. W., 56
Wibberley, H., 396
Wierzuchowski, M., 347
Wilbur, C. B., 259, 451
Wilder, J., 52
Wilder, R. M., 77
Wilens, S. J., 66
Wilkenson, C. F., 37
Williams, H. C., 35
Williams, H. G., 264
Williams, H. W., 147, 172, 293, 318
Williams, R. D., 77
Willoughby, R. R., 113, 117, 133
Winkelman, N. W., 316, 333
Winternitz, M. C., 60
Wisotsky, R., 53
Wladkowsky, E., 390
Wohl, M. G., 70
Wolbach, S. B., 47, 48
Wolff, G., 60, 62
Wolff, H. G., 51, 67, 73, 410
Wolff, S. G., Jr., 51, 67
Woltmann, H. W., 228, 229, 463
Woodward, E., 485, 486
Woodworth, R. S., 383
Woodyard, E., 118, 120
work and adjustment, 466
Worster-Drought, C., 35, 264, 278
Wortis, H., 76, 77
Wosika, P. H., 67
Wright, C., 391

Yacorzynski, G. K., 156
Yiengst, M. J., 53, 56, 60, 62, 63, 65, 66, 68
yogurt, 194
Yudkin, J., 72

Zeman, F. D., 178
Zhorova, K. S., 61
Zimmerman, R., 277, 279
Zohman, B. L., 66
Zunz, E., 52
Zwemer, R. L., 63